Martin the Warrior

The triumphant saga of a young mouse destined to become Redwall's most glorious hero . . .

"Wonderfully imaginative." —*The New York Times Book Review*

"Readers will rejoice." —*Los Angeles Times*

Salamandastron

When the mountain stronghold of Salamandastron comes under attack, only the bold badger lord Urthstripe stands able to protect the creatures of Redwall . . .

"A good yarn . . . grand climax . . . Jacques charms readers . . . another winner." —*Booklist*

"Swashbuckling adventures told with great gusto in rousing words." —*Chicago Tribune*

Redwall

The book that inspired a legend—the first novel in the bestselling saga of Redwall! The epic story of a bumbling young mouse who rises up, fights back . . . and becomes a legend himself . . .

"Charming . . . rollicking good adventure." —*Fantasy Review*

"Reminiscent of *Watership Down* . . . *Redwall* is a thrilling tale of danger and adventure . . . an edge-of-the-seat, can't-put-it-down book with potential for classic status." —*Parent's Choice*

THE LEGEND OF LUKE

Brian Jacques

ACE BOOKS, NEW YORK

THE LEGEND OF LUKE

An Ace Book / published by arrangement with
Hutchinson Children's Books.

PRINTING HISTORY
Published in Great Britain in 1999 by
Hutchinson Children's Books, London.
First American hardcover edition published in 2000 by Philomel Books.
Ace mass-market edition / February 2001

Visit our website at
www.penguinputnam.com

Visit the Redwall website at
www.redwall.org

Check out the ACE Science Fiction & Fantasy newsletter!

ISBN: 0-441-00773-2

ACE®
Ace Books are published
by The Berkley Publishing Group,
a division of Penguin Putnam Inc.,
375 Hudson Street, New York, New York 10014.
ACE and the "A" design are trademarks
belonging to Penguin Putnam Inc.

PRINTED IN THE UNITED STATES OF AMERICA

10 9 8 7

In memory of Tony Jacques

TALL ROCKS

CLIFFS

N

W

SOUTH POINT

CAVES OF
LUKE'S TRIBE

WOO

S

Honeysuckle

SEA

DUNEHOG
DWELLINGS

TUNGRO
HOLT

G

WATERFALL

WATERMEADOW

PINE
FOREST

SHORE

Martin's Journey

NORTHFORK
STREAM

MOSSFLOWER
WOOD

STREAM

GARRAWAY'S
HOLT

MOSSFLOWER
WOOD

CROW
CAMP

PATH

DITCH

REDWALL
ABBEY

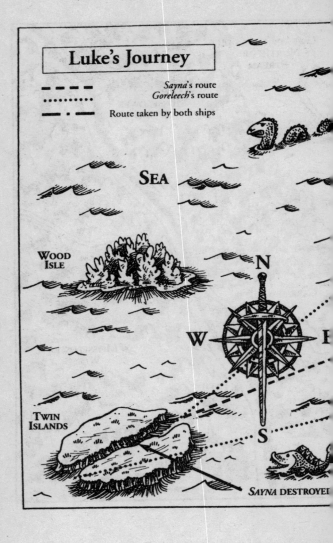

Luke's Journey

- – – – *Sayna*'s route
- ·············· *Goreleech*'s route
- – · – · Route taken by both ships

SEA

WOOD ISLE

N

W E

S

TWIN ISLANDS

SAYNA DESTROYED

CAVES OF LUKE'S TRIBE

CLIFFS

TALL ROCKS

SAYNA

SOUTH POINT

BEAU'S ISLAND

VOLCANO ISLAND

SEA

RANGUVAR
CAPTURED HERE

GORELEECH

The young must grow old,
Whilst old ones grow older,
And cowards will shrink,
As the bold grow bolder.
Courage may blossom in quiet hearts,
For who can tell where bravery starts?
Truth is a song, oft lying unsung,
Some mother bird, protecting her young,
Those who lay down their lives for friends,
The echo rolls onward, it seldom ends.
Who never turned and ran, but stayed?
This is a warrior born, not made!
Living in peace, aye many a season,
Calm in life and sound in reason,
'Til evil arrives, a wicked horde,
Driving a warrior to pick up his sword,
The challenger rings then, straight and fair,
Justice is with us, beware. Beware!

THE
LEGEND OF
LUKE

BOOK ONE

Martin

1

Summer's first morn was like no other!

Trimp the roving hedgehog wandered through the woodlands like one in a dream, drinking in the beauty of Mossflower Country, so different from the cold northland coast whence she had traveled. Dew was still upon each leaf, delicate mist tendrils wreathed into greengold sun shafts 'twixt mighty oak, slender rowan and stately elm. Birds trilled sweetly, butterflies fluttered silently, bees hummed busily over flowers, ferns and lichen-clad rocks. Trimp's heart felt as light as the haversack on her back. She ignored hunger, feasting her senses on the glory of her surroundings and the delight of the new season. Swinging her ash stave jauntily, she skipped a little jig and broke out into song.

"You lark on high,
O minstrel of the sky,
Sing out! Sing out!
Now sing you joyously,
To Mother Nature and her earth,
This is the golden summer's birth,

3

A wondrous sight to see!
Hail, fine tall trees,
Your leaves dance on the breeze,
Rejoice! Rejoice!
And sway so gracefully,
You'll feel your blossom soon give way,
To ripened fruit some sunny day,
Oh please save some for me!
Sing out! Rejoice!
Let all who have a voice,
Call out so sweet and happily,
O'er woodland vale and grassy lea,
Good day my friend to thee!"

As Trimp ended her song a voice hailed her.
"An' good day to thee too, pretty one!"
She halted at the edge of a ditch. Two sturdy old hedge-hogs stood on a path at the other edge, grinning cheerfully. They were alike as peas in a pod. One of them called to her, "We'll 'elp you across yon ditch, missie. Stay there!"
Taking a few paces back, Trimp winked cheekily at the pair. "Nay, you stay there. I'll help myself!"
With a short run and a hop she dug the long ash stave in the bank and pole-vaulted neatly across. Both hedgehogs wriggled furiously until their backspikes rattled, an ancient hog form of applause. Trimp immediately took a liking to the jolly pair. She stood directly in front of them and lowered her head formally, and they did likewise until all three creatures' headspikes touched in the traditional greeting of their species. Introductions were made.
"Good sirs, I'm called Trimp the Rover."
"Marm, I'm called Ferdy an' that fat 'un's my brother Coggs, both of Redwall Abbey."
Coggs snorted, pointing to Ferdy's ample stomach. "I ain't as fat as ole Ferdy, am I, miz Trimp?"
She giggled. "You're as tubby as one another."
Ferdy and Coggs exchanged wry glances.
"She's pretty all right, pretty impudent!"
"Aye, truthful an' pitiless, jus' like all the pretty 'uns!"

"She's thin, though. D'ye think she could 'elp pull a log?"

"Miz Trimp ain't thin, she's slender—but strong, I'll wager, the way she leaped yon ditch. She can pull logs."

Trimp pursed her lips shrewdly. "Of course I can pull logs. I could tow a log with both of you sitting atop of it, if I'd a mind to. But I'm feeling very slender today, owing to the fact that I've an empty haversack on my back. So, towing logs means payment in food."

Ferdy and Coggs exchanged more wry glances.

"Miz Trimp knows wot she wants, don't she!"

"Ho, she certainly does, mate. That 'og ain't soft as moss nor green as the grass. We'll 'ave to feed 'er."

"Only when we gets back to Redwall, though. Then she can tuck into vittles 'til she's like two of us'n's put t'gether. So, is it a bargain, marm?"

Trimp banged her stave butt down on the path decisively. "Done! Lead me to your log, friends."

It was not a very big log, more like a heavy sycamore limb. They attached ropes and pulled, and the wood slid easily along the dewy grass of the pathside. Trimp was full of questions for Ferdy and Coggs.

"What is this Redwall place and how far off is it?"

"Hah, missie, you won't say that someday. Anybeast'll be able to see it from a good league off. Right, Coggs?"

"Right, Ferdy. When we gets round this bend in the path, beyond that big grove of oaks, then you'll see it, Trimp. 'Tis goin' to be a great Abbey, but it ain't properly built yet. Martin reckons three more seasons should see the main Abbey buildin' showin' its spire top."

Trimp suddenly stopped pulling and smote her forehead with an open paw, as if she had just remembered something. "Of course! I've heard other travelers mention the great redstone building in Mossflower. You say there's a Martin there. Is he a mouse, son of Luke the Warrior?"

Ferdy shrugged and beckoned her to keep pulling. "Oh, he's a warrior sure enough, missie. As to his father, I think somebeast mentioned his name was Luke, eh, Coggs?"

Coggs switched the rope to his other shoulder. "Could be,

mate..Nobeast knows much about our Martin—he keeps his past fairly quiet. Mark my words, though, Trimp, the noblest fighter that ever wielded a sword is Martin the Warrior—he fears nothin' an' battles like tenbeasts. Hoho, lookee there, marm, that's Redwall Abbey. See!"

Trimp's eyes grew wide with wonder. Never had she seen anything built on such a grand scale, even though it was still incomplete. The Abbey reared out of the forest on the path's east side, fashioned from mighty blocks of red sandstone. There was a high perimeter wall with battlements and a broad walkway behind them, and visible above this outer wall the main building stood two-thirds finished. Buttresses, arches and columns could be seen between the wooden scaffolding. Mice, moles, squirrels, otters, hedgehogs and voles labored busily, hauling, laying, chipping, carving and carrying, all over the structure. Ferdy and Coggs chuckled at Trimp's astonishment.

"Hohoho. Shows wot honest 'ardworkin' woodlanders can do when they puts their paws t'work, eh, miss?"

"Aye, buildin' Redwall Abbey, a place o' safety an' cheer for goodbeasts to live in, with walls that'd stand the worst any vermin foes could think of!"

Trimp enjoyed the pride in her friends' faces as they spoke of their home. She cocked her head as a hollow booming sound echoed out.

"What's that noise? Are they doing something special?"

Coggs winked at her and patted his stomach. "That's the call for lunch. We're just in time!"

The three hedgehogs pulled their log through the impressively solid wallgates, which were opened for them by a mole. He tugged his snout, saying in quaint mole-speech, "Hurr, gudd day to ee. Boi okey, mates, ee likkle 'ogmaid be purtier'n both of you 'uns. 'Ow be you'm called, miz?"

Trimp shook the formidable digging claw of the twinkle-eyed mole heartily. "I'm Trimp, sir, ten times hungrier than I'm pretty."

A deep smile crinkled the mole's velvety face. "Gurtly pleasured to meet ee, miz Trimp. Oi'm ee Foremole yurrabouts. If'n ee be 'ungered then fear not, us'n's can vittle ee up to yore spoikeytips. Hurrhurrhurr!"

Leaving the log by the gatehouse wall, the three hedge-hogs followed the Foremole across broad lawns to the pond, where scores of Redwallers were washing their paws before lunch. Trimp joined them, while Ferdy pointed out various individuals.

"That 'un swimmin' about is Skipper of Otters, a chieftain. Pretty mousewife by the reeds is Columbine, jolly-lookin' beast with 'er is Gonff, Prince of Mousethieves, an' the liddle 'un is their son Baby Gonflet. Dinny Foremole you already know."

The hollow booming sounded out again, and this time Trimp saw that it was made by a squirrel beating on a hollowed section of tree trunk with two wooden batons. Ferdy nudged her. "That's Lady Amber, our Squirrelqueen. Come on, young 'un, off to the Council afore you sit down to eat."

Trimp followed Ferdy and Coggs to the orchard, where tables and benches were laid in an open square. Ferdy bade her stand back until all were seated. The traveling hogmaid could not wrench her eyes from the food—it was like being at the center of a delicious dream. Cauldrons of fresh veg-etable soup steamed savory aromas around new oven-baked bread shaped into biscuits, batches and loaves. Cheeses, ranging from deep yellow to pale cream and studded with nuts, celery and herbs, were placed between heaped trays of woodland salads. Small tarts showed the rich hues of dam-son, apple, blackberry and greengage through their pastry-latticed tops. Jugs and pitchers of ale, fruit cordial and cold mint tea were being brought to the tables by servers. Trimp held her kerchief politely to her mouth, lest anybeast see it watering. Ferdy tugged her tunic hem and whispered, "Come on, missie, don't be afeared. Nobody will eat ye!" He led her round to the table nearest to the Abbey.

A huge, ancient badger, bent with the weight of many sea-sons, gazed at her with kind brown eyes and nodded. "Wel-come to Redwall Abbey, little one. I am Bella of Brockhall. You look as if you have traveled far."

Trimp curtsied deeply. She liked Bella on first sight.

"Marm, I am Trimp the Rover, so traveling is my business. Since late winter I have been walking from the northlands."

"Fourth clans? Did she say fourth clans?"

Next to Bella, the tiniest, oldest, frailest mouse Trimp had ever seen was sitting in a small cushioned chair, wrapped in a thick warm shawl. The mouse sitting on the old one's other side leaned close to her and spoke loudly.

"Northlands, Abbess Germaine. Our guest has walked all the way here from the northlands!"

He turned, smiling, to Trimp. The hogmaid warmed immediately to the sturdy beast, his strong features and friendly tone.

"'Tis fitting to have one so pretty to grace our table as guest on summer's first day. I'm called Martin."

The mouse named Gonff, seated close by with his wife and babe, winked at Trimp and called out, "Aye, matey, an' he's never called late to table!"

Martin smiled at his friend and closest ally. "Hah! Look who's talking. The greatest grubsnatcher ever to lift a ladle!"

Gonff pointed at himself innocently. "Who me? I hardly ever touch food, matey. A crust an' a beaker o' water's good enough for me!"

His wife Columbine adopted an expression of mock surprise. "Lackaday, it must be the birds eating all those pies an' pasties I'm forever baking. What d'you think, Gonflet?"

Baby Gonflet chuckled uproariously. "It's me'n'daddy, we pincha pies'n'pattees offa windersill when they be's gudd'n'ot, us eatem all up, yumyum!"

Gonff covered his baby son's mouth amid general laughter. "It was his idea, Columbine. He's been leadin' me astray!"

Trimp took her seat amid the happy Redwallers. Old Abbess Germaine waited until Bella brought order to the assembly by tapping a spoon on the tabletop. Heads bowed whilst the ancient mouse recited grace in a quavery voice.

"May good fortune never cease,
Where we build and till the soil,

Mother Nature grant us peace,
And reward us for our toil.

Summer's come now life is sweet,
Food is here for one and all,
In good friendship let us eat,
As one family at Redwall."

Bella served Trimp with soup, Martin passed the bread and
cheese, Columbine piled a platter with salad for her and the
charming squirrel called Lady Amber topped up her beaker
with fruit cordial. Trimp went at it with the best. Dinny the
Foremole shielded his mouth with a paw, whispering to the
Skipper of Otters.

"Hurr hurr, dearie me, oi never afore see'd nobeast tuck
into ee vittles loik miz Trimp. Zurr Gonff be eatin' loik ee
buttyfly alongsoid o' that young 'un!"

Gonff the Mousethief wrinkled his nose at the mole. "I
heard that, matey. Shove that cheese this way an' I'll show ye
what a dainty eater I am. Hoi, Gonflet, get yore spoon out o'
my soup, you liddle bandit!"

Columbine smiled sweetly at Trimp. "Like father, like son,
I always say."

After lunch Trimp volunteered to help Martin and his friends
hoist a roofbeam. Skipper and his crew were atop the half-
timbered dormitory with mallets and pegs, awaiting the
heavy oaken beam. The jovial otter jiggled the rope in its pulley block and called down, "Ahoy, mates, if'n we wait round
much longer up 'ere we'll sprout wings'n'feathers an' fly
off!"

Gonff secured the rope to the beam, and spat on his paws.
"Right, mateys, let's send 'er up with a will. Anybeast got a
good haulin' river song t'help out?"

Bella held up a paw in response. "I'll do 'Grumbledum
Tugg' if you like!"

A groan arose from the hauling party. Baby Gonflet
clapped both paws over his tiny ears.

"Not dat one agin, miz Bell, you allus singin' Grungledun
Tuggs. Ferdy say miz Trimpy be a good singer."

Bella sighed, bowing slightly to the hedgehog maid.
"Trimp, nobeast is forcing you to sing, but it'd be nice if
you'd oblige. D'you know any good hauling shanty songs?"

Trimp did, and she immediately sang out in a fine clear
voice.

"Away O! Away O!
Haul hard an' take her out,
I'll tell ye of the *Greenhawk*,
An' her cap'n, ole Chopsnout.
Away O! Away O! Now bend yore backs an' heave ho!

Ole Reynard Chopsnout was a fox,
A bad corsair to boot,
Who ran his vessel on some rocks,
While searchin' round for loot.
Away O! Away O! Now bend yore backs an' heave ho!

So to the northlands he did steer,
The *Greenhawk* to repair,
A warrior who knew no fear,
Named Luke was livin' there.
Away O! Away O! Now bend yore backs an' heave ho!

That corsair came with all his horde,
I'll tell ye mates 'tis true,
Brave Luke took up his battlesword,
An' that bad fox he slew.
Away O! Away O! Now bend yore backs an' heave ho!

Then Luke called up his gallant crew,
And *Greenhawk* did repair,
He changed her name to *Sayna* too,
Which sounded good and fair.
Away O! Away O! Now bend yore backs an' heave ho!

So Luke the Warrior sailed away,
He left the northland shore,
He swore an oath that one fine day,

He'd come back home once more.
Away O! Away O! Now bend yore backs an' heave ho!"

The beam was halfway up when Trimp stopped singing. Martin had his footpaws dug in firmly, holding the swaying oaken baulk steady with the rest of his friends. He stared at the roving hedgehog, gritting from between clenched jaws: "What've you stopped singing for, missie? Keep on!"

Trimp returned his stare, shaking her head. "But that's all I know. I never learned the rest!"

Gonff slid forward a fraction as the beam began losing height. Urgently, he muttered, "Then start from the beginnin' an' sing it again, matey, afore we're all wearin' an oakbeam for a hat!"

Trimp sang the hauling shanty, as far as she knew the verses, twice before the beam was safe in the otters' strong paws on the dormitory top.

When the others went off to new chores Martin called Trimp to him. Walking on either side of her, he and Gonff escorted her across to the gatehouse and showed her in. The Mousethief took flagon and beakers from a cupboard where he had hidden them, and poured drinks for all three.

"Ninian's cider, I calls this. Comes from the ole place down south on the path, where I live from time to time."

They sipped the cold sweet cider appreciatively, in silence. It was cool and shady in the gatehouse after the bright noon sun outside. Martin leaned forward. "Trimp, where did you hear that song?"

"My grandmum Welff Tiptip used to sing it. She told me that she once knew a little mouse named Martin, too. Was that you?"

Gazing into his beaker, he slowly swirled the cider. "That was me. I am Martin of Redwall, son of Luke the Warrior. My mother's name was Sayna. Strange, I had almost forgotten it, until you sang your shanty. *Sayna* was the name my father gave to his ship as well. Being little more than a babe at the time I don't remember much. But it comes back to me a little now. Tell me, miss, what else did your grandmum say? Anything at all?"

Holding her beaker with both paws, Trimp sipped and pondered. "There were names . . . Coll, Denno, Cordle, and others I can't recall. Is that any help to you, Martin?"

"I'm afraid not. But carry on, please."

"Hmm, now let me see. She used to talk of old Twoola, er, Drunn Tunneller and Windred—"

"Windred! She was my grandmother!" Martin grabbed the hedgehog maid's paws. "Think! Did I have brothers or sisters? A grandsire? What was my father really like? Tell me about Sayna, my mother!"

Even though her paws were hurting in the vicelike grip, Trimp's heart went out to the Warrior. "I can only tell you what I know, sir. Grandmum died when I was very young. She told me that I was born on the northland coast, but we fled when the slavers attacked your tribe's settlement. Our family moved to the midnorth hills. When I became old enough, I left to go roving, and the first place I set out to see was my birthplace on northland shore. Alas, there was nothing left there of our old home, so I carried on roving until I met Ferdy and Coggs, and they brought me to Redwall."

Gonff placed a paw on his friend's shoulder. "Steady on there, mate. You'll crush miss Trimp's paw!"

Martin released her, and went to stand in the doorway, blinking to hold back welling tears. "I used to know things, I'm sure of it. But after the injuries I suffered battling the wildcat Tsarmina, I've hardly been able to recall a single thing. D'you remember Timballisto?"

Gonff nodded. "He was yore friend from the northlands, who was released from slavery and came here. A good mouse."

Martin struck his paw hard against the doorpost. "We must have been crazy, both of us. He lived here, yet for some unknown reason we never discussed our past. Poor Timbal— he died the winter following the great Mossflower war."

Gonff poured more cider for his friend. "Mayhap 'twas too painful for either of you to mention, what you went through when you were young 'uns?"

Martin stood staring out across the sunlit lawns. "You're probably right, Gonff. Perhaps it was. Trimp, can't you remember any more names at all?"

The hedgehog maid smiled pensively. "Only that grandmum used to say if we didn't stop our noise and go to sleep, Vilu Daskar would get us. Aye, Vilu Daskar. Does that name ring a bell, Martin?"

"No, not a thing. 'Tis all too hazy, too long ago now."

The Warrior walked off towards the Abbey. Gonff watched him, sad for his friend and the forgotten past. "I ain't seen Martin like that afore, miss."

Trimp put aside her drink and stood up. "Only since I came to Redwall and sang that song. This Abbey's a beautiful place, Gonff, but I wish I'd never come here and caused Martin such unhappiness. I'd best leave."

Gonff barred her path to the door, chuckling. "Sorry, me young beauty, but I can't allow it, and neither would Martin, or anybeast calls themselves a Redwaller. Come on now, cheer up, earn yore afternoon tea. I'll show ye how I collect honey from our bees—you can lend a paw."

They strolled from the gatehouse towards the northeast wall corner, where the hives were situated.

"But I've never tried taking honey from bees, Gonff. Don't they have a nasty habit of stinging you?"

"What? Sting me, the Prince of Mousethieves? Never! Not as long as I can pretend I'm a bumblebee an' sing whilst I steal the honey from under their noses, missie."

Trimp giggled. "Oh really, Gonff? What do you sing to a bee?"

"Oh, this'n'that, y'know. I usually start like this.

"Ho fuzz buzz buzz, look who's a-buzzin',
Good day sir bee, I'm Gonff yore cuzzin . . ."

Trimp's laughter mingled with the Mousethief's song on the sunkissed noon air as they skipped paw in paw across the lawns of Redwall Abbey.

2

In the days following Trimp's arrival at Redwall Abbey it became obvious to everybeast that something was wrong with their Warrior. Martin was no longer his customary jovial and helpful self. Often he was missing at mealtimes, and he spent more and more time outside the Abbey. It was a worrisome situation: Martin, the very backbone of Redwall, silent and pensive, with a faraway look clouding his eyes. Skipper and Dinny Foremole wandered up on to the east walltop, which was an ideal place to view the beauty of Mossflower Wood in summer. Lady Amber and Coggs were also up on the ramparts. Foremole greeted them with a wave.

"Gudd day to ee. You'm bain't seen Marthen, 'ave ee?"

Lady Amber placed a paw to her lips, cautioning silence. Pointing downwards over a battlement, she said in a low voice, "Martin's sittin' down there alone!"

Skipper crouched below the walltop, shaking his head. "So that's where our Warrior goes when he leaves the Abbey. Still, y'can't blame him. 'Tis a good place for anybeast seekin' solitude from others."

Coggs peeped over at the lonely figure sitting below. "I tell

14

ye, friends, 'tain't like Martin to act this way. He's just sittin' there with his back agin the wall, starin' out at the trees. What'll we do?"

Ever the sensible otter, Skipper began descending the wallsteps, down to the lawn behind the orchard.

"Come away, mates. I'd hate t'think Martin would know we're up 'ere a-spyin' on him. Whilst he's outside we could 'old a quick meetin' with the Abbess to sort the problem out."

All concerned gathered in the gatehouse. Ferdy and Coggs served them elderflower cordial and slices of plum cake. Old Abbess Germaine held a trumpet, made from a spiral seashell with its end cut off, to her ear. Though her body was frail and her hearing none too good, the ancient mouse's other senses were still sharp and her eyes twinkled and shone keenly. She let them rove over the assembly, Bella, Columbine, Skipper, Dinny Foremole and Lady Amber, finally coming to rest on Trimp and Gonff.

"Hmm. My intuition tells me that our guest Trimp and the Mousethief know more of this affair than we do, friends. So I want you to speak up clearly, one at a time please. Start at the beginning, always the best place to begin. Pray keep silent, the rest of you—I'll hear from everybeast in due course. When the story is complete I'll give you my decision as Mother Abbess, based of course on your facts."

There were smiles and nods of agreement all round. Even as a young mouse, Abbess Germaine had possessed great sense and wisdom. Now, with the experience of countless seasons upon her old head, every Redwaller trusted her judgement without question. They were certain that their beloved Abbess could solve any problem.

It was late afternoon when Martin entered the Abbey by the main gate. He was immediately set on by a group of Dibbuns, the infant creatures of Redwall. Baby Gonflet was clearly the ringleader, wrestling fiercely with Martin's footpaw, until the Warrior allowed himself to be laid flat on his back. Martin was immensely fond of the abbeybabes, always managing to make time for them and their odd little games. He gasped as they sat on his paws and held his ears. Baby Gonflet knelt on Martin's chest, shaking a paw under the Warrior's nose.

"You be still, naughtymouse, or we choppa you whiskers off!"

Two baby moles hanging on to Martin's belt giggled uproariously at the idea, adding their own threats.

"Heeheehee, urr, an' us'n's bite ee paws offen!"

"Yurr, an' chuck ee inna pond, hurrhurrhurr!"

Martin looked with mock pleading at his captors. "Oh, lackaday, will no kind creature help me? I'm captured by wild ruffians. Have mercy on me, you savage beasts!"

Baby Gonflet grinned triumphantly at his prisoner. "On'y if'n you comes wiv us!"

Keeping up a pretense of fear, Martin was led protesting to the Abbey by a veritable swarm of mouse, squirrel, mole and hogbabes.

Cavern Hole was a comfortable room inside the Abbey, slightly below ground level. Abbess Germaine sat propped by cushions in her enormous ceremonial chair, surrounded by her Redwallers. Ferdy ran up the stairs and back down again, his spikes quivering excitedly.

"He's comin'! The Dibbuns are bringin' Martin!"

Agile squirrels scampered about with tapers, lighting the colored lanterns which supplemented the customary tallow candles, lending the chamber a festive atmosphere. In front of the Abbess's chair stood a long solid elmwood table, unadorned and bare. Martin was marched up to it by the Dibbuns, and Gonflet raised a chubby paw in salute to Bella.

"Us catchered 'im an' brought 'im 'ere, miz Bell!"

The big badger nodded solemnly. "Thank you, my friends, good work. Sit down now, and we'll deal with him right away!"

Martin held silent, only moving one eyelid to return a wink from his friend Gonff. He was, however, mystified.

Abbess Germaine opened the proceedings by pointing an accusing paw at the Warrior. "What does this creature stand charged with?"

Answers came rattling back like hailstones.

"Always helping others!"

"Defending our creatures with his life!"

"Never considering himself!"

"Being good and kind to all about him!"

"Assisting Abbess Germaine to design the Abbey!"

"Bein' the best friend a mousethief ever had, matey!"

"Hurr, an' keepin' gurt troubles to 'isself!"

Bella restored order by banging once on the table. She appealed to the Abbess. "This could go on all season. Pass sentence on him!"

Germaine's eyes twinkled as she tapped her cane on the chair. "Bring in the instruments of punishment!"

Two trolleys were borne downstairs from the kitchens. One had a big barrel of strawberry fizz and beakers on it, the other a magnificent three-tiered cake, surmounted by a marchpane figure of the Warrior himself. The Abbess looked sternly from the trolleys to Martin and announced in a no-nonsense voice, "I order that you either eat all of this cake and drink the contents of that barrel . . . or share it with us before you embark upon your journey!"

Martin was plainly bewildered. "Er, I'll share it with you all, of course, but, er, what journey is this I'm supposed to be embarking upon?"

Gonff stepped forward, carrying Martin's great sword. It was a plain warrior's weapon, nothing fancy. The hilt was the one that had belonged to his father's old sword: blackbound, with a red pommel stone at its top. But its blade was like no other, fashioned by a Badger Lord from a chunk of metal fallen from the stars. Martin took it from Gonff, his face reflecting in the burnished steel as he said, "This has been used for a lot of things, but never for anything as delicate as a cake."

Gonff indicated a spot on the butter-coloured meadow-cream, between a candied chestnut and a honey-preserved rose petal. "Cut the cackle an' slice the cake, matey!"

A loud cheer went up as the keen blade slid into the massive confection.

"Martin the Warrior! Redwaaaaaaaallllll!"

Columbine took over the slicing and Coggs served drinks, whilst Martin sat in a corner with some of his friends, eating and sipping happily. He nudged the Mousethief.

"Gonff, you tubby rascal, I've a feeling you're at the back of all this. Come on, tell me, where's this journey going to take me?"

The Prince of Mousethieves blew out his cheeks airily. "Huh! You, matey? What makes y'think yore goin' anyplace without me? I'll be with you every step o' the way!"

"Hurr, zurr, an' oi too. You'm bain't a-goin' an' leavin' Dinny Foremole ahind of ee!"

Martin wrinkled his brow in frustration, and put aside his slice of cake, which Baby Gonflet promptly stole.

"Look, will you all stop talking in circles and tell me where I'm supposed to be going?"

Trimp could hold the secret no longer. She blurted out, "To the place you've been dreaming of, where your father Luke the Warrior swore to return someday. The northland shore, where you were born!"

Martin looked this way and that, blinking. His paws took on a life of their own, fidgeting distractedly.

"But . . . but . . . what about the Abbey? I haven't made any arrangements, then there's provisions, directions, a thousand things that would have to be done . . ."

Columbine came over. Wiping cream and cake from the great battle blade with her apron corner, she gave the sword to Martin and sat down beside him.

"No excuses, sir Warrior, 'tis all arranged and taken care of since this afternoon. Provisions are packed for you all, and you've got the entire summer ahead of you. Skipper and Bella will take charge of the building work. I'll look after the Abbess. There's absolutely nothing for you to do or worry about. After all you've done for Redwall and its creatures, the least we can do in return is to allow you a trip to the place of your birth, which 'tis clear you long to see."

Martin squeezed Columbine's paw gratefully. "Thank you—thank you all. What can I say?"

The irrepressible Gonff pounded him on the back. "That's easy, matey, you can either say no, an' sit around with a face like thunder until the flippin' Abbey falls down on us, or you can say yes, when do we leave?"

For the first time in days Martin the Warrior laughed. He

backpawed Gonff in the stomach, knocking the wind from him. "Yes, when do we leave?"

Dinny did not notice Baby Gonflet purloining his slice of cake as he shook Martin's paw with a hefty digging claw.

"Boi dawn on ee morrow at furst loight, zurr matey!"

3

Stars paled into the receding night, as the cloudless sky turned from aquamarine to soft pastel bands of a new day. Out in the vast leagues of Mossflower, birds began singing among still foliage of trees which stood like ancient giants. The sun rose in the east, an immense golden ball, ready to preside over the morning and noon.

Skipper and Bella opened the main gate wide, and all the inhabitants of Redwall crowded out on to the path, surrounding the four travelers. Trimp was sorry to be leaving the beautiful Abbey and its friendly creatures. Words of advice and farewells fell thick as leaves in autumn.

"Fates an' fortunes be with ye!"

"Bringa me back lotsa seashells, daddy Gonff!"

"Go careful now. Watch yore step, Trimp!"

"Aye, an' don't let that Gonff scoff all the supplies."

"Stay away from deep water, Dinny!"

"An' don't climb any tall trees, mate!"

"Keep that sword close t'paw, Martin. You never know!"

"Have you got a clean kerchief, Gonff? I've packed some extra for you. Oh, don't forget your flute!"

Martin kissed Abbess Germaine's wrinkled brow. "Goodbye, Mother Abbess. Watch out for us near autumn."

The ancient mouse sniffed as she straightened his swordbelt over one shoulder. "Come back safe to Redwall Abbey, Martin the Warrior!"

Redwallers stopped out on the path, cheering and waving, until the four figures traveling north were lost in the shimmering dust.

Gonff strode out cheerfully, calling back to Dinny, who was lagging behind at a slower gait, "Come on, Din, keep up, you old wobblechops!"

Shambling along at his own pace, the good mole was not about to be rushed. "More 'aste less speed, zurr. We'm gotten all ee summer afore us'n's. You'm on'y get all 'ot an' wearied boi rushen along loik ee fussy rabbert!"

Martin slowed the pace slightly, allowing Dinny to catch up. "Always take a mole's advice, Gonff. Remember, Dinny didn't get to be Foremole by being hasty and foolish."

Their friend's homely face crinkled into a deep smile. "Oi thankee furr ee koind wurds, Marthen. Moi ole granfer used t'say oi was wise, even when oi was but a h'infant!"

Gonff could not suppress a giggle. "Hah! Yore ole granfer'd say anything for two pieces of pie, as I remember!"

Dinny nodded sagely at this remark. "Aye, an' loik as not ee'd say more furr three pieces o' pie, if'n you'm 'adn't stolen 'em furst, zurr Mouseythief!"

Gonff pulled a sad face at Martin. "Our Dinny can be very cruel at times!"

Martin tweaked his friend's ear playfully. "Oh, I wouldn't say cruel as much as truthful!"

By midday the Abbey was well lost to sight. The four travelers crossed the ditch, leaving behind the path and entering the cool green woodlands. Trimp scouted ahead a bit and found a beautiful site for their early noonday meal. Dabbling their footpaws in a small streamlet, they sat beneath a willow, lunching on apples, cheese and honeyscones, which they washed down with cold clear water. Trimp watched Martin unbuckle the great sword from his shoulderbelt and lay it down within easy pawreach. Admiringly, the hedgehog maid watched reflections of water patterns playing along the blade.

"What a wondrous thing your sword is, Martin."

The Warrior picked it up and held it lightly, testing its flawless balance. "Wondrous indeed, Trimp, but you must always remember what a sword is really made for. It has only one purpose, to slay. In the paws of the wrong beast it could become an awful thing, if 'twere used for evil purposes. As the Warrior who is privileged to carry the sword, I am honour bound to uphold two things: the safety of Redwall, and the memory of my father. The blade was made for me, but the hilt was always his."

Trimp felt slightly sorry for Martin. "This is a long trip we're undertaking and we have only the words of an old ballad to go on. Maybe your father never really said that he would return, or then again, he may have returned long seasons ago and sailed off once more. What I'm tryin' to say, Martin, is this: don't be surprised or disappointed if there is no trace of him on the northland shores when we finally get there."

The Warrior patted his companion's paw fondly. "I've thought of all that, missie, don't worry about me. I've decided to treat the whole thing as a summer journey with three good friends along for the walk. Right at this moment I feel lighter of heart and happier than I've been for quite some time. So hush now and don't fret over me."

Babbling streamwater, combined with distant birdsong and insects' lazy droning, soon had the four creatures taking a short nap in the shade and serenity offered by surrounding trees. They had not been dozing long when Martin became alert. Sitting bolt upright, he reached for his blade.

Trimp opened one eye enquiringly. "What is it, Martin, what's the m—"

The Warrior touched her lips lightly. "Quiet, miss, listen. Gonff, can you hear?"

The Mousethief had drawn his dagger and crawled forward. Crouching against the willow trunk, he strained to hear. "Gourds knockin' together—sounds like little drums. Chantin', too. Bit far off t'make it out proper, mate." He sniffed the air as if hoping for a breeze. "No smell, though, matey, mayhap just as well too."

Martin crouched alongside him and said one word.

"Flitchaye?"

Gonff nodded, still keeping his ears alerted for more sounds. "That's what I was thinkin', but what are Flitchaye doin' this far south?"

Martin shrugged. "Raiding party maybe?"

Trimp looked from one to the other anxiously. "What's a Flitchaye? Do we need to fear them?"

Martin explained.

"Flitchaye are a tribe of runty weasels. We don't fear them, but they're within a day's journey of Redwall, so we'd best go and see what they're up to."

As they tracked their way through silent woodlands towards the distant sound, Gonff whispered, "Flitchayes are a bad lot, missie. They use powerful herb smoke to stun their captives. You wouldn't see a Flitchaye 'til he's right on top of ye, 'cos they disguise themselves with weeds an' shrubs an' live underground mostly. Though if this lot are Flitchaye raiders, they'll stay above ground, not bein' on their own territory. Keep your head down an' stay back with Dinny, behind me'n'Martin."

Trimp's heart beat faster. She was very excited, but not afraid with Martin and Gonff leading the way. Skirting a fern bed they crept up behind a fallen sycamore, and as they stooped in its shelter the sounds grew more distinct. Voices were chanting in unison with the thokking noise of gourds being struck rhythmically together.

"We d'Flitchaye Flitchaye Flitchaye,
Worraworra gonnawinna lorralorra wars!"

Thockthockathockthock, thockathockathockthock!

Bushes rustled and a few twigs snapped. Peeping over the fungus-ridden trunk, Trimp blinked in surprise when she distinguished the shapes moving against the leafy terrain.

Close on twoscore Flitchaye came marching past, brandishing stoneheaded axes and carrying bundles of slender throwing spears. Smeared with plant dye and clad in a disguise of trailing weeds, the vermin were almost as one with their surroundings. It was a barbaric scene, heightened by the sight of a very young squirrel, paws bound and hobbled, being dragged along on a rope of vine thongs attached to his neck. Trimp's eyes began watering as four rearguard passed close to the sycamore trunk, for they carried big earthenware pots on hangers between them, averting their heads from the smoke which wreathed from the vessels. The hedgehog maid rubbed at her eyes, swaying as the smoke fogged her senses. Dinny slapped a glob of mud in her paws, murmuring low, "Yurr, missie, stick this on ee nose an' breathe through ee mouth!"

Trimp did as the mole advised and immediately felt better. She noticed that Martin and Gonff were doing the same thing to counteract the effect of the drugged smoke. When the column of Flitchayes had passed, the four friends sat down in the lee of the fallen trunk, and after a safe wait Gonff indicated that they clean off their noses.

Martin nodded grimly at Trimp. "Well, now you know what Flitchaye are like, the filthy villains. Did you see the little squirrel they'd taken?"

Trimp shuddered. "Poor little fellow. What'll they do to him?"

Martin clasped his swordhilt resolutely. "Nothing if we can help it, miss. Dinny, see if you can gather some ramsons."

The industrious mole was no sooner gone than he was back, carrying two of the broad-leafed plants, still with their tiny starlike flowers in bloom. Trimp took a step back from the pungent garlic-smelling things.

"Whew! Keep away from me with that lot, Din. I can't abide the smell of ramsons!"

Dinny chuckled as he stripped the leaves and rolled them into small solid plugs. "You'm bain't goin' to loik thiz, marm, but et could save ee loif. Yurr, take these."

Trimp's face was a mask of disgust as she accepted a pawful of the reeking wild garlic pellets from Dinny.

"Gurgh! We'll defeat the Flitchaye easily by throwing these at them. What a dreadful stink!"

Dinny passed the pellets around. Gonff chuckled gleefully. "We don't chuck them at the foebeast, missie, we stuff two up our noses an' chew the rest."

The hedgehog maid looked horrified at the idea. "Stuff them up our noses and chew them? You're joking!"

Martin was already plugging his nose with ramsons. "No joke, Trimp. The garlic odor will overpower the smell of any drugged herb that the Flitchaye have. Come on, miss, get on with it, we're losing time!"

With Martin in the lead they set off trailing the Flitchayes. Both Dinny and Gonff were unaffected by the malodorous aroma of ramsons—in fact, they seemed to be enjoying it. Martin endured his in stoic silence, but Trimp felt close to vomiting at the overpowering smell. Traveling silent and fast, they soon heard the foebeast up ahead. Dropping flat amid some bushes, Martin, Dinny and Trimp waited whilst Gonff scouted ahead. Trimp sat miserably in the deep loam, her entire being swamped by ramsons. Gonff rejoined them, quiet as a shadow drifting over grass. The Mousethief made his report swiftly.

"They're camped in a clearin' up ahead—some must've been already there. I counted fifty-one all told, all Flitchaye savages. Saw the liddle squirrel, too, they got him bound to a post in the middle o' their camp. Fifty's too many for us, mateys. 'Tis goin' t'be hard gettin' the young 'un out o' there. Any ideas, pals?"

Martin looked from one to the other before speaking. "Right, here's the plan. Listen carefully, because it all depends on pure bluff. If it works then we get out of there fast. Gonff, here's what you'll do, mate . . ."

4

A mess of bird bones and feathers mixed with squashed half-eaten fruit and vegetables littered the Flitchaye camp. Around the fire undersized weasels squabbled and fought tooth and claw over any morsel of food roasting in the flames. One, larger than the rest, his face daubed blue beneath a helmet of ivy and bugloss, grabbed a half-burnt wren carcass from a smaller Flitchaye. Snarling, the owner tried to retrieve his food from the big weasel, who booted him backward into the fire contemptuously. It was an act of wanton cruelty that caused great hilarity among the other vermin, who sniggered evilly as their scorched companion scrambled shrieking from the blaze and rolled about, trying to extinguish his smouldering fur.

The young squirrel, who was little more than a Dibbun, was trying to shake off the effects of the drugged smoke. He shrank back fearfully against the post he was bound to. Flitchayes with sharp sticks prodded him and licked their lips meaningfully. One weasel took out a blade and was about to start cutting the squirrel's bonds when the big Flitchaye spotted him and knocked him senseless with a well-aimed rock.

He stood over the fallen weasel, baring his stained fangs at the rest and speaking in his high-pitched growl. "Norra yet! Feed de swiggle, fatty 'im uppa plenny!" He thrust the remains of the dead bird at the helpless youngster, snarling into the squirrel's terrified face: "You eat. Commona, eaty allup!"

Martin strode nonchalantly into the camp, as if he was quite used to this sort of thing. A puzzled silence settled over the Flitchaye at the sight of the bold, unarmed stranger in their midst. Pushing them out of his way he went across to the two earthenware pots, still wreathing smoke from the drugged herbs which smouldered inside them. Leaning over, Martin appeared to sniff them both and gave a hard, scornful laugh.

"Hah! Don't think much o' yore cookin', ragbags!"

A gasp of surprise rose from the vermin. The stranger had suffered no ill effects from the fearful fumes! Still shouldering weasels aside, Martin pushed his way forcefully over to the little prisoner. Picking up the knife from the fallen weasel, he made as if to cut the squirrel free.

"Stoppima mousebeast!"

At the shout from their leader the Flitchaye surrounded Martin, hemming in on all sides. Swaggering forward, the big weasel thrust his ugly face close to that of Martin and sneered, "We d'Flitchaye, Flitchaye, Flitchaye!"

The crowd took up the chant, moving around the Warrior in a shuffling, stamping dance. Martin waited patiently awhile, an expression of bored indifference on his face. Then he pointed a paw at his own chest and shouted, "I Martin the Warrior!"

Quiet fell over the vermin, and they stood still. The leader pointed a stoneheaded axe at the lone mouse, repeating Martin's words as best he could. "Ma'tarn de Horrya!" He spat challengingly at the floor in front of the Warrior. Martin coolly returned the gesture, looking the weasel up and down insultingly as he spoke.

"Fish eye, you d'Fish eye?"

The Warrior had anticipated the Flitchaye leader's next move, and he took a pace smartly backward as the weasel swung his axe. The blow was delivered with such force that the Flitchaye could not stop it. He struck himself hard on the shin, cracking his bone audibly. Martin stretched both paws wide. Keeping his eyes on a double-topped oak at the camp's edge, he roared, "Redwaaaaaallll!"

Hidden by the foliage, Gonff held the sword like a spear and cast it accurately. To the Flitchaye it was magic! Seemingly zipping down out of the sky, the great blade thudded point first into the ground at Martin's side.

Wrenching it from the earth, the Warrior swung it skillfully, chopping a nearby vermin's bunch of throwing spears in half with a single swipe. It had the desired effect. Flitchaye scattered to get out of Martin's sword range, leaving him alone by the prisoner. Turning his back on the enemy, Martin gave the little squirrel a quick reassuring smile and whispered, "Don't move 'til I say, matey. Soon have y'out of here." The captive blinked with fright as Martin's sword hissed within a whisker of him, severing the ropes.

Whirring bright in the late afternoon sunlight, the sword weaved a deadly pattern as its owner wielded it. Martin narrowed his eyes to a fierce intensity, glaring slowly this way and that at the vermin.

"I Martin the Warrior, we go now!"

Gently lifting the dazed little squirrel on his shoulders, he turned and began walking from the camp. The leader, his face a mask of agony, limped forward, shouting, "Stoppa mousebeast, sto—"

His cry was cut short when a slingstone smashed his jaw and laid him flat. A female, obviously the leader's mate, dashed forward, but she too was felled by a slingstone which whacked her between the eyes. She fell like a log.

Martin muttered out the side of his mouth to the little one, "Good old Dinny, never known him to miss yet!" Then he turned sternly to the cowering Flitchaye. "I go, you stay, Fish eye, hah!"

At a nod from him, slingstones poured in from Gonff, Dinny and Trimp, causing confusion among the stunned Flitchaye.

Back among the shelter of some big trees, Martin passed his sword to Gonff.

"Good work, mates, but if I know Flitchaye they won't stay still for long. We've got to get out of here, fast!"

Trimp just had time to spit and blow, ridding herself of the hated ramsons, then she was running, paw in paw with Dinny, Martin leading and Gonff behind her, guarding the rear. Trees and bushes sped by in a green blur as the rescuers hurtled through the woodlands, with the first streaks of evening marking the sky. Breathless and quivering, they paused at a wide shallow stream. Trimp stooped and sucked up mouthfuls gratefully. Gonff struck her on the back, causing her to cough out the water.

"Don't drink now, matey, 'twill slow you up. Martin, listen!"

"Flitchayeeeeeeeee! Flitchayeeeeeeeeee!"

The blood-curdling shouts of vermin crying for revenge rang out through the trees. Tapping the back of Martin's head, the little squirrel, who now seemed completely recovered from the evil smoke, spoke for the first time.

"Chugger not wanna get eaten, quick, run!"

And run they did. Martin chose the streambed, to make tracking difficult, though it slowed their pace slightly. Pebbles clacked underpaw, water splashed noisily around the runners, and sometimes trailing crowfoot weeds tried to tangle them up. Gonff turned at the sound of rapidly advancing vermin, as the Flitchaye dashed screaming into the waters upstream.

"Flitchayeeeeee! Flitchayeeeeee!"

The Mousethief held a stone ready in his sling. "They've seen us, mates. I'll say this for the rascals, they're good fast runners. Should we make for the bank and head into the woods, Martin?"

Martin pressed on doggedly with Chugger clinging to his back. "No good, mate, they'd track wet pawprints easily. This water's getting deeper and they can only travel the same speed as us in a stream. Keep going!"

Further downstream the watercourse took a bend, getting deeper. It was now well above waist height and flowing fast. Dinny grunted to Trimp, "Oi doan't loik water, oi'm gurtly afeared of ee wet!"

The Flitchaye, who were still in the shallower water,

seemed to be gaining apace on their quarry. Gonff turned and brought one of the front runners down with a well-placed slingstone, and reloaded his sling immediately.

"They're too close for comfort now, mates. I reckon we'll have t'stand an' fight it out!"

"Gurr, no uz won't. Lookit, we'm be saved!"

In the curve of the streambend a big old crack willow, which had collapsed into the water from the crumbling bank, lay half in, half out of the flow, swaying gently.

Tripping and stumbling wildly, Dinny and Trimp waded through the eddying swirls, coughing and gasping, the food-packs they were carrying hampering them greatly. However, they made it over to the tree and hauled themselves on to its bushy top. Their added weight did the trick. There was a tearing of the last few roots as the willow upended and slid off into the stream.

Martin and Gonff were both slinging stones now, dodging the long thin throwing spears which the Flitchaye flung at them. The little squirrel Chugger clung to Martin's back, yelling hoarsely, "Fro' lotsa stones, don't lerra Fish eyes eat Chugga!"

The Warrior looked to Gonff for his sword. It was evident that ere long they would be battling paw to paw with the vermin in a life or death struggle.

"Hurr, 'urry an' jump on ee boat naow, mates!"

Dinny and Trimp had paddled the tree close up behind them, using long leafy branches they had broken from the willow. Martin pushed Gonff onto the makeshift vessel, and was about to pull himself aboard when a snarling Flitchaye grabbed his paw. For a moment the Warrior was helpless, clinging with one paw to the tree whilst being held by the vermin. Chugger scrambled up onto Martin's shoulder. Leaning over, he bit deep into the vermin's paw. An agonised scream ripped from the weasel's mouth as he let go of Martin's paw. Without a backward glance Martin heaved both himself and Chugger onto the willow trunk.

"Trimp, look after the little 'un. Gonff, you and I'll paddle. Dinny, get your sling and give those scum what for!"

Trimp felt the current pull strongly at the tree, then they were whipped away downstream, with Martin and Gonff paddling non-stop. Wedging little Chugger in the sprouting br____s up front, she went to assist Dinny. The mole was r____uffly as he whirled his sling and flung rocks with d____racy.

"____r, oi'll give ee billoh, you'm choild-eatin' vil-l____e a gurt supper o' stones for ee!"

____ were the volleys of rock and round pebble with ____y and Trimp peppered the Flitchaye that the ver-____or the banks, unable to keep balance and throw ____n the deepening water. Martin chanced a back-____at their molefriend, and winked at Gonff.

"____ld Din there, slinging away like a good 'un!"

____ admiringly, the Mousethief saw one of Dinny's ____Flitchaye squarely between both ears, toppling ____bank into the water.

"____y, that mole's enjoyin' himself all right!"

____hile the travelers made their way downstream, ____d by Flitchaye foes running along both sides of ____Martin peered ahead into the darkness and bit his ____t what he saw.

"____k for us ahead. The stream is dammed right

____ve a cry of dismay. "Look, some Flitchaye ____ahead. I can see the shapes of 'em, waiting on t____ ____ for us!"

____ugh, there were several creatures moving about on ____ dam, shrouded by the enclosing gloom. Dinny groaned.

"Hurr, us'n's be en real trouble naow!"

A hearty voice, quite unlike the Flitchaye, rang out from the dam as shadowy shapes dashed back and forth.

"Whupperyhoooo, cullies, I see Flitchayes. Whuppery-hooooo!"

Gonff began jumping up and down with joy. Cupping both paws around his mouth he yelled to the creatures on the dam.

"Garraway Bullow, ye ole dogswamper, 'tis me, the Mousethief!"

A figure hurled itself from the damtop, cut the water neatly and came swimming at them with the speed of an attacking pike. Chugger nearly fell from his perch with surprise as a large, powerful otter bounded onto the willow as if she had been propelled from the water on a giant spring. Gonff threw himself upon the otter and wrestled her the length of the trunk, both of them laughing and shouting.

"Well frazzle a frog, you ole Majesty, good to see yer!"

"Haharr, Gonffo me ole tatercake, you got a belly on ye like a poisoned plant louse! What brings ye to my neck o' the country, cullie?"

"Yah, we didn't wanna come, 'cept that there's more'n twoscore Flitchaye tryin' to slay an' eat us, mate!"

Garraway Bullow tossed Gonff aside like a leaf and stood up. She looked Martin up and down, shaking his paw firmly.

" 'Strewth, I wager you'd account for a few vermin before they brought ye down, with a sword like that. No matter, cullie, you leave the filthy Flitchaye to my fighters!" Placing a paw to her mouth, she gave a loud ear-piercing whistle, then called to the otters on the dam.

"Whupperyhoooo! 'Tis Flitchayes all right. Go an' get 'em afore they run off. Nought like a Flitchaye hide t'make cloaks for our liddle 'uns, an' winter's on'y two seasons off!"

Otters materialized from everywhere, big warlike beasts, tattooed from ear to tail and armed with double-tipped javelins. Whooping and bellowing, they took off after the weasels, who turned and fled in terror. The tree nosed gently into the dam as Gonff was making introductions.

"That there's Dinny Foremole, the pretty hogmaid's called Trimp, an' the serious-lookin' sword carrier, who ain't nearly so pretty as me, is Martin the Warrior, my matey. Friends, I want ye to meet Garraway Bullow, Queen of all the Nort—the Northern Otter River Tribes!"

Garraway helped them on to the dam, then she hauled the willow in sideways and lashed it to the timber and mud structure, remarking, "No sense in wastin' good wood—'twill strengthen our dam. Come on, Gonffo, an' bring yore mateys too. Seein' as you ain't been ate by Flitchayes, you must be 'ungry, right?"

Gonff laughed impudently at the Otterqueen. "D'ye ever recall a day when I wasn't hungry? I could eat a boiled otter right now, but I ain't got the time to cook ye, burly Bullow, so lead us t'the vittles!''

"Hoi, worra you fink, I'm a likkle flower growin' on dis tree? Worrabout Chugger?''

Trimp rescued the tiny squirrel from the branches, where he had been taking a short nap. He waved at Garraway Bullow.

"'Lo, my name be Chugger, I 'ungry too!''

The Otterqueen swung him up on to her brawny shoulder. "Haharrharr, you ain't back'ard in comin' forward, are ye, master Chugg? Well, I reckon you don't eat much, so we'll find a smidgen o' vittles for ye. Though I don't know rightly where yore from, or if'n our vittles'd suit ye, matey. How'd you get caught by the Flitchaye?''

The little fellow shrugged. "I live inna woods wiv Granny. One day she go 'sleep. Chugger shake'n'shake Granny, but she not wake up. So I on me own, 'til Fish eyes catcher me. But Martin, Trimp'n'Gonffo be's Chugger's friends now. You be my friend too?''

Garraway Bullow wiped something from her eye with the back of a paw. "I'd like t'meet the beast who says I ain't yore friend, Chugger mate!'

5

The otter den, or holt, consisted of a spacious cavern, dug into the bank, directly under where a massive ancient beech tree grew. Thick gnarled beech roots, criss-crossing in all directions, formed a ceiling, wallbeams, and in places long stout seats. It was lit by a great fire in a stonebuilt hearth and mantel, with ovens on both sides and cauldrons suspended over the flames by iron trivets. Otters were everywhere, though mainly babes and oldbeasts, since the mature males and females were out chasing Flitchayes. One wrinkled old male twitched his nose at Garraway, putting aside a wooden spoon he was carving.

"Why didn't ye tell me there was Flitchayes abroad? I'd 'ave gotten me javelins an' gone out with the crew. Young snipfur, y'are, never tell me nothin'!"

The Otterqueen inspected his work approvingly. "That's a fine spoon, Daddo. You put paid to more vermin than any-beast in yore young seasons. Better f'you to take things easy an' whittle nice spoons. We need more spoons."

The oldster sighed and resumed his carving. "Yore tellin' me, daughter. 'Tis those Kitts. They think spoons is boats, go out a-sailin' 'em an' lose 'em, they do."

The little otters, known as Kitts, were anxiously watching an old otterwife putting out spoons on the table for supper. She waggled a paw at them.

"I'll be countin' these spoons after, an' woe betide you Kitts if'n there's a single one gone astray!"

Gonff sniffed at one of the cauldrons appreciatively. "Mmm, Bubblin' Bobbs if I ain't mistaken!"

Trimp allowed the delicious aroma to wreath her face. "Smells marvellous, Gonff. What are Bubblin' Bobbs?"

The Mousethief managed to hook a sip on his knife edge before dodging a swipe from the big fat cook. "Well, first you put on a soup of chopped leeks, parsley an' shredded white turnips, with loads o' secret otter herbs. Then you get a paste made from cornflour, rolled oats an' carrot juice, roll it into dumplin's an' press a good fat watershrimp into the middle of each one. Fry 'em crispy in corn oil, then chuck 'em in the soup. At first they sink, but when the soup starts a-bubblin', the dumplin's bob to the top. That's why otters call it Bubblin' Bobbs. Come on, let's find a seat, Trimp. Supper looks about ready!"

Before the meal started, Daddo laid aside his carving and plucked a few chords with his tail on a flat round instrument, which made a banjo-like sound. He called to Garraway.

"C'mon, daughter, give us yore song afore the rest gits back."

Queen Garraway fluttered her eyelashes demurely and launched into a ballad with a voice that shook the very rafters.

"I'm bound to sing this song,
Though I shouldn't really ought,
I'm Queen of all these otters yet,
They call me Queen of Nort?
Yes Queen of Nort!
My goodness who'd have thought,
One day I'd be a Majesty,
Or something of that sort,
But all the otters that I see,
Must bow and wave their tails to me,

Whilst I just nod back graciously,
I'm Queen of Nort!
Good Queen of Nort,
My northern otter tribe,
Live all along the riverbanks,
And beat their foes with tails like planks,
I rule them wisely and give thanks,
I'm Queen of Nort!
There's nought I'd rather be,
I say to myself constantly,
Your Majesty is really me,
And don't I look like royalty,
I'm Quee-ee-ee-ee-heeeeen of Nort!
N . . . O . . . R . . . T, may I rule long and graciously!'"

Queen Garraway Bullow bowed modestly as the listeners
applauded, clipping the ear of a Kitt who was stuffing a
spoon in his apron pocket and rapping the paw of another
who was making rude gestures at her elders. Suddenly the
pre-supper calm was disrupted, as bounding and hooting the
fighting otters returned, hungry as hunters and flushed with
victory. Trimp found herself sandwiched between two husky
females, who jostled and joked.

"Ahoy there, mate, budge over a bit, will ye!"

"Yah, go an' budge yoreself, barrelbeam!"

Eventually, after much shoving and hustling, everybeast
was seated, and a big rough-looking one-eared male bellowed, "Whupperyhoo! Wheel in the vittles hard'n'fast
there!"

Queen Garraway threw him a frosty glance. "Not afore
you've made yore report, Cap'n Barrool!"

Barrool flicked his powerful tail and winked at her. "Oh,
that! Well, there ain't no more babe-eatin' wicked Flitchayes
plunderin' the land no more, we slew 'em all!"

Daddo eyed him doubtfully. "How d'y'know they're all
slain?"

One of the big females called out, "'Cos we asked 'em real
nice, an' any who said they wasn't got fixed up
good'n'quick!"

This brought roars of laughter from the fighters. Trimp

shook her head sadly, remarking to the female next to her, "How can you joke about killing other creatures?"

The otter's face became severe as she replied, "If you'd seen wot Flitchayes have done to old 'uns an' Kitts when they raided here in bygone seasons, you'd unnerstand, missie. Besides, the crew's only jestin' 'cos they all came back alive an' un'urt. This time we were lucky. Those scum didn't 'ave time to sneak up on us with their smoulderin' herbs an' knock us out, so they 'ad t'fight paw to paw, see."

The Bubbling Bobbs soup was delicious, as was the river-bank salad, arrowroot scones with honey, hotroot celery cream dip and dandelion cordial. Martin sat next to the Queen, explaining where the four were traveling to. Garraway was very helpful.

"Northern shores, eh? You'd be best to go by water, Martin."

"Hmm, maybe so, but you've dammed the stream and we've lost our willow—it's reinforcing your dam, remember?"

Garraway brushed aside his objections cheerfully. "We only dammed the stream to make a liddle waterfall an' a good slide for the Kitts. Another stream cuts in below the falls. We'll lend you a raft. It'll be easy, matey. The river runs straight west t'the sea shores, an' from there you only have t'head north along the coastline, right, Gonff?"

The Mousethief slurped the soup from his bowl. "Right, marm, an' thankee kindly for yore 'elp'n'hospitality!"

Garraway whacked him playfully with her tail. "Lissen, Gonff, you don't get off with it that easy. Come on, out with that flute of yours an' give us a jig. Er, 'Tails in the stream'? Aye, that's wot it was called!"

Gonff pulled out his flute and returned the whack, grinning. "Yore a wicked ole Queen, forcin' pore travelers t'sing for their supper. Right, here goes. 'Tails in the stream'!"

At the first merry trills of the flute every otter in the holt was up and jigging wildly. Martin, Trimp and Dinny had to climb to a high root perch to avoid the flailing tails and whirling limbs. They sat clapping their paws in time to the furious pace. Chugger was down on the floor with a gang of Kitts, linking tails as they whooped and kicked up footpaws, speeding round in a milling circle. Even the oldsters danced

vigorously. Every now and then the floor would reverberate
as otters thumped their tails on it in unison as they sang.

"Tails in the stream mates, tails in the stream,
No time t'sit around the bank an' dream,
Is it a pike perch roach or a bream?
No, 'tis an otter with his tail in the stream!
Whupperyhoo mates whupperyhoo,
Clouds are white an' the sky is blue,
Rap with y'tail an' stamp that paw,
Bow to y'partner an' around once more!
Bread'n'honey'n'cakes'n'cream,
Supper's in the oven an' tails in the stream!"

Gonff tootled faster and faster, and the dance speeded up
until the entire place was a blur of whirling fur and thumping
tails, finishing finally in a glorious collapse of giggling, bellowing otters. Gonff danced nimbly around them, waving his
flute and chuckling.

"Hahaha, c'mon now, you idle lot, up on y'paws. I'm goin'
to play 'Riverdogs ramble round'!"

Panting and blowing, Queen Garraway extricated herself
from the jumble, waving her paws. "Mercy, Gonffo, ye pick-
lenosed rogue, you'll have us danced out of our skins!"

Gonff helped her to a seat. "Right then, ole Majesty, sit an'
rest those ancient paws. Everybeast sit now, but leave a space
in the center. Hi there, Martin, get down here an' show 'em
the Battleblade Dance. C'mon, matey, don't be shy!"

Reluctantly Martin clambered down and unsheathed his
sword. "Gonff, I'm sure nobeast wants to see that old thing!"

The Mousethief appealed to the otters. "Course you do,
mates, don't you?"

Martin sighed. By the furious applause that followed his
friend's remark, it was obvious they wanted to see him perform. Trimp sat Chugger on her lap, settling down to watch
Redwall's Champion, whilst Gonff and Dinny set the stage.
A big red apple was placed on an oaken stump stool, and
Dinny sat on the floor, an upturned cooking pot in front of
him. When he began tapping it with his digging claws, it gave

out a sound like raindrops hitting a thin slate roof. Tock tokkatokka tock tokka tokka!

The Mousethief sat beside his molefriend. Taking two mushrooms he stood one on Dinny's head and the other on his own, then he held his paws straight in front of him, a dandelion held firmly in either one. Gonff signalled Martin with a wink. What Trimp witnessed then she could scarce believe, but it convinced the hogmaid that nobeast living could wield a sword like Martin the Warrior.

Martin began moving slowly at first to Dinny's beat, whirling his blade in all directions. Underpaw and overpaw, round both shoulders and overhead, the sword moved in a slow flashing pattern, humming and whirring, with fireglow playing along its blade. Everybeast stared in silent fascination at the wonderful display. Martin skiphopped, his keen blade tip missing both footpaws by a fraction, then he gave a piercing yell.

"Redwaaaaaaall!"

Dinny speeded up his rhythm, with Martin keeping perfect time, eyes half closed in concentration. Redwall's great sword became a blur of liquid light, traveling so fast that it left patterns upon the air, figures of eight, circles, crescents, even shapes like flowers.

Tocktokkatokkatocktokkatokkatocktokkatokka . . .

Faster and faster the mole's digging claws rapped on the upturned copper pot. Otters held their breath as the perilous blade sang within a whisker of their faces. Trimp nearly bit through her lip at what happened next. Martin gave a wild animal roar, and whirled upon his two friends, the blade striking down on their heads. Once! Twice! Both mushrooms fell apart sliced from cap to base. Like a living thing the sword hummed and flicked round Gonff's paws, lopping off the dandelion heads so that they curled lazily up in twin arcs, landing neatly 'twixt the cut mushrooms on Gonff and Dinny's heads. With a leap and a bound, Martin was at the big red apple, his lethal blade appearing to be six swords at once, chopping like lightning at the apple. Never once was the blade edge heard to strike the oaken stump, on which twelve perfect apple slices lay. Sweeping the flat blade to and fro, the Warrior sent the slices spinning into the watchers' laps. Tossing the sword in the air so that it turned on its own length, Martin took a half-pace backward. With an audible thud the sword came down point first to stand quivering in the floor. Martin clasped both paws on the pommel-stoned hilt and bowed.

The Nort otters went wild. They cheered and danced around Martin and his two friends, lifting them shoulder high and carrying them round the cave. Chugger was already up with his pals, the Kitts, stuffing apple slices in their mouths as they cast about for dandelions, mushrooms and swordlike sticks to repeat the Warrior's feat. Queen Garraway Bullow gripped Martin's paw tight, pumping it up and down fiercely.

"Never seen aught like that on land or water, matey. Hoho! Thought you was goin' to make two moles out o' Dinny an' leave ole Gonffo pawless for a moment back there. You'll have t'show me how t'do it, Martin. Great thunder, matey, wot I wouldn't give for a sword like that'n o' yours!"

When the Warrior could get a word in edgeways, he shook his head ruefully at the crowd of admiring otters.

"Please, 'twas only a fancy exercise in sword control I thought up to relieve the boredom of training. Normally I wouldn't let anybeast see me do it, but I made the mistake of performing it once at a Redwall feast and Gonff's been trying to talk me into doing it again ever since."

Gonff patted his friend's back, obviously proud of his skill. "Fiddley dee, mate, shows yore a real Warrior. Huh, if'n I could do that I'd be at it ten times a day for sure!"

Late that night Martin sat alone on the dam. Inside the holt of Queen Garraway it was snug and warm, and he could hear the snores and murmurs of sleep talkers drifting forth into the soft summer darkness. Martin smiled, recalling how Gonff had grabbed the sword and told a disobedient gang of Kitts about a tail-chopping trick he knew, for naughty little otters who would not go to sleep. It worked like a treat—they fled to their beds instantly. The Warrior stared into the night, wondering what sort of a father Luke had been. He wrestled with fogged memories, confusing the images of his mother Sayna and his grandmother Windred, as they merged together in his mind's eye. He tossed a stone into the water, watching the moon-rimmed ripples. What sort of place had the far north shores been? Had Luke his father ever kept his word and returned there? It was all too puzzling, so he turned his mind to thoughts of the Abbey. What would Redwall look like, one day when it was finally completed? That turned out to be a puzzle too.

Next morning Queen Garraway took the travelers beyond her dam. There had once been a broad waterfall further down the stream, but the damming had cut it down to half its original size, allowing the otters to build a steep mudslide. Squeaking Kitts, covered from ears to tails in wet brown clay, shot down it like stones from a sling, splashing into the pool below and emerging clean of mud. The friends laughed uproariously at their antics. Trimp pointed out one, zooming down backwards.

"Heeheehee, look at that liddle scamp. Bet he'd catch it off his mother if she saw him doing that!"

With a resounding splash the little one hit the water, vanished and came up again, washed recognizable. Trimp hid a smile as Dinny roared gruffly at the culprit: "Yurr, git out'n thurr, maister Chugg. You'm bain't no h'otter—you'm apposed t'be ee squiggle, ee likkle rip!"

Chugger wrinkled his nose at the mole. "I norra swiggle no more. Chugger a notter now!"

Crafty Gonff waved to the squirrelbabe. "Righto then, otter matey, you stay there. We're goin' now."

Chugger scrambled up the bank and clung to Trimp. "Norra notter no more. Chugger go wiv you to da norfen seashores. 'Urry up, Martin, we go now!"

Below the falls, the pool narrowed again into the stream. Queen Garraway lifted the fringe of bushes growing on its bank, showing them their transport.

"Here 'tis, mates, a stout liddle raft. C'mon, Gonffo, lend a paw to pull it out here."

It had a collapsible mast and a sail which would double as a tent, plus four long ash poles, paddle-shaped at one end. They heaved it into the water and leaped aboard. Martin shook the Otterqueen's paw heartily.

"Thank you for everything, Majesty. May your tribe live in peace and plenty here always!"

The brawny otter grinned cheerfully at them. "Thankee, an' may yore journey be a safe 'un. Go now, find what ye seek, an' don't let ole Gonffo git his nose into the grub supplies too often!'

6

By mid-morning the stream had widened out considerably, small white clouds decorated the sunny skies and a gentle breeze convinced the friends they should erect the mastpole and spread sail. Dinny was never fond of water, and had to be dug out of the jumble of sail canvas where he had hidden himself. Gonff, however, took on a decidedly nautical mood, calling out orders.

"Ahoy, mateys, rig up that mastpole amidships, will ye? Set yon sail an' unfurl 'er smartlike to catch the breeze!"

Martin and Trimp chuckled as Dinny threw a derisory salute.

"Aye aye, Cap'n Gonff zurr. Do ee got any more h'orders furr uz common waterbeasties?"

Hiding a grin, Gonff called back haughtily, "I say, Martin, tie a rock t'that fat ole mole's tail an' chuck him in the river, will you? He's slowin' us up!"

Bushy-edged banks slipped by, casting lacy patterns of sunshadow on the translucent waters. Trimp munched on a damson scone and sipped raspberry cordial.

"Ah, this is the life, pals . . . Ouch!"

A muddy stick came spinning out of the northbank bushes, striking her on the cheek, followed by a mocking imitation of the hogmaid's voice.

"This's the life, pals, heeheehee!"

Martin grabbed a pole and punted the raft towards the south bank. Gonff's sharp eyes picked out the culprit.

"There he is, see, runnin' along behind the bushes!"

They followed the direction of Gonff's outstretched paw. A young grey-brown rat was barely visible amid the foliage. Then it emerged on to the bank, pointing back at the Mousethief and mimicking his voice in a nasty manner.

"Runnin' along be'ind the bushes, be'ind the bushes, heehee!"

Martin's grip relaxed on his swordhilt. "Ignore the little villain. He's only trying to annoy us."

The rat flung another stick, but the raft was now too far away from the north bank to be hit. He stuck out his tongue at Martin. "Ignore the liddle villain, liddle villain, heeheehee!"

Chugger looked stern, and shook a tiny paw at the rat. "Go 'way, naughty mouse, or I biff ya!"

Martin took hold of the little squirrel, who was about to jump from the raft, and held him wriggling in the air. "Now now, I told you, ignore the naughty mouse!"

But something unlikeable in the creature's swaggering attitude caught Gonff's attention. He stood up. "I thought that was a mouse at first, but he's a sneaky young water rat. Look at that thick tail, mates!"

The rat stuck his claws in both ears and waggled them impudently at the Mousethief, dancing up and down provokingly. "Oh, look at 'is tail, mates, look at 'is tail. Heehee!"

Gonff whipped out his sling, fitted a small pebble to it and lobbed it expertly off. The stone, which Gonff had not cast with any great force, caught the rat a stinging blow on the tail. It leaped up and down, clinging to its tail and howling tearfully.

"Owowowowow, the mouse nearly slayed me, owowowowow!"

Gonff returned his impression of the whining vermin. "Owowow, naughty mouse nearly slayed me, owow!"

The rat stopped wailing, his face a picture of fury. "You shut ya face. Think ya funny, don't ya?"

Trimp came to stand beside Gonff. "What's the matter, rat, don't you like a taste of your own medicine? Be off with you, go and boil your ugly head!"

The rat kept running along the bank to keep up with the raft, throwing twigs, mud and anything he could lay paws upon. But they fell far short of the travelers. He was livid with rage, shrieking out at them, "Oh, you done it now, wait-'n'see! Nearly slayed Riddig, son of mighty Girfang, Boss of alla streamrats!"

Gonff fitted another stone to his sling, a proper-sized rock this time. "Ah, stop whingin' an' run off home to yore daddy. Quick now, or I'll show ye what a real slingstone can do. I'll give ye t'the count o' three, rat. One, two . . ."

Riddig stopped running and ducked off hastily into the bushes, still calling out threats to his enemies.

"Don't go 'sleep t'night—better not turn yer back. Youse lot are all deadbeasts, wait'n'see!"

Martin sighed, shaking his head at Gonff. "That's all we need, more trouble. First the Flitchaye, now streamrats. Didn't I tell you to ignore him?"

Gonff shrugged apologetically. "Nasty liddle vermin. Couldn't 'elp myself, mate."

Trimp was about to agree when Dinny interrupted.

"Burr, nor could oi, Marthen, tho' oi'd 'a' gotten ee vurmint a gudd crack furst toim wi' moi slinger!"

Chugger thrust out his little jaw truculently. "An' I woulda swimmed over an' bited 'is tail off too!"

Martin tickled Chugger behind the ear fondly. "I wager that would've made him jump, eh, Chugg? Personally I felt a desire to kick that young horror's tail up and down the bank a bit, to teach him a lesson in manners. But keep your eyes peeled, mates. I've a feeling we haven't heard the last of this little incident."

The remainder of a pleasant day was spoiled for Trimp. She watched every rustle of bush or reed along the banks, expecting at any moment to see a mob of rats come springing out at them. However, the situation did not seem to bother her companions a bit. Chugger curled up amid the food packs and snored like a holtful of otters, whilst Martin, Dinny and Gonff chatted amiably, lying back and trailing their paws in the water. Had Trimp observed them more closely she would have noticed that the three Redwallers were alert as hunting hawks, keeping their weapons close by at all times.

Evening fell, and still there was no sign of rats. Martin took precautions by nosing the raft onto a rock which jutted up in center stream, and making a rope fast to it. Dinny fished about until he located a broad flat stone close to the rock. Hauling it aboard, the clever mole built a small fire on it. Martin chopped vegetables with his sword, whilst Trimp dug out dried watershrimp and herbs from a haversack. Gonff filled their small cauldron with fresh streamwater, and Chugger sat warming his paws by the fire. Martin tossed the vegetables into the pot and wiped his sword clean.

"A fire at night isn't the best idea in these parts, Din."

The mole watched his soup carefully as he stirred it. "May'ap 'tain't, zurr, but if'n anybeast be a-goin' to attack us'n's, they'd do et, foire or not. Breezes on ee water be a bit chill. Nought loik a gudd drop o' soup, noice an' 'ot, to keep ee warm an' 'appy!"

Gonff cut a loaf of ryebread into chunks. "Can't argue with mole logic, mate, ole Din's right."

Dinny's soup was good, and they sat around the cauldron, each with a wooden spoon and a chunk of bread, sharing the meal in true traveler fashion. Martin set up two oarpoles and brought the sail forward, draping it over them as a precaution against rain during the night. Trimp found a narrow flagon of elderberry wine and they passed it round, each taking a few sips.

The hogmaid smiled. "There, that should keep the chills away. What now, mates?"

Gonff smiled back at her. "Now you give us a song, missie."

"No no, my voice would carry over water. Let Dinny sing."

A look passed between Martin and Gonff, and they both sighed.

"Never heard a mole sing before, have you, Trimp?"

"No, I can't say I have. Why?"

"Oh, nothin', mate. You're sure you want t'hear molesong?"

"Of course I do, that's if Dinny would be kind enough to oblige us with one of his songs."

The mole's homely face creased deeply with pleasure. "Hurr, 'ow cudd oi refuse a pretty maid loik ee, miz!" Then he placed a paw over one ear in traditional molesinger's manner and launched into a mole ballad.

"Ho doodlum roodlum wurdilum day,
All on ee broight zummer mornin'!
Bold Doogul mole were gurtly brave,
As oi wurr told boi moi muther,
Furr maidens boi the score ee'd save,
Loik chesknutts wun arfter anuther,
Each morn ee rode owt frum 'is abode,
A-mounted on a milky whoit toad,
Surchin' ee danjeruss forest road,
A-lukkin' furr ee maidens.

Ho doodlum roodlum wurdilum day,
All on ee broight zummer mornin'!
Ee spied a gurt fat molewoif thurr,
An' doffed 'is 'at to 'er proudly,
Which froikkened ee molewoif out'n 'er wits,
She'm started to wail roight loudly,
Ee shuvved 'er up onna back of 'is toad,
An' troid t'ride off down ee road,
But two fat moles was an 'evvy load,
An' ee toad wurr crushed loik a beekle.

Ho doodlum roodlum wurdilum day,
All on ee broight zummer mornin'!
Then oop cumm ee gudd an' stoutly mole,
Ee croid, 'Woe thurr bless moi loif,
Thurr be two villyuns tryin' to steal,
Moi dear ole fatty gurt woif!'
So pullin' owt a knotty ash club,
Bowth toad an' Doogul ee did drub,

Ee gave 'em black'n'bloo lumps t'rub,
  An' 'is woif gave 'im cabbage furr supper."

Trimp and little Chugger were laughing so hard that they
had trouble trying to join in on the chorus. Gonff shook his
head at them sadly.

"Don't encourage him, mates. I've heard that song—
there's still another forty-seven verses t'go yet!"

Martin leaped on Dinny suddenly, stifling the mole's
mouth with both paws. Trimp sniffed at the Warrior severely.

"Don't be so bad mannered, sir. Let poor Dinny finish his
song. Chugger and I were enjoying it!"

Martin shot her a warning glance, his voice an urgent
whisper. "Don't make another sound, Trimp. Gonff, throw
some water on that fire, and let's get in the stream, quick!"

They obeyed Martin without question. Gonff flung water
on the flames, which sizzled and hissed in clouds of white
steam. Trimp found herself breathless in the cold stream,
pulled there by Dinny. Keeping their heads low, the travelers
clung to the raft. A hail of arrows hit the sailcloth shelter,
some zipping through, others bouncing off to stick in the
deck timbers. These were followed by a volley of slingstones
and a couple of throwing spears, both of which buried their
points in the food haversacks. Then there was silence.

Chugger clung to Martin's neck, shivering. "I cold an' wet,
not nice inna water!"

Another lot of arrows hit the raft. Martin stroked the little
squirrel's head, whispering softly, "Ssshhh now, Chugg.
Right, let's swim over to the far bank. Try not to make any
splashes, go easy."

As they swam off, a harsh voice called from the opposite
bank, "Give 'em some more just t'make sure, then we'll
board the raft an' have fun with any still breathin'!"

The travelers made it safely to the far bank. Trimp found
some dry grass and rolled Chugger in it. Then she joined her
friends, watching in the thick bushes by the stream's edge.
Swaying under the impact, the raft took several more salvos
of missiles. Gonff nudged Dinny. "D'you reckon we're slain
by now, Din?"

"Hurr, they'm ratters given ee raft 'nuff to finish off ee troib o' badgerfolk, oi be thinken!"

Martin began gathering pawfuls of pebbles from the shallows. "Let's see how they like a spot of sniping. Wait for my word."

Launching crude logboats, the rats made it clumsily across to the raft. There were so many of them that the raft began to tilt crazily. Boss Girfang, their leader, caught hold of his son Riddig, who was trying to undo one of the haversacks, and snarled at the young rat, "Well, where are they, these creatures that tried t'slay yer? I don't see 'em anywheres."

Riddig cowered under his father's angry glare. "I dunno where they went, but there was five o' them, two ole mice, a fat mole, a young 'og an' a liddle squirrel. They all battered me wid slingstones fer no reason at all. I was jus' lyin' on the bank, takin' a nap!"

Girfang tweaked his son's ear sharply. "An' you jus' lay there an' let 'em do it, you, a Boss's son? Stinkin' liddle coward, y'make me sick!"

Riddig squealed as Girfang stamped on his tail, protesting, "I never jus' lay there. I got the 'og wid a stick an' the two mice wid big round stones. They can't 'ave got far!"

A dull thud sounded in the night, and one of the rats toppled into the water. Girfang turned on the rest.

"Be still an' leave them 'aversacks alone or you'll 'ave us all in the stream. Stop rockin' the raft, willyer!"

Thonk! A rat screeched and clapped both paws to his jaw. Girfang grabbed the nearest rat, using him as a shield.

"Somebeast's slingin' at us. Get 'em!"

Splat! Thwack! Crack! Thunk!

Vermin let out agonised yells, two fell in the stream, and the raft rocked wildly as big round river pebbles whizzed out of the darkness, causing injury and chaos.

Girfang leaped with the others into the water. Seizing their logboats' sides, they swam madly back to their own bank, peppered relentlessly with stones. No sooner was Girfang on dry land than the slinging ceased. He grabbed Riddig roughly by the scruff and hauled him ashore, then snapped a willow switch from a young sapling.

"Two ole mice, a fat mole, a young 'og an' a liddle squirrel, eh? Yew rotten barefaced liar!"

Riddig danced in an agonised circle, his father holding
him tight by the neck scruff and whaling away mercilessly
with the willow switch.

"Yeeeee! Oohooh! I wuz tellin' the truth, sir, 'onest I was!
Aaaaagh! Yeekyeek! Owowowow!"

"Truth? Yew wouldn't know truth if'n it fell on yer 'ead
out of a tree, yer mealy-mouthed fork-tongued worm!" Girfang laid on heavily with the switch, punctuating each word
to drive home his message. "There was more'n five beasts
stonin' us there, yew forty-faced toad. Must've been at least a
dozen, all trained warriors by the way they could aim an' hit
so good! Own up, now. There was twelve of 'em, mostly
otters from upstream, wasn't there, ye wretch? Tell the truth
or I'll flay yer!"

Gonff twirled his sling idly, winking at Trimp as they
crouched in the bushes on the far bank. "Does yore heart
good lissenin' t'justice bein' done, missie."

The hedgehog maid listened with satisfaction as she heard
Riddig's wails echoing into the night.

"Wahaaar, there was twelve otters beside the others. Don't
'it me no more, Boss, please! Twelve otters, you was right.
Wahaaahaaahaaa!"

Following this revelation, Girfang could be heard calling
to the rest of his tribe as they deserted him. "Where are you
lot off to? Git back 'ere!"

Derisive shouts followed his command. "Yah, we ain't
scrappin' wid no twelve otters. Go an' fight yer brat's battles
yerself. Yore Riddig started it!"

Gonff grinned, stowing his sling about his waist. "Y'know
what they say, truth never hurt anybeast!"

Martin unbuckled his sword and borrowed Gonff's dagger.
"So they say, mate, but you try telling that to Riddig. I wager
he's sorry he ever threw that stick at Trimp. Wait here, I'll
swim out to our raft and cut it loose."

Next morning, dry and well breakfasted, the friends sailed
onward, staying close to the far bank. Summer warmth raised

their spirits, with Gonff confiding aloud to Martin and Trimp, "I reckon it wasn't Riddig caused all that fuss, y'know."

Trimp looked up from the dough she was kneading for lunch. "Was it not? Who do you think was responsible, then?"

"Dinny's singin', of course. It drove the rats wild an' they attacked us just to stop the 'orrible noise, missie."

"Hurr, you'm turrible crool, zurr Gonffen. Moi ole granmum allus said oi 'ad a voice loik ee lark at furst loight."

"Haha, that's 'cos yore ole grandmum was deaf as a post, Din."

Dinny continued chopping candied fruit, not raising his eyes. "Aye, an' thy ole grandad allus said you'm wurr ee most gurtly 'andsome creature. Noice ole beast ee wurr. Oi used to take 'im furr walks lest ee bump into trees. Bloind ee wurr, pore creetur!"

High noon found them pulled in to a shady inlet out of the hot midday sun. Trimp wanted to bake a candied fruit turnover, but she had no oven. With mole ingenuity, Dinny solved the problem. He cemented flat pieces of shale together with stiff brown clay and water, making a neat little box, which, with the turnover inside, was placed on the fire. Martin and Gonff repaired the torn sail, rent by rat weapons. Nobeast paid much attention to little Chugger. Trimp warned him to stay close to camp, and he did for a while, but whilst Trimp was busy with her cooking and Dinny was digging for fresh roots and vegetables, Chugger wandered off.

Trimp called to her friends. "Come on, lunch is ready. Bring your appetite with you!"

Hastily washing their paws in the stream, they strolled into camp, sniffing the air appreciatively.

"Boi okey, sumthin' smells noice, marm!"

"Mmm, candied fruit turnover, just the thing!"

"Aye, 'tis ages since I tasted fruit turnover!"

The hedgehog maid had discovered a big flagon of new cider at the bottom of Martin's pack. She poured out beakers for all and laid out chunks of hot turnover on a piece of birch bark she had found before saying, "Where's that rascal Chugger got to?"

Dinny shrugged as he helped himself to lunch. "Ho, ee'm abowt yurr someplace, oi 'spect. You see'd 'im?"

Martin took a gulp of the crisp-tasting apple cider. "Me? No, I thought he was with you, Din. Me an' Gonff were busy fixing up the raft. Did you notice Chugg around, Gonff?"

The Mousethief shook his head. "No, sorry, I ain't seen him." Seating himself, he began blowing on his turnover to cool it. "Hah, ole Chugg'll soon come runnin' when he smells yore cookin', miss Trimp, you'll see!"

But Chugger didn't come. They sat and ate lunch, glancing about and giving an occasional shout of the little squirrel's name. Still nothing.

Trimp was worried. "Martin, will you go and take a good look around? I'm sure Chugger can't have gone far."

The Warrior put aside his food. "Let's all take a look!"

Spreading out in different directions they began combing the area. Martin and Gonff went east and west along the bank, whilst Dinny searched in and around the camp area, in case Chugger was having a game with them. Trimp ventured alone into the woodland, knowing that Martin and Gonff would circle inward and meet up with her when they had searched the bank both ways. Tree shelter became thick and gloomy, blocking out most of the sunlight and leaving the depths cloaked in a murky green twilight. The hedgehog maid went cautiously, calling out in a subdued voice, "Chugger, are you there, mate? Come out, my little Chugg!"

Her voice fell dead upon her ears, with no echo. She felt very small amid the tall columns of oak, elm and beech. Then her sharp ears began to pick up the odd noise, and she smiled to herself. That would be Chugger, playing one of his little tricks, stalking her mischievously. She decided to hide and turn the tables on him. Swiftly Trimp ran behind a broad bump-gnarled black poplar, and was knocked flat by the creature that had been following her. She squeaked in fright at the sight of it.

7

The gigantic goshawk took a pace backward, allowing Trimp to rise unsteadily. From its black hooked talons and bright yellow legs up the mighty body, feathered in brown-tipped white plumage, to the mottled headcap, it was the most impressive bird Trimp had ever seen. Twin gleaming gold eyes with savage black pupils stared down at her over a lethally curved beak. The goshawk's voice was rasping, harsh. "What doest thou in my domain, hedgepig?"

Trimp had never been called a hedgepig. Bravely she decided to retaliate, and swallowing hard she adopted a stern tone. "Not that it's any of your business, bird, but I'm searching for my friend, a baby squirrel named Chugger!"

The goshawk twitched his head to one side. He had never been addressed as bird before. "Prithee, have a care, spinedame. I am called Krar the Woodwatcher. None hath called me bird and lived!"

Trimp became bolder. She stared levelly at the goshawk. "Aye, and I'm called Trimp the Rover by those with any manners. None have called me hedgepig and lived—er, that goes for spinedame also!"

It was Trimp's turn to take a backward step. She thought Krar was about to eat her, but a moment later she realized that he was actually smiling at her, an unusual occurrence in a hawk.

"Thou art a bold beast, Trimprover. Thine enemies must be few methinks, or dead. Say again the name of this squirrelmite thou seekest."

"Chugger, but he'll answer to Chugg. He's only a babe."

The forest green was blotted out as Krar spread his colossal wings. He touched Trimp's head with a wingtip. "Do you tarry here, Trimprover, whilst I make enquiries."

Trimp was knocked flat by the backrush of air as Krar flapped his wings and rose among the tree trunks. Leaves drifted down through a golden shaft of sunlight as he shot like an arrow through the woodland canopy.

Gonff came trotting through the woodland, catching sight of his friend as he hurried in from the opposite direction.

"Ahoy, Martin, no sign of the liddle feller?"

"None, mate. Have y'seen Trimp?"

"Hi, you two, I'm over here!"

Both ran over to where Trimp was sitting with her back against the poplar, picking leaves from her headspikes. Gonff stood, paws akimbo, shaking his head at her.

"Well, missie, this's a nice how d'ye do, us two runnin' ourselves ragged along the streambanks an' through the woods, an' you sittin' here coolin' yore paws, very nice!"

Trimp stood up, brushing herself off. "Actually I'm waiting for word of Chugger at any moment. Now I don't want either of you to be afraid."

Martin looked about and spread his paws wide. "Afraid of what, Trimp?"

She pointed upward. "That!"

Entering the woodland through the hole he had made in the treetops, Krar Woodwatcher zoomed in like a thunderbolt. All three travelers were knocked flat by the wind from his wings as he landed.

Trimp patted one of Krar's talons. "Now you'll have to stop doing that, Krar, it'll injure some poor beast one day.

These are my good friends, Martin the Warrior and Gonff, Prince of Mousethieves. Meet Krar Woodwatcher, mates. These woodlands belong to him!"

Martin and Gonff gulped and bowed low at the same time. Krar closed both eyes and clacked his beak politely, as goshawks do when greeting friends. He turned to Trimp.

"Thy friend the squirrelmite is taken captive in the talons of laggardly carrion—crows, I fear. Alas, 'tis sad news."

Trimp was about to speak when Gonff silenced her with a wink. The artful Mousethief addressed himself to the goshawk, cleverly using the bird's own antiquated mode of speech.

"Lackaday, sirrah, and thou callest thyself ruler of this fiefdom? Were I in thy place I'd say fie upon myself methinks, allowing carrion to hold innocent babes in durance. 'Tis not the worthy act of a just lord!"

Much to Martin and Trimp's surprise, the huge goshawk shifted from one leg to the other, his head hanging slightly. "Thou speakest truly, O Mousethief. 'Tis my domain and 'twas fitting I stand chided for lack of vigilance."

Gonff shook his head doubtfully. "I fain would give thee a chance to redeem thyself, lord."

Crouching low, the huge bird spread his wings wide upon the ground, his face a picture of abject misery, his very feathers seeming to droop. "Then truly woe betide me, though I crave a boon from thee, Prince of Mousethieves. Give me leave to effect rescue of thy vassal, I beg ye. Grant me this favour and I will be in thy debt from this day henceforth!"

A wave of pity swept over Trimp as she watched Krar, prostrate at Gonff's footpaws. She could not keep from crying out, "Oh, say you will, Gonff. Let him do it!"

The Mousethief folded his paws stubbornly. Turning his back on the goshawk, he winked at Martin and Trimp as he spoke. "Silence, maid, cease thy prattling! For how doth the Prince of Mousethieves know this creature will cleave true unto his word?"

Martin drew his sword. Touching Krar's bowed head with it, he kissed the blade and announced dramatically, "I, Martin of Redwall, do give my pledge and bond that Krar Woodwatcher, lord of this place, will honour thy trust, O Prince. For is he not a warrior born, like myself, and bound in word and deed to protect lesser creatures!"

Gonff paced up and down, as if digesting this statement. Then he placed his footpaw under Krar's beak. "Say where is this place yon foul crows abide?"

A note of hope crept into the goshawk's voice. "Some pines in a clearing, right close to here, O Prince. Thou and thy friends mayst follow me and watch whilst I free thy servant. But 'tis better it be done soon, for tarrying is unwise, methinks!" He watched avidly as Gonff nodded.

"Mayhap 'tis so. Go then, but hearken, thou hast this warrior to thank for his surety."

A transformation came over the goshawk. He dipped his lethal beak and kissed Gonff's footpaw. "My thanks to thee, O Prince!" Standing tall, Krar spread his immense wings, saluting Martin, who was dwarfed in his shadow. "And my thanks to thee, sire. Karraharrakraaaaaaarrr!"

The goshawk's blood-chilling war cry rang out as he whooshed into the air, bowling the three friends over. Trimp sprang up, pulling leaves from her spines.

"I wish he wouldn't do that! Gonff, how did you know he'd act like that?"

The Mousethief flicked a paw at Martin. "Oh, it was easy. I know how warriors think—I've lived with one most of my life, haven't I, matey?"

Martin tweaked his friend's tail. "Cut the chatter or we'll lose sight of Krar!"

Running as fast as they could, the friends kept Krar in sight as he winged slowly along, just beneath the treetops, taking care not to lose them. After a while they saw a broad green hillock thrusting itself above the woodland. At its top was a pine grove. Krar swooped down, landing alongside Gonff.

"Yonder lies the carrion stronghold, O Prince. I pray thee make no move. We have been seen!"

As he spoke a crowd of grey-black crows of the hooded variety came fluttering out of the pines like ragged dark pieces of cloth blown on the wind, coming to rest on the level sward below the hill. Their bold, harsh chatter filled the air as they swaggered forward to meet the interlopers, wings folded, beaks thrust forth aggressively. In a less fraught situation the sight of their curious rolling gait might have been comical, but these were savage birds, who brooked no trespassers on their land. Krar whispered, "Bide here, friends. Warrior, keep thy blade ready. Now, I will go hence and parley, for I know the carrion tongue."

He strode out, erect and disdainful, and a big crow, far heavier than the rest, waddled forward to meet him. At a point between the crows and the travelers both birds halted. Eye to eye they stood, beaks almost touching. The crow leader hit the soil several times with his beak, casually, as if showing his contempt by digging for worms.

He made harsh cawing noises. "Kraaaw rakkachakka krawk karraaaaak?"

The goshawk rapped sharply back at him. "Arrakkarraka!"

The crow gestured carelessly with one wing. "Nakraaaak!"

Evidently it was not the answer Krar desired. The goshawk made his move without a moment's hesitation.

Charging forward, he slammed the crow to the ground with a ferocious headbutt and began hammering him ruthlessly with beak and talons. Cawing and hopping about excitedly, the crow gang called out encouragement to their leader, but he did not possess the warrior's heart or ferocity of the goshawk. It was over in a trice. A few long grey-black feathers flew in the air and the crow leader lay defeated.

With sharp pecks and talon scratches, Krar forced the crow to stand. The brave goshawk rapped out a command at his beaten foe. "Chavaaragg!"

Humiliated, the crow turned to face his gang, spreading his wings limply and dropping them so they trailed upon the grass.

Trimp nudged Martin. "I know Krar has won, but what's he doing?"

The Warrior had understood it all, he knew. "Those feathers that you see are the crow's pinfeathers. Krar ripped them out. That crow will never be able to fly again. Krar forced him to show his wings to the others as a warning. Hush now, Trimp, I want to see what happens next!"

The goshawk took to the air. Sailing over the heads of the crows, he winged upwards, landing in the biggest nest, atop the highest tree. A female crow shot out of it with a terrified squawk. Krar dipped his beak into the nest and came up with an egg in it. He put the egg back. Spreading his wings he flapped them, screeching harshly at the crows. Then with a powerful thrust he ripped a chunk from the nest with his talons and cast it down to earth. Pandemonium broke out down below. The crows dashed into the pine grove, cawing and leaping about in distress. Martin spoke as he watched them, having interpreted the goshawk's move.

"He's threatening to rip all the nests to shreds, starting with the crow leader's, unless they bring out Chugger. Watch!"

"Trimp! Gonff! It me, Chugg, here I are!"

Dashing out of the pine grove, with the crows behind shooing him on, Chugger hurtled forward, tripping and rolling down the hill, giggling as he went. "Heeheehee, yah yah ole fedderybums!"

Trimp swept him up into her paws, kissing the little fellow and lecturing him at the same time. "Such language, master Chugg. Thank the seasons you're safe. Why did you go wandering off like that, eh? Oh, my little Chugg, you had us worried to death!"

Chugger threw his tiny paws wide, grinning broadly. "See, it me, Chugg! I norra hurted, big birds frykkened o' me, I smacka smacka dem wiv big sticks, ho yes!"

Gonff hugged Chugger fondly, then turned stern. "You liddle fibber, smackin' crows with big sticks indeed. But let me tell you, bucko, remember what Girfang did to young Riddig, eh? Well, any more fibs an' runnin' off when yore told to stay near camp an' you'll get the same off me!"

Chugger hid his face in Trimp's tunic and sulked. Martin threw a paw about Gonff's shoulders. "Big old softie, I'll wager you wouldn't have the heart to lay a paw on Chugger, would you, O Prince?"

The Mousethief struck a regal pose, looking down his nose. "Oh, I don't know, you'd be surprised what us royal types can do when we're in the mood. I usually have any mouse who leans upon me beheaded, so remove your paw, common fellow, afore you incur me wrath!"

Martin looked at Trimp in mock horror. "Such an air of command these royal ones have about them!"

The hedgehog kicked Gonff lightly in the tail. "Yes, O Prince, it's your turn to cook the supper when we get back to camp!"

Krar landed in their midst, managing not to knock anybeast over with his giant wings. He gestured with his beak. "Best we begone from this place. Methinks there be but one of me and too many of yon carrion. Let us away now!'

8

As there was still plenty of daylight left, the travelers opted to sail further rather than lie about in camp. Krar Wood-watcher saw them off on the streambank.

"Fare thee well, O Prince of Mousethieves, fortune go with thee. Thou wilt not see me, but I will guard the air and watch o'er thee 'til thou art gone from my domain. Be you subject to thy Prince's commands and behave thyself, squire Chugg, or I will give thee back to yon carrion. Fortune attend thee, dame Trimp, my friend. Thou too, good Dinny, and thee, sir Martin. I'll not lightly forget that ye forswore thine honour for me. Go now, goodbeasts!"

Chugger began weeping as they sailed off downstream. "Wahaah! Chugg not want Krar t'be gonned!"

Martin let the little fellow work one of the paddles. "Krar isn't gone, Chugg, he's watching over us, even though we can't see him. Give him a wave, go on!" Chugger waved a chubby paw and felt somewhat better. As the Warrior held the paddle with the squirrelbabe, he explained as best he could. "Sometimes friends do go from us—it will happen more and more as you grow up, Chugg. But if you really love your friends, they're never gone. Somewhere they're watching over you and they're always there inside your heart."

Toward evening they saw fireglow in the distance. With complete silence and great caution, the friends approached it, hoping that if it were anybeast hostile, they might slip by unnoticed. But as a voice raised in song echoed on the dusky air, Gonff relaxed, chuckling.

"I'd know that barrel-bellied baritone anywhere, mates. Now there's a fine voice for ye, but don't tell him I said it. Haharr, listen to 'im, will you!"

It was a fine voice, more bass than baritone. Deep and rich, it thrummed out over the babbling streamnoises.

"Hoooooo rum tum toe, follah diddle doh,
Me boots are full of water,
An' the bread won't rise,
So I'm scoffin' apple pies,
An' swiggin' good dark porter.

Hooooooo bless my fur, an' you sit over there,
There's honeycake an' salad,
An' you've got no choice,
But t'listen to me voice,
As I sing you this ballad!"

A look of pure mischief spread across Gonff's face. Cupping both paws around his mouth he sang out in a perfect imitation of the singer's deep voice.

"Hooooooooo you sit there, an' I'll sit here,
An' I won't hear yore ballad,
But I'll scoff yore pie,
An' I'll look ye in the eye,
With me ears stuffed full o' salad!"

From around a bend in the bank, a small neat logboat came shooting out, propelled by a fat shrew with an ash stave. Trimp knew that shrews were usually aggressive and short-tempered, but this one was different. He performed a joyful jig at the prospect of company. It came as no surprise that the shrew and Gonff knew each other. As the former leaped aboard the raft they pounded backs and shook paws.

"Log a Log Furmo, ye pot-bellied son of a waterwalloper, as soon as I clapped ears on that warblin' I knew 'twas the best ballad singer this side o' Mossflower!"

"Haharr, Gonff Mousethief, ye light-pawed rogue, if I hadn't 'ave known that was you singin' back at me I'd 'ave thought 'twas meself. Pull over t'the camp an' bring yore pals with ye, supper's on the go. Ahoy, Martin, is it really yourself, Warrior? Good t'see you, matey!"

Dinny tapped the shrew Chieftain with a digging claw. "Doan't ee know oi, zurr, furr oi'd know ee frum a buttyfly?"

Log a Log Furmo stood back, rubbing his eyes. "Well sink me a log, is that the slim young mole I once knew as Dinny? Wot 'appened, mate, is there another beast inside that skin with ye?"

Dinny chuckled, patting his ample form. "Nay, zurr Log, oi jus' growed more bootiful an' gurtly strong, since you'm bain't been round to rob moi vittles."

Furmo turned to Trimp. "And what is a gentle hogmaid like ye doing with such rogues?"

Trimp smiled. "Keeping them in order."

"I'd best watch my manners then, I'm thinking," laughed Furmo.

The Guerrilla Union Of Shrews In Mossflower, Guosim for short, had always been headed by one traditionally named Log a Log. They ranged all the waterways in their logboats, a great tribe of them. Trimp was almost half a head taller than most of them. Small spike-furred long-snouted shrews, with brightly colored headbands and rapiers tucked in their belts, watched as the newcomers made their way to the fire. Log a Log introduced them as friends, reassuring his band. Guosim shrews are excellent cooks, as the hedgehog maid soon discovered. Their apple and blackberry crumble was pure delight to taste. Two Guosim cooks stood over Trimp, watching anxiously as she sampled some, enquiring gruffly, "Good crumble, that? Made it ourselves, y'know!"

"Aye, to our own recipe. D'ye like it, marm?"

Trimp's smile would have charmed the birds out of the trees. "It's perfect, thank you. I've never tasted a crumble in my life that could compare with it. Beautiful!"

Unused to such compliments, the shrew cooks kicked their footpaws bashfully and began serving more food, calling to one another in bass growls to hide their embarrassment.

"Hoi, Rugger, pour 'er some pear cordial, will ye!"

"Aye, an' give 'er some shrewcheese an' watercress!"

"Look after pore liddle Chugger, will ye, Bindle? Pour some honey o'er the babe's hazelnut pudden!"

"Some streamside salad an' newbaked cornbread for ye, marm!"

Log a Log Furmo smiled at the antics of his younger shrews, trying to impress the travelers with their hospitality, particularly Trimp, for it is a fact that the Guosim had always been partial to a pretty face. Furmo passed Martin and Gonff a tankard of shrew porter apiece, saying, "Haharr, young Trimp's gotten 'er paws well under the table there. They'll feed 'er 'til she bursts!"

Some of the little shrews had never seen a mole before, and they crowded around Dinny, haranguing him as he ate.

"Does all moles 'ave softy nice fur like you, mista Diggy?"

"Ho yuss, moi dearies, us'n's keeps it soft boi eatin' oop all us vittles loik goodbeasts."

"You mus' be the goodest mole of all, mista Diggy, 'cos you be eatin' a h'orful big lot o' vittles!"

"Hurr hurr, thankee, young 'un, oi 'spect oi am!"

"You got very bigbig claws, mista Diggy, wot they for?"

A kindly shrewmum rounded the little ones up. "Don't you be askin' mister Dinny foolish questions, now. Leave 'im in peace to eat 'is supper. Bedboats for you, 'tis late."

Martin was relating the object of their journey to Furmo when the shrewmum stole up and whispered in the shrew Chieftain's ear. He excused himself, explaining, "We'll talk later, friend. I've got to sing the liddle 'uns off to sleep. Won't be long."

Moored to the bank was a logboat, padded thickly with warm cushions and blankets. The shrewbabes lay in it, rocked by the motion of the water, as their Log a Log sang them to sleep in his melodious deep voice.

"The stream flows by and time rolls by,
Now daytime flies so close those eyes,
It's been a long day little one, little one.
Small birds now slumber in the nest,
And fishes in their stream,
Know night has come to send us rest,
And give to all a wondrous dream,
All night hours go, so soft and low,
The lazy stream runs calm and slow,
It's been a long day little one, little one.
Our weary world is waiting soon,
Bright stars will pierce the sky,
As silent as the golden moon,
That sheds her light on you and I,
And when the darkness drifts away,
Some lark up high will sing and say,
Oh welcome to a newborn day, my little one."

Gonff crept up, carrying Chugger. The squirrelbabe was
fast asleep. Sliding him aboard the logboat with the dozy little shrews, Gonff patted his friend's shoulder.

"Wish we could take you all the way with us, Furmo mate,
ole Chugg went out like somebeast'd whacked him with a
slingstone once you started singin'. How d'you do it?"

Log a Log Furmo shrugged, gesturing at the logboat. "I've
had plenty o' practice, mate. Eight of them are mine."

It was about an hour after dawn when Trimp opened her eyes.
The previous night had been a late one, with lots of good
shrew food, singing, storytelling and even a bout of tail
wrestling by two lithe young Guosim shrews to impress her.
Some shrew cooks were up and about, rekindling the fire and
preparing breakfast. The Guosim were very fond of sizeable
breakfasts when they were at summer camp. Feigning sleep,
the hedgehog maid peeped out from under her blanket,
savouring the day. Downstream looked like a long winding
green hall, with alder, bird cherry and weeping willow trees
practically forming an arch over the sundappled stream,
which was bordered by bright flowering clubrush, sedge and
twayblade. Blue and pearly grey, the firesmoke hovered,

making gentle swirls between sunshine and shadow in diagonal shafts. Snatches of murmured conversation between early risers were muted in the background, with the sweet odors of smouldering peat and glowing pinebark on the fire. Trimp wished that she could stay like this forever, happy amongst true friends, in tranquil summer woodlands by a stream.

"Oatmeal'n'honey, fresh fruit an' hot mint tea, marm!"

It was the two shrewcooks from the previous evening, tempting her to partake of breakfast. Trimp needed no coaxing. She sat up gratefully, wondering how one night's sleep could leave her with such a fine appetite.

"Thank you, friends. My word, this looks delicious!"

Gonff and the Log a Log were in friendly dispute as they broke their fast.

"Hearken t'me, Mouseythief, we're sailin' with you, at least as far as the seashore, an' that's final, mate!"

"No no, Furmo, we wouldn't think o' pullin' ye away from yore summer camp. We'll be all right travellin' on alone."

"Hah, will y'lissen t'the mouse, turnin' down an offer of safe voyagin' in convoy. He's mad, Martin, tell 'im!"

Wiping wild plum juice from his paws the Warrior agreed. "Safety in numbers, Gonff, I'm all for it. Where's your manners, mate, d'you want to offend Log a Log Furmo by refusing his kind offer? Ignore him, Furmo, I accept!"

Dinny and Chugger seconded the Redwall Champion.

"An' h'i except, too, as well an' all, mista sh'ew!"

"Hurr, oi too, zurr, ee shrews be gudd company an' gurt cookers. Burr aye!"

Trimp licked her oatmeal spoon and held it up. "That goes for me too, unless Gonff wants t'do all the cooking and paddling aboard that raft!"

The Prince of Mousethieves clapped the Guosim leader's back. "Quit yore arguin', matey, 'tis no good wot y'say, yore goin' with us, like it or not, see. Yore goin'!"

A real shrewish voice rang out. Furmo's wife Honeysuckle bustled up, waving a ladle. She was bigger than him and had a temper that none could match on land or water. "Goin'? Goin' where may I ask?"

Even though he was a chieftain, Furmo wilted under her

fierce eye and sharp tone. "Er, just down the stream apiece, my fragrant woodrose."

Gonff interrupted, standing between both shrews. "Ah Honeysuckle, you delightful morsel, we've asked your husband to accompany us with some of his shrews, to show us the way and guard us against attack. But of course he says he can't possibly leave yore side on such a foolish errand. Not that I blame Furmo. Anybeast leavin' a dark-eyed beauty like you to go off sailin', huh, he'd be out of his mind, mad as a frog an' daft as a bluebottle!"

Lips pursed grimly, Honeysuckle waggled the ladle under Furmo's nose and spoke threateningly. "An' you, y'great lazy lump, you said you wouldn't go, eh?"

"But petal, 'ow can I leave you an' all the liddle 'uns?"

Furmo winced. His wife had hoisted him upright by one ear. "In the boat, Log a Lazypaws, this instant. You Guosim there, wot are you standin' grinnin' about, eh? Now get those logboats ready t'sail, now, while I'm still in a good mood. Shift yore mossbound behinds!"

Four logboats were lashed to the raft's sides, each with six Guosim paddlers. Honeysuckle tossed supplies aboard with furious strength and energy. Gonff murmured under his breath as Dinny dodged a sack of vegetables, "Matey, I'd hate t'see 'er in a bad mood if this is one of 'er good moods!"

Honeysuckle scowled at him. "What was that you said?"

The clever Mousethief gestured at the provisions. "I was just sayin', marm, after so much bad food 'tis nice to see some good food!"

She pointed a warning paw at the pair. "Don't let me hear of you two wastin' any!"

Dinny tugged his snout respectfully. "Hurr, 'ow cudd us'n's be a-wastin' vittles loaded aboard boi such ee furr paw as yourn, moi gurt booty?"

Honeysuckle dipped the mole a deep curtsy, actually smiling. "Why thankee, sir mole, wot a gallant thing t'say!"

Halfway downstream between the camp and the next bend, Log a Log sighed with relief and shook Dinny warmly by the paw.

"You clinched it, Din, all that fair paw an' great beauty stuff. Where'd you learn it?"

The mole twitched his nose at Trimp. "Burr, oi diddent lurn nuthin', zurr, h'oim jus' a reg'lar silver-tongued molerogue, bain't oi, miz Trimp?"

The hedgehog maid twitched her nose back at him. "Aye, especially when it comes to lappin' up oatmeal'n'honey you are. Great fat fraud!"

Furmo did a perfect imitation of his wife's voice. "One more remark like that, young 'og, an' I'll rap yore ears with my pudden spoon. That mole's a real gentlebeast!"

Meandering happily down the broad waterway through the sun and shade, the travelers and their shrew friends jested and chuckled with each other.

A watermeadow appeared on their left about midday. The Guosim had ceased paddling because the current was carrying them along with sufficient speed. All aboard both raft and logboats sat admiring the serene beauty as Log a Log pointed out its features.

"Looks peaceful, don't it? But mark my words, mates, midst all that brookweed, water lilies, crowfoot an' gipsy-wort, there're more skeeters than y'could shake a stick at. Mayfly, caddisfly, stonefly, alderfly, pond skaters, big lacewings an' o' course the ole Emperor dragonflies. Makes it a rare ole fishin' spot—fish all come there to hunt the flies."

Gonff winked craftily at the shrew. "Aye, an' Guosim go there to hunt the fish, I'll wager."

A sturdy old shrew elder snorted at the Mousethief's remark. "Yore jokin', of course. There's eels an' pike in there longer'n a logboat. 'Tis them'd be huntin' us if'n shrews was fool enough to try fishin' that watermeadow!"

Log a Log pointed downstream. "Look, there's dragonflies comin' up this way. They ain't tarryin', either. Wonder wot's upset 'em?"

A half dozen of the huge insects came straight at the raft, suddenly veering off into the watermeadow, their iridescent wingbacks and black-green banded bodies making a brave sight. Log a Log addressed Martin. "Somethin's upset the dragons. We'd best be on our guard, 'specially when we round that bend ahead—there's a creek to one side of it. Stay on the alert, Guosim!"

Trimp sat in the center of the raft, holding on to Chugger.
Half the shrews took to paddling the logboats lashed to the
raftsides, the rest joined Martin, Log a Log, Dinny and
Gonff, who stood for'ard on the raft, weapons close to paw.
As they rounded the bend, it became only too clear what dan-
ger they were in.

Like some fantastic snowstorm a male swan came billowing
out of the creek entrance. The sight of it took Trimp's breath
away. Spreading awesome wings, the colossal bird reared out
of the water, its long neck bent, hissing loudly like a serpent.
Log a Log roared at the paddlers, "Back water! Back water,
Guosim!"

Furiously the shrews backpaddled against the current, but
the raft's stern hit the bank on the bend's incurve and lodged
there. The elder shrew seized a long paddle and bravely
swung it at the swan, sizing up the situation for his companions as he did so.

"He's a mute swan. Prob'ly the female's guardin' 'er
young up that creek, an' this feller thinks we're goin' to 'urt
'em. Looks fairly mad t'me. Ain't goin' to let us pass or
retreat. This is his stretch o' water, an' he'll protect his family
an' this area with his life, mates!"

Though they were in great danger, Martin could not help
admiring the giant bird. With its tough orange beak, which
had a hard black lump at its base, and its neck thick as a
rowan sapling, the mute male swan was a fiercely wondrous
sight, snow white, with wings powerful enough to cripple
and kill an adversary. The Warrior picked up a paddle to fend
it off, knowing that he had not the heart to kill or injure such
a magnificent creature with his sword. However, the swan
had no such finer feelings, but came at them hissing and making a peculiarly strange squeak, far out of character given his
bulk and ferocity. Gonff swung his paddle.

A gigantic wing descended on him, snapping the paddle
like a twig and buffeting him from the raft into the water.
Martin's paddle clacked hard against the bird's beak, sending
a jarring pain through his paws, and the swan came at him.
Dinny caught it a hefty blow in the neck, which merely
seemed to bend gracefully under the impact. Two shrews

were swept off into the water by another clout from the swan's wing. It reared high and gripped the raft timbers in its wide webbed claws, trying to hoist itself aboard. Trimp and Chugger slid backward, yelling, as the raft began tilting with the swan's weight pressing on its front end. Martin grabbed his sword and held it up quickly, so that the swan's beak hit it with a loud echoing sound. Pang!

Nobeast was expecting what happened next. Something hit the swan's head like a stone, sending a cloud of small white feathers into the air. There was an ear-splitting screech from above. It was Krar Woodwatcher! The courageous goshawk came in for another dive, even though it must have been dizzy from the first blow. The swan swung its beak and retaliated. There was a thudding noise as both birds struck one another simultaneously. Krar landed in a heap on the raft. Savagely shaking off Dinny, who was trying to help it recover, the goshawk struggled upright, panting, "Use thy raftpoles and get thee off downstream. Hasten now, whilst I hold off yonder battler!"

Krar launched himself into the attack once more. Feathers flew amid the hissing and screeching, streamwater was thrashed into foam, leaves and branches showered wide. Punting the raft out from the bank, whilst shrews either side paddled madly, they skimmed out under the arch formed by the swan's neck and Krar's wings, into the midstream current and off down the waterway. Still paddling and poling with great vigour, they turned their heads to see what the outcome would be. Krar Woodwatcher was as brave and hard a fighter as the swan, but not so foolish. The moment he saw everybeast was out of danger he zoomed off into the woodlands to nurse his bruises, leaving behind a bewildered and still angry mute swan. Trimp could not stop herself from trembling as she called out, "He's coming after us, the swan's coming after us!"

Log a Log gritted his teeth. "Don't look back, mates, it'll slow us down. Keep paddlin' fast as y'can. The swan'll only foller us to the edge of his territory, then he'll go back to guard his family."

The shrew's prediction proved true, though it gave them a hair-raising moment. The swan came after them in no uncertain fashion. It was almost upon the raft, hardly two logboat lengths from it, when suddenly it gave a final hiss and turned about, traversing back upstream lest any other intruder had shown up to menace its brood. With a sigh of relief, the friends collapsed to the deck, shaking all over from exertion and the shock of the swan's attack. The irrepressible Gonff grabbed the sailcloth, holding it wide and flapping his outstretched paws at Trimp. "Wot's the matter, matey, never seen a swan before?"

The hedgehog maid hooked a paw under the teaser and pulled him flat on his tail. "Oh, I've seen a swan all right, Gonff, though if I never see another one in my life 'twill be too soon, thank you!"

Through the thinning trees, Dinny scanned the sky. "Hurr, whurr be ee 'awkburd gone?"

Martin indicated the changing terrain. "We're coming out of the woodlands, Din, leaving Krar's territory, too, I imagine. I wish I could have thanked him. What a great fight he put up on our behalf. I'll never forget that brave bird. Never!'

9

Once they left the trees behind there was very little shade. The water became deeper, the current more sluggish. Throughout a long hot day, the travelers did their share, taking turns to relieve the Guosim paddlers. Only little Chugger seemed unaffected by the blistering heat. With a damp shrew headband bound round his brow and an ash twig in his paw, he cavorted and leaped everywhere, doing battle against a score of imaginary swans.

No sooner had shadows begun to lengthen than Log a Log shipped his paddle, calling out the order they were all waiting upon. "Pull into that curve on yore right, mates. We'll rest there an' camp until tomorrow!"

Gratefully, Trimp watched their lumbering craft nose into the shallows of a cove. It had a good flat bank and protruding rock ledges to provide much-needed shade. Guosim cooks immersed canteens of drinks in water which was cool and shaded by the overhang. Some went out scouting for fresh food, others began preparing a meal from their supplies. Eyeing their leader hopefully, the rest sat on the raft in silence, awaiting his command.

Log a Log Furmo wandered up and down the bank, peering into the crystal-clear water. He scratched his chin, as if undecided, then wagged a cautionary paw at his crew. "No further'n the end o' that raft, now. Stay out o' the current an' deep parts, an' keep close to the bank. I don't want to carry back news of any drowned Guosim to yore kin." Before he had finished speaking, several of the younger shrews hurled themselves yelling into the stream.

"Yahahoooooo!"

Jumping ashore to avoid the splashes of the bathing party, Log a Log shook his head at Martin. "Look at 'em, like a flippin' shower o' Dibbuns!"

A secret wink passed between Gonff and Martin as the Warrior shrugged free of his sword and belt. Grabbing Log a Log between them, they leaped into the water. The shrew Chieftain surfaced breathless, blowing spray from both nostrils.

"Yah, y'rotten 'orrible creatures, what'd ye do that for?"

Gonff flung himself on Log a Log and ducked him. "Gerrout, ye ole fogey, you were dyin' for a play in the water, weren't you?"

Log a Log swam deftly out of the Mousethief's reach. "Of course I was, mate, but don't tell my shrews that. I'm supposed to be a serious leader who acts responsibly!" He sank beneath the surface again as Chugger landed on him.

"You norra leader, you a big fish, Chugger wanna ride on you back. C'mon, fishy, hup hup, gerra move on!"

Everybeast had tremendous fun in the stream, laughing and splashing, ducking and diving and behaving exactly as Log a Log had said, like a shower of Dibbuns. However, they deserted the water en masse when the foraging party returned, hailing them from the banktop: "Lookit, mates, we found strawberries!"

Two haversacks filled with wild strawberries, small, sweet and juicy, were carried into camp. Refreshed after her swim, Trimp sat with Chugger and Dinny on the sunwarmed rocks, sharing a heap of the delicious fruit.

One of the foraging party reported to Log a Log. "Saw a pile of otter tracks on the heathland back there, mebbe fifteen or more, all big 'uns!"

The shrew Chieftain shrugged, selecting a big strawberry.

"Otters are goodbeasts, we've no reason to fear 'em. They're welcome to a pawful o' vittles if'n they visit us."

As evening shades tinged the skies, the otters came upriver and emerged dripping from the stream. A big wiry fellow, obviously their Skipper, held forth his paws in greeting.

"Peaceful evenin' to ye, friends. Is that a fruit salad with strawberries in it I see? Looks 'andsome, don't it?"

Log a Log smiled at the hungry otters, indicating that they were free to help themselves. "Sit down an' welcome, friend. Haven't I seen you afore?"

Balancing back on his rudderlike tail, the otter answered, "Prob'ly crossed paths once or twice, matey. I'm Tungro— my tribe have a holt on the river north o' here."

The shrew nodded. "Ah, Tungro. Heard yore name someplace. What are you'n'yore crew doin' hereabouts, mate?"

Tungro accepted food from Trimp and thanked her. He acted rather nonchalant, but Log a Log suspected he was either hiding something or not telling the full story when he replied airily, "Oh, not much, y'know, jus' takin' a look t'see wot's on the other side o' the hill, so t'speak. Ain't you or none o' yore crew caught sight of an old-lookin' raggedy otter 'round here today, have ye?"

Log a Log threw a pebble into the stream, watching it sink. "No, mate. Why d'you ask?"

Tungro did not reply. He nodded to his crew, finished eating and bobbed his head courteously. "Obliged to ye for the vittles, friends. Go in peace an' good fortune travel with ye. Oh, if'n you should bump into the ole otter I mentioned, tell 'im that he can come back to the hold if'n he's mended his ways." Tungro handed Furmo an otter tailring. "Give 'im this an' say that yore all mates o' mine. Fare ye well, now!"

Without creating a single splash the otters slipped into the water and were gone. Martin and Gonff came to sit alongside Log a Log, and the Mousethief expressed his bewilderment.

"Phew, that was a speedy visit. What d'you suppose 'twas all about, Furmo?"

The shrew's answer was guarded. "Ye'll forgive me if'n I don't tell all the story, 'cos I ain't certain of the full facts meself, but here's as much as I'm willin' to say, mates. I've heard of Tungro, aye, an' his brother Folgrim. Both great warriors, 'tis said, but Folgrim was knowed t'be fiercer, even though he was smaller than Tungro. Well, when their ole father died, they was joint Skippers of their holt. One winter they were attacked by a mixed band o' vermin, but otters ain't beasts to mess with. They gave those vermin scum a real good drubbin' an' drove 'em off. Now Tungro reckoned that was enough, but not Folgrim. Off he went alone in pursuit o' the vermin. Wasn't 'til two seasons later Folgrim returned 'ome. They say the vermin laid a trap an' captured 'im. Starved, beat an' tortured somethin' 'orrible he was, wounded, crippled an' with only one good eye. Sick in the brain too, 'cos Folgrim was never the same after wot those vermin did to 'im. I know from lissenin' to travelers, Folgrim be'aved so bad an' strange that Tungro's banished 'im more'n once from the holt, but Folgrim always returns, an' Tungro forgives his ways an' takes 'im back. Well, you couldn't banish yore own brother forever, just 'cos he ain't right in the head, now could ye?"

Martin had to agree with the shrew. "No, you're right, blood's thicker than water. What was that he gave you to give to his brother?"

Log a Log held up the beautiful otter tailring, carved from the backbone of some great fish. "Nice, ain't it? Though I hope we don't meet Folgrim an' have t'give 'im it."

Gonff took the tailring and inspected it. "Why not, Furmo? He's not as bad as all that, is he?"

The shrew took the tailring back and stowed it in his pouch. "I can't say, Gonff. I won't tell ye all I've heard 'cos I'm not sure I believe it, an' I can't tell ye wot I haven't seen. I'm for a spot o' shuteye now. You two can sit up an' natter all night."

Nothing further was mentioned of Tungro's brother Folgrim. The friends lay down to rest that night with their own thoughts about the story they had heard. Purely out of insatiable curiosity, Gonff wished that he could meet the strange otter. Finally the Mousethief slept, not knowing that he was to get his wish on the following day.

• • •

Next morning was damp and humid, with the sky clouded over a dirty grey and drizzle falling continuously. Pushing on downstream the craft sailed slowly along on the rain-flecked waters. Trimp and Chugger sat beneath the awning the shrews had set up from the single sail. The hogmaid watched the others, droplets spilling from their whiskers, soaked through, paws slipping on paddles, as they pushed doggedly on. As noon approached, there was no change, and the drizzle persisted. Guosim paddlers looked pleadingly to their leader. Log a Log wiped moisture from his eyes, seeking a suitable spot along the same bank they had camped on the previous day. Eventually he called, "Head 'er in, mates. Looks like an ole cave yonder!"

A tent was rigged over the cavefront, and the provisions were stacked under it to keep them dry. Everybeast crowded under the canvas and in the small cave. Chugger was wearing a rough hooded cloak which Trimp had fashioned from an empty apple sack. Evading the hedgehog maid, who looked after him like a mother duck, the little squirrel toddled off to explore the country. Trimp looked right and left. Where had the little imp gone? Poking her head from under the shelter she spotted him. Chugger had climbed the rock ledges and was up on top of the bank. He wrinkled his nose and waved at Trimp. "No worry 'bout Chugg, jus' goin' to fight swans!" Waving his ash twig, he vanished from sight. Trimp took off in pursuit, scrambling up the wet stones.

Martin had just lit a small fire when he heard Trimp calling urgently from above, "Help! Come quick, mates!"

Grabbing his sword, Martin dashed out ahead of the shrews. Together he, Gonff and Furmo took the ledges in a series of bounds, with Dinny and the Guosim following swiftly behind. Trimp was crouched down, protecting Chugger. She pointed. "There, Martin! Oh, help him, please!"

Two water rats were tormenting another creature. Martin peered through the curtain of misty drizzle. It was an otter, limping along, clad in a ragged cloak and bent almost double. Kicking him and striking him with whippy willow withes, the vermin spat at him, taunting, "Move yerself, yew dodderin' ole ragbag, we're goin' to tie rocks to yer paws an' sink yer in the stream, nice'n'slow. Come on, yer hobblin' addle-brained idiot!"

Martin lifted his sword and took a pace forward. Log a Log placed a paw on his shoulder. "Stop there, Warrior, don't interfere. That's Folgrim you see, fightin' the enemy!"

Gonff nodded towards the two rats, who were still unaware of their presence. "He's fightin' them, d'ye say? Huh, it looks the other way round t'me, mate!"

Log a Log shook his head grimly, murmuring to his shrews, "Get Trimp an' the liddle 'un back down t'the cave—this ain't fit fer 'em t'see. Keep silent, Martin, crouch down by me an' watch. You too, Gonff."

One rat stuck out his footpaw and tripped the lame otter, who fell heavily. Both rats laid on savagely with their switches as he pleaded, "Please, sirs, don't drown me, I'm nought but a pore wayfarin' beast who's lost his way. Don't beat me. Owow!"

This continued for a moment. Until one of the rats got too close to the victim. Like a wolf, Folgrim was upon him with lightning speed. He seized the rat in a death hug, sinking his teeth deep into the vermin's throat. Shocked beyond belief, the other rat stood trembling a moment, then he dashed off wailing in terror. Folgrim lifted a bloodstained mouth from his prey's neck, calling, "Run run run, ratty, I'll track ye down, Folgrim'll get yer."

At a signal from Log a Log the travelers backed off unobserved and clambered down to their camp. Gonff sat by the fire, sipping a beaker of hot mushroom soup. He stared into the flames and shuddered. "Ugh! I never seen a creature killed like that afore!"

Martin passed a beaker of soup to Log a Log. "So that's Folgrim, brother of Tungro. Well, Furmo, d'you believe what they say now?"

Log a Log nodded. "Every word, mate, every awful word!"

A sound of somebeast scrambling down the ledges alerted them. Next moment Folgrim limped in, still with a blood-smeared mouth. Chugger's eyes grew big and round at the sight of the fearsome beast. The otter winked his single eye at them and sat by the fire. "Ah, nice fire. Chills a beast t'the bone, drizzle does!"

Swiftly, Dinny filled a beaker from the soup pot. "Yurr, zurr h'otter, drinkee summ noice 'ot zoop up!"

Smiling, Folgrim shook his head. Martin saw that his teeth were filed, or broken into jagged points. "Not fer me, mole. I got food back up there."

Trimp approached bearing a loaf and a hunk of cheese. "Then take these with you for tomorrow, sir." She took a step backward at the sight of the otter's face. It was painted thickly with plant dyes and mud, to cover the horrible wounds and scars etched into it. The single red-rimmed eye stared crazily at her.

"No thankee, missie, I'll 'ave more food by tomorrow when I track that other 'un down. You, shrew, can you let me 'ave tinder an' flint? Beast needs a good cookin' fire in this country an' I ain't got the makin's."

Log a Log gave Folgrim a bag of soft dried moss and two chunks of flintstone to make fire with. "Take 'em an' welcome, friend. Yore brother Tungro said that I should give you this tailring too. He says yore welcome back at the holt if'n you've mended yore ways. We're friends of your brother's."

Folgrim reached out and grabbed Trimp's paw, pushed the tailring over it with a swift movement and released her. "Pretty bracelet for a pretty maid, eh! If'n you see my brother, tell 'im that I said 'e's a good beast. The holt's better off widout me—it's far too late fer me t'mend my ways. Got t'go now, light a fire, do a spot o' cookin'. Travel on, catch the other rat, light another fire, do more cookin'!" Baring his pointed teeth at the horrified friends, Folgrim stood up and stumped out into the rain.

Trimp covered her mouth with both paws, her normal good pallor taking on a greenish tinge. Log a Log sat her down by the fire, placing a dry sack round her shoulders.

"D'you feel sick, missie? Y'don't look none too chirpy."

Trimp took a deep breath before replying. "Didn't you hear? That otter is going to cook a rat and eat it. Oh, I can't believe it!"

Gonff winked at the others as he patted Trimp's paw. "You

didn't believe him, did ye, Trimp? Haha, that's a good 'un, ain't it, Martin, ain't it, Furmo? An otter eatin' a water rat!"

They both laughed hollowly.

"Er, haha, shouldn't believe all y'hear, Trimp."

"Aye, he was only joking, miss, haha . . ." Martin's half-hearted laugh trailed off miserably.

Further along the bank, in the shelter of another rock ledge, Folgrim was kindling a fire and holding a one-sided conversation with the slain water rat.

"Pity I never got yore mate, he was fatter'n you are. Still, don't fuss, I'll lay 'im by the paws afore sunset tomorrow night. Fire's nice, ain't it? Chills a beast to the bone, this drizzle does. Nice fire, I likes a good fire!'

10

They slept late next morning. The rain had ceased and sunlight was beaming from clear summer skies when Chugger roused himself and trundled out on to the bank. Steamy mist from the rain, hung over the whole bankshore in a thick low layer, waiting for the sun to evaporate it. The tiny squirrel raced through it, giggling as he tried to catch the elusive tendrils in his paws. "Yeeheehee! All be's covered in frog, lotsa frogs. Heehee!"

Gonff and Trimp emerged from the cave yawning. Upon hearing Chugger's cries, Gonff became alert. "What frogs? Who's covered in frogs?"

Trimp shoved the Mousethief playfully. "He means fog. Look out!"

The mist parted and Chugger bowled head over brush into them. Gonff swept him up, tickling the little fellow and swinging him about. "I'll give ye frogs, y'villain!"

Soon the whole party was up and about. Furmo and his shrews lit a fire and began cooking breakfast. Dinny appeared out of the mist, toting a pail of water.

"Hurr, doan't be furr frum ee seashores naow. Lookit all ee frog yurrabouts, Marthen."

79

Martin climbed halfway up one of the ledges and peered over the mist curtain. "Right, Din. We don't normally get heavy bankmist like this inland. Sea can't be too far off now. Hush! Everybeast be still. I can hear someone coming this way!"

It was the otters, Tungro and his crew. As soon as Martin recognized their voices, he hailed them from the bank. "Morning, friends. Breakfast's almost ready, y'welcome to share it with us!"

Tungro waded ashore, dripping from the stream. "Thankee kindly, goodbeasts, we wouldn't say no to a bite o' brekkist. The crew ain't eaten yet t'day."

Nudging Log a Log Furmo, Gonff raised his eyebrows. "Better git more shrewbread on the hot stones. Here was I, thinkin' I was goin' t'get a nice big peaceful breakfast—now it'll be a small noisy one with this lot as guests!"

The rest of Tungro's crew came ashore in a huddle. They had Folgrim with them, a rope lead round his middle and both paws bound by a long hobble, which had allowed him to swim. He winked his one good eye at Trimp. "Good day to ye, missie. 'Ope I finds yer well?"

The hedgehog maid shuddered, though she bobbed him a curtsy and managed a quick smile. "I'm well, thankee, sir."

Tungro drew Martin and Furmo to one side. He seemed slightly embarrassed and hesitant. "Er, I 'opes you'll fergive me, er, bringin' my brother Folgrim to yore camp fer brekkist like this. He ain't a bad beast really, 'tis just that 'is mind's troubled."

Martin nodded understandingly and patted Tungro's shoulder. "Don't worry, friend, we know a bit about Folgrim and the bad times he's had. He dropped by here yesterday afternoon. There was no trouble, he behaved himself quite well."

Tungro looked relieved. "We caught up with Folgrim just after he'd tracked an' slain a rat. He'd lit a fire, that was 'ow we spotted 'im. Me'n'the crew had t'jump on pore Folgrim a bit, but we managed, tied 'im up an' buried the rat carcass afore he, er, well . . ."

Furmo poured a beaker of pennycloud cordial for the otter. "'Tis all right, y'don't have to explain. We know from the other rat Folgrim managed t'get his paws on, just over the banktop there. Come on now, get somethin' to eat."

Furmo and his shrews had made a delicious breakfast. There was hot shrewbread, strawberries and a batch of vegetable pasties, with a choice of cordial or hot mint tea to drink. Tungro sat slightly apart with his brother, trying to make him eat a little, but Folgrim kept his mouth firmly shut, refusing the food in silence. Everybeast tried to get on with their meal, but they kept taking secretive glances as Tungro encouraged his brother. "Come on now, Fol, these're prime vittles, made by the best o' Guosim cooks. Try some o' this pasty, me ole mate!" Folgrim merely shook his head stubbornly. Tungro noticed the watchers and shrugged embarrassment. "Sorry, he won't eat nothin', though there ain't a thing wrong wid yore food, friends. 'Tis the best I ever tasted."

Trimp was trying to hold on to Chugger, but he wriggled out of her grasp and went swiftly on all fours to Folgrim. Smiling up into the otter's scarred face, Chugger grabbed a pasty and lectured him like a mother squirrel. "Eaty all up now, or y'don't grow bigga strong like me. H'i eatim up if'n you don't, silly ole riverdog!"

Suddenly Folgrim burst out laughing at the little squirrel's antics, and took a big bite out of the proffered pasty. "You ain't eatin' all my brekkist up, liddle sir, ho no!"

Chugger nodded his head in agreement. "Good h'otter, now Chugg getcher sh'ewbread an' minty tea!"

Folgrim gobbled another mouthful of pasty. "Why thankee, mate, though I likes cordial better'n mint tea. Mebbe you could fetch me a couple o' them strawberries too, they look nice!"

Tungro shook his head in amazement at the sight of Chugger feeding breakfast to his brother, both of them chatting away amiably, as if they were old friends.

"Well wallop me rudder, will y'look at that? Folgrim never was the most civil o' beasts—back at the holt 'e spoke to nobody, much less smile an' chat like that. I reckon my brother's took a shine to yore liddle squirrel!"

Trimp was slightly apprehensive. She confided her fears to Dinny in a whisper that only he could hear. "I'm not so sure I

like Chugger being around Folgrim. He's an otter who's
eaten his enemies and is troubled in his mind. Who can tell
what he'd do if the mood took him?"

The mole put aside his food, watching Folgrim and Chugger. "Oi doan't think ee gotten much t'wurry o'er, missie.
Hurr, jus' you'm looka yon h'otter. Whoi, ee'm loik an ole
molemum wi' 'er h'infant molebabe. Wuddent 'arm an 'air o'
maister Chugg's liddle 'ead, burr no!"

Trimp watched as Chugger fed Folgrim some shrewbread.
The little squirrel was talking to the otter as if he were a
naughty Dibbun.

"Now if'n you don't eat alla sh'ewbread up, I won't not let
you 'ave no st'awbees, mista Fol!"

The hedgehog maid nodded in agreement with her molefriend. "I think you're right, Din. They're firm friends!"

When the meal was over, Martin and his group struck
camp. Warm summer sun had lifted all the mist and the broad
stream glistened invitingly. Tungro hailed them as they were
packing supplies aboard.

"My 'earty thanks to ye, friends. We've got t'go now. Safe
journey to you'n'yore mates, Martin, an' fair weather attend
ye to the north coast!"

However, it was not that simple. Folgrim refused to go
with his brother. Digging himself into the banksand, he resisted all their attempts to move him. Tungro stroked his strange
brother's head coaxingly.

"C'mon, Fol, let's go back 'ome together, matey. Yore ole
bed's waitin' for ye, an' everybeast's wantin' to give you a
great welcome. Wot d'you say, eh?"

Chugger leaped from the raft and threw himself upon Folgrim, hugging the scarred otter and wailing piteously. "Waa-
haah! Don't take mista Fol 'way. Waahaahaa!"

As if this were not sad enough, Folgrim joined in, tears
streaming from his one eye. "Buhurr! Don't take me away
from me liddle pal. I wants t'go with 'im. Buhuhurr!"

Tungro was greatly moved. Dashing a paw across his eyes,
he appealed to Martin. "Tell me, mate, wot do I do?"

The Warrior leaped ashore. Two swift slices of his sword
set Folgrim free from the ropes at his waist and paws.
"There's only one thing to do, friend. Let your brother come

with us. We'll deliver him safe to your holt on the return journey, I promise."

Folgrim jumped up. With Chugger perched on his shoulders, he boarded the raft, both of them grinning from ear to ear. Tungro shook Martin's paw fervently.

"I know my brother'll be safe with goodbeasts like you'n'yore friends, sir. Mayhap 'twill be good for 'im."

They sailed off downstream, waving goodbyes to the otters standing on the banks.

"See you sometime about autumn!"

"Aye, we'll be waitin', with a potful of shrimp'n'hotroot soup to welcome ye!"

"Good, we'll be lookin' forward to it!"

"Watch out for Folgrim at night, he's a terrible snorer!"

"Hurr hurr, if'n ee can outsnore this lot, zurr, ee must be a good 'un!"

"You speak for yourself, Dinny mole. I don't snore!"

"Ho yuss ee do, miz Trimp. Don't 'er, zurr Gonff?"

"I wouldn't know, Din. When you're snorin', it drowns out everythin', even thunderstorms!"

The curious raft, with logboats tied to both sides, sailed off downstream into the soft summer morning. Tungro and his crew gave a final wave before sliding into the water and gliding sleekly upstream, home to their holt.

It was midday when Log a Log Furmo steered into a curving recess. Martin looked up at the shrew as he scrambled atop the steep rocky bank.

"What've we stopped for, Furmo? Surely it's not time to eat already. We've hardly been afloat today."

"Come up 'ere'n'look at this, Martin."

The Warrior joined his friend on the banktop. Far ahead he could see thick extending pine woods, flanking both sides of the stream. Martin peered hard at the dark mass. "Trouble, d'you think?"

The Guosim Chieftain voiced his thoughts. "I noticed the stream's startin' to run swifter, so I thought it best t'pull in an' scout the land. No sense dashin' into danger, that's if there's any there."

Martin mused for a moment, looking from the raft to the

pines and back again, before making up his mind. "Right, here's what I suggest. You take Gonff, I'll take Folgrim—I wager he can smell vermin a league off. We split up and go both sides of the bank to scout those pine woods out. Leave the rest with the raft. Throw a kedge anchor over the stern—that'll slow them up so they won't be speeding into the pine wood area."

Furmo agreed with Martin's strategy. An old waterlogged willow limb, forked at one end, was weighted by lashing big chunks of rock to it. When it was cast over the raft's stern, it dragged heavily on the streambed, slowing the vessel's progress considerably.

Furmo and Gonff took the north bank, the raft dropped Martin and Folgrim off on the south bank. Chugger shook a tiny paw at the Warrior. "You take good care of mista Fol, or I smacka you tail!"

Martin nodded seriously at the little fellow. "Aye aye, cap'n Chugg, I'll watch out for him, never fear."

Log a Log Furmo had been right. The broad stream was surely moving faster, running deeper, too, Martin noticed as he trotted along the bank with Folgrim at his side. Without the kedge anchor on its stern, both raft and logboats would go hurtling downstream.

At noon they reached the fringes of the pine woods. Gonff and Furmo waved across at Martin on the opposite side. He held both paws up, signaling them to wait. After a while Folgrim returned from scouting inside the fringe. He was carrying some ashes and a clump of grass, stained dark purple, along with a dab of ochre, still wet from the stream. Urgently he gestured for them to back off, away from the pines.

When he judged they were far enough from the conifers, the otter signalled them down to the shallows, where they could converse across the stream. Gonff and Furmo waded in as deep as they dared. Martin and Folgrim followed suit, the strong current pulling at them. The otter held up the stained grass and spoke. "Painted Ones, in the woods. Beware!"

Gonff and Furmo waded back to dry land. Folgrim called after them, "See you back at the raft!"

•   •   •

Trimp helped the Guosim shrews haul her friends aboard, and looked questioningly at Furmo as he ordered the craft into the south bank, behind a curve. "What is it, what's happening?"

The shrew Chieftain explained. "Painted Ones are in those pine woods ahead. Folgrim found traces o' the blaggards."

Trimp was plainly puzzled. "What d'you mean, Painted Ones?"

"Nobeast knows fer sure, missie, but most of us thinks they're some kind o' tree rats. My Guosim ain't been down this far in seasons—weren't any about then. I reckon they must've been driven out o' their own territory an' settled in the pines yonder. Painted Ones is vicious savages, never just a few, always come in big gangs. Those woods'd be ideal for 'em— they paints themselves all over, like sunlight stripes an' shadows. Painted Ones live up in the trees, an' woe betide any pore traveler tryin' to pass through their stampin' grounds. Killin's second nature to 'em! They're very good at disguises—you could be walkin' in the pines, thinkin' nobeast is there, then bang! The villains 'ave got you, an' yore a dead 'un!"

Dinny shook his head sorrowfully. "Et be a gurt pity, 'cos we'm be orfully near ee seashores. Oi cudd feel et in moi diggen claws."

Trimp sighed sadly. "But we can't go any further now."

Gonff chucked her gently under the chin. "Lackaday, lookit that long face, like a toad with toothache. Cheer up, pretty one, or you'll have it rainin'. Leave it to me, I've got a plan!"

Dinny wrinkled his nose. "You'm got ee plan, zurr?"

Gonff adopted his devil-may-care expression. "Why d'ye think they call me Prince of Mousethieves? Of course I've got a plan, you ole tunnel-grubber!"

Martin prodded his friend's well-fed middle. "I hope 'tis a plan that'll work, matey?"

"Oh indeed, an' did you ever know any o' my plans that didn't work, O swinger of swords?"

"Aye, lots of them, O pincher of pies!"

"Well this won't be one of that sort, O noble whiskers!"

"It had better not be, O pot-bellied soup-swigger. Now tell on."

"We won't wait 'til light—we'll set sail and shoot past them in the dark. They won't expect that."

• • •

The raft stayed tied to the bank until midnight, then they cut loose the kedge anchor and hoisted the sail. Drifting out into a moonless dark midstream, Gonff nodded to Furmo, who was seated in the logboats with his Guosim. Digging paddles deep, they shot the craft off downstream, with Martin, Dinny and Folgrim punting long poles at the stern. A light breeze caught the sail, billowing it out beautifully. Gonff and Trimp laid out slings and heaps of well-rounded stream pebbles where they could be easily reached. The Prince of Mousethieves chuckled. "The speed she's goin', we'll be through an' past 'em afore they even guess we've arrived, eh, missie?"

Covering Chugger's sleeping form with foodsacks and loose canvas, Trimp snuggled down by him. "I hope you're right, Gonff, for all our sakes, but mainly for this little mite's. I don't know what I'd do if any harm befell Chugger."

Folgrim turned from his pole, file-sharpened teeth glinting in the darkness, his one good eye roving wildly. "If'n yer wants t'see deadbeasts, pretty miss, take a look at any vermin puttin' a paw near my pal Chugg!"

Trimp shivered, certain that the scar-faced otter did not issue idle threats.

As the flotilla of raft and logboats neared the pine wood, myriad eyes, aglow with evil intent, watched it from the bankside trees on both sides. Small harsh excited whispers sounded through the conifers.

"Yikkyikkyikkyikk! Heerdee comm!"

"Many many lotsa shroobs'n'micers too. Yikkayikka!"

"Betcher deez viddlez too, loddza viddlez!"

"Fassta fassta inta dee trapp. Yeehikkayikka!"

"Fattee moledigga an' 'edgepiggee, avva fun wid dose!"

Then the raft was into the wooded area. Martin congratulated Gonff quietly on his daring scheme. "Well done, mate. We're shooting through like a shaft from a bow. Not much can stop us now!"

No sooner had the words left his mouth than the raft hit a thick series of vine ropes, stretched at different heights above and below the water. Everybeast aboard was thrown flat with the impact, and both leading logboats and the front of the raft were jammed fast in the cunning trap.

11

Martin was first to spring upright. He lashed about with the long punting pole as Painted Ones dropped from the trees onto the raft. Several were sent screeching into the water. Furmo and his shrews began laying about them with their logboat paddles, hollow thonking noises sounding as they struck tree rats in midair. Screams and splashes mingled with roars and shouts rent the blackness of the stream between the dark spreading pines. It was a scene of total chaos. Folgrim groped his way to the canvas protecting Chugger and Trimp and stood over them, flailing viciously, the air thrumming as he wielded his long pole. Whack! Thwock! Thunk! Splat! Gonff and Dinny were hard at it with their poles.

Panting heavily, Martin called to them, "There's too many of 'em—we can't keep this up. Hold the vessel as best you can. I'll be back soon. If not, go without me. That's an order!" He broke his pole over the backs of three who were trying to climb aboard, then dived into the fast-flowing stream.

As soon as he felt himself hurled against the ropes by the current, Martin latched his footpaws onto the heavy vines

87

and unsheathed the great sword from his back. It was tremendously hard trying to swing his blade in the rushing water, but swing it the mouse Warrior did. He hacked and hewed with might and main until his grip was frozen to the sword by cold water and weariness. By a superb feat of will he forced himself to continue. Heavy wet strands struck his face as the razor-sharp blade whipped through them, and water filled his mouth as he roared like a wild beast, battling the powerful woven ropes of wet vine. Lowering the blade underwater, Martin sawed furiously at the ones that he had twined his footpaws into, ducking his head beneath the surface and hunching both shoulders to put more force into his efforts. Then the raft was running overhead, scraping his back as it was liberated from the trap. Martin went head over tail, automatically shifting the sword to one paw and reaching out frantically with the other as the vessel sped forward.

Dinny felt somebeast grab his footpaw as he stood astern, swinging his pole. He was about to deal whoever it was a resounding blow with the pole butt when Martin's head emerged from the streamwater.

"Dinn, the pole, quick!"

The mole shot his pole into the water and Martin grabbed it. Throwing his sword onto the raft, he struggled aboard with Dinny's help. The raft was still swarming with Painted Ones. Martin seized the fabulous blade, and whirling it aloft, he gave full cry to the battle call of Badger Lords.

"Eulaliaaaaaa!"

Screeching with fright the tree vermin threw themselves from the raft, splashing frenziedly for shore.

Gonff threw back his head and roared with laughter. "Hahahaha! Look at 'em go! The ole Eulalia's worth a dozen fighters, an' let me say, matey, that 'un of yores was a right blood-freezer. I near jumped out o' my fur!"

Martin was grinning as he slumped wearily down to the deck. "Let's just say it was an additional idea to make your plan work. I was far too tired t'do anything except shout. Owow! What're you villains doing to me?"

Trimp and Chugger scrubbed roughly at the Warrior with clean dry foodsacks. The little squirrel growled, "Be still an' stoppa shoutin', we dryin' you off. Don't wanna catcha deff o' cold, do ya?"

The hedgehog maid was hard put to keep a straight face. Her squirrelbabe was becoming quite a one for being severe with otherbeasts. She cleaned Martin's ears out roughly. "That's the stuff, Chugg, you tell him. Warriors have to get dry too, same as any other creature!"

Luckily none of the friends were seriously injured, though there were the usual number of bumps, cuts, scratches and scrapes sustained, as in any rough-house encounter with vermin. Trimp and Log a Log Furmo set about ministering to the slight casualties, whilst Gonff and Dinny kept a weather eye out for any likely berth, now they had left the pine wood behind. A small midstream island loomed up out of the darkness, perfect as a resting place for the remainder of the night.

However, after their hazardous scrape with the Painted Ones, they were far too keyed up for sleeping. Guosim cooks built a small fire in the shelter of some bushes and cooked up a cauldron of vegetable soup. Gonff took some soft bread and chopped scallions, made Bubbling Bobbs and tossed them in the cauldron. Trimp sat round the fire with the rest, feeling a strong sense of camaraderie with them, laughing, chatting and fishing for Bubbling Bobbs with clean sharp twigs. Furmo regaled them with a comic song called "The Festive Fight."

"One dark an' stormy night,
As the sun set in the east,
To granma's house I went,
For to partake of a feast,
With frogs an' fat hedgehogs,
Some otters an' a sparrow,
An' a squirrel who attended too,
Armed with a bow an' arrow.
The seedcake had been served,
When a dormouse in a bonnet,
Took one bite, oh what a sight,
She broke her teeth upon it.

Then backward fell a mole,
Tail first into the custard,
Ole granpa grabbed his spoon,
An' lookin' quite disgusted,
He hit the mole a smack,
Then like a flash of lightnin',
An otter brained him with a flan,
That started off the fightin'.
We fenced with celery sticks,
With pies an' puddens pelted,
The squirrel with the bow,
By a pot of soup got belted,
A sparrow flung a scone,
It laid the otter senseless,
Then granma swung her pan,
An' left us all defenseless,
Two frogs sailed out the door,
A hedgehog up the chimney,
Whilst me an' ole granpa,
To the mantelpiece hung grimly.
So hark an' hear my tale,
Stay safe at home an' starve sir,
Steer clear of granma's house,
When there's goin' t'be a feast there!"

Chugger had fallen asleep leaning against Folgrim, a soggy Bubbling Bobb still clutched in his grubby paw. After the fight with the Painted Ones, Trimp trembled fitfully, thinking what might have happened had they fallen into the claws of the foe. However, the feeling passed as she looked around at the cheery faces of her friends. Ribbing one another good-naturedly and chuckling, they sat around the fire, finishing off the meal with gusto. Nobeast would guess that but a short while ago, they had been battling for their lives, and hers. Allowing her eyes to close slowly, she snuggled down on some dry moss. Who would not feel safe in the company of such brave creatures?

Murmuring streamwater soon had them all lulled, with the exception of Martin and Folgrim, who sat, outwardly relaxed, but inwardly alert. Fading to glowing embers, the fire burnt down. Somewhere a nightjar called, and moon-shadows cast soft patterns through lazy breeze-stirred foliage. Peace lay over the little island in midstream, await-ing the calm hours of dawn.

Day broke fine and clear, with a warm summer wind blowing westerly. Log a Log Furmo hopped aboard the raft, wetting a paw and holding it up. "Hoist that sail, mates, an' ship the paddles. We're on a good fast run t'the big sea!"

Picking up speed, the raft fairly zinged along the broad watercourse. With his bushy tail blowing forward over both ears, Chugger perched in the bows of a lead logboat, shout-ing aloud with exhilaration. "Whooooeeeeee! Us goin' a sea!"

Dinny clung nervously to a stayrope, not too sure whether he was fond of the vessel's wild ride downstream. "Hurr, zurr Log, bain't us'n's a-goin' ee bit farst yurr?"

Log a Log laughed and performed a nimble jig round the edges of the logboats flanking the raft. "Fast, me liddle fat mate, fast? See the way those banks down yonder take a deep dip? When she 'its there you'll know wot fast means!"

The mole shut his eyes tight, grabbing the stayrope tighter as Furmo gave it a mischievous twang. Folgrim and Trimp rescued Chugger from his precarious position and tied a line to his chubby middle, whereupon he promptly hopped back to his former position. Furmo began booming out a song in his wonderful bass voice.

"You stay aft mate, I'll stay fore,
Mind the rocks an' watch the shore,
Like good shipmates you an' me,
Roll down t'meet the sea!
Fast as fast as you can wish,
Through the waters like a fish,
Our ole craft do wend its way,
On this bright summer's day!
Wid spray in yore face,
An' a crackin' pace,
An' a runnin' stream afore,
If y'never lack a wind at y'back,

Then who could ask for more!
Ooooooh rum a doodle aye doh
Go where I go
Rum a doodle aye doh follow me!"

The raft bucked sharply, entering a canyon of buff-hued
rock. Everybeast yelled and held on to something. Chugger
was thrown into the water from his perilous perch. Trimp
screamed in alarm, but Folgrim had a good grip on the line,
and with a powerful heave he swung the little fellow back on
board.

"Up y'come, rascal. 'Ere, Gonff, look wot I caught, a
Chuggfish! Funny liddle critter, never seen one wid a tail that
long!"

Shaking water from his ruffled fur, the baby squirrel drew
himself imperiously to his full height. "I norra Chuggfish, h'i
a likkle squiggle!"

White water boiled about the surface, whilst high banks
narrowed and dipped sharply downwards. Furmo gave orders
to stow the sail, and his Guosim shrews took up their positions
at the logboats' oars, keeping the vessel in midstream with
strong skillful strokes. Soon they were all thoroughly
drenched by spray and unable to hear each other talk because
of the roaring waters. Log a Log and Martin with long poles
sculled at the after end. The Warrior mouse noticed that the
shrew Chieftain was no longer singing and smiling. Grim-
faced and silent, he struggled to keep the raft on course.

Now the raft really began to buck, side to side and up and
down, sometimes rearing high out of the stream and returning to hit the water with a resounding splash. Twice it was
whirled completely round on the treacherous current, Martin
and Furmo poling furiously to turn it. Trimp knew they were
in trouble when Gonff pushed her and Chugger flat, shouting
at them to hold tight. Gripping the tough vines that held their
craft together, Trimp locked both footpaws around her little
friend. Lifting her face, the hedgehog maid took a quick
glance ahead. What she saw took her breath away.

A rainbow bridged either bank, shining through a misty
curtain of cascading watermist. The raft rushed through it.
Then there was nothing!

Martin heard himself yell with surprise as his pole snapped on a rock at the waterfall's edge. The entire vessel, raft and logboats, sailed out into space. Log a Log's voice cut across the sudden silence.

"Hang on, maaaaaaaaaaates!"

Then the thunderous roar of falling water took over. They were falling, down, down, with a view of beach and sea to the front and an awesome sheet of rushing water at their back. Gripping fiercely to anything within reach, the breath torn from their mouths, they plunged downwards, tilting as the raft went head first, for what seemed like an eternity. Down, down, down . . . Whooooooom!

The broad surface of a pool at the bottom exploded with the impact. By its own momentum the vessel was plunged deep into the pool, breaking into pieces as it went.

Water rushed into Trimp's mouth. Her eyes opened. Everything was cold, silent and vague. Half conscious, she stared about. Somewhere high above, the water was billowing in thick white clouds, and she tried to fight down panic as she felt Chugger pawing feebly at her. They were both trapped under a log from the raft, which had become wedged in the rocks at the pool's bottom. Then the little squirrel's paws went limp. Panic surged through Trimp with the sudden realization that both her and Chugger's lives were going to end, trapped underwater and alone. Bubbles burst from her mouth as water flooded relentlessly in. Forgetting her plight for a moment, the hedgehog maid felt a tremendous wave of pity tug at her heart for Chugger. The little squirrel was still a baby. What a sad way for him to end a tragically short life. She reached down and held his paw, thinking that at least he would have her with him. Then the arrival of Folgrim jolted her failing senses.

Setting himself between the rocks, he bent his body, levering outward with all four paws, veins standing out on his neck as he added the strength of his rudderlike tail and the back of his broad skull. Folgrim pushed until the scars on his face stood out like blue ropes. There was a grinding crunch, followed by a muffled clonking noise. The log floated upwards, free, the rocks trapping it having been forced apart by the otter's wild strength. Folgrim seized Chugger by his tail and Trimp by one paw. Setting himself firm in the sand, he thrust mightily upward, tail and footpaws working in unison. In a stream of bubbles all three shot to the surface. Willing paws pulled them ashore.

Martin took a quick check of his crew. "Dinny, where's Dinny?"

The words had hardly left his mouth before Folgrim plunged in again, streaking underwater like an arrow. White sand and shell fragments, together with weeds and grains of rock, clouded the bottom a pearly grey color. Folgrim swam to an overturned logboat and wormed his way underneath. The otter's head broke water in a small air pocket trapped in the upturned vessel, and Dinny's head was facing him. The mole tugged his snout in polite relief. "Gudd day to ee, zurr. Oi 'oped sumbeast'd cumm afore ee air runned out in yurr. Oi doan't moind tellin' ee, oi'm gurtly affrighted o' liven unnerwater. Us moles be loik that, 'appy unnerground, but sad unnerwater, ho urr!"

The otter showed his filed teeth in a smile. "Then shut yore eyes, 'old yore breath an' 'ang on t'my paw, mister Din. Soon 'ave y'back on land, matey!"

Chugger shot fountains of water everywhere as he recovered. Trimp, who was no worse for her ordeal, sat watching Furmo anxiously. "Oh, say he's going t'be all right, sir?"

Chuckling, the Guosim leader pressed gently on the little squirrel's stomach and another jet of water arose. "This 'un'll be fine, missie, don't git yoreself in a fret. I seen shrewbabes swaller twice that amount—it never seemed to 'arm the liddle fellers a bit!"

Chugger opened one eye, his paw rising to point accusingly at Furmo. "You keep punchin' Chugga's tummy an' I swirt water in you eye, sh'ew!"

Furmo held Chugger upside down and shook him thoroughly, letting the baby squirrel go as he snapped at his footpaws. "See, I told yer, miss, he's stronger'n a growed eel!"

Dinny rolled himself into the warm sand until he looked like a white moleghost. He went and sat by Martin, who shook his head and burst out laughing.

"Have a rest, go to north shores, make it a holiday, take all summer! Some rest, eh, Din? Some holiday!"

Gonff dug a big raft splinter from his tail and sighed with relief. "Well, look at me, mates, I'm enjoyin' meself no end. Only one thing missin' though . . ."

Martin knew what was coming, so he interrupted Gonff. "Food! That's what it is, isn't it, you felonious famine-faced soup-stealer!"

Gonff picked his teeth nonchalantly with the splinter. "How'd you guess, noble britches? Ahoy there, Furmo, wot's the position on vittles, matey?"

One of the Guosim cooks answered for his leader. "Flour's ruined, fruit's all right though, plenty o' fresh water in that pool. Biscuits we baked this mornin' are lost in the stream. I reckon we could stand a few fresh supplies of wotever the land has to offer 'ereabouts."

Martin took charge, issuing orders. "Right, anybeast who feels up to it can forage for food. We'll split up around these hills and dunes on the shoreline. Dinny, you stay here with miss Trimp and Chugger and take a rest. See what you can salvage from the wreckage."

12

Trimp was still feeling a bit sick and dizzy from her ordeal in the pool, but with Chugger about it was difficult to rest.

"Chugger, come away from that water, it's very deep!"

"Ho, Chugg know it deep, I beena bottum of it!"

"Yes, well that's where you'll find yourself again if you don't come away. Come on, this instant!"

"Yah, lea' me alone, me an' mista Din doin' a job, see!"

The mole picked him up with one huge digging claw. "Oi can doo ee job on moi own thankee, maister. Naow, you'm do loik miz Trimp tell ee an' no cheek frumm ee!"

A fox appeared as if from nowhere. Behind him were four roguish-looking vermin, an assortment of rats and ferrets.

The fox looked the wickedest of all five. He was obviously their leader, and wore big hooped brass earrings and tattered silks. Faded tattoos showed on the paw holding a sharp single-headed axe. He gestured at Chugger.

"Haharr, young 'un, you lissen t'yore elders an' don't be cheekin' 'em. Avast now, cullies, wot 'ave we 'ere?"

One of the vermin sniggered. "Dinner, that's wot we got!"

Shaking his head in censure, the fox growled, "Stow that

kind o' gab, Fribb, these 'ere are gentlebeasts—a mite grubby, but respectable. Ain't that right, missie?"

Trimp had decided instantly that she did not like the vermin, or their leader, but her voice showed no fear. "Who are you and what do you want?"

Strutting insolently about, the fox rummaged through the salvaged supplies with his axeblade. He chose an apple, polishing it on his ragged sleeve. "I could ask you the same question, me pretty."

Trimp picked up a solid spar of raftwood. "I'm not your pretty, and 'tis usually considered good manners to ask before helping yourself to the food of others!"

Scornful sniggers echoed from the four vermin. Pausing with the apple halfway to his mouth, the fox grinned. "This 'un's got me quakin' in me boots, mates. Gut me, she's a right mouthy liddle baggage, ain't she?"

Trimp brandished her wooden spar, trembling slightly, but still game for trouble. "Aye, but you'll find I can back up my words when dealing with bullies. Now who are you and what do you want here?"

Making as if to go, the fox sidled past Trimp. Suddenly he turned, knocking the spar from the hogmaid's paw with a deft flick of his axeblade. Dinny went for him with a deep growl, but one of the vermin tripped him with a cutlass blade. He tried to rise, only to find another one menacing his throat with a pike. Biting into the apple, the fox pulled a face and spat the piece out. He held the axe under Trimp's chin, his voice hard and commanding.

"I'm Sholabar, lord of these coasts. See that boat out there? Well, 'tis mine. I patrols these waters an'—"

Trimp interrupted him sharply. "I don't see any boat out there!"

Sholabar growled at one of the vermin. "Where did ye berth the boat, Grimleg?"

"Be'ind the point, like y'told me to, cap'n."

The fox shrugged. "Well, no matter. Point is, missie, yore on my land. All around ye, far as y'can see, belongs t'me. Even this freshwater pool. So yore a trespasser, see!"

Trimp pushed the axe away from her chin and laughed in

the bully's face contemptuously. "Haha! Don't talk stupid, nobeast owns the shores and sea!"

Shaking with rage, Sholabar raised his axe at her. "Snot-nosed liddle spikeback, I'll skin yer alive!"

Chugger bounded forward and sank his teeth in the fox's leg.

"Yahowww! Leggo! Gerrim offa me! Yaaarrgh!"

The little fellow clung like a limpet, sinking his teeth deeper and growling fiercely. One of the vermin grabbed him by the tail. Trimp seized Sholabar's paw, trying to stop him swinging the axe at Chugger. The fox roared, "Aaaargh! Stretch 'im out, Grimleg! Yaaaah! I'll chop the liddle brat in two!" He shook his arm, trying to loosen Trimp's hold, while Chugger's little teeth dug deeper and deeper. "Fribb, get this brat offa me! Eeeyarrr! He's bitin' me leg t'the bone! Owowow!"

Before the fox could issue another yell, Folgrim came hurtling out of nowhere and struck him like a thunderbolt. There was an ominous crack. The fox's head went backward at a crazy angle under the force of the otter's blow, and he fell slain upon the sand. Taking one swift look at Folgrim, the four vermin fled for their lives. Martin and Gonff were rounding the corner of a nearby dune, carrying wild onions and dandelion shoots, and two of the fleeing vermin ran straight into them. Gonff butted one in the stomach, laying him out, gasping for air. Martin tripped the other one and grabbed him hard by the scruff. The other two vermin ran the opposite way, only to find themselves surrounded by Guosim rapier points.

Hauling the four vermin roughly along, the foragers arrived back at the poolside. Martin had to place himself between the captives and the scar-faced otter, who was trying to get at them with the dead fox's axe. Martin spoke calmingly to him. "No more slaying, friend, they've had enough. You four, sit down there and explain yourselves. What's been going on here? The truth, now!"

Grimleg the ferret managed a good act, whining pitifully. "We're nought but porebeasts, sir, we roams the sands, lookin' fer vittles t'keep skin an' bones together, sir. Woe is us, sir, we fell foul o' this robber band. We begged 'em for food but they attacked us. That liddle 'un tried to eat our cap'n, er, Sholabar, an' yon 'ogmaid was goin' t'brain us wid a club. Sir, 'tis the truth I tell ye. See that savage riverdog? That 'un slew our mate Sholabar fer no reason at all, sir. An' that mad mole 'ad a sword 'e was goin' t'kill me wid!" Grimleg picked up the cutlass he had dropped when he fled. "Aye, this is the very blade, I swears it on me mother's eyes, sir. They'd 'ave murdered us if you 'adn't arrived!"

Trimp noted Martin's wink before he turned to her stern-eyed and demanded, "Is this true, did you attack these poor creatures? Speak!"

Trimp caught on immediately. Cringing and rubbing her paws nervously, she groveled on the sand, performing a passable imitation of a vermin lying its way out of trouble.

"Oh, 'tis true, yer honor, 'tis true, we 'ad a wicked upbringin' y'see. But spare our lives an' we'll give up bad livin', on me granma's whiskers I swear we will. Kind sir, just let us sail off in our boat, that's moored be'ind the south point, an' you'll never see 'ide nor 'air of us agin, on me oath!"

At the mention of a boat, Furmo exchanged glances with Martin. "So they've got a boat. What d'you think, matey?"

Surveying the wreckage of what had once been their vessel, Martin nodded, as if considering the matter. "Aye, it'd save us long days of walking, eh, Gonff?"

Gonff drew his dagger and stood over the four vermin. "Fear not, friends, justice has come to yore aid. These ruffians, the hogmaid an' her crew that attacked you so wickedly, here's how we'll deal with 'em. My friends an' I will confiscate their boat an' take them with us as deck slaves for punishment. That way they'll bother honest creatures like yoreselves no more. What d'ye say to that?"

Grimleg and his vermin companions were nonplussed. In one fell swoop they had been foiled of their prey, lost their boat and also their captain to boot. The ferret was about to object when Furmo drew his rapier and stood facing him, cold eyed. His voice, when he spoke, was like ice.

"I'd say 'twas a good idea. These honest beasts should make no objection, as long as the tale they told us is true. 'Cos I can't abide a liar, y'see! Liars is worse than thieves or murderers, I always say. Show me a liar an' I'll silence his untruthful tongue for ever. Gurr! I can't stand liars!"

Gonff placed his paw on Furmo's rapier hilt. "Put up yore blade, matey, these are honest creatures!" Grimleg and his vermin nodded furiously, trying hard to look poor but honest. Gonff pointed an accusing paw at Trimp and her friends. "Now this lot, they're a different kettle o' fish. They've got the look o' savage murderin' villains t'me!"

Folgrim narrowed his one eye and squinted wickedly. "Aye, I'm a bad lot, allus 'ave been. Ain't 'appy 'less I'm slayin' pore honest beasts wid me axe."

Chugger bared his teeth and emitted a small growl. "Ho, we's villings sure nuff, choppa tail off an' cutcha froats us will. Gurrr!"

Dinny squinched up his snout and made evil gestures with his digging claws at all and sundry. "Burr aye, an' stuffen ee tails up'n ee noses. Gurrurr!"

Trimp kicked sand at the seated vermin. "Hah! Gimme a sharp blade an' a cookin' pot, an' I'll show ye what I do to pore honest beasts. Yarrrrr!"

Gonff gave a shudder of mock horror. "Enough o' that foul talk, ye blaggards! Off t'the boat with you an' keep a bridle on those wicked tongues!"

Martin drew his sword and marched the miscreants off. Gonff and the Guosim shrews had to bite their lips to keep from bursting out laughing.

Log a Log Furmo kept his face solemn. He patted the backs of the four miserable vermin heftily, then shook each one by the paw, with a grip that caused them to wince. "Lucky for you we came along, my friends, very lucky!"

One of the Guosim cooks whispered to Gonff in a voice that all could hear. "I 'opes they thanks the Chief—he can't stand ungrateful beasts. Why, I've seen Furmo take 'is blade an' . . ." Before the sentence was finished the vermin were gabbling aloud in panic.

"Aye, lucky indeed fer us, sire, thank ye!"

"Don't know wot we'd 'ave done without ye, Chief!"

"True, true, we'll never forget 'ow you saved us!"

"Thankee, thankee kindly, sir!"

Gonff gathered up the vermin weapons, tut-tutting like an

old mousewife. "Nasty sharp things. Don't fret, friends, we'll take care o' these lest you injure yoreselves on 'em!"

Furmo presented them with the piece of wood that Trimp had intended using. "Sorry about yore friend the fox. You can dig a nice restin' place for him with this. Goodbye to ye."

As they marched off down the beach, one of the vermin, a big skinny rat, kicked the sand ruefully. "Huh, why did we ever come 'ere in the first place, that's wot I'd like ter know?"

Grimleg whacked him over the head with the piece of wood. "Ah shuddup, screwnose!"

Log a Log Furmo was delighted with the new vessel. He splashed about in the shallows, admiring it as the others clambered aboard. It was a long flat-bottomed skiff, with a single square midsail. Bluffed at the stern and pointed at the bows, fashioned from seasoned beech, elm and rowan wood, it had oarlocks and paddles, four to each side, plus a fine carved tiller and rudder. There was a stern shelter of canvas, stretched over a frame of willow, for cover in rough weather.

When Furmo climbed aboard he went beneath the shelter, then emerged crowing with joy. "Lookit, Guosim, a liddle stone hearth an' a clay oven, an' three good bench seats. I reckon this craft'd hold a score an' a half of crew. I tell ye, mates, whoever built this vessel knew wot they were doin'. True craftsbeasts they must've been. A real beauty, eh, Gonff?"

The Mousethief shook his head in amazement. "I wager 'twill go like the wind too. Where'd those ole badbeasts ever lay paws on a marvellous craft like this?"

Chugger swaggered about, now immersed in his new role as a pirate captain. "Us robbed it offa ole frogdad an' boiled 'is tail for vikkles. Heeheehee!"

Trimp reprimanded him sharply. "That's quite enough of that kind of talk, thank you, Chugger."

The miscreant shot up the mastpole scowling darkly. "I norra Chugger no more, h'i a villyun, a orful bad 'un!"

Dinny went to sit beneath the stern awning. "Well oi bain't a bad 'un no more, zurr, ho no. Et 'urts moi face, a-scowlin' an' a-snarlin' all ee toim. Oi'm nought but a good ole mole, oi surpose."

• • •

Tacking close to the shore they threaded northward. Furmo and his Guosim shrews were in absolute ecstasies about their new craft. Being great boatbuilders they could readily appreciate the skill and ingenuity which had gone into its construction.

"I thought you were only traveling with us as far as the shore, my friend," Martin reminded the shrew gently. "Weren't you supposed to return to your camp and tribe, once we were safely downstream?"

Furmo was sniffing the deck, licking the mast, listening to the prow timbers and rapping his paws experimentally on the carved elm oarlocks. He smiled absently at Martin. "Oh, y'mean goin' back upstream t'the domestic life? Well I tell ye, matey, I'd get a right ole tellin' off from me wife if'n I went back to tell 'er we lost the logboats an' raft together. Huh! I might be a Log a Log, but my missus Honeysuckle, she's the real ruler of our tribe. She'd skelp the ears off me if'n I went back boatless!"

Martin nodded his agreement. "So what are you going t'do?"

A crafty smile flitted across the shrew's rugged face. "I'm goin' t'stay with ye, 'til yore adventure's done. Then you can sail back 'ome with me an' explain to me darlin' wife how you couldn't 'ave done without me'n'my Guosim crew. In fact you'll be so pleased with me that you'll present me with this boat, t'make up fer the ones we lost. In return I'll throw a smashin' feast for you'n'yore crew, an' we'll top it all off by namin' the vessel *Honeysuckle* in me dear wife's honour. Done?"

Grinning broadly, Martin clasped Furmo's paw. "Done, you golden-tongued rascal!"

13

The days that followed were sunny and uneventful, and good progress was made by the little ship *Honeysuckle*. She was ideally built for skimming the coastal waves, responding quickly to any vagrant wind, sliptide or rockshoal by just a touch on her tiller. Chugger was a constant source of amusement. The little squirrel had promoted himself to captain, still keeping up his new identity as a villainous sea rover. Folgrim and Trimp often had to stifle smiles and chuckles at his antics. Swaggering about the deck, armed with a stick for a sword, he growled out orders to all and sundry.

"Gerra vikkles cooked, or I fro y'to a sharkers!"

"Keepa tiller straight, mista Furmo, or cap'n Chugg make ya scrubba deck!"

"All singa funny song, or I choppa tails off!"

Gonff saluted him smartly. "Cap'n Chugg sir, I've checked the provisions, an' we're runnin' low on everythin'. We need more vittles."

Chugger stroked his chin reflectively, as he had seen Martin do, then he waved his tiny paws irately. "Well saila ship to d'shore an' get lotsa more vikkles. Hmph! Don't 'nnoy me, mouse, I busy bein' cap'n!"

Gonff looked to Furmo. "Well, we do need more provisions."

The shrew Chieftain tacked the vessel artfully across two cresting rollers, watching the shoreline intently. "We'll sail 'til evenin' then put in t'shore. A night on dry land'll do us good. Tomorrow will be time enough to send out a foragin' party. Er, if'n the cap'n approves."

Chugger was binding a colored shrew headband around his brow to make himself look more dashing. He nodded. "Good good, dat's wot we do. All 'ush now an' be quiet. Cap'n Chugg gonna take 'is nap!"

By evening the weather had grown noticeably brisker. Folgrim pointed shoreward, to where the beach was sandy and rockstrewn, dotted with dunes and backed by grassland with stunted trees and bushes. "Best chance a landfall there, afore the light fades."

Leaning on the tiller, Furmo sent the *Honeysuckle* skimming towards the beach. Wading ashore, the crew took up the ship's bowline, waiting on Furmo's word. Watching the incoming waves carefully, he yelled as a high one caught the stern. "Take 'er in, me hearties. Heave!"

Without any difficulty they ran the vessel up high and dry above the tideline, where it lay safe.

Dinny immediately trundled up the beach, pleased to be on dry land, calling back to them, "Thurr be an owd boat up yurr. Oi thort et wurr a rock!"

Upside down and half buried in the sand, the boat lay, long forgotten on the deserted shore. Folgrim viewed it wistfully. "Wonder who it belonged to?"

Trimp ventured closer, peering into the dark cavern formed by the upturned craft. "I don't know, but it'd make a snug shelter for the night. We could get a fire going and make a decent meal with the last of our rations. Come on, it'll be fun!"

Before anybeast could stop her, the hedgehog maid stooped and scurried under the wrecked hull.

"Yeeek!" She came scampering out hastily, with a huge

redbacked crab chasing her, its claws open and extended aggressively. She hopped clear, but the crab stood outside on the sand, menacing them, protecting its shelter. It was joined by another crab of equal size and ferocity. Trimp was shaking like a leaf, and Chugger hid behind her.

"Yaaah! It a bigga spider! No, two bigga spiders now!"

Martin stayed Folgrim's paw as it strayed to the axe he had taken from the vermin. "Easy now. Killing's not necessary, friend. They're not spiders, Chugg, they're crabs, pretty big 'uns too. But not to worry, our Prince of Mousethieves knows how to deal with crabs, don't you, O chubby one?"

Gonff bowed low, muttering to his friend, "Less of the chubby one, matey." He turned to Trimp. "Fear not, pretty one, crabs an' I are ole chums. Furmo, build a fire over yonder an' bring me two long pieces o' wood, will you? Stand clear the rest of ye!"

Whilst Furmo and his Guosim shrews built a fire of driftwood, both crabs held their ground, never going forward or back, but scrabbling sideways with their fearsome pincers wide open, giving out danger signals to the intruders. Gonff took the two long wooden spars offered by a shrew and bound them at both ends with rags soaked in lamp oil, keeping one eye on the crabs.

"These should do fine. Now watch this an' remember, mates, a crab's the daftest creature livin'. Once he latches on to somethin' he won't let go, unless 'tis food he can push into his silly mouth, an' these poles ain't food!" He charged the nearest crab, with the pole held out horizontally, shouting, "C'mon, ole shellback, bite on this!"

Clack! The creature's powerful claws seized the pole.

"Now one for your ole pal there. Bite on this, stalkeyes!" Gonff thrust the second pole at the other crab in like manner. Obediently the fearsome pincers grabbed it. Boldly the Mousethief stood a hair's breadth from both crabs and turned his back on them to face the audience. "Y'see, they ain't got enough brains between 'em to let go of those poles, an' while they're hangin' on to 'em, they can't hurt us with their nippers. Now, they'll stand there like that 'til the crack o' doom if I let 'em. But here's the best way to get rid o' crabs. Watch!"

Taking a blazing piece of wood from the fire, Gonff raced nimbly round both crabs, touching the flames to both ends of each pole. Agitatedly, the big crustaceans continued their sideways patrol, stalk eyes waving wildly in the firelights they were carrying, stumbling and tripping in dumb panic. The Mousethief advanced upon them, swinging his crackling torch.

"You rock-backed oafs, go on, get out o' here afore yore nippers get burned. Go on, into the water with yer!"

He chased them a short distance down the beach, until the crabs' tiny brains realized the answer to their burning problem. They scuttled off sideways into the sea. Gonff skipped back up the beach, chuckling. "Ain't got the sense they was born with, those two!"

Everybeast waited whilst the fearless Gonff went beneath the boat hull with his lighted torch. "Come on in, buckoes, the place is empty!"

Guosim cooks like nothing better than to improvise with their cooking. That night they did the crew proud. Barley broth with wild onions and dried watershrimp, hot mint and dandelion tea, and the *pièce de résistance*: a big pan, lined with thick slices of honey-soaked shrewbread, into which they placed all their dried apples and pears and hazelnuts, mixed with the last of their fresh berries—blackcurrants, strawberries and raspberries. The pan was covered with a flat slab of stone and placed on the fire. After a while, the aromas drifted temptingly around in the shelter formed by the upturned boat. Whilst Folgrim was not looking, Chugger emptied his barley broth into the otter's bowl and sat happily licking his seashell spoon.

"Cummon, mista Fol, eaty up all barley broff, or you don't get no pudden. See, Chugg eat all his up, yum yum!"

The scarred otter tugged his friend's bushy tail fondly. "Ain't it strange 'ow a bowl can fill itself up agin? Yore a forty-faced liddle skinnamalinker, cap'n Chugg!"

The pudding was perfectly cooked, a triumph. Everybeast had their bowls heaped, and they tucked in willingly.

"Mmmm, this is marvellous!"

"Best I ever tasted, pipin' 'ot an' delicious!"

"Burr aye, gurtly noice an' turrible tasty et be's!"

"Any chance o' second 'elpings there, cooky?"

"If'n you wants to end up in the sea wid yore crabmates, Gonff, jus' keep callin' me cooky!"

"Oops, sorry, O well-furred an' beautiful Guosim Boss!"

"Oh, all right, pass yore bowl 'ere!"

Outside the night grew cold, with a stiff wind driving sand spirals across the shore. Fortunately, the shelter was in the lee of the wind, and they sat around the cheery fire amid the good food and banter. During a lull in the conversation, Trimp cocked an ear to the opening. "Listen. Can you hear anything, Martin?"

Martin listened. "Aye, like a sort of moaning."

Furmo refilled Dinny's bowl. "Prob'ly the wind."

But Martin's paw was on his sword. He leaned forward, alert. "That's not the wind. Listen carefully!"

In the silence that followed they all heard the audible moaning from outside, eerie, ghostly.

"Oooo oo ummmm, ooo oooo aaaahhhh . . ."

It seemed to fade and rise with the lonely wind out on the moonless stretches of coastline. Furmo shuddered. "Don't sound like nothin' livin' t'me!"

This remark started off a lot of fearful speculation.

"Mayhap 'tis the spirits of deadbeasts?"

"Aye, mate, could've been the long-dead crew o' this boat!"

"They say strange things 'appen on ole lonely shores!"

"I've 'eard tell o' that, too. Bet they comes back on dark nights, to visit the spot where they perished!"

"Ooh urr, us'n's should've stayed aboard ee boat on ee sea!"

"Hark, I can 'ear 'em singin' words!"

Sure enough, the words came clear and distinct. Beneath the boat, fur stood on end, paws trembled and creatures drew closer to the fire. They could not avoid hearing the wailing dirge, which rose and blended with the sighing winds.

"Ooooo ooo ummmm! Ooooo ooo aaahhhh!
From the deep cold seas afar,
Spirits of the dead arise,
Rattling bones and sightless eyes,

From the deep mysterious sea,
Wand'ring lonely beach and shore,
We must walk eternally,
Wand'ring, seeking evermore,
When the pale moon sends its light,
Or in dark and starless night,
Roaming near and traveling far,
Ooooo ooo ummmm! Ooooo ooo aaaaaaahhhhhhhhh!"

Trimp's face was blanched with fear. Chugger was trembling like a leaf, and she hugged him close to her. The breath caught in her throat as a spectrally hollow knock sounded on the upturned boat hull—Whock! Whock! Whock!—followed by unearthly-sounding voices.

"Leave the coast, desert our shore,
Or stay here for evermore,
Go by land or go by sea,
Heed these warning words and fleeeeeeeeeeeeeee!"

Martin looked at the terror-stricken faces around him. Drawing his sword, he turned to the only one, beside himself, who did not appear to be affected by the eerie chants. "Well, what d'you make of that little lot, Gonff?"

The Mousethief drew his dagger. "Don't see how a ghost could be solid enough to knock its paws on a boat hull, mate. You stay here in case it's some kind o' trap—take care of these ditherin' daisies. I'll go an' take a look out there!"

Gonff slid out into the night. A moment later he reappeared, a great deal faster than he had left. Martin gripped his friend's paw as the dagger slid from it. This was not like Gonff, who sat ashen-faced and trembling. The Warrior gazed into his haunted eyes. "What is it, mate? What did you see out there?"

Gonff swigged down a beaker of dandelion and mint tea. He regained his composure slightly, though it was some time before he managed to speak. "I tell ye, matey, I never want to see aught like that again. Tall they were, very tall, with 'orrible faces an' long white bodies that seemed to flutter'n'float!"

One of the Guosim shrews recoiled in horror, his paw shaking as he pointed out beneath their shelter entrance. "Eeaaargh! I see one! There 'tis!"

A vague misty shape was gliding about outside. Martin sheathed his sword and seized a long paddle. "I've had enough of this nonsense. Let's see what these ghosts have got to say for themselves!" As the apparition drifted by again, Martin struck out with the paddle, giving it a good hard sweep.

The ghost gave a yell of surprise and collapsed into a heap. Martin grabbed the struggling mass and dragged it inside the shelter. Ripping off the flowing white cloth, he exposed a hedgehog on stilts.

The creature's face was daubed thickly with some kind of white clay, and long seabird feathers were stuck into the clay. Blackened beneath the eyes and painted bright red about the mouth with plant dyes, it gave the hedgehog a fearsome appearance. It glared at Martin defiantly. "Arrah now, an' aren't you the bold ould Sea Rogue! Goo on now, cullie, kill me an' get it over wid. That fine blade you carry looks fit t'do the job. You durty murtherin' omadorm!"

Martin grabbed the hedgehog firmly by its clay-encrusted ear. "Listen, my friend, keep a civil tongue in your head or I'll box your ears for you. We're not Sea Rogues and we don't go about slaying others willy-nilly!"

A huge grin cracked the white-clayed face. "Muther of all the seasons, now ain't that a mercy! By the spikes o' me fat uncle, does that fine pudden taste as good as it smells? Could y'not serve me up a large morsel of the luverly stuff, an' could meself not sit next t'that pretty darlin' hogmaid whilst I show her the powers o' me turrible appetite, sir?"

Martin was smiling as he extended a paw. "I'm Martin the Warrior of Redwall, and these are my friends, who no doubt will introduce themselves."

The hedgehog shook the proffered paw vigorously. "An' 'tis pleased I am to meet ye, Martin sir. I'm Murfo, son o' Chief Dunespike, Allcoast Champion Spinetussler."

Gonff immediately took to Murfo. Sensing in him a kindred spirit, he exchanged a wink with the newcomer. "Don't y'think you'd better ask yore dad an' the others in out o' the

weather, Murfo? They'll catch their death o' cold, stumpin'
about in long white nighties on a night like this. Go on, give
'em a shout."

Murfo stuck his head outside and roared, "Hoi, da, these
beasts are friends, an' they've got pudden on the hob. Bring
the boyos over, will ya!"

In the blink of an eye, the shelter and the beach surrounding it was packed with hedgehogs, all untying stilts
from their footpaws and casting aside their long white ghost
robes. Murfo's father, Dunespike, was possibly the biggest
hedgehog Martin had ever set eyes on. Introductions were
made all round, with Dunespike offering his apologies for
frightening them.

"Ah, 'tis sorry I am for puttin' the fears into honest craturs
like yerselves, but we've seen that sleek boat of yours afore,
so we'd be forgiven for thinkin' that you were the durty scut
of a fox an' his flotsam that usually sail in it. Ah yis indeed,
Martin me ould son. Well now, isn't this all grand?"

As one all the hedgehogs nodded and chorused, "Ah, 'tis
grand, grand indeed, sir!"

Furmo scraped his ladle around the big pan, comment-
ing, "Sorry there ain't enough pudden t'go round all yore
tribe."

Chief Dunespike accepted the last bowl and passed it to
his son, shaking his head ruefully. "More's the pity, but those
who get none'll never know what they missed an' be no
worse for the missin' of it! Here, me son, get that down yer
gob an' don't go tellin' your ould da how grand it tastes. Bad
cess t'this rotten tooth o' mine, it won't abide the sweet stuff
an' torments the very life o' me if I go near anythin' sweetish,
so it does."

All the hedgehogs' spikes rattled as they shook their heads
and chorused in unison, "Ah yis, the ould tooth torments the
big feller turrible!"

Trimp could not resist asking a question. "But why do you
parade around the shore at night dressed as ghosts?"

Whilst Dunespike sat nursing his tooth, Murfo explained,
"Sure, to scare off the sea vermin. They're all superstitious
wretches. Scarin' them is far simpler than gettin' the half of

our tribe slain in battle. It works just grand, missie. Ain't that right, boyos?"

Again all the tribe nodded their heads and spoke together. "Ah yis, 'tworks just grand, grand grand!"

Still nursing the side of his jaw, which looked painfully swollen, Dunespike glanced admiringly at Martin's sword. "By the spike of the great hog himself, 'tis a grand an' powerful blade you have there, Martin sir!"

Martin unsheathed his sword, holding it forth for all to see. "Aye, that it is. The hilt was my father's and the blade was forged by a Badger Lord from a piece of a star that fell from the skies. This sword is a magic weapon!"

Dunespike shook his huge head in amazement. "Magic, you don't tell me! How so?"

He did not see the wink that passed between Martin and Gonff. Martin turned the sword, so that the red pommel stone at its hilt top twinkled in the firelight. "This stone can soothe pains and heal wounds!"

The big hedgehog Chief stared reverently at the stone. "And toothaches?"

Martin smiled. "Aye, toothaches too!" Digging a hole in the sand with his swordpoint, he pushed the sword in upside down. He held it in the deep wet sand until he judged the stone was cold enough. "Sit down here, sir. Gonff, will you get the other side of the Chief and hold his head?"

Dunespike sat down gingerly. Gonff braced the hedge-warrior's head still by leaning against the uninjured side. The hog looked uncertainly at Martin, who was withdrawing his sword from the sand. "You wouldn't be goin' to hurt me now, would you, Martin?"

The Warrior smiled reassuringly. "Me, hurt you? I'm not even going to touch you, Chief. 'Tis the pommel stone does all the magic. Sit still and relax." Very gently, Martin began moving the cold stone in slow circles around the patient's swollen jaw, murmuring as he did so, "Easy now, easy. How does that feel, nice and cool?"

Dunespike closed his eyes, leaning heavily against Gonff. "Ah, 'tis grand, grand, like a butterfly's breath on a morn in spring. Don't stop, Martin, keep doin' that, round an' round me ould rotten, achin' tooth."

Martin whispered soothingly in Dunespike's ear. " 'Round and 'round with the magic stone, that's the stuff. Is your tooth in the middle of this area I'm circling?"

Dunespike sighed contentedly. "Yis, so 'tis, so 'tis."

Gripping the crosshilt with both paws, Martin whacked the pommel stone, hard and sudden, right at the middle of the swelling, where the tooth was located. Thump!

"Yaaaargooooogh! I'm destroyed, he's killed me! Aaargh!"

The entire tribe of Dunehogs leaped forward. Martin swung his blade aloft, halting them with his fearsome war cry. "Eulaliaaaaa!"

Dunespike stopped roaring. He opened his eyes, felt the side of his jaw, then spat out a blackened molar. "Haharrharr! Look at that now! I'm free of pain—me ould tooth's out! Oh, seasons preserve y'grand name, Martin sir!"

Trimp put a pawful of sea salt in warm water and stirred until it dissolved. She gave it to Dunespike, saying, "Take this and swish it around where the tooth came out, sir. 'Twill clean the hole and help it to heal."

The big hedgehog patted Martin's back so heartily that he almost knocked him flat. "Sure, an' I wish ye'd done that when we first met, then I would've been able to tackle that grand pudden of yours. Martin of Redwall, yer a mighty cratur, sir, heroical, y'are."

The Dunehog chorus echoed their Chief's sentiments.

"Ah yis yis, heroical indeed!"

"Isn't he the grand mouse!"

"Oh, that he is, grand, grand!"

Murfo appealed to his father. "Da, would y'have Martin an' his friends sittin' the night out under some battered ould boatwreck? Sure an' 'twould only be good manners to invite them back t'the roundhouse."

14

Trimp walked ahead of the main party with Murfo and a party of admirers, all of whom, it seemed, wanted to hold her paw lest she slip. They were deep among the dunes when Murfo stopped and tapped the side of his nose. "Well, missie, what d'you think of our roundhouse?"

Trimp looked round. All she could see was sand dunes. "Where? I can't see any roundhouse?"

The hedgehogs danced with glee, highly amused.

"Can ye not see it at all, pretty one?"

"Ah sure, maybe she's got her eyes shut!"

"An' the roundhouse starin' her right in the face!"

"She's pretty all right, pretty short-sighted. Hahaha!"

At that Trimp lost her patience. "Very funny, I'm sure. Now would one of you stilt-legged, clay-faced buffoons show me this roundhouse?"

Murfo stepped forward to the side of the biggest dune and slid aside a screen of brushwood and dead grass, revealing an opening. Bowing low to Trimp, he bade her enter. "How d'you like it, me beauty? This whole big dune is our roundhouse, an' none can find it except the Dunehogs."

It was an ingenious structure, built from stones, timber, clay and wattle, completely disguised as one massive sand dune. Inside, it was lit by lanterns and a fire glowing beneath a stone oven, with secret air vents to the outside. Everybeast sat upon woven rush mats, and a silence fell as Dunespike entered and threw up his paws. "Do we know who we are?"

Every hedgehog held up their paws and answered, "Sons o' the sand an' daughters o' the dunes!"

The Chieftain looked round until he had selected a very young beast, who was still learning the tribe's rules. A question-and-answer session started between master and novice. Older Dunehogs watched, nodding sagely.

"Do we fight our enemies?"

"Dunehogs would rather use fright than fight!"

"How tall is a Dunehog?"

"As tall as his stilts!"

"Where do Dunehogs live?"

"In a roundhouse where nobeast knows!"

"Why don't they know?"

"'Cos we cover our tracks!"

"An' when is it your turn to cover tracks?"

"Dawn 'til night, first quarter o' the moon!"

"Right. You did grand, young 'un, just grand!"

"I thankee, Chief Dunespike!"

Food was served amid a babble of chatter. Dunespike plumped his huge bulk down between Martin and Trimp, knocking Murfo out of the way. "Ah, that's better now. My turn t'sit next t'the pretty maid." He tweaked Trimp's head-spikes before turning to Martin. "These young 'uns must learn the rules, y'know. Sit ye an' welcome to our ould home. Eat hearty now."

The crew of the *Honeysuckle* soon got into the habit of eating like Dunehogs. There was a board, piled high with wafer-thin ryeflour pancakes, and between each four creatures two earthenware pots were placed, steam arising from both. One of the pots contained a thick stew, consisting of overboiled potato, finely chopped cabbage, wild onions and various types of shellfish. This was spooned on to a pancake and rolled up carefully. One end was twisted a couple of times to stop the contents spilling out.

Gonff was an expert within seconds. He nudged a nearby Dunehog. "Good idea, this, mate. Saves a lot o' platewashin'."

"Oh, that it does, sir. 'Tis a grand ould idea!"

Gonff, the perfect mimic, answered him in Dunehog idiom. "Ah sure 'tis. Grand, grand!"

Everybeast within hearing chuckled appreciatively.

When the first pot was finished, there was still about half the amount of pancakes left. These they used in like manner with the contents of the second pot: a sweet hot mass of pulped berries and honey, with some strange tangy spice mixed in.

Dunespike chomped away blissfully. "Ah, thank ye, Muther Nature, for the good ould sweet stuff. 'Twas meself was thinkin' I might never taste it again until yourself magicked me rotten tooth away, Martin!"

For entertainment the Dunehogs laid on an exhibition of Spinetussling. A circle was cleared and two contestants tied on pairs of half-size learning stilts. They stood balancing at the ring's inner edge. Then a few oldsters, acting as referees and judges, shouted, "Hold y'circle, no paw touchin' now. Get set. Tussle!" The pair stumped adroitly out, charging one another. They were two fully grown males and had lots of supporters.

"Ah, g'wan there, Doggle, make him eat sand!"

"Get into the great lump, Paykel. Throw him spike o'er stilts an' let's see the soles of his footpaws!"

"Watch the divvil now, Doggle, look out fer those sweeps with his stilts!"

"Go on, Tussle will ye, Tussle!"

Both hedgehogs circled awhile then met in the middle with a resounding bump of heads. They locked headspikes and began trying to throw each other over. Not being allowed to touch one another with their paws made it very hard. Sweating and grunting, they pushed back and forth, every now and again trying a side hop to unbalance the unwary one.

"Now, Doggle, now, give him the ould sidehead twist!"

"Use the one two forward butt, Paykel, an' you'll Tussle him!"

In the end Doggle triumphed. He took the advice, using a combination of the sidehead twist and a left stiltsweep. With a roar of surprise, Paykel spun once in the air, stilts flying high, to land flat on his back. Cheers rang out from Doggle's supporters as he leaned down and rapped on his opponent's stilts thrice, which is considered a very sporting gesture in Spinetussling circles.

Now the Dunehogs were calling for the Chief to enter the ring, but he shook his head, smiling.

Murfo yelled across at him. "G'wan, da, show 'em how a real champion Tussles, or is yer belly gettin' too grand?"

This aroused jeers and laughter. Still smiling, Dunespike plodded down to the ring's edge. "Are you fit to be thrown, Doggle?"

Doggle performed an agile dance on his stilts. "Aye, Chief, I am that. Though I'm thinkin' 'twill take somehog younger an' faster than yerself to throw me, ye fat ould omadorm."

Dunespike raised one eyebrow. There was menace behind his smile as he tied on one stilt. "Ah sure mebbe I am gettin' on in seasons, but let's see if we can't make ye kiss the sand wid yer backspikes!"

A gasp arose from the audience as Dunespike stood erect.

"Will ye look at that, he's goin' to Tussle wid only one stilt. Doggle will make crab bait of the ould fool!"

One of the judges pointed at Dunespike. "D'ye not know yer wearin' only one stilt, Chief?"

"I do!"

"An' y'wish to Tussle like that tonight?"

"I do!"

The judge shook his head in resignation. "Right. Hold y'circle now, no paw touchin', get set. Tussle."

The agility and skill of one so old and heavy shook Martin. Dunespike bounded across the ring on his one stilt, meeting Doggle who was yet not halfway across. Down went the Chief's huge head, spikes bristling, and he caught his opponent a mighty butt, locking spikes and twisting powerfully. Doggle went sailing through the air sideways, to land amid the spectators. Roaring with laughter, Dunespike hopped over to knock his opponent's stilts thrice amid wild applause. Then he looked at Martin. "Would ye like to tie the ould stilts on an' Tussle wid me, Martin of Redwall?"

Shaking his head, Martin held up both paws, laughing.

"I'd sooner tangle teeth with a shark than Tussle with you, sir. You're a warrior born!"

Gonff chimed in. "Martin's a warrior too, y'know, an' sure he's a grand one with the ould sword. Let him show ye!"

Martin shook his head wearily at the Mousethief. "Gonff, if you want any exhibitions of sword dancing you can do them yourself. I don't like showing off every time we meet new friends."

Gonff shrugged glumly. Trimp felt sorry for him and immediately tackled Martin.

"It's not a case of you showing off, Martin, it's wanting to show you off to our friends. He's so proud of you, as we all are. Couldn't you manage just one little example of your bladeskill?"

Martin threw his paws about them both. "When you put it like that I've no option, missie. Forgive my bad manners to you, Gonff. Right, let's see what we can do with these stilts!"

At Martin's request the Dunehogs thrust two stilts upright in the sand and balanced another one across their tops. The three stilts looked like a doorframe standing freely in the middle of the ring. The Warrior bade everybeast stand clear. A silence fell as they eagerly watched Martin take up position, holding the sword over one shoulder in a classic fighting stance. After weighing the stilts up, he hopped a half-pace back and went into action with a roar. "Redwaaaaaaaalllllll!"

Like a shimmering blur of light the fabulous blade hit the topmost, horizontal stilt, sending it flying in the air. Almost within the same breath the sword zipped left and right, chopping both the upright stilts clean through their middles. Before the top stilt had hit the ground, Martin's sword severed it in midair. Even before the thunderstruck audience could shout or applaud, Martin had sheathed his battleblade and was sitting calmly next to Dunespike.

Amid the tumultuous applause, stamping footpaws and rattling spikes, the hedgehog Chieftain found his voice. "Well stagger me spikes an' pickle me paws! Martin of Redwall, ye'd be a useful mouse t'have around anyplace! I thought me own two eyes were tellin' fibs t'me. Sure an' I still don't believe I seen y'do what y'did, sir!"

It was enough to end the battleplay. A great old hogwife

took out a curious stringed instrument and began twanging it with her headspikes, another began shaking a tambourine, and a third took up his little pawdrum and beat a lively tattoo.

Murfo seized Trimp's paw. "Haharr, can y'dance an' sing, miss?"

Trimp skipped down to the ring ahead of him. "Just try me. I recognize that tune, 'tis 'Hogstamp Pawclap'!"

Setting the sand flying, both young creatures went at the dance with a will, putting in all the fancy steps they knew.

"Hogstamp pawclap all around the floor,
Shake those spikes that's what they're for.
Day is ended work is done,
Hogstamp pawclap everyone!

Curtsy the pretty maid bow down sir,
You've never danced with one so fair.
Take y'partner one two three,
Swing to the left, love, follow me!

Rap rap rap! Let's hear those paws,
I'll stamp mine if you stamp yours,
'Round an' round now jump up high,
Lookit that young hogmaid fly.

Hogstamp pawclap, move to the right,
I could dance with you all night,
Skip into the middle o' the ring,
Raise y'voice let's hear you sing!

Can't you see, merry are we,
Here's the land and there's the sea.
Promenade let's hear you say,
Honour your partner, jig away!

With a hog an' a stamp an' a clap clap clap,
Raise the dust up slap slap slap,
Beat that drum an' pluck those strings,
Ain't we all such lucky things!
Easy with the spikes now . . . Hedgehogs!"

As Trimp and Murfo halted, the music struck up again and nearly everybeast began dancing. Dunespike and Martin sat tapping time with tankards of Seafoam, a fine beer that the Dunehogs brewed themselves. Martin smiled as he watched Chugger kicking up his heels with a tiny hogmaid, and leaned towards Dunespike. "Guess who's just changed from a squirrel to a hedgehog. Haha, yesterday he was a Sea Rogue captain!"

Dunespike took a deep swig and wiped a paw across his mouth. "An' good luck t'the liddle sprig, sez I. See, Martin, yore pal the otter thinks he's a bit of an ould hedgehog too!"

Martin was amazed at the transformation that had come over Folgrim. The scarred otter was roaring with laughter as he whirled a hogmaid round and round. Dunespike nudged Martin. "Sure an' I wish that otter was one o' me hogs. The boyo looks as if he'd stand no ould buck from anybeast!"

The Warrior winked at his friend. "That's the truth, mate, nobeast messes with Folgrim twice!"

Dunespike was still watching Folgrim as he answered, "Beasts without fear are far'n'few. I knew soon as I clapped eyes on you'n'Folgrim that you were two of that rare ould stock. Only other two I ever heard of was a mouse like yerself an' a black squirrel. 'Twas said that they were a grand ould pair of battlers who didn't know the meanin' o' the word fear, no sir!"

Martin came alert. "What were their names? Where did they come from, Chief, do you know?"

Dunespike had eaten and drunk copiously, and he was tired. "D'ye know, I'm not certain. The mouse had a short kind o' name, the squirrel now, was her name Rangfarl or somethin'? I can't think properly some days, me ould head must be turrible muddled from all that Spinetusslin'. Wait now! I heard it said that the mouse came from north of here, up the coast a ways, though 'tis meself'd be lyin' if I told ye any more. Sometimes I wonder if there are more butterflies flyin' 'round in me head than there are out on the dune flowers."

Martin patted the old Chieftain's paw. "Never mind, matey. Though I'd be obliged if you could tell me how far the north shore is?"

Dunespike lay back on the rush mats and yawned cavernously. "Oh, four days about. You'll easily know, 'cos the weather gets much colder an' you'll see a great ould rocky point stickin' out into the sea. Martin, I can't keep me eyes open, so I'll bid ye goodnight an' peaceful dreams."

When the festivities had ceased and the lanterns had been doused, Martin sat awake in the firelight's glow. All around the Dunehogs' shelter creatures sprawled, snoring, murmuring, some even chuckling or singing broken snatches of song in their sleep. For some reason unknown to himself, a great weight lay on him, and tears sprang unbidden to his eyes. Then the Warrior realized what the cause of his distress was. He had been laughing, singing, drinking, eating and dancing, with hardly a thought for them.

"Them" being the father and mother he could hardly remember, who had lived only four days away from the place where he now sat. A vision of a ship, sailing off into a snowswept day, sprang into his mind, a memory of overwhelming sadness and pain. He gripped his sword tightly, knowing it was the only link between himself and the small young mouse who stood on the shore, watching the ship vanish into swirling snow and heaving waves. Weariness overtook Martin of Redwall. He lay down and let his eyes close. The small mouse, the ship and that long ago day grew dimmer and dimmer, then vanished into the realms of merciful dreamless sleep.

15

Over the following days and nights Martin, hardly rested or ate. He was unusually silent, and spoke only when he had to. Draped in a blanket and sailcloth, he sat at the prow of the *Honeysuckle*, regardless of the hostile weather, which grew colder by the day. Dunespike and his tribe had given them a marvellous send-off, plying the crew with stores of food and delicacies. Trimp and the others had been sorry to sail off, the hedgehogs were so hospitable and funny. Martin's somber mood affected the crew of the *Honeysuckle* deeply, and they were not the jolly bunch of companions who had traveled downstream together.

Log a Log Furmo cooked a special damson crumble, with Trimp assisting two of his Guosim shrews to make tempting arrowroot and redcurrant sauce for it. They sat beneath the stern shelter whilst Gonff dished it up to the crew, filling each bowl brimful and remarking, "Dig in, mateys, this'll put the roses in yore cheeks an' a smile on yore faces. Best skilly'n'-duff I ever saw!"

Furmo raised his ladle warningly. "Ahoy, Gonff, I'll raise a good lump 'twixt yore ears if'n I hear ye callin' my best damson crumble an' miz Trimp's sauce skilly'n'duff. Hmph! Skilly'n'duff indeed! What does he think we are, missie, a pack o' sea vermin?"

Trimp held out a bowl to Gonff. "Fill it up, friend. I'd better take some to Martin. He only had a beaker of mint tea for breakfast, and 'tis late noon now and he hasn't had a thing since."

Gonff heaped a good portion into the bowl. "Best let me take it, pretty 'un. I know him better'n anybeast, 'cept my Columbine. Wish she was here now—liddle Gonflet too. They'd cheer him up."

Dinny's homely face creased in a smile. "Hurr, oi'm thinken ee h'infant an' yore pretty woif wudd cheer you'm up gurter'n anybeast, zurr Gonffen."

Gonff sat down. Putting the bowl to one side he wiped at his eyes with a piece of rag. "That's the truth, Din. I miss Columbine an' the liddle feller a lot. I ain't the cheerful rovin' type I used t'be."

Chugger leaped on to the Mousethief's lap and hugged him. "Shush now, mista Gonff, I be yore likkle one, eh?"

The Mousethief could not help smiling through his tears. "Bless yore 'eart, Chugg, course you will, though I 'ope you ain't a Dune'og no more—they're too prickly to hug. Beggin' yore pardon, miz Trimp. No reflection on you."

Martin came striding astern. He threw off the blanket and sailcloth, nodding to Furmo. "Tell your shrews to trim the sail and take up oars. I can see the rockpoint standing out in the distance!"

Furmo went up the mast like a squirrel. He peered ahead at the dark jutting line far off, then came back down. "Aye, that'll be the start o' the northlands right enough. Folgrim, will ye take the tiller an' keep 'er dead ahead? Gonff, 'elp tie off the lines. We'll make landfall tonight if'n she holds a tight sail. Stir yore stumps, Guosim, show our friends wot a shrew rower looks like!"

The *Honeysuckle* sprang forward, only having to tack the slightest bit, running before a wind out of the southeast. Martin took the for'ard port oar, with Gonff plying the opposite one. The Warrior set a vigorous pace, though Trimp cautioned him. "Easy now, Martin, not so fast. Think of the others."

Gonff blew off spray that was tickling his nose. "That's the stuff, Trimp, you tell 'im, otherwise we'll all be flat on the deck afore we're halfway there. Don't forget, it's not safe to row like a madbeast on a full stomach of skilly'n'duff. Yowch!"

The Guosim rowers chortled gruffly as Furmo stood over Gonff armed with his stout wooden ladle. "I told ye wot I'd do, you insultin' rascal. Now, say after me. 'Damson crumble with good hot sauce!' "

Gonff repeated it dutifully, and Furmo made him say it again. The phrase made such a good rowing chant that the Guosim shrews took it up, bending and straightening their backs in time to the cadence.

"Damson crumble an' good hot sauce! Damson crumble an' good hot sauce!"

Chugger was acting captain again. He strode officiously up to Gonff and nodded approvingly. "Mista Gonff, you like a damser crum an' good 'ot sauces?"

The Mousethief licked his lips appreciatively. "I certainly do, me liddle mate!"

Patting his tiny stomach, Chugger growled fiercely, "Well you can't avva no more, I eated it all up, an' I not yore likkle mate now. I cap'n Chugg, see!"

Not stopping for anything they rowed doggedly on, trying to keep up the pace, which Martin had unconsciously increased again. Midnight had gone by an hour when they rounded the point. Everybeast lay back, panting with exhaustion, as Furmo gave orders to ship oars. Everybeast except Martin. As the *Honeysuckle*'s hull scraped to a halt in the shallows, he was upright, staring at the deserted shore, which was bathed in pale moonlight. Like lonely sentinels, the cliffs stood high in the background, topped by sparse vegetation. Darkened caves, partially covered by weather-warped driftwood and rubble, which had once disguised them from hostile eyes, lay forlorn and abandoned. A floodtide of memories poured in on Martin's senses. Every rock, even the wind-driven sand drifts, looked familiar to him. Turning to his tired companions, the Warrior spoke in a hoarse whisper.

"I was born here, I know this place!"

Slipping overboard he waded through the shallows.

Drawing his rapier, Log a Log Furmo signalled to his Guosim. Folgrim picked up his axe, determined to go ashore with them. Gonff backed to the rail and stood in their path, holding up both paws.

"No, mates. Let our friend go alone. 'Twould not be right to intrude on him this night!"

The crew of the *Honeysuckle* laid aside their weapons and sat down to await Martin's return.

Striding slowly up the beach, Martin turned to his right, the cave which had once been his home drawing him to it like a magnet. At first he thought his eyes were deceiving him. Halting, he stared hard at the feeble glow emanating from the cave. It *was* a light. Somebeast had lit a fire there recently, which had died to glowing embers. Drawing his sword, the Warrior of Redwall crouched, moving forward silent as moonshadow. Entering the cave, he flattened himself against the rock wall, waiting until his eyes were accustomed to the dim light.

Covered by a long traveling cloak, an old mouse sat dozing by what was left of the fire. Martin crept close, extended his blade and tapped the mouse's paw lightly with its point. He did this once again, then the creature stirred, turning its face to him. The old mouse spoke in an awestruck voice. "Luke, is that you?"

Wordlessly Martin placed some broken twigs on the fire. Laying aside his sword he sat down opposite the ancient creature, staring at it through the rising flames. A slow smile of pure joy stole across the old one's lined face.

"Oh, Luke, Luke, it is you! But how . . . ?"

The Warrior spoke softly, so as not to frighten the old fellow. "I'm Martin of Redwall, son of Luke the Warrior. Pray, what is your name, sir?"

Rising slowly, the old mouse shuffled around the fire. Sitting next to Martin, he reached out and touched the Warrior's face. Martin watched in silence as tears rolled down the mouse's cheeks and his head began to shake.

"Ahhhh, so many seasons, so long ago. I've returned here through snow, rain and sun, many many times, and sat waiting alone, always alone."

Tears overcame further speech. Martin drew the old mouse to him, placing a paw about his scrawny back and wiping away the tears with the cloak hem. He rocked him gently. "There, there, no need to weep further, friend. I am Luke's son and I have come. You are not alone."

The old mouse's eyes searched Martin's face. "Aye, you are Martin, so like your father, so like him. D'you not remember me? I'm Vurg, I was Luke's best friend."

Martin could not remember him, but he nodded. "Of course. I didn't recognize you in the dark. Vurg, my father's strong right paw. I recall you now. How are you, Vurg?"

Holding forth his withered paws, Vurg chuckled. "How am I? I'm old, Martin, old, old, old! Heeheehee, I've got more seasons on me than a hedgehog has spikes!"

Martin hugged the scrawny form to him fondly. "Nonsense, I think you look just the same as you always did. I'll wager your appetite's still as good. Are you hungry, Vurg?"

"Heehee, anybeast tough enough t'be livin' on the northlands coast is always in need o' good vittles!"

Martin sheathed the sword across his shoulder. "Right, come on back to the boat with me. I've got a crew of Guosim shrews there who'll feed you 'til you burst!"

Vurg rose creakily, retrieving a beaded linen bag from the sand. This he stowed beneath his cloak. "Well, young Martin, what're we standin' 'round here waitin' for? Lead me t'the grub!"

Together they crossed the shore, Vurg leaning heavily on Martin's paw for support, chattering away.

"Guosim shrew cooks, eh? Bet they know 'ow to serve up proper-made vittles. Not like ole Cardo, now there was a mouse who'd burn a salad. Cook? Cardo couldn't boil water to save his life. You remember Cardo, don't you?"

Martin lied as he kept the oldster on a steady course. "Oh, Cardo! How could anybeast forget that buffoon!"

Gonff was on watch, sitting in the prow. He saw the two mice approaching the *Honeysuckle* and roused the crew from their slumbers.

"Ahoy, mates, Martin's comin' back. Looks like he's brought company, too. Stand by—he might need help."

Furmo and Folgrim assisted in getting Vurg aboard. The

old mouse winked at the scarred otter. "Heehee, bet you could take care o' yerself in a scrap?"

Folgrim's pointed teeth bared in a savage grin. "I've taken care of a few in me time, sir!"

Vurg mused absently as they seated him comfortably under the stern awning. "Aye, so did Luke an' Ranguvar, they took care o' more'n a few. Heeheehee!"

Furmo patted the old one's paw fondly. "How's yore sweet tooth, Grandad?"

"I tell ye, young whipsnout, a sweet tooth's about the only one I got left in me mouth. Heehee!"

The shrew stoked up his stove with seacoal and driftwood. "Then how does a baked river roll with hot maple syrup sound t'ye? I makes it with sweetflour an' all manner o' candied fruit, folds it careful-like into a big roll, bakes it to a turn an' pours 'ot maple syrup over it. Got a beaker or two of Dunehog Seafoam ale t'go with it. Sound good?"

Vurg wiped a paw across his lips. "I'll tell ye when me mouth quits waterin', young 'un!"

Morning came, with overcast skies and a bitter wind. Martin sat beneath the stern shelter with his friends, sipping barley and carrot broth. Vurg lay behind them, close to the oven, wrapped snugly in his cloak, sleeping off the feast he had consumed.

Gonff sat Chugger on his lap, allowing him to steal his beaker of broth. "You finish that all up, matey. An' don't be dashin' about kickin' up a rumpus. Old Vurg needs lots o' sleep. Well, Martin, did y' find out what you needed to know from the ole feller, about yore dad an' so on?"

Martin shook his head as he watched Vurg sleeping. "Didn't want to rush him. Vurg will tell me when he's ready. Though I did hint that I needed information."

Dinny looked over the top of his beaker. "Wot did ee'm owd feller say 'bout that, zurr?"

Martin shrugged. "Not much, though he did say I'd find out all I needed to know when we took him back home to someplace called Tall Rocks."

Chugger was beginning to wriggle out of Gonff's grasp. Trimp took charge of him, stroking the tiny squirrel's head soothingly. She looked enquiringly at Martin. "Tall Rocks? Where's that?"

The Warrior stared out at the grey wintry seas. "Somewhere up north of here. Vurg said he'd show us the way."

Furmo picked up the linen bag from where it had fallen out of Vurg's cloak, and passed it to Martin. "What d'you suppose is in this?"

Martin sighed deeply, and placed the bag carefully back in the folds of Vurg's cloak without disturbing him. "He'll tell us when he's ready, I suppose. Though I'm not certain I want to know now. I have a feeling inside that 'tis going to be a long and tragic tale."

Vurg woke before noon feeling much refreshed, and to prove it he ate a huge breakfast. Under his directions they pushed off and continued north. Martin watched, silent and pensive once more, as his birthplace faded into the distance.

16

It was a late noon, two days out from Martin's former home, when Tall Rocks hove into view. Rain was falling heavily and the wind had died completely. The sea surface, though pitted constantly by rainfall, was relatively calm, with a notable absence of the huge foam-crested rollers usual in the area. Vurg stood in the bows, Martin at his side, and relayed directions. Furmo and Dinny held the tiller between them, listening out for instructions.

"Keep her head out to sea a bit. Stick to that course!"

Furmo obeyed, but voiced his doubts. "Wouldn't we be better tackin' in closer to the land side?"

Martin swiftly gave him his answer. "No, no! Stay seaward. Vurg says the underwater reefs are close to the surface inshore. Out here the sea runs very deep, so the reefs are far below us. Keep her head out!"

"Right enough. Just as well the tide's runnin' smooth t'day."

Martin agreed. "Aye, Vurg says that if any waves start up you must steer right out to sea, away from Tall Rocks, and forget the whole thing until ebb tides arrive. Otherwise the

Honeysuckle'd be smashed against the rocks!"

Dinny glanced fearfully to the horizon. "O seas, keep ee gurt waves clear of us'n's. Thurr be nuthin' wurser'n a drownded molebeast, no zurr!"

Trimp and the remainder of the crew stood aghast at the size of Tall Rocks. Monumental pillars of stone, they reared out of the sea like monsters from the dawn of time, huge and forbidding. For leagues of the coastline the seas were dotted with them, colossal and weirdly shaped, some cylindrical, others triangular or square-sided, their bases festooned with seaweed, kelp and dark moss above the columns of dark basalt stone. The *Honeysuckle*'s sail was taken in, and the most expert Guosim oarbeasts sat at the rowlocks, knowing their lives depended on the accuracy and sureness of their strokes. The order came when they were almost abreast of a cluster of columns, fronted by one half as big again in girth and height as the rest.

"Take 'er in steady. Keep the big 'un on yore portside!"

Trimp held tight to Folgrim's paw. "Good grief! Look at the size of those rocks, Folgrim!"

Chugger, who had climbed on to the otter's shoulders, clung there like a leech, whimpering. "I frykened, mista Fol, Chugg no like this!"

Folgrim tickled the little squirrel's footpaw. "Aye, I'm frightened too, matey. So is the whole crew, an' even Martin, so we're in good company, I reckons!"

All else was forgotten as the monstrous pinnacles loomed close. Fear echoed in Furmo's high-pitched yell. "Bring 'er 'round! 'Round the big rock! Push 'er off'n'take 'er 'round, mates! Now!"

Rising in a smooth high swell, the sea swept the skiff, like a cork, straight for the big rock. Paddlers on one side banked her, rowing furiously, whilst Martin and Gonff joined the others, fending the rock off by pushing against it with oars and long poles. With an audible sucking and gurgling the swell receded. Down they shot into a deep trough, with the *Honeysuckle* swerving bravely in a swift arc around the basalt monolith. No sooner were they on the lee side of the rock than the peril of their position increased. Now they were in a narrow channel betwixt the main column and the others grouped behind it. Obeying Vurg's orders, the Guosim Chieftain sang out, "I'm steerin' for that pack o' rocks! Make ready to tie up, for'ard, aft an' amidships! But don't tie 'er fast, mates, leave slack so she can ride the swells!"

The moment they were in reach of the grouped pinnacles, Martin whirled a weighted line, as did Folgrim in the midships and Gonff at the prow. Again the swell lifted them and Furmo shouted, "Heave those lines out, mates!"

The strong slender ropes snaked out and up. Three iron grapnels clanked simultaneously into the stone crevices. The *Honeysuckle* was secured safely, and bobbed up and down alongside the rocks, with the slack lines allowing her to ride easily on the swells.

Log a Log Furmo could not stop his paws shaking. He wobbled along the deck and leaned against Martin, pale, breathless and shaken. "By the fur'n'blood o' the great Guosim, at least ten times there I thought we was a goner, matey!"

Martin grasped his friend's paws, steadying them. "You did it superbly, Furmo. Nobeast could keep her on course like you did—'twas nothing short of a miracle!"

Stamping his footpaw against the deck, Furmo smiled proudly. "Aye, an' no other craft in all the rivers'n'seas could've done it like our *Honeysuckle*. Wot a ship! I'll tell some stories about 'er t'my tribe when we gets back!"

Vurg took a deep breath. Cupping paws around his mouth, he called out in a quavery voice, "Ahoy the *Arfship*! Ahoy there, can you 'ear me?"

There was no answer. Furmo felt recovered enough to roar out in a thunderous baritone, "Ahoy *Arfship*, 'tis Vurg an' some company. Ahooooooy!"

Martin pulled the shrew to one side just in time to avoid a hefty rope ladder with timber rungs which came down out of the rocks and clattered to the deck.

Gonff stared in puzzlement at Vurg. "Who are we shoutin' to, an' wot's an arfship, mate?"

On the ledge above them a hare appeared. He looked as ancient as Vurg—older, in fact. Shaking a tremulous paw at Vurg he called down, "Where in the name of my auntie's apron have you been, wot? I've been sittin' up here like a blinkin' sickly seagull, worryin' about you, sah! Now y'come sailin' up here, pretty as y'please, in charge of this jolly old rats' regatta. Wot!"

Vurg mounted the rope ladder with Trimp's assistance, followed swiftly by her friends. The old mouse argued with the hare as he climbed up to the ledge.

"Oh, give yore flappin' jaws a rest, Beau. These creatures are friends. They brought me back from the north shore. Which is more'n I can say for you. I'd grow whiskers t'me footpaws waitin' on you t'come an' fetch me, y'great flop-eared bag-bellied droopy-pawed rockrabbit!"

The old hare's ears stood up indignantly as he helped Vurg on to the ledge. "Hah, rockrabbit is it, you blather-bottomed old dodderer, wot wot. I've had a barnacle casserole bubblin' here for two confounded days waitin' for you. Bad form, sah! I was goin' t'make a plum pudden too, but I flippin' well ain't now. So you can go an' jolly well whistle f'your blinkin' dessert for all I care. An' I hope the casserole keeps you awake all night. Ungrateful bounder!"

Martin popped his head over the ledge. "When you two creatures have stopped arguing, would you mind moving aside? We've got a ship's crew to get up this ladder."

The hare fitted a rock crystal monocle into one eye and glared down at Martin. "Oh, have you now? Well my compliments t'you, sah, an' your crew, wot! I s'pose you've come to eat us out of house an' home without a by your leave or jolly old toodle pip!"

Vurg interrupted the hare's tirade. "Ahoy, Beau, mind yore manners. Take a close look at yon mouse an' tell me who ye think he is?"

Beau crouched down, holding his back and grimacing. He brought his face level with Martin's. The eyeglass popped out with surprise as he stared at the Warrior mouse.

"Luke! Well burn my auntie's taters, wot! You're a bounder, a rotter an' a curmudgeon, sah! How is it that you've stayed so jolly young whilst we've grown old? Not the done sort o' thing, I'd say. Bally cad!"

Martin sprang up onto the ledge. Smiling, he grasped Beau's paw and pumped it up and down.

"I'm Martin of Redwall, son of Luke the Warrior. Whom have I the pleasure of addressing, sir?"

The hare shook his hoary silver head, returning the smile. "Knew y'father well, sah. Excellent chap! I'm Beauhair Fethringham Cosfortingsol. No I ain't, I'm Beausol Fethringhair Cosfortingclair. No I ain't, wait a tick. I'm Beauham Fethringclair Confounditall. Tchah! I'm so old I've forgotten me own name. What a disgrace, wot!"

Vurg sniggered. "Heehee, try Beauclair Fethringsol Cosfortingham. That's yore silly long name."

The hare scratched his scraggy whiskers. "Ah! Of course it is. Thank you, old chap." Then, scratching his whiskers again, he turned on Vurg. "On the other paw, who asked you, sah, you battered old mouserelic? When I need somebeast to tell me m'name I'll jolly well ask m'self. Pish tush! The very idea, tellin' a chap his own moniker!"

Vurg approached him until they stood nose to nose. "Battered ole mouserelic? Well of course I am, an' who wouldn't be, lookin' after you all these seasons. Should've left you on Twin Islands, that's wot I should've done!"

Martin clapped a paw to his brow, looking beseechingly to Gonff. The Mousethief pushed Beau and Vurg apart. "Quiet now, you two, an' lissen t'me. Aboard our ship we got a way of settlin' arguments. We let any quarrelsome beasts settle things by challengin' our argument counselor. Folgrim, come over 'ere!"

Testing his axe edge by licking it, Folgrim strode over. Baring pointed teeth, he turned his scarred face from Vurg to Beau. The otter's voice sounded like a blade hacking ice.

"Well now, anybeast got an argument t'settle wid me, choose yore weapons. Axes or teeth, it don't make no odds t'me!"

Vurg immediately hid behind Beau, whose throat bobbed like an apple on a string as he gulped. "Arguin'? Who's arguin', old chap? Merely a bit o' humorous banter 'twixt my erstwhile companion and m'goodself, wot? I say, Vurg, hadn't we better get these seagoin' types aboard the good vessel *Arfship*? They look jolly hungry an' tired t'me. We could fricassee a shark or two for friend Folgrim, or maybe he'd prefer just to gnaw on the messdeck table. Er, ahaha, follow me, chaps. No offense, mister Folgrim sir, merely a jocular jest, wot wot!"

Vurg and Beau led them through a perfectly round tunnel in the rock. They emerged on the other side amid the massed pinnacles and stood gazing up in openmouthed awe at the sight that greeted them. Beau managed to make an elegant leg and bowed slightly. "Welcome to the vessel *Arfship!*"

Jammed between the column they stood upon and the one immediately next to it was half a ship. High overhead it stood, lodged between both pinnacles, more than two-thirds of the way up. From midships to for'ard end it was wedged firmly, a huge rusting iron spike at its forepeak driven into the rock by some tremendous force. The thing had once been red, but now through seasons of harsh weather, seaspray, sun and rain, it was faded to a rose-pink hue.

Dinny's voice cut the silence. "Well fill moi tunnel! Arf a ship oop in ee air!"

Ascending another rope ladder, they climbed up to the old habitation. Trimp stared about in astonishment at the immensity of it all. It was like being in some great chamber. Timbered bulkheads with holes for oarports let in the light, as did the opened hatch covers high above them. Furmo's voice echoed spectrally in the vast space as the crew of the *Honeysuckle* walked through it wide-eyed.

"An' this is supposed t'be only arf a ship! I tell ye, mates, could you imagine it afore it was broken, with the other arf attached? It must've been like a floatin' village! I wager there wasn't anythin' that size ever sailed the seas!"

Vurg nodded his old head. "Oh but there was, an' this is what's left of it. See through those open hatch covers? There's another deck above this an' another one above that again. Yore lookin' through three decks up t'the main one, which if y'count it makes four altogether. We keeps the 'atches open to give light, battens 'em down in bad weather. Up these stairs is the for'ard cabins. Come on, I'll show ye!"

Martin shook his head as he passed rows of benches, with chains dangling from them and long broken oars hanging through the ports. They looked well worn from constant use. "Beau, was this a slave ship?"

"Indeed it was, old lad, the foulest, most evil vessel that ever plied the ocean. Now 'tis our home, our beloved *Arfship.*

Actually, 'twould have been *Half Ship* if I'd had me way, but
the others called it *Arfship*, so *Arfship* it is, wot. Come an' eat
now, questions later, that's the drill!"

Following him up the ornately carved staircase, they
entered a roomy cabin with its skylights thrown open. It was
a complete living area. Tables, chairs, bunks and cupboards
were all about, clean and neat. Two mice, old and grey, were
working at a table next to a big glowing stove with its
smokepipe thrusting through the edge of the skylight. Vurg
introduced them.

"This is all of us left from those who sailed off long ago
from the north shores. Myself, Dulam and Denno."

The mouse called Denno went straight to Martin and took
the Warrior's face gently in both his flour-dusted paws. "No
need to tell ole Denno who you are—I know. Luke's son
Martin. Couldn't be no otherbeast. Yore the spittin' image o'
the great Luke, though you got yore mother Sayna's eyes."

Martin shook visibly, blinking hard. "You knew my
mother?"

Denno nodded. "Course I did, an' a prettier, more gentle
creature there never was. I knew 'em all, Martin, everybeast.
But we've got all night to talk of that. Sit and rest now, the
food will be ready soon."

Barnacle casserole was a delicious concoction of sea vegetables and shellfish. Guosim cooks hurried back to the *Honeysuckle* and brought up more supplies. Beau relented, and
aided by Folgrim and Trimp he began mixing a big plum
pudding. Gonff helped the Guosim cooks to bake scones and
bread. Martin and Chugger cut up an excellent cheese, studded with beech mast and hazelnuts. Dinny put together a
salad with any spare vegetables he rooted out. Mint tea was
put on to boil and dandelion and burdock cordial poured
from a keg into serving jugs.

After the tables were pushed together and set, they sat
down. Gonff proposed a toast.

"To the end of a journey, to my best friend Martin the Warrior an' to the wonderful vittles an' good hospitality showed
to us by the crew of the *Arfship*!"

Everybeast raised their beakers and drank cheerfully. As

they ate, Furmo could not resist asking the question which was puzzling him greatly.

"Tell me, Vurg, 'ow did the for'ard half of a great ship land up 'ere? It just don't seem possible."

Vurg munched shrewbread and cheese as he explained. "Yore right, mate, I wouldn't 'ave believed it meself if'n I hadn't been aboard at the time, but 'ere's how it came about. Durin' the biggest storm anybeast'd ever seen, the *Goreleech*—for that was once wot this ship was called—struck that big rock pillar out in front. I tell ye, waves twice as high as this vessel were runnin' on a sea driven by wind an' rain. 'Twas more like a hurricane than a gale. Well, she whacked that big rock side on, with a force you couldn't imagine. Smashed the *Goreleech* clean in two, like an 'ot knife goin' through butter. On board the for'ard part were oarslaves an' Sea Rogues doin' battle. We were flung to the decks like wet leaves in a wind. There was screamin', shoutin' an' weepin'—everybeast was sure they'd met their deaths. The stern half fell backward into the sea, and sank in the blink of an eye.

Now, the same great wave that sank it carried us, an' the other half, swirlin' round to the back of the big rock. Down, down we went as the wave ebbed away in a torrent of suckin' an' whirlin', an' we thought we was surely done for. Then another giant wave rounded the rock an' lifted us, easy as a paw lifts a grain o' sand. Up we rose, up, up, high in the air. From where I lay on the deck, I saw the two pinnacles as the wavecrest flung us forward. Suddenly a shudderin' shock ran through me from tail to eartips. Then everythin' went still.

"I opened me eyes and stood up. We were wedged fast, right up 'ere, the broken midships restin' flat on a ledge of one column, the prow on another, with the big iron spike that stuck out front, driven like a nail, deep into the rock!"

Gonff forgot the beaker which was halfway to his lips, and sat shaking his head. "An' what happened next, Vurg?"

The old mouse chuckled as he speared a scone with his knife. "Me'n'Beau rallied our fighters fast an' finished off those scummy Sea Rogues afore they 'ad a chance t'get us. We've lived 'ere ever since. Nothin'll shift the ole *Arfship*.

She's weathered time'n'tides, storm an' seasons, aye, an'
never budged a splinter. After a while we made a rope cradle
an' rigged a line over t'the cliffs on shore. Many creatures
left an' went off t'find their ole homes. A score of us stayed
'ere. But that was long ago. Now there's only Dulam, Denno,
me'n'Beau left out o' them all. Most o' our mates died.
They're wrapped in sailcloth, weighted down with stones,
sleepin' on the seabed far below us. Fates be kind t'their
memories!"

Martin decided that the time had come. "Tell me, Vurg,
what became of my father, Luke the Warrior?"

Beau rose stiffly and went to a cupboard. He returned to
the table with a large, dusty volume. "'Tis all within these
pages, Martin, everything, as best as the four of us can recall.
We spent many a winter an' autumn night recordin' the entire
tale. 'Twas a joint work. D'y'know, I thought it might be
found by somebeast, long after we were gone. But fate an'
fortunes've smiled on us, laddie buck. There's food'n'drink
on the table an' a long night ahead of us, wot! Here, Denno,
you young whippersnapper, you can understand your own
writing best. Read the journal to our friends, there's a good
chap!"

Denno polished a tiny pair of glasses. Perching them on
his nose, he looked over at Martin. "I was the scribe, y'see.
Right, let's start at the beginning. I 'ope you like the title. 'Tis
called 'In the Wake of the Red Ship,' this being an account of
Luke the Warrior, written by his friends."

Outside, the eternal seas washed against Tall Rocks, and
breezes sighed a wistful dirge about the basalt columns
where seabirds wheeled and called. In the cabin, high among
the pinnacles, Martin of Redwall listened as the saga of his
father, Luke the Warrior, unfolded.

BOOK TWO

Luke

There were other mice in the tribe, older and more experienced, younger mice also, bigger and stronger. But everybeast regarded Luke as their natural leader. As mice go, he was nothing special to look upon, of average height and stocky build. However, on closer observation it became obvious that Luke was a warrior born. Behind his calm dark eyes there lurked a flame, his stance bespoke fearlessness, some indefinable quality in his whole attitude marked him as one in whom others could put their unquestioning trust. A mouse tribe could look to him for guidance, and he could always be counted on for fairness and wisdom in his decisions. Such a creature was Luke the Warrior.

Over many seasons the tribe had wandered under his leadership. Long ago they had left the warm areas of abundance, those places where verminous villains preyed upon any who sought the peaceful life. Constant warfare against outnumbering odds had forced Luke's tribe into the nomadic way, always seeking and searching for some place where they would not have to sleep paw on sword, with one eye open. From the fertile middle lands they roamed north, where the

weather was cold and the land bleak and sparse. On the day
they reached the northland coast, Luke thrust his sword into
the earth. This would be his tribe's new home. It was a lonely
place, quiet and undisturbed.

The tribe approved Luke's decision. Hardworking beasts
could wrest a living from the ground here, providing they
were left in peace to do so. There were caves in the base of
the cliffs which backed the shore, a high rocky cape thrusting
out into the sea at the southern point. It felt safe, with cliffs at
the back and the seas in front of them. There was good soil
on the clifftops, which could be planted and farmed in spring,
summer and autumn.

For the first few days they kept a low profile, living off
what supplies they had stored, making the caves habitable.
During this time, Luke and his friends patrolled the area,
watching out for enemies, robber bands and vermin raiders.
Luke knew that his tribe was only a small one, wearied by
constant travel, and would not be able to resist any major
attack from a large force. But happily there was neither sight
nor trace of foebeast.

Then, on the fourth day, Luke strode ahead of the rest as
they made their way back to the caves. His step was light,
and a shudder of joy ran through him. He felt that this forsaken northland coast was already bringing him happiness.
Only two days before, his wife Sayna had given birth to their
first little one, a son. They would call the new baby mouse by
the name of Martin. Luke's grandsire had been named Martin, and when he was young, Luke had often listened to tales
that were told of the formidable Warrior mouse. It was his
sword that Luke carried in the sheath on his back, given to
him by his own father. Luke was the third of his family to
carry the old battleblade, and one day, when the time was
right, little Martin would be the next.

The tribe were busy preparing a feast for Luke and Sayna's
son, the first little one to be born on the northland coast.
There was to be a great bonfire, too. As Luke came within
sight of the caves, he could see the ever growing mound of
driftwood and dead timber being piled above the tideline.
Two young mice were struggling to drag a big chunk of drift-

wood along the shore. Luke approached them, a smile hovering on his face at their efforts.

"Well well, Timballisto and Fripple, when d'you plan on gettin' that log to the bonfire pile, next season?"

Both mice were little better than three seasons old. They sat down wearily on the log, big round eyes imploring Luke.

"'S too blinkin' big for us, Luke. Will y'lend a paw?"

The Warrior mouse drew his ancient battlesword from its sheath on his back and swung it high overhead, bringing the sharp blade down to bite deep into the wood.

"Righto, you two rascals, grab ahold of the swordhilt with me. We'll see if it moves any easier with us three strong beasts pulling it. Come on!"

Heaving energetically, Luke tugged the lump of wood through the sand. He watched fondly as the two little mice pulled valiantly, each latched on to the crosshilt.

When they brought the log to the pile of timber, Luke allowed Fripple and Timballisto to help him loose the swordblade, though he could have easily done it alone. He passed a paw across his brow, winking at them. "Whew! Thankee, mates, 'twas a job well done!"

The little mousemaid Fripple took hold of Luke's paw. "Please Luke will y'take me to your cave to see your new baby Martin please Luke?"

Luke could not help chuckling at the beseeching look on Fripple's face. He tweaked her paw gently. "Of course I will, pretty one. What about you, Timbal?"

Timballisto scowled fiercely. "I'll stay 'ere an' guard our wood 'til y'get back!"

Martin's cradle was a hollowed-out log, lined with soft moss and a woven blanket. The only family Luke had left in the world sat by it, his wife Sayna and her mother Windred. Crowing with delight, Fripple leaned over the cradle and took the baby's paw in hers. "Oh my my, isn't he a lovely likkle feller!"

Sayna held the mousemaid's smock, lest she fall into the cradle. "Aye, he's a good baby, no trouble at all. I think he will grow bigger and stronger than his daddy."

Martin's eyes watched solemnly as his father loomed over him. He raised a tiny paw, reaching for the hilt protruding over his father's shoulder. This delighted Luke.

"Hoho, look at this bucko, tryin' to draw my sword!"

Windred hovered around the cradle anxiously. "Be careful, he might cut himself on that blade!"

Luke reassured the fussing old mousewife. "Oh no he won't. Martin's a warrior born, I feel it. Let my son hold the sword. It'll be his one day."

Sayna watched her serious-faced babe trying to wrap his little paws round the blackbound haft with its redstone pommel. She shivered slightly. "May the fates forbid that he'll ever have to use it in war."

Luke released Martin's hold and stood up straight. "Don't worry, Sayna. That'll never happen whilst I'm around. Besides, I don't think we'll be bothered here, being this far north. We searched the shores an' cliffs both ways. There's nothin' much to the south, an' if you go further north there's only some great tall rocks stickin' up out o' the sea about three days from here. Not a pawprint of vermin anywhere. Now, what about our son's feast?"

Windred turned to the cave entrance. Out on the shore the mice of the tribe were setting out what food they had foraged by the unlit bonfire. Each had brought what they could afford to spare, but it was not much. Windred spoke. "Hah! Feast, you say? 'Tis a wonder we keep fur around bone on this forsaken coast. You've brought us to a cold an' hungry place, Luke!"

Sayna checked Windred reprovingly. "That's not fair, mother. 'Tis not Luke's fault. Where the food was plentiful, so were our enemies. At least we have safety up here, and when spring comes we'll be able to farm and plant the clifftop lands. Luke says there's good soil up there. What about those berries old Twoola saw yesterday?"

Luke glanced from one to the other. "What berries? Where did Twoola see them?"

Sayna explained. "He took a walk last evening, north along the shore, and said he saw lots of berries growing in a rift near the clifftop. But there were great seabirds up there, too, nest-ing. I thought it might be dangerous, which is why I didn't mention it yesterday. Seabirds can be very fierce creatures."

Luke patted his swordhilt. "Aye, an' so am I when our tribe needs food. Leave it to me. I'll take some good well-armed fighters with me, and Twoola can show us the spot. We won't harm the seabirds if they don't attack us, and I don't think they will, for what need have they of berries? Seabirds live on what they can scavenge from the sea and the tideline. We'll gather the fruit and uproot a few young bushes to plant on the clifftops back here. Now there's no cause for worry or fuss. I'll leave some warriors back here to guard our camp, and I'll be back as soon as I can, with whatever we find up there. Carry on with the feast—the youngsters are expecting it. I'll try to return before 'tis finished."

Sayna placed Luke's warm cloak about his shoulders. "You'll need this. It gets cold out there at night. Bring me back a little blackberry bramble, and I'll plant it so that Martin will be able to help me pick the berries in a few seasons."

Windred adjusted the cloak around Luke's sword. "Aye, and be careful out there. This is still strange country to us, Luke."

With a score and a half of good mice that he could depend upon, Luke set out north along the shore. However, they could only travel as fast as old Twoola, and the ancient mouse hobbled along at a slow creaky gait. It was close to midnight when the foraging party reached the high crag where the berries grew. Twoola sat down wearily upon the sand, pointing upward. "That's the place, Luke, but I ain't goin' up there. Some o' those seabirds are big as eagles!"

Luke took off his cloak and wrapped it around the old fellow. "You did well getting us this far, Twoola. Stay here and rest—we'll go up. Vurg, Denno, bring those ropes."

By those who knew the coasts and high seas, one name was whispered with terror and loathing.

Vilu Daskar!

The pirate stoat was known by other names. Butcher, thief, torturer, murderer. But none more frightening than his own.

Vilu Daskar!

Captain of the biggest vessel ever to plough the main. A trireme, with three banks of oars, pulled by wretched slaves. Crimson red, from the pennants fluttering at its forepeaks, down through the four mighty sails to its gigantic keel. Always leaving behind it a thin red wake, from the dyes which oozed out of its timbers. Jutting out from the prow stood an immense iron spike, rusted red by long seasons of salt water. Such was the red ship, named the *Goreleech* by its master.

Vilu Daskar!

Evil was his trade, the red ship his floating fortress. Aboard it he could disappear into the trackless wastes of seas and oceans, materializing again to prey on the unwary. Coastal settlements, inland hamlets, even the island havens of other Sea Raiders and Corsairs. None were safe from the *Goreleech* and its bloodthirsty crew, a mob of wild cruel vermin. Mercenaries, assassins, cutthroats, the flotsam and jetsam of earth and waters. These Sea Rogues were ruled by two things alone: a lust for plunder and slaughter, and a blood-chilling fear of their lord.

Vilu Daskar!

He revelled in the dread his name instilled into all.

In the 'tweendecks of the *Goreleech,* relentless drums pounded incessantly. Chained to the oars, masses of gaunt slaves bent their backs and pulled, straightening with a joint groan as they heaved on the long wooden sweeps. To the accompaniment of slave drivers cracking their whips and the ever present drumbeat, the red ship sailed into the waters off northcoast.

Vilu Daskar leaned against the stern gallery rail, his alert dark eyes watching constantly, like a snake about to strike. Unlike other seagoing vermin, he was highly intelligent, well-spoken and modestly garbed. He wore a long red cloak, beneath which was a plain black tunic, belted by a broad red calico sash through which was thrust a long bone-handled scimitar. The only concession to finery was his headgear, a white silken scarf bound about his brow, atop of which he wore a rounded silver helmet with a spike at its center. Tall and sinewy, he cut a quietly elegant figure, unlike the crew under his command, all arrayed in a jumble of tattered finery and sporting heavy tattoos and masses of gaudy earrings, necklets and bracelets.

Evening light was fading fast over the cold seas when, from high on the mainmast, a searat called Grigg sang out from the crow's nest: "Laaaand awaaaay off larboard, cap'n. I sees a light onshore, sire, to the north o' that rocky point!"

Vilu flicked his eyes in the direction given, without moving his body. Akkla, the ferret steersbeast, held the ship's wheel steady, awaiting his captain's command. Even if it meant running the *Goreleech* onto rocks, he knew better than to change course without Vilu's order.

The stoat spoke without raising his voice. "Sweep south and take her in behind that big rock point."

Two other vermin stood waiting as Vilu peered hard at the faint glow, far off on the shoreline. He issued orders to them without turning, knowing they would obey instantly.

"Reef and furl all sails, and increase the oarstroke to double double speed. We need to get out of sight quickly."

Abruptly he strode off for'ard, where his bosun, the searat Parug, had a better view of the shore.

"So, my keen-eyed bosun, what do you see?"

Parug scratched at his beribboned whiskers, plainly bewildered. "'Tis 'ard to tell, cap'n. Ho, that's a fire right enough, an' a good big 'un, t'be seen from this distance, sire."

A thin smile hovered on Vilu's lips. "But?"

The bemused bosun shook his head. "But anybeast'd be mad t'light a fire that big on northland shore. Wot are they up to, cap'n?"

Vilu lost sight of the glow as the *Goreleech* turned south, the headland blocking his view. "Well, no creature in their right mind would set up a signal beacon on that shore, so they are either out of their minds, or ignorant of the danger. Maybe that's it, Parug, they might merely be simple beasts having some kind of celebration, eh?"

Parug's dull face broke out in a grin. "Oh, like a kinda feast, y'mean, sire?"

The stoat's paw strayed to his bone-handled scimitar. "Quite. Not very courteous of them. The least they could have done was to invite us!"

Parug's grin widened. "So we anchors the other side o' yon point, comes over the rocks, an' invites ourselves, eh, cap'n?"

Vilu stroked the white bone scimitar hilt. "Exactly. We might not attend the feast, but the least I can do is present my calling card."

Parug stared blankly at his captain. "Callin' card? Wot's a callin' card, sire?"

With lightning speed the scimitar blade's tip was touching the bosun's throat. "This is my calling card!"

Parug's throat bobbed nervously under the sharp bladetip. "Oh, er, I see, sire, er, haha!"

Vilu Daskar tired of the one-sided conversation. He put up his sword and strode off.

Darkness had fallen. Luke's tribe laughed and sang around the bonfire, unaware of the big red ship anchoring on the other side of the south point.

18

Luke threw the first rope up into the darkness. A moment later he heard the wooden bar tied to its end clack upon some rocks. He tugged it, making sure the bar held in the rocks it had wedged itself among. Paw over paw Luke went up, whispering to Vurg, "Follow on with the other rope, mate, but be quiet. We don't want to disturb any of those seabirds."

Vurg climbed up after him, and they balanced together, lodging their footpaws in the sides of the fissure. Luke took the second rope and began twirling it, paying the coils out as he swung it wider before throwing it strongly upward.

This time there was no sound of wood striking stone, but the rope went taut. A gruff friendly voice called down in quaint speech, "Oi got et, zurr, oi'll make ee rope farst whoilst ee clamber up yurr!"

Vurg grabbed Luke's paw in the darkness. "Sounds like a mole t'me. What d'you think, Luke?"

"Aye, 'tis a mole sure enough, though what he's doin' up a cliff I don't know. He sounds friendly enough, anyway. Come on!"

Both mice climbed until they reached a flat ledge, where

there were several other moles and some hedgehogs to meet them. The mole who had hailed them took tinder and flint and lit a lantern, rumbling on in his curious mole dialect.

"Burr, us'n's doan't be gettin' mouseybeasts a-clamberin' up to call on uz, zurr, but welcumm to ee anyways. Oi be Drunn Tunneller, these 'uns be moi fambly, yon 'ogs be ee Tiptip brood, an' that 'un be Welff."

A friendly-looking hedgehog wife in a broad rough apron twitched her spikes and curtsied. "Pleased t'meet ye, I'm sure, but what be you goodbeasts a-doin' up 'ere in the dark night?"

Luke introduced his party as they climbed up to the ledge. Then he explained the reason for their visit.

"We came to take some o' those berries an' maybe some young plants whilst the seabirds were sleepin', marm. I'm sorry, though, I didn't realize they were your property."

Welff brushed the apology aside cheerfully. "Oh, you take all the berries an' shoots y'need, my dearie. Rain's washed good soil into this crevice for many a season. We got raspberry, blackberry, all manner o' berries growin' 'ereabouts. Ole Drunn's father tunnelled through to 'ere from the clifftops long ago. We've got a cave back there. Now don't ye be afeared o' the seabirds. We leaves 'em be an' they don't bother us a mite. Matter o' fact, they makes good watchbeasts in daytime, warns us if'n Sea Rogues be a-comin', so we can go an' hide in our cave."

Luke stared questioningly at Welff Tiptip. "Sea Rogues?"

"Oh, lackaday, sir, ain't you knowin' about those badbeasts? Why, they comes to this northcoast often as not."

Luke began to feel the first stirrings of unease. "But there's nothing t'be had on northland coast. Why do they choose to put in here?"

Drunn Tunneller waved a huge digging paw. "Thurr be nobeast yurr to wurry abowt, zurr, so they'm cummin' to take on fresh water, patch ee sails, repair ee ships an' so forth. Burr, they'm all scum'n'villyuns!"

Welff nodded agreement with her molefriend. "So they are. We hides in our caves an' stays well clear until those badbeasts are gone. Else we'd get slayed, or taken for slaves by 'em. Oh, Luke sir, what be the matter wi' ye? Do y'not feel well?"

Though the night was cold, Luke felt suddenly hot and sick. "Further south, down the shoreline, my tribe have lit a big bonfire on the shore. We didn't think there'd be any danger this far north!"

Drunn's big digging claws took hold of Luke's shoulders. "You'm must 'urry, zurr. Do ee take yore mouseybeasts an' get ee back with all 'aste. Dowse ee flames, an' put out yon fire. Et be loik ee beacon to Sea Rogues. Oi beg ee, 'urry!"

Welff called after the party of mice scrambling down the cliff, "Good luck go with ye, sir Luke. We'll follow ye on in the morn, with baskets o' berries an' wotever plants you may need. Aye, an' Drunn's moles will show ye how to hide yore dwellin's from the sight of Sea Rogues!"

Welff's words were lost upon Luke and his friends. They were already down and charging along the shoreline headlong, with old Twoola hobbling in their wake.

Dawn came wild and angry. Cold howling easterly gales swept the shoreline sand, piling it in buttresses against rocks and whipping grains widespread across the ebbing tide. Drunn Tunneller and Welff Tiptip led their little band along the beach, bearing between them the promised baskets of berries and young plants. Wearing cowled cloaks and mufflers over their noses and mouths, they pressed on gallantly towards Luke's encampment, heads bowed against the weather's onslaught. To cover her anxiety Welff chattered feverishly to her molefriend.

"Now if 'twere late spring an' the weather milder, a body would expect Sea Rogues visitin' our shores. Anybeast afloat in stormy seas like we get this time o' season is nought but a fool. I know 'twasn't wise for Luke an' his mice to light great fires in full view onshore, but I reckon mayhap no harm will've befell them, eh, Drunn?"

The mole was about to agree with her when a fierce gust of sandgritted wind caused him to turn his face seaward. He groaned aloud and dropped his basket. "Guhuuuurr noooo! Look yon, 'tis ee gurt redship!"

Through the fleeting spume of sand and seawater, Welff glimpsed the mighty bulk of the *Goreleech*, her crimson stern riding high on the main, red sails bellying tight as she sped westward out onto the deep. The good hogwife stood watching the fearful sight, tears mingling with the grit sticking to her face, and she moaned like a stricken beast. "Waaaow, lackaday, the redship! Fortunes an' fates 'a' pity on those pore mice!"

Drunn grabbed her paw, signalling to his friends to follow. "Coom on, missus, ee beasts be needin' our 'elp!"

Vurg was covered in swirling wood ashes from the scattered fire embers. He sat on the shore, lost in a dumb trance. Between them, Drunn and Welff shouldered his paws, steering him to the meager knot of survivors who huddled forlornly in the mouth of Luke's cave. Old Twoola was the only mouse who seemed able to explain what had taken place. "Friends, you come at a terrible time for us. Many graves will need to be dug in these bloodstained sands."

Welff spoke softly to the old one. Now that she had recovered from her first shock, she was all business. "Aye, 'tis so, but first we must attend to the living. Drunn, will you light a fire in this cave and set water to boil? Our family will prepare food for you. Dig out any ole linen you possess—we'll need bandages!"

As the moles and hedgehogs took care of the shoremice, their dreadful tale came out piecemeal.

"There was hundreds of 'em. We didn't stand a chance!"

"It was a massacre. Only those out lookin' for firewood escaped. We could do nothing to stop those evil killers!"

"Windred was lucky. She ran out on the shore with the babe, stumbled an' fell. Her cloak was over them both, an' the wind covered it with sand an' hid them. 'Tis a wonder little Martin wasn't smothered."

Windred sat by the fire, washing sand from the babe's face with warm water and the hem of her dress. "Aye, an' he never made a single sound the whole time. Pore liddle mite, they slew his mother. Scum, they are! I'll remember that 'un's name to my dyin' day. Vilu Daskar! She tried to fight him off with a stick, but he had a big curved blade. He was shoutin' his own name, Vilu Daskar, an' enjoyin' what he was doin'. That stoat was laughin' as he cut my daughter down. Laughin' like a madbeast!"

Drunn looked up from a wound he was attending to. "Ee maister o' redship shows mercy to nobeast, marm. Yurr, but whurr be zurr Luke gone to?"

The young mouse Timballisto, who had survived by climbing the cliff face, nodded towards the sea. "Luke's out there, but nobeast can come near him, sir."

Waist deep in the sea stood Luke, buffeted by the cold waves, with ice forming on his tear-stained features as he gazed westerly after the red ship which was now naught but a blurred dot far out by the horizon.

Twoola shook his head sadly. "He will not even look upon his own son, or his wife's mother. Alas, he has no ship to sail after the murderers. But he would have ended up slain if he did. Either way, I think Luke will die and be swept away when the tide turns. His life has been destroyed and he cannot exact a warrior's vengeance upon the Sea Rogues. Luke has no will to live."

Welff hitched up her apron decisively. She turned from the sight of the forlorn creature standing in the sea to those who stood watching. "I ain't havin' this, by the paws'n'prickles I ain't! You there, Cardo, go and fetch a stout rope. Vurg, give that stave you carry to Drunn. That liddle mousebabe's not growin' up without a father. Twoola, get every able-bodied beast out here. Move!"

Galvanized into action by Welff's no-nonsense manner, they dispersed quickly to their allotted tasks.

Drunn Tunneller tied the rope end around his middle and gripped Vurg's stave tight. "Hurr, oi never was one furr pagglin' in ee sea, marm."

The hogwife eyed him sternly. She was not about to be disobeyed in any circumstances. "Go to it, Drunn, afore Luke freezes t'death!"

The mole trundled dutifully into the sea. "Hurr, 'tis a good job oi trusters ee, missus!"

Luke was totally unaware of the mole wading up behind him, his eyes fixed on the horizon where the *Goreleech* had disappeared from sight. Drunn heaved an unhappy sigh.

"Whurrrr! Oi 'ates t'do this, zurr Luke, but 'tis furr thoi own gudd an' furr ee h'infant too, burr aye!" With one blow of the stout beech stave he knocked Luke unconscious. Looping the rope about Luke so that they were bound together, Drunn called back to the watchers onshore. "You'm 'eave away farst. Oi'm most colded t'death out yurr!" Willing paws pulled the rope swiftly in to dry land.

The days that followed were hard upon the survivors. They buried their dead and would have gone on mourning all season, but for the help of the moles and the hedgehogs. Welff chided them ruthlessly and Drunn bullied them cheerfully, until they began to pick up the pieces and get on with the business of living. Luke recovered, but he spoke to none, sitting silently at the back of his cave, gazing into the fire. Every once in a while, he would wander out into the night, and then sleepers would be awakened by his roaring down at the water's edge, shouting one name.

"Vilu Daskar! Vilu Daskar! Vilu Daskaaaaaaar!"

The morning following one such night, Luke's cave had become the meeting place for everybeast. They were gathered around the fire, breakfasting on hot oatcakes and blackberry preserve. Welff brewed a big pot of mint and comfrey tea, which they sipped as they ate. Luke had returned from the sea's edge, and he lay on a rocky ledge, wrapped in his cloak, sleeping. Cardo had a flat driftwood board, and his knife was heating in the flames as he announced to the gathering, "I'm going to burn the names of our lost ones onto this wood with my knifepoint. Don't let me forget anybeast. I'll fix it in the sand on top of the big grave, agreed?"

Young Timballisto sniffed and rubbed a paw at his eyes. "Will you put Fripple's name on it, sir?"

Cardo took his blade from the fire. He smiled sadly. "Of course I will, Timbal. How could I forget my own daughter? I'll put a little flower after it, she'd like that."

To break the atmosphere, Welff turned their attention to the baby Martin. "Dearie me, will you lookit that mite, he's out of his cradle again. Where's he a-crawlin' to now?"

Windred knew. "He's after his father's sword again. Watch."

The solemn chubby mousebabe crawled over until he could get his paw on Luke's swordhilt. He sat quietly enough, trying to lift the weapon, which was twice his height.

Drunn squinted his eyes admiringly at the babe's efforts. "Ee vurmints beware when that 'un grows!"

Windred looked across to Martin's sleeping father. "Aye, an' bad fortune to any Sea Rogues when Luke awakens properly. He will, you mark my words. I know him!'

19

In the seasons that followed, Luke and his surviving tribe did
well and learned many things. No longer were they hungry—
farming the clifftop land, foraging further afield in good
weather, and gathering mollusks, shrimp and shellfish from
rockpools and tide shallows. Drunn and his moles taught
them how to create screens of rock, driftwood and overhang-
ing vegetation for their caves, disguising them from the gaze
of unwanted visitors and providing windbreaks against harsh
weather. Windred looked after little Martin, who had become
a sturdy toddler, living the simple life, still as solemn and
well behaved as ever.

Luke, however, was a different creature from the easy-
going, good-humoured leader he had been before his wife's
death. His tribe learned to give him a wide berth and ask no
questions of him. He kept a cave apart from the others, in
which he was making and storing weapons. He came and
went at odd times, returning with materials he had gathered
in his wandering. Martin was the only one he would confide
in, though he constantly questioned Drunn and Welff on the
habits of Sea Rogues. How often did they visit the north

coasts? Did they ride at anchor or beach their vessels? What sort of discipline did they employ, what was the average size of a crew, what type of weapons and tactics did they favour? If a ship was sighted out on the main, all creatures ran for cover, but Luke would lie on the clifftops with Martin, watching it. The little fellow listened carefully to what his father had to say.

"I hope that vessel doesn't put in here, son. I'm not ready for them yet. Better that it stays out to sea and sails off. But when I'm ready, the day will arrive when I'll be looking for a ship to land here, and then we'll see what the seascum are made of. Look, she's veering off southward. We won't be bothered by that one, thank fortune. Come on, you can help me to build up our weapon supply."

Luke showed his son how to make arrows, whilst he himself attended to the bows. "See these, they're ash branches, good heavy wood. I've chosen the ones that are medium thick and straight, and dried the ends out by standing them in warm sand around the fire. Now, we make a slit in the opposite end and fit a piece of feather in it, like so, then bind above and below the feather with twine. Next, I place the dried end of the wood in the fire, let it burn, but not too much, then rub it to a point on this rock, burn a little more, rub a little more. Here, Martin, try the end of this with your paw. Be careful."

Martin dabbed his paw gently on the needlelike point his father had rubbed on to the fire darkened ash. He smiled. "Oo, it shark!"

Luke smiled at his little son, who was still learning to pronounce words. "Aye, 'tis shark all right, very shark. Sea vermin don't wear armour, so an arrow doesn't need a metal or flint tip. A good hefty ash shaft with a firepoint will stop 'em!"

Vurg entered the cave, and indicated Martin with a nod. "His grandma Windred is lookin' for him. Dinner's ready in the big cave. Are you coming, Luke?"

Luke glanced up from the bowstring he was twining and greasing. "I'll be along. There's still work to do here."

Vurg looked around at the rows of stakes waiting to be sharpened, flint axeheads, unstrung yew bows, and gnarled driftwood limbs waiting to be fashioned into clubs. "A fair ole bit o' work I'd say, Luke. Why don't me'n'Cardo an' some of the others help you?"

Luke knotted off the end of his finished bowstring. "My son's a good little helper, but I could do with some like you to lend a paw. Why didn't you offer sooner, Vurg?"

His friend smiled wryly. "Because none of us fancied gettin' our heads bitten off."

Luke offered his paw. "Sorry, mate. I accept your help gratefully. 'Tis not your heads I'm lookin' to bite off, just the Sea Rogues'."

Vurg took Luke's paw and shook it warmly. "Good. Let's go an' get some dinner, then every able-bodied beast in camp will pitch in with pleasure!"

From then on Luke became a real Warrior Chieftain, directing his creatures in the making of weaponry, drilling and training his fighters and marking off the shoreline around the caves in various strategies and plans for when the time was ripe.

It came unexpectedly, one evening the following summer. Having finished their day's chores, the tribe sat about after dinner in the big cavemouth, their backs warmed by the fire within, enjoying the pleasant evening. Windred was singing an old song which had been passed down through her family.

"Old Ninian mouse and his goodwife,
Needed a house to build,
They had a family grown so large,
Their tent was overfilled.

To setting sun the old wife toiled,
From daybreak in the east,
But Ninian was a lazy mouse,
Who loved to sleep and feast.

The wife heaved stone and carried wood,
For door and wall and beam,
Whilst Ninian idly in daylight,
Snored on in peaceful dream.

She raised the gables, built a roof,
Her back was bent and sore,
As Ninian ate up all the food,
And loudly called for more.

So when the house at last was built,
His wife nailed up a sign,
Which stated 'THIS AINT NINIANS!'
She said, 'That shows 'tis mine!'

Then when the countless seasons passed,
And all within had died,
The rain and storm of ages long,
Had swept the sign outside.

It washed the first three letters out,
But left the rest intact,
That sign now reads, 'S AINT NINIANS!'
A church? A joke? A fact!

So traveler if you read the sign,
Then take my word 'tis true,
A dreamer can become a saint,
So can a glutton too!"

Welff applauded with the rest, chuckling and shaking her head at Windred's song.

"Tell me, Windred m'dear, is it true, is there such a place as Saint Ninian's, or is it really a joke?"

Luke answered for her. "'Tis a fact, marm. I was born at Saint Ninian's, as was Sayna my poor dear wife. We were driven out, when I was a babe, by an evil warlord, a wildcat named Lord Greeneye Verdauga who had a horde of vermin at his command, so they told me, but I was far too young to remember. This is our home now, and nobeast will ever drive us from here whilst I am about."

Drunn Tunneller dashed towards them, waving. He was panting hard, having clambered down from the clifftops.

"Burr, git ee insoid, guddbeasts all, ee Sea Rogue ship be a cummen yurr!"

Immediately the tribe began pulling out driftwood and vegetation to disguise the cave's entrance as they had been shown. Luke nodded to Vurg and Dulam to accompany him down to the tideline.

Shading their eyes against the westering sun, the three mice stood in the ebbing tide shallows watching the ship. Vurg scratched his head and looked to Luke. "Doesn't look quite right t'me, mate. What d'you make of it?"

Luke scrutinized the vessel keenly. It was still a good distance from land. "Hmm, could be just an honest merchant trader, but in these waters I doubt it, Vurg. It doesn't seem to be making good headway—if it's trying for land, it won't make it here until near daybreak tomorrow at the rate 'tis goin', eh, Dulam?"

Dulam watched the strange craft take a north tack, as if trying to catch the wind. He pointed. "See, she's got a broken mast, I think. That's why the going's so hard for that ship!"

Luke checked Dulam's sighting. "You're right, mate. Maybe this is just what we've been waiting for. Back to the cave and rouse our fighters!"

Reynard Chopsnout, captain of the vessel *Greenhawk*, was in high bad humour. His ship was taking on water, and to make matters worse, add a broken mainmast and ten days on short rations. Moreover, the crew were becoming mutinous and he was hard pressed to maintain command. The Corsair fox pawed irritably at the hard polished blob of pitch which served him as a snout. It was stuck on where his nose had been until he came off worse in a swordfight with a skillful ferret.

Chopsnout roared at the hapless weasel who was wrestling with the tiller. "Hold 'er fast to the wind, Bootbrain. What's the matter with ye? To the wind I said, wagglepaw, the wind!"

Some of the vermin crew were aloft, trying to rig a jury mast. One of them called down mockingly, "Don't shout too 'ard, Choppy, yer nose'll fall off!"

Chopsnout grabbed a belaying pin and hurled it up at the

rigging. It fell back, almost hitting him. Amid the hoots and jeers of the crew, he yelled, "Who said that? Come on, own up, ye lily-livered poltroon!"

Another insult rang out from below, where other crew members were baling out the water the *Greenhawk* was shipping. "Bootbrain'd 'andle the tiller better if yer fed us proper, yew ole vittle robber!"

Chopsnout could not see who made the remark. He danced and stamped in anger on the deckplanking. "Liar. Filthy foultongued liar. I get the same amount o' vittles that everybeast aboard gets!"

There was an ominous clack. Chopsnout quit stamping and dropped on all fours, scuttling about the deck. This caused great hilarity among the crew, and bold ones began yelling.

"Oops, ole Choppy's lost 'is hooter agin, mates. Hahaharr!"

"Let's 'ope it don't bounce down 'ere an' kill somebeast."

"Give 'im a chance, mateys, 'e's on the scent of it. Heehee!"

"Arr now, don't say that, bucko, 'e'll go an' get all sniffy on us. Hohohoho!"

The irate fox soon found his pitchblob nose and stuck it on hastily. He paced the deck waggling his cutlass ominously. "Go on, laugh, ye slabsided slobberin' swabs, but don't come whinin' t'me for aid or advice. I'm finished, d'ye hear, finished!"

He strode off huffily to his cabin. Bootbrain dithered at the tiller, not sure of which way to swing it. "Harr, cummon, cap'n, we was only funnin'. Wot course d'yer want me to set?"

Chopsnout poked his head round the cabin door and cast a withering glance at the weasel. "Course? I couldn't give a frog's flipper wot course you set. Sail where y'fancy, let the ship leak 'til she sinks, leave the mainmast broken. 'Tain't my bizness. I'll leave the command o' the *Greenhawk* to youse clever-tongued beasts, an' see 'ow *you* like it!"

There was an uneasy silence from the crew. Darkness was falling fast and nobeast was about to take on the responsibility of running the vessel. Chopsnout smiled triumphantly. "So, what've ye got to say t'that, me fine buckoes?"

Bootbrain, who was never given to teasing or insulting his

captain, could not help making an observation. "Cap'n, yore nose is on the wrong ways round. Ye've stuck it on backwards."

The final straw came when a strangled titter rang out from below. Reynard Chopsnout slammed his cabin door shut and sat sulking in his cabin.

Sometime after midnight there was a rap on the cabin door. Chopsnout snarled at the beast without, "Go 'way an' leave me alone!"

The rapping persisted, accompanied by a voice. "But cap'n, lissen, 'tis yore ole mate Floggtail. I've spotted somethin' on the shore. Come an' look!"

Adopting a stern face, Chopsnout emerged from his cabin. The crew were gathered on deck, peering at a fire burning on the beach some distance away. The Corsair fox could not help smirking as he addressed Floggtail, the searat first mate.

"Well well, a fire, eh? Looks no different from any other I've seen. What d'ye plan on doin' about it, mate?"

Floggtail stared hard at the firelight, scratching his fat stomach distractedly. "Er, er, Scritchy an' Wippback reckons we oughter tack a bit an' sail beyond that point stickin' up south'ards, cap'n."

Chopsnout smiled encouragingly at the two searats. "Hmm, clever thinkin', you two. Wot next?"

Both searats hastily explained their plan.

"We drops anchor t'other side o' the point, cap'n."

"Aye, then, er, we climbs over that point an' drops in on 'em."

"That's right, then we slaughters 'em all an' robs any vittles we find!"

Chopsnout shook his head in despair at their stupidity. "How d'ye know that those creatures on shore ain't already sighted us an' armed theirselves up, eh? An' tell me this, wot's t'stop this ship sinkin' if'n you takes the time to tack around be'ind yonder point? Well cummon, I'm waitin' fer an answer off'n some bright spark?"

There followed a deal of paw shuffling and blank looks, then Floggtail appealed sheepishly to Chopsnout. "Er, cap'n, 'ow would yew go about it, sir?"

Chopsnout snorted airily. "Ho, yore in trouble now, so youse need yore ole cap'n agin, eh? Well I ain't makin' a move 'til I gets a full apology off'n this crew for the insults I've bore!"

Staring at the deck as if the answer lay there, the vermin crew mumbled disjointedly.

"Sorry, cap'n, er, about yore no . . ."

"About wot we said to yer."

"Aye, we didn't mean it, cap'n."

"'Twas on'y a joke, cap'n, we won't say nothin' no more."

"Yore the best cap'n ever t'sail the seas, sir!"

Chopsnout attempted a sniff, holding onto his nose, which was starting to wobble slightly. "Well all right, so be it. But next time you start any o' that I'm done with ye for good. Now, 'ere's the way I sees it. That fire on shore is only a liddle 'un, an' all I can see is two beasts sittin' by it, mouses mebbe. If'n there were a full tribe o' them there'd be a great big fire, so I figgers there's on'y the pair of 'em, prob'ly some ole hermit an' his wife. They're either daft or blind, 'cos they ain't seen us, or they wouldn't've lighted a fire an' give themselves away. Hark t'me now, this is my plan. Leave off fixin' the mast an' balin' out water, all four paws on deck 'cos the tide's starting to ebb. Grab any spare planks, timbers or oars an' start paddlin' 'er for the shore double quick. We'll run the *Greenhawk* up on the sand an' beach 'er high'n'dry. Then we'll capture those two mice an' torture 'em 'til we finds out where they've hid all their vittles. After they've cooked us a good feast the rest's simple. We fixes the leaks an' the mainmast, chops the ole mouse'n'his wife up fer fishbait, then sails off south fer a bit o' sun an' plunder!"

Bootbrain nodded his head in admiration of Chopsnout. "Stripe me, 'ow d'you remember it all, cap'n? Yore a clever 'un, no two ways about it!"

The Corsair fox drew his ragged frock coat about him haughtily, staring down his imitation nose at the astounded vermin crew. "Aye, that's why I'm a cap'n, so mind yore manners an' git about yore business, you dumbclucks!"

Vurg raised his eyes from the fire on the beach that he and Luke were sitting by. "She's headed straight for us. They've put out paddles. You were right, Luke, that ship'll land here around dawn."

Luke reassured himself by touching the sword concealed beneath his cloak. "Good. Is everything ready, Dulam?"

The mouse who had crawled up in the sand behind Luke made his brief report. "Aye, ready. Old 'uns an' the babes are well away, hidden beyond the cliffs, an' our fighters are waitin' in the caves."

Luke watched the *Greenhawk* moving closer to land, speaking to Dulam without turning his head. "Tell them to make every shaft count—'twill be kill or be killed. We'll only get one chance to capture that vessel."

Dulam wriggled off back to the caves. Luke sensed Vurg's trembling, and he placed a steadying paw on his friend. "Take it easy, Vurg. This is the best chance we're ever goin' to get of startin' to avenge our loved ones. Trust me."

His companion stole a glance at the hard-eyed warrior sitting beside him. There was not a shred of pity or unsureness showing on Luke's face, just cold wrath and determination. Vurg suddenly stopped trembling.

"I'm all right, Luke. I trust you. All of yore tribe do!"

The *Greenhawk* was aided by a light breeze caught by her square-rigged aftersail, speeding up the vessel's progress, drawing her closer to the pair of forlorn figures huddled about the guttering fire onshore. Reynard Chopsnout drew his cutlass and climbed up to the prow. He crouched there, putting a final edge to his blade on an iron cleat. Already he could mentally hear the whimpers of the two shorebeasts, pleading for their lives. This was going to be as easy as falling off a log!

20

Somewhere on the clifftops a small bird raised its beak to herald the dawn, as day's first pale streaks washed the sky outward from the east. The crew of the *Greenhawk* sweated and cursed as they pushed their craft onshore with makeshift paddles. She rose on a swell and forged forward, scraping her hull into the sand and listing to port, keeling slightly as the ebbing water dropped her on the beach. Roaring and shouting, Chopsnout urged his vermin over the side. "Grab 'em, mates, I want those two alive!"

Luke shrugged off his cloak. Raising his sword he watched the savage-looking Sea Rogues pounding up the beach. Vurg took up his position, spear at the ready, steeling himself against the wild war cries of the charging foe.

"Haharr, let's see the color o' yer innards, mice!"

"Lop off'n their footpaws so they can't run away!"

"Gimme a cloak made out o' mouse's skin!"

"Eeeeeyaaaaargh!"

Chopsnout could scarce believe his eyes. Leaping down from the prow to bring up the rear, he saw the first wave of ten or so crewbeasts vanish into the ground.

• • •

Halfway up the beach, Luke's fighters had dug a trench, lining it with sharpened stakes and covering it with rush mats strewn thinly over with sand. Vermin screamed in shocked agony as they plunged into it. Luke gave the signal, letting his swordpoint dip as he bellowed aloud to his companions, "Now! Strike now!"

Both Luke and Vurg dropped into a crouch. Arrows hissed angrily overhead, thudding into the vermin who were hovering on the edge of the spiked trench. Two more flights of shafts followed speedily, then Luke leaped upright, wielding his sword as the archers dropped their bows and seized fire-hardened lances.

"Chaaaaarge!"

They dashed forward, with Luke and Vurg out in front, leaping the trench and hurling themselves upon the enemy.

Chopsnout had lost his pitchblob nose as soon as he hit the sand. He stood yelling hoarsely at his vermin crew. "Retreat, back to the ship, retreat!"

However, they were suddenly outflanked. The rest of Luke's small force thundered out from a cave situated on the far edge of the point, armed with long cudgels and slings. Rocks whistled through the morning air, cutting down several of the routed vermin, then they were hit from both sides by Luke's lances and the swinging clubs of grim-faced, ruthless mice. Reynard Chopsnout leaped ineffectively at the high beached bulwarks of the *Greenhawk*. He slid awkwardly back to the moist sand, half raising his scimitar as Luke's battlesword found him. It was over in less time than it had taken for the vermin to beach their boat.

Luke was now every inch the Warrior Chieftain of his tribe. Sheathing his blade, he nodded curtly at the stunned faces of the fighters surrounding him. "Well done, we've gained ourselves a ship!"

Cardo let his lance drop, obviously shocked. "Luke, they're dead. We've slain them all."

Luke picked up the lance, pressing it into his friend's paw.

"Aye, that was the idea, mate. Or would you sooner that we were caught nappin' an' murdered like our families were?"

There were loud cries of agreement with Luke. Friends crowded around to shake his paw or pat his back.

Luke glanced up at the clifftops. "Steady, mates, plenty o' time for that later. Some of you fill in that trench. Dulam, you an' the others roll those vermin carcasses into the sea, the ebbin' tide'll carry 'em out. I don't want the young 'uns to see any of this. Vurg, come with me. We'll have to rig up some means o' haulin' the ship above the tideline, so she don't get carried back out on the floodtide."

Luke and Vurg hurried to the cliffs, intercepting Drunn, who was climbing down to see the result of the battle.

"Burr, you'm winned, zurr Luke. Oi allus knowed ee wurr a gurt Wurrier, ho urr!"

Luke took the friendly mole's outstretched paw and shook it heartily. "Drunn my old mate, how are ye at movin' ships up beaches?"

The mole sized up the situation immediately. "Et be the least oi c'n do furr ee, zurr!"

Before the incoming tide had arrived Drunn, with the aid of his moles, some mice and the hedgehogs, had dug a shallow channel from the *Greenhawk*'s prow to a spot above the tideline. This he lined with slabs of cliff shale, well wetted down with seawater. On the vessel's forepeak was a windlass, a simple mechanism for hauling up the ship's anchor, with a horizontally revolving barrel. Welff Tiptip and her hogs helped to carry the anchor up onshore, where they wedged it firmly between two big rocks jutting up out of the sand. Now the ship was attached to the land by its anchor rope. Drunn chose the stoutest creatures to turn the windlass, which they did by ramming home stout poles into the housing. Once the slack of the rope was taken up, they began turning the windlass in earnest.

The young ones and oldsters had come down from the clifftops. Extra paws were needed, so they all joined in. Windred and old Twoola ran back and forth, splashing more water on the shale slabs as the ship slid forward, up onto shore, creaking and groaning. Martin and young Timballisto pushed with all their might against the windlass spokes, along with the rest.

It was a happy day. A sprightly breeze moved the clouds away, sunlight beat down on the workers. Joyfully they toiled, turning the windlass bit by bit, moving their ship up the shore on its own anchor rope. Some even improvised a shanty to keep up the rhythm of the task, and soon everybeast was singing it.

"Oh don't it make a sight so grand,
A ship that travels on the land,
Keep that windlass turnin', bend yore backs an' push!

We'll soon have her above the tide,
Then we'll clean an' scrape each side,
Keep that windlass turnin', bend yore backs an' push!

We've got to find a good tree fast,
Then we'll build a new mainmast,
Keep that windlass turnin', bend yore backs an' push!

With pitch an' rope we'll make her right,
All shippyshape an' watertight,
Keep that windlass turnin', bend yore backs an' push!

You vermin scum, oh mercy me,
Beware when Luke puts out to sea,
Keep that windlass turnin', bend yore backs an' push!"

Gradually the ship slid over its runway of wetted shale slabs, finally coming to rest above the tideline, with the bow end firmly wedged between the two standing rocks that had secured the anchor. Luke was smiling broadly, as he patted the barnacle-encrusted hull. "Well, there she is, a right old slop bucket if ever I saw one, mates, but by winter I guarantee she'll be good'n'ready." He called to Martin, who was down by the tideline with Timballisto, stowing things behind a rock. "Ho there, son, what are you doing?"

Martin beckoned his father to join them and explained, "We collected all the weapons for you, see."

He unrolled an old length of sail canvas, revealing a jumbled assortment of swords, daggers and various blades that had been once owned by the crew of the *Greenhawk*.

Luke ruffled his young son's ears approvingly. "Well done, Martin. You too, Timbal. These are far better than our makeshift weapons!"

Timballisto selected a short sword for himself. Martin picked up a longish curved blade and began thrusting it into his belt. But Luke took the sword from his son and tossed it back with the other weapons.

"No, you're far too young to carry a blade yet, son. Timbal, you may keep your blade. 'Tis about time you had one—you'll be fully grown in another couple o' seasons." Seeing the disappointment on Martin's face, Luke threw a kindly paw about his son's shoulders. "Martin, you don't need the blade of any seascum. My sword is yours by right. It was passed on to me by my father and one day I will give it to you."

The young mouse's piercing grey eyes searched his father's face. "When?"

In his mind Luke saw himself asking the same question of his own father. He gave Martin the same answer he had received long ago.

"When I think you are ready."

Throughout the remainder of summer and all of autumn, the tribe of Luke worked long evenings, after their day's chores of farming food and foraging the shores was done. Gradually the once rickety Sea Rogue ship took shape. The hull was careened, ridding it of weed, barnacles and other saltwater debris. Unsound and rotten planking was torn out and replaced with good stout oak, which they traveled far to find and haul back. Cauldrons of pitch and pine resin bubbled continuously. Lengths of rope were woven and hammered in between the ship's timbers. Then the pitch and resin were poured into the joints, sealing them and making the vessel watertight. Any spare food was cooked and preserved in casks for ship's stores, along with new barrels for fresh water to be carried in. Luke oversaw everything, paying careful attention to the slightest detail.

"Do it proper and 'twill serve you well!" Everybeast in the tribe became familiar with their Chieftain's constant motto.

Winter's first icy breath was coating the northern coast with rimefrost when the new mainmast was raised. Vurg and Drunn had chosen a good tall white willow, which would bend with the wind where other wood might crack and break. Newly patched and hemmed, the wide single mainsail was hoisted, fluttered a moment, then bellied proudly out in the cold north breeze. A cheer went up from the creatures who had worked so hard to repair the vessel. Luke stood back upon the shore with Martin and Windred, surveying the new craft. It had three curving sails from the bowsprit to the mainmast, with the big triangular sail and a tall oblong one either side of the new willow. At the stern was a smaller mast with one other triangular sail. It obviously met all Luke's requirements. He smiled at Martin. "She'll have to have a new name, son."

Martin, like all youngsters, always had a question. "Why do they always call ships 'she'?"

Luke had to think about that one for a moment. "Truth t'tell, son, I'm not sure, but I think they call ships she because, well, she's like a mother to her crew."

Another enquiry followed immediately from the serious-faced young mouse. "I haven't got a mother. Will she be my mother?"

Luke's eyes were sad as he replied, "No, son, I'm afraid not."

Windred stared reprovingly at Luke. "D'you mean you're not taking Martin along with you? He's your son, Luke!"

The Chieftain nodded. "Aye, he is, and that's why I'm not goin' to risk his young life out there on the seas. Beside that, Windred, you're his grandmother, so he'll have to look after you—the only family I have left in this world is you two. Now let's hear no more of it. Would you like to name the ship, son?"

Martin would not let anybeast see tears in his eyes, so he rushed off along the shore, calling back to Luke, "Call her *Sayna* after my mother!"

Windred watched her grandson dash down to the sea, where he stood throwing pebbles into the waves. "I'm sorry, Luke, I should have kept my silly mouth shut."

Luke rested a paw gently on her shoulder. "Don't be sorry, Windred, I'd have had to tell him sooner or later. Martin's made of tough stuff. He'll grow to be a fine warrior, though the only way he'll learn is to be told the plain truth. 'Twould be no good telling him lies."

That night a feast to mark the completion of the vessel *Sayna* was held in Luke's cave. Autumn's harvest had been good and the cooks had excelled themselves. Martin cheered up as he and Timballisto joined a young hogmaid called Twindle and Drunn's nephew Burdle. The four sat together, giggling and joking beneath a lantern at the rear of the cave, ruddy firelight twinkling in their eyes. They had never seen such a sumptuous spread. "Yurr, lookit ee gurt plum pudden!"

"Oh, an' see those likkle tarts, they've got cream on top that looks like a twirl. Bet my mum Welff made those!"

"Mmm! Have you tasted the soup yet? 'Tis full o' rock-shrimps an' veggibles!"

"I want a slice o' that big cake, the one with honey an' red-currants all over the top!"

They sipped Drunn's fizzy apple cider and munched hot wheat scones that contained chunks of candied pear. The elders drank special barley beer and cut off slices of celery and onion cheese to go with it. Old Twoola raised his beaker and broke out into song.

"Oh the weather's cold outside outside,
But we're all snug in here,
With thee an' me, good company,
An' lots o' barley beer!

Oh the snow comes down outside outside,
An' winter winds do moan,
But sit us by a roarin' fire,
An' you'll not hear one groan!

Oh the night is dark outside outside,
But the soup is good an' hot,
Good food, fine friends an' happy hearts,
I'd say we've got the lot!"

Amid the laughter and applause that followed, old Twoola
poured himself another beaker, crying out, "That's the stuff.
'Tis a feast an' we be here to enjoy ourselves. Who's got a
song?"

Drunn began using a gourd as a drum, beating out a
rhythm on it with two wooden spoons. "Goo urr, missus
Welff, show 'um 'ow ee can sing!"

Goodwife Welff was immediately up, apron swirling as
she danced a jig, clapping her paws and singing.

"Two plums grew on a pear tree,
A wise old owl did say,
Oh dearie me I'm certain,
They shouldn't grow that way.

For beechnuts come from beech trees,
Whilst Mother Nature rules,
As long as acorns come from oaks,
No wisdom comes from fools!

Then came a little hedgehog,
Who said with simple smile,
Good day to you wise creature,
Now list' to me awhile.

Why does a tree stay silent,
And yet it has a bark,
An' why do shadows fall at night,
But never leave a mark?

Though you may think me silly,
I know 'tis only fair,
Most any fool can tell you,
That two plums make a pair!"

The mice had never heard this quaint ditty before, and they chuckled at the logic of the little hedgehog.

Dulam poured Welff a beaker of cider, offering her his seat, so that she could catch her breath. "Good song, marm, that was very clever."

The hogwife winked at him. "If'n you think that's clever then ponder on this. How many pears in a dozen pair, six or twelve?" She watched the bemused mouse trying to work it out.

"Er, six, I think, aye 'tis six."

Goody Welff chuckled. "Then I wouldn't send you to the orchard for my pears."

Dulam scratched his head and did some more figuring. "No, twelve, the answer's twelve!"

"Twelve pair o' pears, are you sure?"

"Er, er, aye! I'm sure, marm!"

Goody Welff drained her beaker, eyes twinkling. "But that's twenty-four, twelve pairs o' pears."

Dulam scratched his head furiously. "You've got me all mixed up, marm!"

Drunn patted the puzzled mouse's back heartily. "Ee try wurkin' et out in apples, zurr!"

Late into the night they carried on feasting, singing and setting riddles. The fire was burning low when Windred moved the cave barricade a little and peered outside. She shuddered and hurried back to the fire. "Brr, snow's beginnin' to fall out there!"

Luke took his cloak and spread it over Martin and Burdle, who had drowsed off together in the corner. Windred waited until Luke returned to the fire, then asked, "Couldn't it bide until the spring?"

Luke stared into the red embers. "No. I have stayed too long already. Snow or not, I'm bound to sail in the morning."

Windred sat silent awhile, listening to the snow-laden winds sweeping the shore outside. Suddenly she leaned forward and gripped Luke's paw fiercely. "Go then, and seek out Vilu Daskar. Slay him and destroy his blood-coloured ship. Steal the life from him who robbed us of our Sayna. I'll take

care of Martin and when he's grown enough, he'll care for
me. But swear to me that one day you'll return here to the
creatures who love you, Luke the Warrior!"

Holding his swordblade over the fire, Luke watched the
embers reflecting red against it. "I swear that when I'm done
the seascum will murder no more innocent creatures. On my
oath I will return here when my work is done!"

21

It was a bitter winter noon when the ship *Sayna*, crewed by Luke and a score of his fighting mice, slid down its shale runway on the ice the season had provided. With one fluke buried in the sand, the anchor held the ship against an ebbing tide. Even though her sails were furled, the *Sayna* strained against the anchor rope, as if eager to be gone. All the farewells had been made, and the crew had sent their friends and families back into the caves, not wishing them to stand out tearful and freezing to wave the ship off. Luke was last to leave. Martin sat stone-faced outside the cave. Luke could not reason with him.

"Son, son, you would not last two moons out there on the high seas. I cannot risk your life pitting you in battle against the seascum I am sworn to do war with. Listen to me, I know what is best for you!"

But Martin would not listen. "I want to sail on the ship and be a warrior like you!"

Luke spread his paws wide and sighed with frustration. "What am I going to do with you, Martin? You have my warrior spirit and your mother's determination. Listen, son, take my sword."

It was a fighting sword and well used. Luke pressed it into his son's paws. The young mouse gazed wide-eyed at the battle-scarred blade and gripped the handle tight as if he would never let go.

Luke smiled, recalling the time when his father had passed the sword on to him. Tapping a paw against the crosshilt, he said, "I can see it is in you to be a fighter, Martin. The first thing warriors must learn is discipline."

Martin felt as though the sword were speaking for him. "Tell me what to do and I will obey."

Relief surged through Luke as he commanded the would-be warrior. "You will stay and help defend our cave against all comers, protect those weaker than yourself and honour our code. Always use the sword to stand for good and right, never do a thing you would be ashamed of, and never let your heart rule your mind." He tapped the blade once more as its pitted edge glinted in the winter morning. "And never let another creature take this sword from you, not as long as you live. When the time comes, pass it on to another, maybe your own son. You will know instinctively if he is a warrior. If not, hide the sword where only a true warrior who is brave of heart would dare to go and find it. Swear this to me, Martin."

"I swear it on my life!"

The young mouse's grey eyes reflected the wintry sea as he spoke. Luke saw that the tide would soon be turning.

"It might be some seasons before I return, but I'll be back, son. Meanwhile, Timballisto is a promising and sensible creature, with more seasons under his belt than you, and I have left him in charge of our tribe. Obey him."

A determined smile, reminiscent of his mother, hovered on Martin's lips. "Of course I'll obey him, but one day I shall be in charge."

A great feeling of pride enveloped Luke. "I'm sure you will. Farewell, my son."

Rigging ropes hummed around broad-bellying sails as the *Sayna* skimmed the deeps like a great white swan, headed west out onto the main. Luke turned for a moment from the tiller and looked back astern. He saw the small figure standing on the pebbled strand alone, waving the sword in a warrior's salute. The vessel dipped, bow into a rolling trough, and when she rose on the next wavecrest, the shoreline was lost in an afternoon of snow and icy winter spume. Luke turned back to his crew, certain he had chosen fighters whom he could trust to be at his side through thick and thin. Vurg, Cardo, Dulam, Coll and the rest, they stood waiting his orders, clinging to the taffrails to stay upright on the heaving deck. Cardo was not looking too well. Luke shook his head. "Get below decks, all of you. Batten down everything and stay there. 'Tis goin' to get rough. I'll take tiller an' first watch. We have t'learn to be sailors now, seabeasts, so like all beginners we can expect to be sick—me too. There's nothin' to be ashamed of. We'll get used to stormy seas in a few days."

Cardo had definitely taken on an unhealthy pallor. "Permission to jump over the side an' drown myself, cap'n!"

Just looking at his friend made Luke feel queasy.

"I'll drown you myself if you start that cap'n business. My name's Luke an' that's what you'll call me. Permission denied. Now get below, all of you!"

The entire crew shouted back at him, "Aye aye, cap'n!"

Luke was glad they had not lost their sense of humour.

It was three days before they were out of the stormy latitudes. The evening of the fourth day saw calm seas with no trace of snow. Luke realized they must have drifted southwest instead of holding the northwest course. A meeting was held in the captain's cabin, and Luke told the others what had happened. "'Twas my fault, really. I'm still only learning about bein' at sea. You may've noticed the weather's changed for the better—well, that's because we've drifted south."

But Vurg would not hear of his friend taking the blame. "Oh, frogfeathers, mate, it's the fault of everybeast here, we've all taken our turn at the tiller. Bein' seasick or sleepy didn't help things. Little wonder we drifted off course. Ain't that right, pals?"

The crew agreed, though Coll had a question.

"Er, just what *was* our original course? Seems to me we've just been sailin' willy nilly, eh, Vurg?"

"Well, I s'pose there's little else y'can do when you're searchin' the seas for that red ship."

Luke gestured at the empty shelves round the cabin. "What were we supposed t'do? There's not a chart or a map aboard the vessel. Most of these pirates sail by instinct. I've been thinkin', maybe 'tis best what we're doin', lettin' the winds an' currents carry us."

Cardo had regained his color, as had the rest of them. "Why do you say that, cap'n, er, sorry, Luke?"

"Well, look at it this way. Seascum hate the cold stormy seas as much as we do, so it stands to sense they'd sail to warmer waters. I've a feelin' the further south we sail the more chance we have o' meetin' up with Vilu Daskar."

Dulam spoke up as he headed for the door. "Great idea. I'm with ye, Luke. But after three days sick I'm feelin' much better, 'cept that I'm famished. Let's break out some vittles an' get a decent feed inside us!"

Dulam's suggestion was welcomed wholeheartedly. The crew were much happier now they were in calmer climes with a plan of action worked out.

A full moon beamed down on the *Sayna* as she drifted south on calm seas. Luke let Denno, a fat jolly mouse, take the tiller.

"Let her sail easy, Denno, just keep your eyes open and check the tiller from swingin' wide in another direction. I can tell by the smoke comin' from our galley there's some serious cookin' goin' on. Better take a peek, eh?"

Denno shook his head, chuckling. "You'll prob'ly get chased away. There's more cooks in that galley than y'could shake a stick at, an' that Cardo's the worst of all. Thinks 'e's cap'n o' the stewpot!"

Lantern light and steam came from the open galley window. Out on the darkened deck, Luke shook with suppressed laughter as he watched the antics of his crew. They bustled and bumped into one another, each trying to advise or outdo the other with tips on cooking expertise.

"Not too much o' that dried barley, Vurg, go easy."

"Oh, rubbish, my ole mum always put plenty o' barley in everythin' she cooked!"

"Aye, I thought yore mum's fruitcake tasted a bit funny."

"Well it didn't stop you scoffin' it, y'great lard bucket!"

"Lard bucket yoreself, mate. Hoi, Dulam, where are you goin' with the salt? Ship's stew needs lots of salt!"

"How d'you know? 'Tis the first time you've been on a ship. Put any more salt in that stew an' we'll drink the water barrels dry afore mornin'."

"Aye aye there, chop those carrots smaller, mate!"

"Gerrout, I like big cobs o' carrot!"

"So that means we've all got to 'ave great lumps o' carrot?"

"Huh, won't 'urt you. Hey, 'tis my turn to stir. Gimme that ladle."

"I'll give ye it on yore nose, see 'ow y'like that!"

A large cauldron of stew was carried into the big cabin, where Luke had set out beakers of ale and an oatcake by each place. Doing his utmost to keep a straight face, he tried sniffing appreciatively. "Mmm, that smells good. What is it, Cardo?"

A heated debate broke out over the cauldron's contents.

"I call it Cardo's Carrot Seastew!"

"Ho, do you now, well I calls it Vurg's Veggible Delight!"

"I did all the work, so 'tis goin' t'be called Coll's Combination Concoction!"

"No it ain't, it's Dulam's Delicious Shipstew!"

Luke banged the mess table with the serving ladle. "Enough! I won't have mutiny aboard my ship over a pot o' grub. I'll name the stew. Put it down here!"

They watched as Luke ladled a portion into his bowl. Blowing on a spoonful he sampled it gingerly, with his crew looking on anxiously. Bravely Luke chewed at the stew, his face expressionless. He put down the spoon and took a deep draught of ale.

They all spoke the word at once. "Well?"

Luke picked something from between his teeth and looked at it quizzically before returning his verdict.

"I think it should be called crunchy barley, half cooked carrot lump, far too salty 'otwater stew. So if you'll excuse

me, I'll just stick to oatcake an' ale for tonight's meal, mates
Eat up, an' see how you lot like it!"

Luke wandered out on deck with his frugal meal. "I'll take
the tiller for a while, mate. You go an' get somethin' to eat."

Denno immediately stopped gazing at the peaceful moon
flaked waves and relinquished his watch. "Certainly smelled
great when they carried it to the cabin, Luke. Thankee, mate
I'll enjoy some o' that stew."

Luke smiled wryly. "Oh aye, I'm sure you will!"

Soft pastel-hued skies heralded the dawn. A mouse named
Cordle dozed at the tiller, a canteen of water held loosely in
his paw. Coll came to relieve him, sipping from a beaker.

"Huh, fine one you are, sleepin' on watch. Good job Luke
never caught ye or he'd 'ave whacked yore tail off!"

Cordle blinked sleepily and took a quick swig of water
"Leastways while I'm sleepin' I'm not drinkin'. I tell ye
Coll, I never drank so much water in all me life!"

"Aye, no more o' that blinkin' stew fer me, mate. Yo
could've stood a spoon up in the salt that went into it! If w
capture any Sea Rogues, I reckon we should feed it to 'em
that'd teach 'em a lesson." But Cordle was not listening—h
was staring eagerly out to sea. "What's up, Cordle?"

"Look, land! I'm sure of it, that's land of some sort dea
ahead. Laaaaand hoooooooo!"

Instantly the ship came alive. The mousecrew tumble
from their bunks and staggered out on deck, rubbing slee
from their eyes as they followed the outstretched paw o
Cordle.

"It's land! Land!"

"Dead ahead, Luke. Cordle's spotted land!"

Luke climbed to the bowsprit and viewed the dark blot o
the horizon. "Aye, 'tis land sure enough, an island by the loo
of it. Take in the bow an' mainsails, Coll, an' steer north
We'll sail in nice'n'easy round the other side of that islanc
No sense in chargin' at it full sail. Right, mates, I want you a
armed an' alert. Cordle, Denno, Dulam, stay with the ship an
guard it close. The rest of you'll come ashore with me. Mak
no noise, tread careful an' follow my lead. There's no tellin
what we might meet!"

• • •

The *Sayna* dropped anchor in a sheltered inlet on the island's west side at early noontide. It was sunny, silent and windless. Luke inspected the high rocks surrounding the cove. Seabirds nested in the crags beneath a jumble of trees and vegetation growing on the clifftops. Climbing over the ship's side, the shore party waded through clear sunwarmed shallows to a narrow strip of sandy beach.

Vurg gripped his spear tight, whispering to Luke, "I don't like it, mate. 'Tis far too quiet—place gives me the creeps. I feel like somebeast's watchin' us!"

Luke drew a scimitar he had chosen from the former crew's weaponry. He pointed it at a strange sight, a flight of steps carved into the cliffs. "I wonder who took the trouble t'do that? Looks as if they've been there a long time. Let's take a look."

In single file they climbed the smooth, well-carved steps, which, though narrow, were easily negotiable. They ascended in several zigzag shapes to the clifftop. From above, the *Sayna* looked very small in the cove below. Cardo uprooted something from the ground which he wiped on his tunic before beginning to eat it.

"Mmm, young onion. Wonder how that got here?"

A loud, frightening cry rang out from the trees.

"Oohoohoohaaaaaarrrrreeeeeeegharr!"

The hair on Cardo's nape stood straight up, and he dropped the onion. "What'n the name o' frogs was that?"

Luke and Vurg began creeping forward, gesturing to the rest not to follow them. "Stay here. We'll go an' take a look." Crouching low, they made their way into the thickets.

A small bird whistled somewhere, but other than that the only sound the two mice heard was their own footpaws rustling through the ferns. After a while Luke straightened up. "Well, whatever it was, there's neither sight nor sound of it now, matey."

Vurg uncrouched and something bumped lightly against the back of his head. He turned cautiously. "Hoho, pears, a whole treeful of 'em!"

It was a pear tree, laden with fine ripe fruit.

Vurg picked one, squeezed it gently, nodded approvingly,

then took a huge bite. "Mmm shlumphh! Sweet'n'juicy, mate, wunnerful!"

Luke reached for a pear, grinning at his friend's juice-wetted face. "Ole greedyguts, are you eatin' that pear or takin' a bath in it?"

Fffffsssssst . . . Splack!

A thick piece of wood with a metal point at either end whipped out of nowhere and thudded deep into the tree trunk between them both. It was followed by a loud booming voice echoing out of the stillness of the trees.

"Seascum! Touch not my food. Go from this place or Werragoola will tear you limb from limb and devour you!"

Luke threw his pear to the ground. "Do as I say, Vurg. Drop your pear an' let's get back t'the crew. Don't argue!"

Vurg was not about to disagree. He dropped the half-eaten pear as if it were a poisonous reptile and followed Luke back the way they had come. When he figured they were both out of sight, Luke dropped down behind a fallen tree.

Vurg was still wide-eyed and trembling. "Did ye hear that voice, matey? It must've come from a beast ten times bigger'n a badger!"

"You lay low here 'til I get back. Give me your spear." Before Vurg had a chance to argue, Luke plucked the spear from his paws and was gone.

Bellying down, Luke crawled back to the pear tree. Then he lay still, checking the area keenly, eyes darting back and forth as he searched the trees for any sign of movement. Satisfied he was not being watched, Luke picked up his fallen pear and stuck it on the point of Vurg's spear. Acting speedily, he flung the spear, butt end first, into a thick bush, where the pear on the spearpoint remained clearly visible, sticking out of the leaves. Next Luke gave the pear tree a good shake, calling out aloud, "Hah! These must be the pears the cap'n tole us about!" Then he wriggled off into the shrubbery with his teeth clamped tight around the scimitar, and lay still, watching.

Suddenly another metal-tipped wooden club struck the pear from the speartip and a mad, booming voice howled angrily, "You did not heed my warning! Now Werragoola says you must die! Yakkahakkaheeeyhooooo!"

A wild, ragged figure hurtled across the tiny clearing and flung itself into the bush, undoubtedly hoping to come to grips with whoever was holding the spear. Luke was after it in a flash. The beast was immediately at a disadvantage, trapped with its bottom sticking out of the bush. The sturdy mouse dealt the target a tidy whack with the flat of his blade and shouted sternly, "Come out o' there, ye savage!"

The reply came back after an agonised gasp. "Haharr! Stabbed me from the rear, eh, seascum? You pirates are all the same. Just wait'll I get out of here!"

Luke gave the bottom another whack with his bladeflat. "Mayhap this'll help ye, Wellaguller, or whatever y'call yoreself. Here, have another taste o' my blade!" He laid on another stinging blow and the beast almost somersaulted out of the bush in a cloud of leaves and broken twigs.

"Owowowouch! Typical vermin pirate type, wot! Can't slay a chap without jolly well torturin' him t'death first. Oooh! My posterior's aflippin' flame, y'great lout!"

It was a hare, garbed ridiculously in rags, seashells and strands of vegetation, its face stained purple with berry juice. Luke watched it cautiously as he put up his sword.

"I'm no seascum. My name's Luke an' I'm a chieftain from far across the seas."

The hare stood up, rubbing his tail area ruefully. "Oh I see, and that gives you the blinkin' right to land up here an' whale the tar out of chaps' bottoms with your sword. Huh, prob'ly why you had to leave the place you came from—everybeast got fed up with you wallopin' all an' sundry 'round the nether regions with swords an' whatnot, so they banished you from the blinkin' land. Say then, scurvy cad, beaten up any other poor creatures t'day, wot wot? Speak up, sah."

Luke was astonished at the nerve of the hare. "Hold on a tick, flop-ears! First you go terrifyin' my crew with your howlin' an' wailin', then you try to kill me by flingin' those funny-lookin' spears of yours, an' then you got the brass neck to complain when you get caught at it. Just who d'ye think you are?"

Puffing out his narrow chest, the hare clapped a paw to his stomach and bowed curtly. "Who do I think I am, sah? I am smoke on the wind, a creature of many resources! To the ver-

min inhabiting this island I am Werragoola the purple-faced
terror. In a far more elegant life than this I was known as
Beauclair Fethringsol Cosfortingham. Fondly referred to as
just Beau by m'family, friends an' dear old nanny, wot!"

Vurg stole cautiously up, brandishing a stick. "Ah, there
y'are, Luke. But who's this creature?"

Luke made the introductions. "This is the one who was
doin' all the shoutin' an' throwin' weapons at us. Vurg, meet
Beau."

The hare regarded Vurg's outstretched paw suspiciously.
"Vurg, eh? Sounds a right murderous vermin name if ever I
heard one. Chap looks shifty, too. D'y'know, I'm not totally
convinced that you two aren't Sea Rogues."

Luke sighed impatiently. "Well we're not standin' 'round
all day just to convince ye. Come on, Vurg, let's round up the
crew an' get back aboard the ship. We're wastin' time here."

They had only gone a few paces when Beau leaped in front
of them with a broad grin pasted on his purpled features.

"You're mice, silly old me, wot? Mice aren't seascum,
they're good chaps like m'self. Have y'really got a ship,
Admiral Luke? Are y'sailin' away from this confounded isle?
Take me with you, sirs, I beg of you. I'll even provision your
vessel with the food I grow here. You won't be sorry. Old
salty Beau they call me on shipboard, can turn m'paw to anythin' nautical. Hoist me mains'l, loose those anchors, take a
turn round the riggin' an' boggle me bilges, wot wot! I can
spout that sort o' rot all season . . ."

Luke could not help smiling at the lanky excited creature.
"Keep that up, Beau, an' we'll make ye swim behind the ship
to give us a bit o' peace. You say you've got provisions?"

"Provisions, grub, rations, scoff, vittles, tucker, you name
it, Luke m'mouse, an' I've got it!"

Luke was forced to place a paw across Beau's mouth.
"Enough, mate. You can sail with us, but on two conditions.
Cut the cackle an' show us to the provisions!'

22

The crew of the *Sayna* spent the rest of the afternoon gathering produce which Beau had grown. They carried pears, apples, wild grapes, mushrooms, carrots and all manner of fresh food back to the ship. Luke was wondering whether he would regret his decision, because the hare never once stopped chattering.

"Heave ho, me hearties, that's the ticket, wot wot! I say there, what a jolly little ship, absolutely tiptop! Far nicer than the great red monstrosity that delivered me here, by the left, I should say so!"

They were filling pails from a lively trickle of fresh water running down the cliff face to the shore. Forming a chain, the crew passed it aboard, where it was emptied into the casks to top up the *Sayna*'s water supply. Beau was chattering on as he shoved another pail beneath the running water.

"Oh yes, this's the stuff t'put fur on y'tail, wot! Good fresh water, sweet an' clean, drink it m'self, y'know, mornin' noon an' night. Feel those muscles, see how my eyes sparkle, have y'ever seen teeth as white as mine, wot!"

Luke pulled him to one side. "Beau, did you say a great red ship brought you here?"

"Indeed it did, sah, filthy great thing, name o' the *Goreleech*."

Luke's paw tightened like a vice over Beau's. "Tell me everything you know about the red ship!"

Beau rubbed his paw and looked quizzically at Luke. "Of course, old chap, no need to crush a fellow's paw. It all started some seasons ago when yours truly got the jolly old urge to go seafarin'. Shipped out on a small merchant craft, tradin' round the coast, y'know. Good crew, couple o' shrews, some hedgehogs an' a mouse or two. We were doin' quite well, until one night our ship was lyin' at anchor an' we were all in our hammocks snorin'. Well, the *Goreleech* sailed up an' took us by surprise, rammed our little boat with its great iron spike, sunk us like a stone, wot.

Sea Rogues everywhere, slew most of the crew, took the remainder captive. I'll never forget the captain of the red ship, a stoat, Vilu Daskar, cruel murderin' villain! I spent two seasons chained to an oar in the red ship's middle decks, starved, whipped, kicked an' beaten. Still got the scars if y'd like to see 'em. I was the only beast out of my old crew left alive after a while, then I fell sick, too weak'n'thin to be of further use at the oar. Vilu Daskar had me thrown overboard. Prob'ly thought I was about t'die, so the fish an' the tides could finish me. Hah! But I came off stern stock. My old nanny could have told him that I was a Cosfortingham, an' we don't die too easily, y'know. I was washed up here an' this has been my home ever since. Island's full o' vermin, though, searats an' such, deserters, runaways an' some who've been marooned—evil lot. The rogues would've skinned an' scoffed me, but I've spent my seasons here livin' in secret, growin' my own tucker an' fightin' 'em from the shadows'n'tree cover. That's when I became Werragoola Purpleface, regular one-hare army, wot!"

Luke smiled in admiration at the brave hare. "You did well, Beau. Tell me, have you ever sighted Vilu Daskar's vessel again?"

"Rather. Passed here three moons ago, put in for water an'

sailed off bound south. I hid on the clifftops an' watched the red ship come an' go. D'you know, your ship's the first decent craft with honest crew I've ever seen put in here. Jolly lucky for me I'd say, wot wot!"

Screeching war cries cut the conversation short, and Beau hurled himself at Luke, knocking him to one side. A rough, sharp spear buried itself in the sand where Luke had stood a moment before. Down the steps in the cliff face, a huge mob of ragged vermin were dashing towards the *Sayna*'s crew.

The Warrior mouse acted swiftly. Grabbing the spear, he ran forward, shaking it to feel the balance. From halfway between the tideline and the stairs he made a mighty throw. A searat, slightly ahead of the rest, took the spear through his middle and toppled over screaming. Those behind could not stop their mad charge and stumbled over the slain rat. Luke's roar snapped the crew out of their shock.

"Back to the ship at the double!"

The vermin who had tripped on their fallen comrade did not have far to fall. They sprawled in the sand momentarily, then scrambled up and gave chase after the mice.

Weapons drawn, Luke, Vurg and Beau stood in the shallows, hurrying the crew past them. "Get aboard quick, mates, loose all sails an' up anchor!"

Cordle, Denno and Dulam helped the first few over the side and set to, turning the windlass to haul up the anchor.

Wild with their desire to capture a ship, vermin thundered recklessly into the water. Luke swung back and forth with his sword, slaying and wounding wherever he struck. Vurg hit out with his spear and Beau went at them, a club in each paw. "Yaaah! Back, back, ye scum!"

Other vermin were coming in from both sides now, to cut the trio off from their vessel. Aboard the *Sayna*, Coll and some others went to work. Hanging over the stern, they whizzed arrows and slingstones at the mob in the shallows. It was Cardo who saved the day, though. Grabbing an axe, he chopped the rear anchor free of its rope, then, heaving until he had pulled a fair length from the windlass, the resourceful mouse cast the thick line into the sea. "Grab ahold, mates, we'll haul ye aboard!"

Luke held off the closest foes whilst Beau seized the rope and knotted it into a wide loop, which he threw over Vurg and Luke with one wide cast, then ducked inside to join them. Bound together within the noose of anchor rope, they struck out at the surrounding attackers, with Vurg bellowing back to the ship, "Heave away, mates, fast as y'like!"

Billowing sails caught the wind, whipping the *Sayna* out to sea. Every available crewmouse bent his back at the windlass spokes, making it fly round. Luke smashed a spearhead with a swipe of his swordblade, but before he could strike at its owner, his footpaws left the seabed and he was swept away backwards with Vurg and Beau pressed either side of him. Even spraying seawater sloshing at his mouth could not silence the hare.

"Fare thee well, vermin, glub glub! G'bye, chaps, *gluggle*!"

With the *Sayna*'s outward momentum and the windlass winding them in, they soon outdistanced the maddened vermin. Vurg felt his back bump hard against the ship's side as Beau hooted, "Steady on, chaps, *glub*! We ain't the blinkin' enemy. *Gluggle ug*! D'ye mind lettin' us live a trifle longer! Pshaw! This seawater tastes jolly foul, wot!"

Willing paws pulled them aboard, and Luke wriggled free of the rope. They stood astern, watching the island recede as the enraged mob fought among themselves in the shallows. Luke put aside his blade and took off his sopping tunic.

"How did we do, Cardo? Everybeast safe?"

"Aye, they're all alive, mate, one or two wounds. I took a slingstone right across the paw meself!"

Vurg inspected the cut on his friend's paw. "Nasty! Is that the paw you use t'cook with?"

Cardo smiled cheerfully. "No."

Vurg gave a disappointed sigh. "Wot a pity!"

The crew laughed heartily at the indignant Cardo.

Beau looked from one to another, unable to fathom the joke. "What's so funny? Is the blighter an awful cook?"

This caused further laughter and more indignation from Cardo. "Take no notice of 'em, Beau. They're all lousy cooks. You'll be sorry you signed aboard this ship, mate, 'specially when y'taste the grub. It's dreadful. Even the fishes throw the scraps back aboard!"

Immediately the hare cast off his raggy garb and began wrapping a length of canvas around his waist like an apron. "Lucky you found me then, chaps. Aboard my old ship I was voted the choicest chef to be chosen from all chief chefs!"

Coll nudged the hare. "Bet you couldn't say that again?"

Beau dismissed him with an airy twiddle of both ears. "Couldn't I though, hah? I was the cheese chosen chief of all choosers, no, wait a tick, I was choked by a chosen chief chook, no, that ain't right . . ."

Luke interrupted him. "If y'can cook, then stow the blather an' get t'the galley. Cardo, you can be Beau's assistant. Denno, attend the wounded, you were always good at healin'. Coll, you take the tiller. Keep that westerin' sun at your right shoulder—we're followin' the red ship south. The rest of you trim the sails an' see she moves along steady!"

Beau turned out to be an excellent cook. That night he served the crew of the *Sayna* a meal to gladden their hearts. Being a hare, he cooked victuals in generous portions, so there was more than enough for all.

"Right ho, I know this'll be wasted on you famine-faced chaps, but here's tonight's menu, wot. Starters, cheese an' onion turnovers, with my own flaky pastry, followed by shrimp an' mushroom bake in a parsley an' turnip sauce. For afters there's a pear an' plum pudden. To drink, mint an' dandelion tea or some rather good cider I found in your ship's stores. Hold hard a moment there, don't touch a bally crumb till I've said grace, you savages!"

Luke lowered his eyes, admonishing the crew. "He's right. No need to get sloppy an' bad-mannered 'cos we're not at home. Carry on, Beau."

The hare intoned the grace at tremendous speed.

"Fate'n'fortunes smile on us,
An' of this crew take care,
But let no greedy robber try,
To guzzle up my share!"

Before anybeast could raise an eye or pick up a spoon, the hare was tucking in as if there were no tomorrow.

Vurg passed the turnovers to Luke. "Our cook can certainly shift the vittles, mate!"

Luke sniffed the hot turnovers appreciatively. "Beau can do wot he likes, long as he keeps servin' up meals as good as this 'un!"

"Aye. Better put some aside for Cordle—he's on tiller watch."

The *Sayna* ploughed steadily south on fair seas under a waning moon. Weary after the day's exertions her crew lay down to rest, though food seemed to have the opposite effect on the garrulous cook. Beau quoted endless rhymes, danced and sang ceaselessly, now that he was not alone but in the company of friends. Luke sent him on deck to guard the tiller, and he did a double watch, serenading the sea and the night skies. Dulam wadded his cloak about both ears, complaining bitterly. "A good cook he may be, but a tuneful singer he ain't. Sounds like somebeast attackin' a plank wid a rusty saw out there. Hoi, give yore gob a rest, will ye, Beau!"

But insults and pleas had no effect on the off-key warbler.

"Oooooh flunky dee an' a rum tumtum,
The good ship *Flinkydogg*,
Set sail with a crew o' fishes,
An' fat ole cap'n frog.

Oooooh doodle dey make way make way,
The frog said to the fishes,
'All fins on deck an' use yore tails,
To wash these dirty dishes!'

Oooooh skiddle deedoo, a fig for you,
The fishcrew boldly cried,
'Just chuck 'em in the ocean,
They'll be washed up by the tide!'

'Tis mutiny oh woe is me,
The frog did croak so sad,
'If I'd a crew o' boiler crabs,
They'd not be'ave so bad!'

'Twas after dark, a passin' shark,
Heard what was goin' on,
So for his tea, impartially,
He ate up everyone.

Oooooh goodness me hoho heehee,
The shark smiled, 'Lackaday,
I can't abide a feckless frog,
Nor fish who won't obey!'"

Beau neatly dodged an apple core flung at him from the cabin. His ears stood up indignantly. "Rotten bounders, fancy chuckin' missiles at a chap who's doin' his level best to sing y'to sleep, ungrateful cads!"

He was answered by an irate bellow. "Y'great lanky lollop-eared breezebarrel. Shuttup!"

Beau lay back on the deck, tending the tiller with a long footpaw.

"A wink's as good as a nod t'me, old lad. If y'don't appreciate good music then I'll withdraw the privilege of my melodious meanderings. But I'll finish this little ditty first. Stay calm, there's only another forty-six verses to go."

23

In the following weeks the *Sayna* covered many sea leagues. They were well out of the cold latitudes and the weather became almost tropical, with constant sunshine beating down out of clear blue skies. But Luke was getting edgy and frustrated. There had been no sign of the red ship, which could be anywhere in the trackless wastes of ocean they were searching. Between them, he and Denno began drawing up a chart, from the northern shores to the isle where Beau had lived and onward. Luke was disappointed that there were no other landfalls to act as route markers.

"We're sailin' blind, mate. At least if we sighted land there might be some news of the red ship, but all we've seen for ages now is nothing but sea on every horizon."

Denno put aside his quill pen, nodding agreement. "Aye, we could do with takin' on some fresh water, too, an' the supplies are runnin' low. That hare must think his one job in life is dishin' up mountains o' vittles to the crew. Lookit the stomach I've put on!"

Luke, however, was not about to criticise his cook. "You leave ole Beau out o' this, Denno. That hare can do no wrong as far as I'm concerned, mate. I never tasted such wonderful food in all my seasons."

But Denno's words proved prophetic. It was on the afternoon of the following day that Vurg scraped bottom of one water cask with the dipper.

"If'n we don't sight land soon then I reckon we're in trouble, matey. Water's all but finished!"

Beau emerged from his galley swinging a ladle. "No water? Well, we'll have t'make do with cider an' whatnot. Cardo, what's the jolly old position on drinks other than water? You're my assistant seacook."

There was a rattling and scuttling from the galley, then Cardo popped a mournful face around the door. "Down t'the dregs, Beau, down t'the very dregs!"

The irrepressible Beau began climbing the rope ladder of the center mast. "Well, no use standin' 'round with a face like a squashed apple, comrade o' mine. Just have t'scan the bloomin' horizon for land, wot wot!"

Cardo cast a withering glance up at Beau. "Oh, just like that?"

The hare was now clinging to the mainmast top, one paw shading his eyes as he gazed eagerly all around. "Well of course just like that, y'silly fat mouse. Hello there, chaps, is that a smudge way out to the southwest? Land ho! Or at least I'll bet it's somethin' jolly close to land. Hah, well done that hare! Mentioned in dispatches, maybe jot down a line o' praise or two in the ship's log at the very least!"

Luke shoved Denno playfully. "Y'see, matey, told you I wouldn't have a word said against ole Beau! Cordle, set a course sou'west. If that's land, we might make it before tomorrow mornin'."

Tacking against the prevailing breezes, the *Sayna* lay off the island three hours before dawn. A huge cone, of what Luke took to be an extinct volcano, reared dark and forbidding against the night sky. Though it was difficult to see much in the darkness, Beau noted that there were forests of trees growing on the slopes and a shoreline of kinds. Luke spoke his thoughts to the hare as he sized up the situation.

"We'd best stay offshore until 'tis light—there might be

reefs 'twixt here an' the beach. Don't see any signs o' life ashore, but we'd best not chance anythin' until daylight. You go an' get a bit o' shuteye with the crew, Beau, I'll call ye when 'tis light."

"Wouldn't think of it, old lad. You and I shall stand watch together, 'til the ravenwinged shades of night are flown and earth is reborn in fiery sunlight to day!"

Luke leaned on the taffrail, eyes searching the shoreline. "Well said, Beau, very poetic, mate."

The talkative hare perked up. "Thank ye kindly, Luke. I'm rather glad you appreciate poetry. Here's a modest effort I composed m'self, to while away the hours back on my island. 'A mole and a duck went strolling one day—'"

Luke's strong paws clamped round Beau's jaws, holding his mouth tight shut. "Either be quiet or go t'sleep. If you don't I'll put ye to sleep with a belayin' pin!"

As dawn broke Luke roused the crew, and they sailed cautiously in towards the shore. Now the island could be viewed clearly. The beach was dark bluey-black volcanic sand. A thin plume of white smoke drifted lazily from the top of the rock cone which dominated the place, denoting that the volcano was not altogether extinct. Purple and scarlet flowers bloomed thick in the foothills, and many of the trees had huge spear-shaped leaves. It was an exotic scene, though the total silence made it rather sinister. As Vurg watched the *Sayna*'s prow nose into the sandy shallows, he conveyed his misgivings to Luke.

"I'm gettin' that same feelin' I had last time we came to an island—I don't like it, matey. Too quiet for a place that looks so fertile. There's got to be some sort o' creatures livin' here!"

Luke pointed to the shore. "You're right, Vurg. See there? Slightly above the tideline? What d'you make o' that?"

Beau elbowed his way to the prow. "A great pile o' fruit! The creatures must be jolly friendly leavin' a gift like that for us."

Luke frowned. "Too friendly, perhaps. Let's not be too hasty. There's something about this little offering that doesn't ring true."

But Beau was already leaping the side. "C'mon, you chaps! I'll be food taster. My stomach's as steady as a jolly old rock, wot wot."

Before Luke could stop them, most of the crew had followed the hare, bounding overboard into the shallows and splashing ashore towards the heap of luscious fruit piled on the beach. Vurg chuckled as the hare picked a grape, tossed it and caught it deftly in his mouth. He waited a few seconds and then waved a large bunch of wild grapes at the ship. "Still standin', me hearties. Delicious! C'mon, everyone, tuck in!"

Luke and Vurg watched as they all pounced hungrily on the mysterious gift. "Ahoy, Beau," called Vurg. "Bring some back for us."

"Right y'are, Vurg. I say, chuck the empty casks overboard an' we'll see if we can find a stream to fill 'em from."

Being the only two left on board, Vurg and Luke rolled all the casks out and tipped them over the side. Vurg tied the tiller in position so the ship would not drift.

"I was wrong, Luke. This island seems quite friendly now. P'raps Beau was right, an' whoever left the fruit out doesn't mean us any harm. Mayhap they'll show themselves before the day's out."

A stream of freshwater actually flowed across the shore, not far from the heap of fruit. Dulam and Cardo filled the casks and got them back to the ship. Luke rigged a rope through the mainsail's top block, and between them he and Vurg hoisted the casks of water aboard. Dulam and Cardo waded back to join their friends ashore.

Luke called after them. "Make the most of it. Tell the crew I want them back on deck by sunset. We sail at first tide tomorrow."

Luke was busy stowing the casks in the galley when Vurg shouted urgently from out on deck. "Onshore, mate. Come an' see!" He left what he was doing and hurried out.

Some of the crew were lying down amid the fruit, some were sitting aimlessly nearby, whilst one or two of the remainder were staggering oddly about. All appeared to have slack grins on their faces. Luke yelled, "Ahoy, Coll, Dulam, Beau, what's the matter, mates?"

Dulam collapsed on the sand, Coll fell on top of him, only
Beau remained standing. The hare gave a faint giggle, tried to
wave, then his legs gave out and he sat down awkwardly,
staring at the ship, smiling foolishly.

Luke smote the taffrail. "That fruit, I should've known it.
C'mon, Vurg!"

But Vurg was pointing to where the foothills met the shore.
"Wait, those bushes are movin'!"

Halfway over the side, Luke checked himself. He could
scarce believe his eyes. The entire hillside had come to life,
literally hundreds of bushes were moving across the shore in
a massive screen of foliage. On instinct he leaped back
aboard and dragged Vurg down flat.

A veritable hail of missiles struck the boat: arrows,
javelins, spears and stones. Drums began pounding aloud and
an eerie wailing rose from the bushes, followed by another
salvo of missiles. Luke grabbed a long boathook.

"Get your spear, Vurg. Pole her off into deeper water."

Scurrying forward, they pushed the vessel into the ebb
tide, grunting with exertion as they pressed hard against their
poles. An arrow thwacked into Vurg's shoulder, and Luke
ignored a deep javelin graze across his cheek.

"Push, Vurg, let's give it all we've got, mate!"

The *Sayna*'s keel scraped free of the sand. Luke dashed
recklessly astern and slashed the rope which held the tiller
rigid. Wheeling sideways, the *Sayna* caught the tide. Luke
flattened himself as another rain of death peppered the ship,
then she was bow out, sailing free. Arrows, sticking up from
the deck timbers as if from a pincushion, snapped against
Luke's footpaws as he dashed back to Vurg's side.

Wincing, the brave mouse tugged the shaft from his shoulder. "Lucky that arrow's flight was near spent an' my tunic's
a good thick 'un. I'm not bad hurt, Luke, what about you?"

Luke pawed blood from the cut on his cheek. "Only a
scratch, mate, I'll live. Whoever they are, 'tis plain they can't
shoot straight. Great seasons, look!"

Vurg stared in amazement at the diminishing shoreline.
Silent and deserted the beach lay, as if nobeast had ever been
there. All that remained was a pile of squashed fruit. Vurg
turned in bewilderment to his friend. "Where've they gone?

Denno, Cordle, Beau, the whole crew are gone. What do we do now?"

Grim faced, Luke gazed at the shoreline, his warrior blood pounding furiously as he strove to control himself. "Let's make sail, it'll look as if we're runnin' away. We'll wait 'til dark, Vurg, then we'll go back an' get 'em!"

Drums pounded everywhere. At first, Cardo thought they were inside his skull, causing the massive headache which woke him. However, he saw that they were all too real when he opened his eyes. It was a scene that turned his blood to ice water, though strangely, everything was wrong side up. Like the rest of his crewmates, he had been bound tight and slung lengthways on a stout pole, so that his head hung down. The poles had been hoisted up on ropes, close to the ceiling of a big cave, with a fire burning at its center. Rock ledges had been carved around the cave walls in tiers, and these were crowded with hundreds of small fierce ratlike rodents, unlike any Cardo had ever seen. They were covered with intricate patterns of red, orange and white dyes, with clattering seashells affixed to ears, paws and tails.

At the rear of the cave were two massive drums, atop of which forty or fifty of the rodents performed a stamping dance. The sound boomed and banged relentlessly, increased fourfold as it echoed around the cave's interior. Crouching by the fire was a figure far larger than the rest, obviously a female weasel, draped from ears to tail with long necklaces and bracelets made from painted crab claws. Her face was daubed thick with white clay, black charcoal lines accentuating the features.

Beau was hanging alongside Cardo. He opened his eyes, looked around, then squinched his ears flat peevishly and called downward to the rodents, "Put a flippin' bung in it, you chaps, wot! Those drums are makin' my old noggin throb dreadfully. I say there, you! Yes you, marm, tell these blighters t'desist. Hmph! Rank bad manners t'go thumpin' drums like that when a body's feelin' out o' sorts. Now pack it jolly well in!"

As if by magic complete silence fell. The remainder of the crew had awakened, and Beau winked at them knowingly.

"Voice of command an' discipline, that's the thing t'give the blinkin' troops, wot wot!"

The weasel sprang upright. Grabbing a long wand ornamented with dried sea urchins, she shook it, pointing first at the captives, then to somewhere at the back of the cave between the two drums, and finally making a long sweeping gesture at the crammed masses of rodents.

"Rabbatooma! Slarisssssssss! Ya Aggoreema!"

This seemed to drive the rodents into a frenzy. They laughed savagely, howling back at their leader, "Ya Marrahagga! Slarisssssssss! Ko, Slarisssssssss!"

Coll strained his head over towards Beau. "Huh, 'ope you ain't said the wrong thing, mate."

The hare was quite indignant. "Wrong thing, laddie? Me? I should say not. Tact an' diplomacy are the pawmark of us Cosfortinghams. Hang on a tick, I'll have a word with that vermin lady, see what the position is as regards loosin' us from our bonds, wot. Now then, my good villainess, d'you think y'could spare a few of those runty types to unbind me'n'my stalwart comrades? Sort of save us hangin' around, pardon the pun."

Ignoring the hare's request, the weasel crouched and began making mysterious weaving patterns upon the cave floor with her wand. The small ratlike creatures pointed at the captives and chanted aloud, "Ko Slarisssssss Rabbatooma! Slarissssss eeeeeeyoh!"

Denno shook a droplet of perspiration from his nosetip. "Phew! I'm roasted!"

Dulam closed his eyes, as if trying to block out his thoughts. "Quiet, mate. That could be a bad choice o' words. They might be flesh eaters."

Now the rodents who had been dancing on the drumheads deserted their posts, swiftly scrambling onto the ledges alongside the rest. Casting something into the fire, the weasel caused the flames to burn green. Then she went to the drums and began tapping her wand alternately against the side of each one, calling out in a sibilant voice, "Slarisssssss Slarissssssss Slarissssssssssssss!"

Ever the optimist, Beau suggested brightly, "D'y'know, I'm not familiar with their lingo, but I'll wager Slariss is some sort o' greeting, like how d'ye do, or good evenin', chaps. P'raps I'd better return the compliment, show some manners, wot. I say, marm, Slariss t'you too. Slarissssssssssss. Howzat?"

From a hidden opening behind the two drums Slariss emerged.

Beau's mouth went suddenly dry with fear—even he was not ready for this. The snake's head was bright green and huge. It slid slowly out in a seemingly never-ending ripple of sleek coils. As if searching, its flickering tongue quested in and out restlessly, eyes glittering in the firelight, twin diamonds of primitive evil. Lazily the green and black chevroned coils formed into several loops, one atop the other, with the flat reptilian head resting at their peak. Standing at the other side of the fire, the weasel poked the tip of her long wand in the flames until it was glowing. Not one creature in the cave made a sound or moved a muscle. The snake was hunting, seeking a victim. The crew hung motionless, stiff with terror. Beau was not aware of the glowing wand's end approaching behind his head. Suddenly the weasel touched it against the tip of his long right ear.

"Yowchowoop!" He shook his head.

"Slarissssss!"

Not a paw's length away the snake swayed its head, mouth open, fangs bared dangerously, hissing its challenge. The hare found himself staring into the reptile's eyes. Frozen with nameless dread, he hung there helpless.

24

The night was humid, still warm from the day's sun. The *Sayna* came back to the island on the floodtide, showing no sail. Luke and Vurg dropped anchor offshore.

Vurg was muttering to himself as they went over the side. "Can't tell if'n anybeast's watchin' us. I 'ope none spotted us comin' in. Suppose they did, though? Mebbe one of us should've stayed behind as guard on board."

Luke chuckled dryly. "I thought o' that meself, mate, but it'll take the two of us to rescue our crew. Besides, if we get caught, too, then what use is a ship to us? Stow your chunnerin', Vurg, y'gettin' to sound more like an ole mousewife every day."

They stole up the deserted beach, using any rocks they found as cover. Closer to the foothills, Vurg held up a paw. "Sssh, lissen, can you hear anythin'?"

Luke stood quite still and listened closely. "Thought it was the waves at first, but it sounds like some sort o' chant—drums, too. Aye, that's the sound o' drums!"

Vurg pointed to the foothills, slightly to the right of them. "Comin' from there, matey, I'm sure 'tis!"

Sword and spear at the ready, they pressed on into the foliage stretching uphill before them. The sounds of drums and chanting grew louder, closer. Luke whispered, "Stay there, mate. I'll go an' take a peek."

The cave entrance was a short winding tunnel. Luke sized up the lie of the land, then beckoned to Vurg. They crouched behind a bush at one side of the entrance whilst Luke explained his plan.

"See that round boulder, just uphill there? D'you reckon we could shift it between us, Vurg?"

"Aye, at least we'll give it a try, mate!"

"Good, but first we need to dig a bit of a hole here."

"Where, right here in the entrance to the tunnel?"

"That's right. Ground's pretty soft, we'll use our weapons."

Between them they scraped out a shallow depression in the tunnel's mouth. Luke searched about until he found a size-able chunk of rock, which he placed to one side of the hole, tamping it down firmly.

"Right, now let's move that boulder."

It was a large round stone, but it moved slowly when Luke set his back against it and Vurg used his spearbutt as a lever. Luke fought for control as they rolled it down towards the entrance.

"Whoa, go easy now, mate, easy does it, just a touch more. There, that should do it!"

The boulder was checked from rolling into the hole at the cave entrance by the rock Luke had placed there, which now served as a wedge to hold the boulder back.

Luke drew his sword, then paused. "Those drums've stopped. Come on, somethin' must be goin' on in there. Be careful not t'make any noise, matey."

The friends crept through the tunnel and, keeping to the shadowed walls, entered the main cave, hardly able to believe their eyes at what they saw. Sinister green firelight flickered over the massed faces of the rodents packed on the ledges, all staring fascinated at one thing. The great snake! The reptile's thick neck was quivering as, rearing back and hissing coldly, it prepared to strike at Beau.

Luke sprang into immediate action. Grabbing Vurg's

spear, he hopskipped forward a pace and hurled the hefty
weapon with all the force he could muster.

Speechless with horror, Beau saw the reptile's mouth open
wide, revealing sharp deadly fangs as it struck forward at his
unprotected face. Then, like a lightning bolt, the spear went
smashing into the gaping mouth, driving half its length out
through the back of the neck column. Thrashing wildly in its
death throes, the snake fell back to the floor, its powerful
body flailing like an immense bullwhip, battering rodents
from the lower ledges and scattering the fire into a cascade of
flying sparks and embers.

The weasel scarce had time to turn before Luke was upon
her, ramming the vermin leader flat against the rock wall, his
swordblade at her throat. "One move an' yore dead meat,
scum!" the Warrior roared into her painted face.

Though the weasel could not understand Luke's language,
the message was clear. The only part of her which moved was
her throat, as she gulped against the swordblade.

"'Tis Luke, mates. We're saved!"

A ragged cheer rang out from the crew. Below them the
dead snake was still causing great damage. Rodents were
flung high, smashed against the cave walls, crushed and
beaten senseless by the writhing coils of the monster. It
seemed like an eternity before the reptile's body went limp
and still. However, a great number of the rodents had escaped
serious injury, huddling together on the highest cave ledges.
Several of them now grabbed weapons and advanced on
Luke and Vurg, screeching savagely.

"Marrahagga lagor Rabbatooma! Lagor!"

Vurg swiftly freed his spear from the snake's carcass and
joined Luke, pressing his spearpoint at the weasel's heart.
Luke kept the sword at her throat as he growled, "Tell 'em to
back off an' cut my crew loose!" He nodded to the bound figures hanging on their poles from the cave ceiling. "My crew.
Cut 'em down afore I cut you down. Now!"

The weasel raised a paw slowly and pointed at the crew.
"Rabbatooma, lagor, Ko!"

One rodent, obviously some kind of minor chieftain, bowed
curtly to the weasel. "Ya Marrahagga!" Turning sullenly to the
rest he indicated the prisoners. "Lagor Rabbatooma."

Beau had recovered from his shock and rediscovered speech.

"I should jolly well say so, you foul little fiends. You heard him. Let us Rabbatoomas go, this very instant!"

The rodents obeyed. Swinging out on ropes, they perched on the poles and sawed through the crews' bonds with their daggers. With shouts of relief and pain, Beau and the *Sayna*'s crewmice fell to the dusty cave floor, where they lay groaning.

Cardo whimpered as he tried to rise. "Paws've gone numb with bein' tied tight for so long!"

Luke's reply was brusque. "We can't linger here, mates. Crawl out on your bellies, move yourselves. That's an order!"

Luke and Vurg were still menacing the weasel as the crew hauled themselves out in a sorry complaining bunch.

"Ow ow, I got pins'n'needles in all me paws!"

"My pore head's achin' fit to split, mate!"

"Look, that rodent slashed m'tail when he cut the ropes!"

"Huh, you should complain, my backfur's all scorched from hangin' over that blazin' fire!"

Luke kicked the last one's tail lightly. "Mebbe next time you'll wait my orders afore dashin' ashore to stuff drugged fruit down yore faces!"

When the crew were gone, Luke spun the weasel round and held the blade across her throat from behind.

"Keep an eye on those savages, Vurg. Stick 'em if'n they get too close. Right, weasel, we're backin' out of here nice'n'easy. Don't move or yore a dead 'un!"

As they retreated, the rodents followed them, crying, "Lagor Marrahagga!"

Luke was beginning to understand what they said. "Don't fret, buckoes, we'll let go of yore Marrahagga as soon as we're out o' this stinkin' place. Now back off!"

They negotiated the short winding tunnel. Waiting outside, the crew were massaging life back into numbed paws. Luke guided the weasel round the shallow pit they had dug, and the rodents had just reached its edge when he nodded to Vurg. "Knock that wedge aside, sharpish!"

Vurg hit the piece of rock a sharp tap with his spearbutt, moving it aside. The boulder rolled forward half a turn and landed in the shallow hole with a bump. It blocked the tunnel

entrance off completely and muffled the squeaks of rage
sounding from behind it.

Vurg leaned on his spear, grinning. "A good tight fit, I'd
say, mate!"

Luke ordered his crew to get back aboard the *Sayna*, whilst
he and Vurg took the weasel and forced her to sit next to the
pile of squashed fruit. With his swordpoint Luke drew a picture of the *Goreleech* in the sand, then he transferred the
point back to the weasel's throat.

"Marrahagga see red ship sail by here? Red ship, big one?"

The weasel watched Luke's face as he repeated the question several times over. Carefully she drew three circles in the
sand, with squiggly lines radiating from them and an arrow
pointing south. Whilst Vurg squinted at the drawing, the
weasel tapped Luke's sketch of the ship thrice.

Luke understood. "Three suns, that's three days," he
explained to his bemused friend. "She says the red ship sailed
by here three days back, bound south."

Vurg dusted his paws off in a businesslike manner. "That
means we ain't far behind her, mate. Better get under way.
What do we do about this 'un, Luke?"

The weasel looked unhappily at the Warrior. Touching the
swordblade with a paw, she tried to shake her head. A mischievous smile crept over Luke's face, and he thrust a big
squashed plum at the weasel's mouth. "Eat!" She shut her
lips tight in revulsion. Luke swung his blade aloft as if to slay
her with one blow. "Marrahagga eat! Eat!"

The weasel gobbled the fruit with great alacrity.

Vurg giggled like a mousebabe, and selected a bruised
pear. "Cummon, Marryhaggit, try some more o' yore own
medicine!"

The weasel was forced to down two more plums and a
peach. She sat unhappily, juice dribbling down her chin.

Vurg turned to Luke, full of mock sympathy. "Dearie me,
she don't look too 'appy, mate. D'ye think she's still hungry?"

Luke passed the weasel a half-eaten apple that one of his
crew had sampled earlier on. "Oh, I wouldn't worry about ole
Marrahagga, mate, she'll cheer up soon. Come on, let's get
goin'."

When they looked back, the weasel had picked up a piece

of fruit and was about to hurl it at them. She swayed, dropped the fruit and sat down with a bump, a silly grin plastered on her painted face.

Vurg waved to her. "G'bye, ole Marryhaggit, 'tis nice to see we're leavin' you happy. I can't abide sad farewells!"

Luke waved too. "Aye, an' take care of that headache you'll have tomorrow!"

As the *Sayna* left the island in her wake the crew sat sipping hot tea of a herbal remedy brewed by Denno. Cardo, voted spokesmouse by his crewmates, addressed the Warrior.

"Luke, we're sorry we raced ashore an' ate that fruit. 'Twas silly of us. But we'd like to offer a hearty vote of thanks to you for savin' our lives. Yore a true warrior!"

Luke held up his paws to silence the cheers. "Aye, I saved you because I was able to, mates. Pity I wasn't there when the red ship hit the northlands shore. Every night an' day I think of my son Martin back there, growin' up without a mother to care for him, nor a father, with me off here chasin' the red ship. But we'll catch her, I swear we will. An' I'll make the name Vilu Daskar just a dirty memory in the minds of honest beasts!"

The crew went off to their sleeping places as the ship sailed south in the soft warm night, each with their own memories of family lost or left behind. Luke stood in the prow, keeping watch, lost in thoughts of Martin's small figure on the strand, waving his father's old battlesword. He stared forlornly at the gentle bow wave dispersing into the calm dark sea.

"Someday I'll come back and find you waiting for me, son."

25

On an island many leagues to the south, black smoke billowed above the crackling flames of what had once been a peaceful community of squirrels. Vermin, armed to the fangs, roamed in bands through the forestlands, slaying anybeast who dared to oppose them. Screams rent the air, whips cracked as pitiless rogues rounded up those left alive. Bound neck and paw into a straggling line, the bewildered captives were dragged out of the sheltering trees, into the dunes above the tideline. Akkla, the ferret mate, sniggered evilly, watching the prisoners' horror as they glimpsed their home to be: the red ship *Goreleech*, riding at anchor in the sea offshore.

"Move yerselves, me beauties, we'll soon find yer a snug liddle berth aboard the pretty red boat!"

Vilu Daskar sat on the beach, chin on the bone handle of his scimitar, pensively watching whilst Parug, his bosun, forced the terrified squirrels to kneel and bow their heads before the master of the red ship. Vilu stayed silent until the pitiful heap of provisions and plunder was piled in front of him. Lazily the stoat's eyes flicked over the crewbeasts standing around the pile.

"Is this the best you could do?"

One, a burly weasel called Rippjaw, shrugged. "Dat's all we be findin', cap'n!"

Vilu stood slowly, his eyes fixed on a necklace of yellow beads, which Rippjaw sported about his neck.

"So, where did you get that trinket, my illiterate friend?"

Rippjaw glanced down at the necklace with his good eye. "Oh, diss. I take 'im offa deadbeast, cap'n."

Vilu's scimitar made a noise like an angry wasp as he slew the weasel with one powerful stroke of the sharp blade. With a look of bored disdain, he flicked the necklace from Rippjaw's severed neck onto the pile.

"Must I keep reminding you addlebrained fools that all loot belongs to me? You do not steal from Vilu Daskar." He turned to the prisoners, as if noticing them for the first time. "Hmm, you're a pretty wretched lot. No mind, though, you'll soon learn to pull an oar—either that or die. Well, lost your tongues? Nobeast got anything to say?"

An ancient squirrel, silver-grey with uncounted seasons, raised his bound paws and pointed at Vilu. "The one that follows upon the wave, will steer you one day to your grave!"

The stoat could not explain the shudder that ran through him, but it was gone in an instant. He dismissed it, observing to Akkla, who stood awaiting orders, "I make it a rule never to take notice of threats by those I've conquered. If any of them were true I'd have been dead long ago. Take that dithering old relic and the rest of his tribe aboard the *Goreleech*, and chain them on deck."

The captives were being moved off when wild commotion broke out at the woodland fringe. More than a score of crewbeasts fought wildly to control a single squirrel. Vilu leaped nimbly onto a grass-topped dune, viewing the scene with evident enjoyment. Noosed ropes held the maddened squirrel by her paws, neck, tail and waist. The vermin dug their footpaws into the sand, hauling on the lines to keep them taut and prevent her attacking them. She was a huge sinewy creature, with unusually black shining fur which glistened in the sunlight. Though wounded and scarred in several places, she heaved and bucked against the ropes, sending vermin sprawling, baring strong white teeth at them.

Stopping safely out of reach on his perch, Vilu smiled. "Whoa! What have we here, a real fighter?"

The searat Grigg, his paws cut and burning from rope friction, reported in a strained voice, "This'n's killed four crew single-pawed, cap'n. 'Tis like tryin' to 'old a pack o' sharks at bay!"

Vilu leaped down from the dune. "Hold her tight, now!" Advancing on the bound squirrel, he soon had his scimitar tip under her chin, forcing her head back.

"Be still now. I am Vilu Daskar and I could kill you with a flick of my blade. Be still!"

Snorting for breath against the noose around her neck, the squirrel fixed her blazing eyes on the stoat, hatred and loathing ringing fearlessly in her harsh voice.

"I know who you are, scumface. Let's see you put down that blade an' loose me. I'm Ranguvar Foeseeker an' I could rip *you* t'bits without need of a weapon to do the job!"

Vilu pressed his bladepoint harder, causing a drop of blood to stand out against the jet black fur.

"Ranguvar Foeseeker, eh? Hearken then, you're in no position to throw out challenges, and I've no intention of fighting you. I don't do battle with my slaves."

Ranguvar tried to push her chin further onto the blade. "Coward! Then slay me an' be quick about it!"

Vilu withdrew his scimitar, shaking his head. "Never thought I'd live to see the day, a berserk female squirrel! No no, my friend, I'm not going to slay you. What a waste that would be. With mad strength like that you could do the work of a score of oarslaves alone. A few seasons of Bullflay's whip and short rations will humble you. Down on the bottom deck, front row. The seaspray day and night should cool you down a bit. Take her away!"

"You won't break me, dirtbrain," Ranguvar yelled as she was being dragged off. "Don't close your eyes to sleep whilst Ranguvar Foeseeker is aboard your cursed ship!"

Vilu Daskar picked up a pawful of dry sand and watched the breeze carry it away, remarking to Grigg, "Huh, insults and threats, they're like sand in the wind to me, Grigg: here one moment, gone and forgotten the next."

• • •

Minus the use of oars, using only her sails, the red ship
coursed south. Bullflay the chief slave driver, and his assis-
tants unchained all the galley slaves and herded them up on
the trireme's high maindeck. The *Goreleech*'s new squirrel
captives were shocked by the sight of the oar-wielders.
Starved to emaciation, hollow-eyed and ragged, barely alive
in some cases, the wretched slaves blinked against the bright
afternoon. Bullflay cracked his long sharkskin whip low,
pulling several of the slaves flat as it curled around their
footpaws.

"On yer knees, ye worthless fishbait, don't yer see the
cap'n's present?"

Ranguvar had been chained and covered with a weighted
cargo net, through which she watched the scene.

A huge baulk of timber had been attached to a rope reeved
through a block halfway up the mainmast. Vilu stuck his
scimitar into the mainmast at shoulder height.

"I've brought you thirty-six new oarbeasts, Bullflay. How
many do you need?"

The big fat weasel saluted with his fearsome whip. "I'll
take every one you got, cap'n Vilu!"

The pirate stoat signalled for some refreshment and a seat.
Hurriedly four crew members brought his chair, a flagon of
his favorite damson wine and a grilled fish. Seated comfortably he picked delicately at the fish and sipped wine from a
crystal goblet, watched by the hungry slaves. Wiping his lips
on a silken kerchief he nodded briefly to his chief slave driver.

Bullflay grabbed the rope which had been reeved through
the block and hauled on it until the baulk of timber was
hoisted level with the scimitar sticking from the mast. "Haul
the wood this high, or else!" He let the baulk drop to the
deck. The weary oarslaves stood in line for their turn to haul
up the baulk. Then he picked up his whip and cracked it over
the new arrivals. "Come on, you lot, get below. We'll get yer
chained up to an oar nice an' tidy like. Hahaharr!"

Getting the black squirrel Ranguvar below was an awesome task. Keeping her bundled in the cargo net, a score of
vermin dragged her through the decks until she was at the
front seat of the vessel's bottom level. Eight of the Sea
Rogues suffered wounds and injuries, but they finally got the

berserker chained alone to a long thick oar handle. Ranguvar sat relatively quiet. She waited until the other oarslaves were brought down and shackled into place at the sweeps. She questioned one, a tired old otter, who looked as if he had seen many seasons slaving.

"What was all that about up on deck, the timber an' the rope? Why did you have to haul it up, all of you?"

The otter blinked back a tear from his craggy face. "Didn't yer know, mate? Vilu Daskar an' Bullflay got to 'ave their bit o' fun. Thirty-six new oarslaves means they got to get rid of thirty-six old 'uns, so they finds the sickest'n'weakest by makin' us hoist the log."

"What happens to those who can't haul the log?" Ranguvar could not stop herself asking.

The otter's husky voice shook as he explained. "That's when the real sport starts, mate. They sails the red ship out 'til land's too far away for a fit beast to swim back to it, then they runs out a plank. Vilu gives the pore creatures their freedom, tells 'em they're free to swim back t'shore an' forces 'em t'walk the plank."

Ranguvar's fur stood up on the nape of her neck. "Do any ever make it, friend?"

"What d'you think? You saw the state of some o' those slaves. If'n the big fishes don't get 'em the sea does."

Ranguvar turned and murmured softly, "Well at least you survived it. What's yore name?"

Bowing his head until it touched the oar, the otter replied, "Norgle's my name. My father's name was Drenner. He used to sit where yore sittin' now, that's his oars yore chained to. My ole dad was one of those who couldn't haul the log."

Slaaaash! Crack!

"Shaddup, yer scurvy bilge swabs!"

Slavemaster Bullflay swaggered up to his rail, directly in front of Ranguvar. He wielded the whip at Norgle, but the black squirrel sat up straight and took the blow. A big skinny rat positioned himself alongside Bullflay. Picking up a drumstick, he stood ready at the big drum which was used to keep the oarslaves pulling in time with each other.

Bullflay winked at him, nodding towards Ranguvar. "See

that, Fleabitt? Cap'n Vilu said this squirrel's a real tough 'un. We'll 'ave ter pay 'er some special attention, won't we?"

Fleabitt's narrow frame shook with unconcealed glee. "Special attention, right, chief. We'll learn 'er!"

Ranguvar's piercing stare raked the rat scornfully. "What could I learn from you, cocklebrain?"

Craaack!

Bullflay's whip struck her. Ranguvar transferred her dead stare to him without even blinking.

"Is that the best you can do, barrelbelly?"

Choking with rage, the burly weasel flogged away at his new oarslave, using all his strength. When he finished, his stomach was heaving in and out, and both his paws were shaking violently with the exertion.

"You . . . you dare talk ter Slavemaster Bullflay like that! I'll flay yer to dollrags!"

Ranguvar, who had ducked her head to protect her face, raised her eyes. There was death dancing in them as she growled at Bullflay, "You big useless lump o' mud, one day I'll kill yer with my bare paws, even if'n I have to bite through these chains to get at yer. Remember that, weasel!"

Bullflay could not bring himself to answer or raise his whip again. Ranguvar's eyes had frightened him. He strode off down the walkway, laying left and right with his whip at the other oarslaves.

"Silence there, quiet! An' be ready ter row when my drum starts to beat, if you want t'keep fur on yore backs!"

Two hours after daybreak next morning, a searat called down from his watch in the crow's nest, "Away to the north, a sail, cap'n, a sail!"

Vilu Daskar leaned out over the stern of the *Goreleech*, shading his eyes, peering hard at the faraway smudge.

"Sail? Are you sure? What kind of craft is she?"

"Too far off t'tell, cap'n sir, but 'tis a sail fer sure!"

Akkla kept the tiller steady, awaiting Vilu's order.

Striding the afterdeck, the pirate stoat stroked the yellowed bone handle of his scimitar pensively. "Hmm, a sail, eh? How far off are the Twin Islands, Akkla?"

"We could make 'em by tomorrow midday wid all sail an' full speed on the oars, cap'n."

His eyes still fixed on the far-off object, Vilu replied, "Too fast, we'd lose her. No ship can keep up with mine under full sail and oars. Take her to half sail and tell Bullflay to set the rowers a steady beat. We'll let her keep us in sight, and that way we'll land at Twin Islands tomorrow night. Set your tiller south and a point west."

The red ship sailed off on her new course, with the whips cracking on all three decks below. Oars rose and fell, pulling the *Goreleech* through the waves. The fresh captives groaned miserably as they bent their backs under the lash.

26

Vurg snuggled deeper in his hammock. Morning sunlight streamed through the cabin window, and he tried to ignore it, closing both eyes tight, but he could not close his ears to the raucous duet which the cook and his assistant were yelling from the galley. Other crewmice were already awake, hurling objects at the galley door, haranguing the singers within.

"You'll turn the grub sour wid that noise!"

"Aye, belt up, you two, stop that awful racket!"

"I thought somebeast was tryin' to squash a dozen frogs!"

But Beau and his assistant Cardo were in full cry and not about to give up for mere threats and insults.

"Ho wot d'you give to a saucy crew,
Stew! Stew! Stew!
Wot's better than a bowl o' stew?
Why a bowl o' stew or two!
We fries the varnish off the mast,
Then adds some ole rope ends,
An' the cap'n's boots all boiled up slow,
Good flavour to it lends.

So scoff it up 'tis good for you,
Stew! Stew! Stew!
Made with a drop o' lantern oil,
An' a barnacle or two,
Some fine sail threads an' fishes' heads,
Then roast the cook's ole socks,
An' add to that some o' the fat,
They use to grease the locks!
Ho stew, stew luvverly stew,
No skilly'n'duff or brown burrgoo,
Just swallow the lumps that you can't chew,
An' fill a plate for yore worst mate,
Then sit an' watch him temptin' fate,
With face so green an' nose all blue,
Stew! Stew! Steeeeeeeeeeewwww!"

Luke was guiding the tiller, smiling as he listened to the crew voicing their doubts about breakfast.

"D'you think they really mean it, Cordle?"

"I don't know, mate. Mebbe they're just jokin'."

"But they wouldn't use lantern oil an' lock grease, would they, Vurg?"

Vurg winked at Luke as he answered Denno, who was prone to bouts of seasickness at the slightest thing. "Who knows, mate? Ole Beau's a great 'un for playin' pranks an' I remember that salty stew Cardo made when we first set sail. Wot d'you think, Luke?"

The Warrior was hard put to keep a straight face. "No, Vurg, I don't think Beau an' Cardo'd do that to our vittles, though I couldn't find my seaboots this mornin'."

The cook and his assistant staggered out of the galley, bearing between them a steaming cauldron. Denno's usually ruddy face took on an unhealthy pallor. "Urgh! I ain't eatin' none o' that stuff!"

Grinning wickedly, Beau dipped a beaker into the cauldron. "Wot? After all the blinkin' trouble we went to preparin' this delicious stew? Now see here, Denno m'laddo, I'm goin' to see you eat this, even if I have t'feed it t'you m'self. It'll put the jolly old roses back in your cheeks. Now open your mouth wide, old chap!"

"Yaaaah! I'm too young t'die!"

The crew of the *Sayna* shook with laughter as Beau chased Denno round the deck with the beaker of stew.

"Oh, c'mon, you great big silly, stan' still an' open wide!"

"Gerraway from me, you lop-eared poisoner! Help, some-beast stop 'im! Do somethin', you rotten lot!"

Beau pursued Denno from stem to stern, stew slopping from the beaker as he coaxed and cajoled. "Never grow up strong an' handsome like me if you don't eat all your blinkin' brekky up, wot wot?"

Denno scrambled up the mainmast for the crow's nest, with Beau scaling the rope ladder close behind him. When he reached the topmost point, Denno suddenly yelled, "Sail, I see a sail!"

Beau grabbed his footpaw, chortling. "No excuses now, laddie buck. I'll pour it down your ear if you don't hold still!"

Luke's sharp command caused the hare to release the crewmouse.

"Beau, let him be! Are you sure it's a sail, Denno?"

"Aye, Luke, I saw it a moment ago, but it's gone now!"

Beau let the beaker drop and clambered swiftly up along-side Denno, his keen eyes following the mouse's paw.

"Over there it was, south, mebbe a touch west!"

The hare concentrated his gaze upon the horizon for a while, then he climbed down to the deck and made his report to Luke.

"There was somethin' out there, but bad weather's risin' from the sou'west—sea's gone quite choppy an' the clouds are lowerin'. Mayhap 'twas a ship—couldn't really tell."

Luke came to a decision speedily. "Vurg, steer her over that way—south goin' west. Coll, Dulam, Cordle, pile on all sails. Beau, get the food to my cabin, an' the rest of you, make sure everythin' is battened down tight. Looks like we're in for a storm."

When the orders had been carried out the crew gathered in Luke's cabin to share the meal. Contrary to Denno's belief, the stew was delicious. Beau was quite huffy that anybeast should think it otherwise.

"Phuff! Never cooked rubbish or wasted good food in all m'life, wot. Vegetable stew, sah, with lots of carrot, dandelion root, leeks, dried mushrooms, onions, taters an' my own special barley'n'oat dumplin's. Puts fur on the chest, a glint in the eye an' a splendid spring t'the paw. Stuff t'give the crew, eh, Luke?"

The Warrior cleaned his bowl with a chunk of bread. "It certainly is, mate. D'you think we should allow Denno a second helpin'?"

Denno licked his spoon sheepishly. "Not my fault. The way they were singin' that song, well, I thought . . ."

Beau kindly ladled him another portion. "Thought, laddie? Y'know what the shortsighted vole thought. Listen an' I'll tell you.

"A shortsighted vole climbed out of his hole,
His glasses he'd lost I fear,
Some blossom petals in the breeze,
Fell on his head, oh dear!

'I thought 'twas summer but winter's come,
'Tis snow!' that vole did shout.
'I think I'd better go and warn
The creatures hereabout!'

He bellowed 'round the woodland wide,
'I think 'tis going to freeze!'
He shooed some sparrows from a nest,
'Back to your hive you bees!'

And squinting dimly at the ground,
He lectured tufts of grass,
'All hedgehogs now should be indoors,
'Til wintertide does pass!'

'Go join your family round the fire,
Don't sit there all alone,
'Tis no fit weather for a mole,'
He scolded at a stone.

'And as for you,' he told a bush,
'You badgers aren't too smart,

I thought you'd be the first to know,
When winter's due to start!'

So gather 'round and listen all,
My moral's clear and true,
I think 'tis best to stop and think,
When thoughts occur to you!"

As Beau finished his poem, the ship gave a lurch. Luke
saved the stew cauldron as it slid by and laid it safe on the
deck, wedging it 'twixt the table and his chair.

"Don't panic, crew, it's the bad weather. Sit tight an' wait it
out in comfort—there's little else we can do. I'm goin' out on
deck. Vurg, you come with me. We'll take tiller watch two at
a time until the storm passes. When you go out there, use
ropes an' tie yoreselves to that tiller. I don't want any crew
washed overboard."

The little ship began to sway crazily as mounting waves
buffeted her, up and down, side to side. Luke gritted his teeth
as he and Vurg strove to hold the tiller on course. Spray
lashed both mice until, despite their heavy cloaks, they were
saturated. A high-pitched whine, like that of a stricken beast,
rose above the storm's din. It was the wind, playing on the
tightened rigging ropes as if they were the strings of some
instrument. Pawing saltwater from his eyes, Vurg glanced
anxiously up at them.

"If we don't slack off some sail, this gale might rip us
t'pieces, Luke. Can't we take her t'half canvas?"

The Warrior stared straight ahead into the onslaught.
"'Tain't possible, Vurg. I couldn't risk the crew's life by
sendin' 'em up into the riggin' to shorten sail. Also I'm near
certain 'twas the red ship that Denno an' Beau sighted. I
don't figger on losin' her. We're bound to follow!"

Beau and Cardo struggled back to the galley across the
seesawing deck, bearing the empty stew cauldron between
them. Coinciding with the boom of thunder overhead, the
galley door slammed open wide. A flash of white lightning
illuminated the scene as they were both swept inside by a
wave crashing over the ship. Smoke wreathed them as the
galley stove was extinguished into a hissing mess by the

water. The seacook staggered inside, yelling to his assistant, "Lock all y'can in the cupboards—keep the blinkin' vittles dry. I'm goin' to fetch a rope and secure those water casks before they start rollin' about!"

No sooner was Beau out on deck again than a crackling bolt of chain lightning struck the *Sayna*'s foremast. Like a dry twig the stout timber split, sending the long lower jib swinging like a scythe. Vurg saw the danger and shouted, "Beau, look out, mate!"

As Beau turned, the jib caught him a mighty clout in the midriff, hurling him ears over tail into the sea.

Luke was already on the move. Releasing the tiller he quickly tied the stern line about his waist and plunged in after Beau, with Vurg bawling above the mêlée, "All paws on deck! Hare overboard! All paws on deck!"

Down, down went the Warrior, into a world of boiling confusion, with the roar of storm and sea ringing in his ears. Luke felt his progress checked as the line pulled tight, and immediately began striking upward, his eyes searching the racing bubbling surface for signs of the hare. Air started escaping his nostrils and mouth as he fought his way bravely to the wavetops. Gasping for breath, he surfaced in a deep green valley, then the maddened seas crashed down upon him. Next moment he was swung up high on the crest of a huge roller. Luke took the opportunity to scan swiftly about for Beau. Below him he could see the stern of the ship, but no other sign of life upon the watery wilderness. Then he was dropped into another deep trough, only to be swept aloft again. About his middle, the line tightened painfully as he was pulled along in the ship's wake, spitting seawater, paws flailing, searching constantly for Beau, despite his own predicament.

Vurg called out to the crew, "Haul Luke in, mates, afore the line snaps an' he drowns. Beau's gone, can't do nothin' about that. Haul in there!"

Willing paws heaved on the line. Luke felt himself pulled through the buffeting waves, and relaxed, half stunned and too helpless to resist. Vurg was waiting with a dry cloak and a beaker of elderberry wine, and Cardo helped to carry Luke to his cabin.

The Warrior coughed and spluttered as the wine revived him. He sat up, shaking his head.

"It was too wild t'see anythin' out there. No sign of Beau?"

Cardo was weeping uncontrollably. "None at all. That ole hare was my best matey, an' the finest cook afloat. The sea's a cruel beast, cruel!"

Luke passed the remainder of the wine to him. "Drink this, now, Cardo. 'Tis a terrible thing, poor Beau. But we must concentrate on keeping this ship afloat or we'll all finish up on the seabed if'n this storm keeps up."

He was interrupted by joyous shouts from out on deck as the ship gave a mighty shudder and stopped rolling.

"The wind's turned. We're saved, mates!"

Wrapping the cloak about him, Luke hurried from the cabin.

Evening was streaking the skies westward, and to the east the thunder boomed dully, with a sporadic bolt of lightning far off. Vurg scratched his head in amazement. The wind was still blowing, but strong and warm, flattening the sea with its power. The *Sayna* was shuddering lightly, her damaged rigging thrumming as she responded to Dulam's touch on the tiller and sped southwest.

Relief among the crew was evident. Coll laughed. "Hahaha! Quickest thing y'ever did see, Luke. One moment we're near sinkin' in a storm, then swift as a flash the wind turns east an' suddenly veers west. We're saved!"

Dusk was creeping in. Luke's cloak fluttered straight out behind him as he stood, with the crew, looking back over the stern at the distant area where Beau had been lost. Cardo had composed a short verse.

"Our friend was taken by the sea,
He rests now, who knows where,
A good an' gen'rous beast he was,
A brave an' cheerful hare.

We've got no flow'rs or blossoms,
To cast out on the deep,

No stone will ever mark the spot,
Where he sank down to sleep.

Beau Fethringsol Cosfortingham,
Sweet as long summer days,
Your memory lies in our hearts,
You'll be our mate, always!"

The crew stood in silence, heads bowed, tears falling onto the deck. Everybeast had loved the hare dearly.

Luke took a deep breath and wiped his eyes. "Cordle, take first watch aloft, keep yore eyes peeled for the red ship. Coll, your turn at the tiller. Right now, while me'n'Cardo put the galley straight an' piece together a meal, the rest of you get rope an' pitch, bind that mast as best you can, then take in all sails. She's runnin' fast enough in this sea. In future storms I don't want to see anybeast out on deck without havin' a life-line attached to 'em. 'Twas a terrible thing that happened to Beau, but I know he'd want it to serve as a lesson to us all."

The sun's fiery orb sank below the westering horizon, and the *Sayna* sped smoothly into the night. A splash announced that the shattered jib had been jettisoned overboard. Luke stood at the galley fire, which he had rekindled, longing to hear just one merry chuckle from Beau, but knowing it was not possible. They would have to sail onward without their friend the hare.

27

Vilu Daskar was used to freak weather in tropical waters. When the storm struck he ordered his oarslaves put to work. With no sails to aid them they were forced to row double time as the drums pounded out and whips cracked. Daskar himself took the wheel, tacking the *Goreleech* skillfully on a direct westerly course. As the tempest began slackening, he swung the vessel due east, came around the far side of the Twin Islands and anchored a safe distance offshore, behind the easternmost of the two massive hills.

Savouring the night air, Vilu sat out on deck, sating his appetite on a plate of baked fish and a flagon of nettle beer. Akkla the ferret hovered nearby, watching the stoat pick his teeth with a fishbone. Vilu dabbed at his mouth with a silken kerchief and stood up. Akkla gazed anxiously at the remains of the meal, hoping Vilu had finished.

"Had anything to eat yet, Akkla?"

Edging eagerly near the barrelhead table, the ferret bowed cringingly. "No chance ter eat durin' that storm, cap'n."

Vilu held out a paw, as if inviting Akkla to finish the meal, then clouted the ferret's face sharply, knocking him to the deck. "Go and get your own food, famine-face!"

From below decks there was a bellowing roar which mounted to a screech, quickly followed by the thudding of paws up the companionway. Bullflay, the weasel slavemaster, assisted by some of his cronies, stumbled out onto the deck. He was pressing a wadded rag to staunch the blood from one side of his head.

Vilu could see he was in great pain. "Hmm, nasty injury. How did you come by that, Bullflay?"

The weasel's toadies took up the tale with relish.

"'Twas the black squirrel, sire!"

"Aye, the berserk female. Tore master Bullflay's ear off, sire, with 'er teeth!"

"She'd 'ave 'ad 'is other ear if'n we 'adn't rescued 'im, sire. Madder'n a shark that 'un is!"

"No use floggin' 'er, sire, two whips master Bullflay's broke on 'er. Two!"

Vilu sat back, a smile hovering across his eyes. "So, and what would you have me do with this berserk warrior, Bullflay my friend?"

The weasel's flabby jowls quivered with rage. "I wants yer t'let me kill 'er, sire, tie rocks to 'er neck'n'paws an' slide 'er into the water nice'n'slow. Let the other oarslaves watch 'er drown bit by bit!"

Vilu nodded understandingly. "You'd like that, eh, Bullflay?"

A drop of blood spattered the deck as the slavemaster nodded. "Aye, sire, I'd like it fine after wot she did t'me!"

Vilu dallied with the bone handle of his scimitar. "I've no doubt you would, but I'm captain aboard this ship, not you. I decide who lives or dies and that squirrel is not ready for death yet. Cut her food and water for a few days. That should do the trick."

Bullflay was about to protest when he saw a dangerous glint in Vilu's eyes. He saluted sullenly. "As y'say, sire."

Vilu smiled sweetly, perilously. "Precisely, my lard-bellied friend. As I say!" He beckoned to Akkla, who was still crouching on the deck, holding his face where he had been struck.

"Stop slobbering about down there. Get up! Take four

crew and go ashore. Climb that hill, and mount a lookout for the ship that was following us. Report to me when you sight it. I'll lay an acorn to an apple that they'll do like any other vessel does when they come to Twin Islands. Parug, do you know what they'll do?"

The searat bosun shook his head. "No, sire."

Vilu closed one eye and squinted towards the channel separating both islands. "They'll sail straight up the middle of there, always do. We'll be waiting for them when they emerge from the channel mouth and meet them head on with our spike, eh, Parug?"

A quiver of evil joy shook the bosun. "Stick 'em like a gnat on a pin, sire!"

Vilu filled a beaker with nettle beer, passing it to Parug. "Like a gnat on a pin. What a quaint turn of phrase!"

Far below on the bottom deck of the trireme, Norgle the otter sat on the second row, staring in admiration at the back of Ranguvar, sitting alone on the front bench. Lashmarks scored and quartered the black squirrel's back, where Bullflay had done his best to flog her into submission. He had failed—every slave chained to an oar throughout the length and breadth of the *Goreleech* knew it. It brought fresh life and the spark of defiance into the hearts of even the oldest and most timid. Norgle heard the heavy pawstep of Bullflay descending and murmured softly to Ranguvar. "'Tis Bullflay, matey. Get yoreself ready for the worst. Like as not he'll slay ye for bitin' off his ear."

The black squirrel's eyes glowed with fierce battle light. "Hah! Not before I've bitten his other one off!"

"Silence down 'ere. One more peep an' I'll flay yore backs t'the bone, y'bilge scrapin's!"

A hush fell as Bullflay's whip cracked aloud. Still holding the rag to his ear, he strode up and stood by the drum. Raising the whip high he glared at Ranguvar. "An' you'll be the first t'git flayed, squirrel!"

The eyes of Ranguvar bored into her hated enemy. "An' you'll be the first to die, lardbucket!"

Bullflay quailed under the berserk stare of Ranguvar. He let the whip fall and strode off, muttering, "We'll see 'ow bold yer are after a couple o' days without vittles or water. That'll cure you!"

However, when food was served up to the oarslaves, even though it was only a crust, one bowl of thin gruel and a cup of water, everybeast saved a small portion. When the oardecks were quiet, the food was passed from paw to paw until it reached the captive berserker.

Mid-morning of the following day saw Dulam, whose watch it was at the topmast, bellowing, "Laaaaaand hoooooooooo!"

Luke joined him at the lookout point. The high, humped hills of Twin Islands stood out fresh and green in the warm sunlight. He patted Dulam's back.

"Well done, mate. You'll get an extra portion at lunch for bein' the first to spot land!"

Dulam sighed mournfully. Luke was a warrior, not a cook. "An' will I have to eat it too?"

Luke tweaked his friend's ear playfully. "There's gratitude for ye, after me slavin' over a hot galley stove since dawn makin' skilly'n'duff for ye."

Dulam sighed wistfully. "My ole mum used t'make the best skilly'n'duff on the northland coast."

Luke chuckled as he climbed out of the rigging. "Well, I ain't yore ole mum. Mayhap we should've brought her along, Dulam."

"Aye, mayhap we will next time. She's as good with a ladle as you are with a sword. Dear ole mum, yore liddle Martin used to come round to our cave for her apple pies. Sweet apples, golden crust, steamin' hot, dusted with spices an' warm arrowroot sauce poured over 'em. I can taste 'em right now."

Luke helped Dulam down to the deck. "Well, let's hope she's still feeding my son, make him grow up big'n'strong. Now will you stop natterin' on about those pies, 'tis turnin' me off my own cookin'!"

"Huh, that wouldn't be hard to do!" Vurg remarked in passing.

Luke heard him. "What was that you said, Vurg?"

"I said the sky's far up'n'blue, mate!"

Luke glanced upward, remarking quietly to Vurg, "There's far worse cooks aboard than me."

Vurg cupped a paw to his ear. "What?"

The Warrior winked slyly at his friend. "I said, the sky's as blue as the sea."

Afternoon shadows were starting to lengthen as the *Sayna* lay offshore of the Twin Islands. Luke called up to the topmost watch, "Any sign of the red ship?"

Cardo shielded his eyes. "None at all, Luke!"

Vurg leaned against the tiller. "So what now, mate?"

Luke studied the Twin Islands carefully before replying.

"No good chasin' out into unknown waters with the *Sayna* in a bad state. No tellin' what might become of us. I think we should sail her into that channel which separates the two islands, 'tis calm an' sheltered in there. We could make the *Sayna* shipshape again, fix the mast properly, make a new jib an' sew up those torn sails. Sort of put everythin' to rights afore we set sail again, eh, Vurg?"

"Aye, sounds sensible, but what about the red ship, Luke?"

"Well we ain't in a fit condition to chase her right now. We'll have to make up two days when we're sailin' again. Strange though, Vurg, I've got a funny feelin' that red ship isn't too far off somewhere. Hmm, mayhap 'tis just a fancy an' it'll pass. Right, head 'er in there, mates. We'll make fast to the east channel bank about halfway along."

Later that evening Akkla tapped nervously at Vilu Daskar's splendidly carved cabin door.

Vilu put aside the charts he and Parug were studying. "Come!" the pirate stoat's voice called imperiously.

Akkla entered respectfully and made his report.

"Sire, 'tis like you said: towards evenin' a ship sailed into the channel an' put in 'alfway up on the east side."

Vilu could not resist a triumphant smirk at Parug. "Just as I predicted." He turned back to Akkla. "What manner of vessel is it?"

"Like an ole Corsair barque, cap'n, but ain't no Corsairs aboard of 'er, they're all mice, tough-lookin' beasts. She took some storm damage, sire—I think they've put in there for repairs."

Parug drew his cutlass and licked the blade. "It's dark outside, cap'n. We could come stormin' up the channel like an 'awk onto a wren, jus' when they're least expectin' us!"

Vilu shook his head despairingly at the searat bosun. "No no, my impulsive friend, why wreck a ship that's in need of repair? Leave the mice awhile, let them work and sweat fixing up their craft, get it all good and seaworthy again. Then we'll swoop on them and sink it. Let them see all their efforts destroyed. Much more subtle, don't you think?"

Parug thought for a moment, then his features creased into an evil gap-toothed cackle. "Haharrhahaharr! Yore a bad 'un all right, cap'n!"

Vilu adopted a modest expression. "Oh, I do my best to be the worst. Akkla, what was the name of this ship?"

"I don't know letters, sire, but Fleabitt does, an' 'e said 'twas called the *Sayna*, I think. Aye, that's the name, *Sayna*!"

To both Sea Rogues' surprise, their captain poured wine for himself and them. Akkla and Parug sipped appreciatively at their goblets. Vilu Daskar's wine was the best.

Vilu himself merely wet his lips as he mused, "Hmm, *Sayna*. What do you think, my friends, 'twould have been saner for *Sayna* to give Twin Islands a miss?"

Akkla and the bosun stared at him in dumb silence. Vilu put aside his wine and sighed.

"That's called a play on words, you bumpkins. Saner, *Sayna*, 'twas a pun, don't you see?"

The pair stood in slack-jawed silence, trying to understand what their captain had said. He turned his back, dismissing the slow-witted crewbeasts. "Dimwitted idiots, get out of my sight before I lose patience with your thick-skulled ignorance. Begone!"

Akkla and Parug set their goblets down gingerly, not daring to finish the wine, and hurried from the cabin. Vilu's former good humour had deserted him. He detested being surrounded by stupid witless vermin.

Slouching in his chair, he began to focus his mind upon the *Sayna* and her crew. Why would a vessel of such small size be pursuing a ship as huge as the *Goreleech*? What possible harm could a score or so of mice inflict upon Vilu Daskar, terror of the seas? They must be totally insane, or recklessly brave. Well, one way or another, he would soon find out. Hah! And so would they, the fools!

Vilu left his cabin and strolled out on deck, almost colliding with a searat called Drobna. His claws dug viciously into the rat's cheek, drawing the frightened rodent close. Vilu smiled disarmingly at him. "Tell me, what chance does a minnow stand if it chases a shark?"

Drobna's cheek was pulled awkwardly on one side, and spittle trickled from his lips as he blabbered out a reply. "Nuh . . . nuh . . . none, sire, minnow agin a shark's got no 'ope!"

Vilu released him, patting Drobna's cheek tenderly. "Well said, my friend, well said. Even a moron like you can solve a simple problem now and then."

He strode on up the gently swaying deck, leaving Drobna rubbing a stinging cheek, completely baffled.

28

Luke was already up, having taken last watch of the night. The *Sayna* lay moored on the east bank of the canal-like channel running between Twin Islands. Luke leaned on the starboard rail, watching the day break still and humid, with leaden overcast skies. Cardo came out of the main cabin, bearing an old shield that he used as a tray. On it was a beaker of hot mint and dandelion tea, accompanied by a warm scone spread with stiff comb honey.

He winked at Luke. "Mornin', mate. Here, get that down you. I was up awhile before dawn, so I tried me paw at bakin' scones."

Luke seated himself on a coil of rope, sipping gratefully at the hot tea and nibbling gingerly at the scone. He surveyed the islands' two massive hills, which looked silent and oppressive with the heavy grey sky cloaking their summits in mist.

"Hmm, wouldn't surprise me if'n we had a spot o' rain today, Cardo. Well, this scone tastes good, matey. Where'd you learn to bake stuff like this?"

Cardo stared down the channel to the open sea beyond.

"'Twas a recipe Beau taught me. I miss that ole hare. He was a good friend t'me."

Luke put a paw round Cardo's shoulder. "Aye, so do I. Strange, but we never know the true value of friends'n'family 'til they ain't with us any more. Come on, matey, buck up. I can hear our crew wakin'. Mopin' about won't help us. Best t'keep ourselves busy, eh?"

The crew of the *Sayna* had nothing but praise for Cardo's good cooking, and it cheered him greatly. After breakfast Luke reviewed their position and gave orders.

"Cardo, see if y'can cook up a lunch t'show us that breakfast wasn't just a flash in the pan. Cordle, pick a couple o' good patchers to help you repair the sails. Coll, Denno and Dulam, I want you to strip down the mainmast an' bind it round tight with strong greased line. That willow never broke, it only cracked. 'Twill be good as new once it's bound an' tightened proper. Vurg, get yore weapons an' come with me. We're goin' up that big hill yonder. Let's see if we can find a decent piece o' wood to fashion a new jib from. Right, off t'work now, crew, an' keep yore wits about you an' both eyes open. 'Tis strange territory."

The hill turned out to be a complete disappointment. There were no proper trees with trunks and stout limbs growing there. Luke snorted in disgust as he swiped with his sword at one of the tall feathery bushes which grew in profusion on the slopes. Vurg picked up the branch his friend had lopped off and inspected it.

"Huh, too thin an' brittle. Wouldn't even make decent firewood. Won't find a decent jib spar growin' 'ereabouts."

Luke peered uphill into the warm humid mist. "Looks pretty much the same all over, Vurg. Why don't we go back down an' try searchin' the channel edges for a good piece of driftwood? Might've been some timber washed up there. Vurg? What's the matter, mate?"

Vurg was rubbing his paws together furiously and flapping them as if he were trying to fly. "Yukk! Some kind o' filthy insects. Must've come off those bushes. Look, they're all over me paws!"

Luke pushed his companion forward, urging him downhill. "Well don't stand there flappin' y'paws, mate, let's get to the channel. Good salt water'll wash 'em off!"

Further uphill than the two mice had ventured, Vilu Daskar's spy patrol lay among the bushes. They watched Luke and Vurg hurry off down to the water. Ringpatch, the ferret in charge of the group, said, "If they'd reached the 'illtop they'd 'ave seen the *Goreleech* anchored below on the other side. Good job they never."

"Yah, they woulda never got past us," a small searat called Willag scoffed airily. "There wuz only two of 'em. We'd 'ave chopped 'em up fer sure!"

Ringpatch eyed him contemptuously. "Huh, what d'you know about it, spindleshanks? Those two mice looked like warriors to me. I wonder why they turned back an' ran off?"

"Said it was some kind o' insects, least that's wot I thought I 'eard one of 'em say," replied one of the patrol vermin.

"Huh, insects," Willag sneered. "They can't 'ave been much as warriors if'n they ran from insects!"

Suddenly, one of the patrol leaped upright, hitting himself left and right with both paws and dancing wildly. "Yaaaagh! Insec's! I'm covered in 'em! Yeegh!"

Tiny moist brown slugs from the surrounding bushes were all over the patrol, writhing and crawling, sticking to any patch of fur they came in contact with. The vermin thrashed about in the bushes, beating at themselves.

"Yuuurk! Gerrem offa me, I can't stand insec's!"

"Uuugh! Filthy slimy liddle worms!"

"Yowch! They sting too. Owowow!"

"Sputt! One got in me mouth. Oooogh!"

Ringpatch dashed off uphill. "Patrol, retreat. Let's get out o' here afore they eats us alive!"

Stumbling and crashing through the bushes, they retreated over the summit, driven by the sticky slugs to seek a saltwater bath.

Vurg had just finished scouring his paws in the channel shallows when he cocked an ear upward. "Listen, did you hear something? Like a kind of high-pitched squealin' noise? Came from up near the hilltop there."

Luke stood still, cupping both paws about his ears. "Aye, I heard it, mate, though I couldn't imagine anythin' but insects wantin' to live on this forsaken place. Prob'ly some seabirds, feedin' off those horrible grubs."

Vurg dried his paws in the coarse grass. "Well let's 'ope they eat 'em all. I detest squigglies!"

It was noon by the time they got back to the ship. Denno was atop the mast, binding the last bit tight with greased line, and he saw them approaching.

"Ahoy, crew, looks like Luke'n'Vurg found us a jib spar!" Willing paws helped the pair carry a long stout limb of some unidentified wood aboard the vessel.

Coll inspected it, nodding his approval. "Tough oily-lookin' wood. Let's strip the bark off an' measure it agin the broken jib for size."

It proved an ideal replacement for the old spar. By mid-noon they had it fixed. Rigging and fresh-patched sails were hauled, and Luke paced the deck, checking all was shipshape.

"Good as new the ole tub looks, mates. I'm famished. What happened to that lunch Cardo was supposed t'be cookin'?"

Cardo popped his head around the galley door. "Go an' seat yoreselves in the cabin. 'Tis about ready."

The *Sayna*'s cook had triumphed again. Cardo had used most of the dried fruit to make a hefty steamed pudding, covered with a sauce made of pureed plums and arrowroot, and there were beakers of old amber cider to drink with it. Luke voted the meal so delicious that he proposed Cardo be made Ship's Cook for life. Ladle clutched to his chest, Cardo bowed proudly as the crew applauded.

"Hoho, good ole Cardo. More power to yore paw, mate!"

"Any second 'elpings there, cooky me darlin'?"

"Aye, an' keep them scones comin' for brekkist every day!"

"Wot's for supper tonight, matey, anythin' tasty?"

Knowing he had a new-found power to wield, Cardo laid the law down to them, shaking his ladle officiously. "So I'm Ship's Cook now, eh? Then cook it is! But I ain't washin' dishes an' scourin' pots'n'pans, so there!"

To appease his touchy cook, Luke sided with Cardo.

"Agreed! From now on everybeast washes their own dishes. We'll take turns with the pots'n'pans. I'll do first duty!"

A splatter of heavy drops pattering on the bulkheads announced the arrival of rain. Vurg opened the cabin door and slid his plate and beaker out onto the deck. "I vote that the rain washes our dishes tonight, buckoes!"

Soon, raindrops could be heard pinging merrily off the crew's dishes scattered across the deck. Through the open door Luke watched a distant lightning flash, and he heard the far-off rumble of thunder.

"Looks like we're in for heavy weather, mates. Best batten down an' lay up in this channel 'til it's over."

Rain continued into the late evening, but the crew were snug and dry in the cabin, glad of the respite from sailing. Cardo sat apart from the rest, his face gloomy.

Vurg tweaked the cook's ear. "C'mon, wot's up now, y'great miseryguts?"

Cardo shrugged. "Don't know, Vurg, just got a bad feelin' an' I can't explain it. Somethin' seems wrong."

Denno nudged Vurg, pulling a wry face at the unhappy cook. "Oh dearie me, just like the ole farm mouse, nothin's right."

Coll winked at him. "Which farm mouse was that, matey?"

Denno began tapping a beat on the tabletop.

"There was an ole farm mouse, lived in an ole farmhouse,
Who always thought of a reason,
To rant an' complain, again an' again,
Whatever the weather or season.

If rain came down, he'd scowl an' frown,
Shake a paw at the sky an' say,
'Rains like these are good for the peas,
But they ain't much use for me hay!'

Then if wind came along, he'd change his song,
Cryin' out 'Oh woe lackaday,

'Tis all I need, a wind indeed,
To blow all me apples away!'

He'd gnash his teeth about shaded wheat,
At the sign of a cloud in the skies,
An' the very sight o' cloudless sunlight,
Would bring tears to both his eyes.

He'd simmer'n'boil, as he pawed the soil,
An' got himself worried an' fussed,
'Lookit that sunlight, 'tis far too bright,
'Twill turn all me soil to dust!'

Oh botheration trouble an' toil,
Life don't get peaceful or calmer,
If I'd gone to sea, a sailor I'd be,
Instead of an ole mouse farmer."

The crew were all laughing heartily when Cardo said,
"What's so funny? We were all farmers once."

The laughter died on their lips. Luke patted Cardo. "Aye,
yore right there, mate. Farmers we were, fightin' the weather
an' seasons to put food on the table. We didn't have much,
but we were happy with our wives an' families until Vilu
Daskar an' his red ship showed up. Now we're seamice,
rovers, fightin' evil an' ill fortune. Though I tell you this: one
day, when 'tis all over, we'll return home an' pick up the
threads of our old lives again."

Outside the elements increased their fury. Thunder reverberated overhead, rain lashed the heaving seas and flaming
webs of chain lightning threatened to rip the darkened skies
with their ferocity. The crew of the *Sayna*, without guard or
watch on the galeswept decks, allowed sleep to close their
weary eyes.

Most of the night the storm prevailed. Three hours before
dawn a strong warm wind blew up from the south. Driving
the tempest before it like a rumbling cattle herd, it hurtled on
northward. Peace and calm was restored to the seas in its

Brian Jacques

wake. Humidity returned, bringing with it a dense foggy bank, which hung over the Twin Islands and their channel like a pall.

The *Goreleech* put out to sea, then Vilu Daskar ordered her turned about, a league out, to face the channel. An hour before dawn he gave the command.

"Bullflay, tell your drummer to beat out full speed. Don't spare the whips. I want this ship to run up that channel as if hellhounds were chasing it. Stand ready, my scurvy Sea Rogues, there's slaves to be taken!'

Vurg woke with a raging thirst. He got up quietly, so as not to disturb his sleeping crewmates, and picked his way through the darkened cabin to the door. It was foggy on deck, silent and damp. Vurg padded to the galley, dipped a ladle into the water barrel and drank deeply. A second measure of water he tipped over his head to waken himself properly. He was about to start lighting the galley fire from last night's glowing embers, so that Cardo would have a good fire to cook breakfast, when he heard the sounds.

It was like a steady drumbeat and a deep swishing noise which grew louder by the moment. The noises seemed to be coming from somewhere farther up the channel. Vurg made his way to the forepeak. Leaning out, he strained his eyes against the blanket of milky white mist. The sounds increased in volume, and the *Sayna* began to bob gently up and down on some kind of swell. That was when the world turned red!

Towering over him like an immense leviathan, the *Goreleech* came thundering down upon the ship *Sayna*. Vurg was flung high into the air and landed hard on a rock in the

shallows, swallowed by the merciful blackness of uncon-
sciousness. A horrendous rending of ship's timbers rent the
air as the *Goreleech* ploughed into the *Sayna*, ripping the
entire starboard side out from stem to stern. Masts fell before
the wicked iron spike on the red ship's prow, snapping off
like dried twigs. Vilu Daskar roared with evil joy at the sound
of screaming crewbeasts in shock.

Half stunned, Luke splashed about in the water. He
grabbed a floating object for support. It was Cardo. The dead
cook's eyes stared unseeingly into his until Cardo sank
slowly beneath the channel. Luke came to life then. Bellowing like a creature possessed, he seized a rope trailing from
the red ship's side and began hauling himself, paw over paw,
up the *Goreleech*'s massive hull. Soaked, bruised and
weaponless, the Warrior climbed with the speed of fury,
grappling his way over carved galleries, swarming over the
heavy seawet mats of rope fenders.

• Vilu Daskar was just turning to shout further orders to his
vermin crew when Luke came storming over the gallery rail.
He was upon the pirate stoat like a wolf, grabbing him around
the neck. Both beasts crashed to the deck, Luke's eyes filled
with bloodlight as he throttled his mortal enemy. Vilu Daskar
could do nothing against the Warrior's furious strength. He
saw crewbeasts dashing to his aid and managed a panicked
gurgle. Akkla swung a belaying pin, once, twice, thrice, to
the back of Luke's unprotected skull. Another two crashing
blows laid the Warrior mouse low, and Vilu slipped from his
faltering grasp. Vermin crewbeasts rushed the stoat captain to
his cabin, where he lay on a table, making a croaking sound
as they forced warmed wine between his lips. He reeled off
the table, nursing his neck with a silken cloth.

"Dirr . . . we . . . sinkam?"

Bullflay stared at Akkla. "Wot did 'e say?"

The ferret turned to Vilu. "Don't try to talk, sire, yore
throat's damaged. Aye, we sunk 'er all right. Crew's just
draggin' aboard any mice that are still livin'."

Still clutching the silken cloth about his neck, Daskar staggered out on deck. Bullflay waddled ahead of him, drawing a
cutlass and straddling the limp form of Luke. "This's the one

who strangled yer, lord. Let's see if'n I kin take off 'is 'ead
wid one swipe!"

Vilu kicked the slavemaster, sending him sprawling.
"Gggghaaa, I wan' 'im alive. Hhhhraaaggghh!"

The pirate stoat tottered unsteadily back to his cabin.
When the door slammed, Fleabitt whispered to Grigg, "Talks
awful funny, don't 'e?"

"So would you if'n you'd been near throttled ter death,"
Grigg whispered back. "Better not let 'im 'ear y'say that 'e
talks funny, or you won't 'ave a tongue t'talk wid at all,
matey!"

Dulam was chained to deckrings like the others of the
Sayna's crew who had survived the ramming. He dabbed
gently at the back of Luke's head with his wet tunic, but it
was some considerable time before the Warrior began to stir
and show signs of coming around. On his other side, Denno
pressed Luke gently back to the deck. "Lie still, mate. You
should be dead by rights, the poundin' yore head took back
there. I saw it as I was hauled aboard."

Luke lay still, eyes closed, head throbbing unmercifully.
"What about our crew?"

He felt Denno's tears drip on to his paw as he said,
"There's only us three left, Luke: you, me'n'Dulam."

Luke felt numb. He could hear his own voice echoing in
his ears. "I saw Cardo, but Coll and Cordle and the others . . .
Vurg! Where's Vurg?"

A seaboot thumped cruelly into his side. Bosun Parug
stood over them, grinning.

"Fishbait the lot of 'em. Bit of a mistake, us 'ittin' yore
ship so 'ard. Shoulda just sneaked up an' burned it, then we
would've caught ye one by one as y'dived inna water." He
kicked Luke once more, obviously enjoying himself. "Huh,
three mis-rubble prisoners. 'Twas 'ardly worth it. Three
mice! Hah! May's well call it two, 'cos cap'n Vilu's got special plans fer you, bucko. I never knew a beast laid paws on
Vilu Daskar an' lived t'see the sun go down. I'd 'ate t'be you,
mouse. Death'll come as a mercy to ye when the cap'n's finished wid yer!"

But Luke was hardly listening. He was consumed with grief and guilt over his slain crew. Mentally he told himself that this was the second time he had lost dear ones by leaving them unguarded. It did not matter what happened to him now, though there was one thing he longed for ere death claimed him. One chance, just one opportunity to slay Vilu Daskar!

Twin Islands lay bright and still in the afternoon sunlight. The fog had gone; so had Vilu Daskar and the *Goreleech*. Slowly Vurg became aware of a tickling sensation on his face. A tiny hermit crab, burdened by a periwinkle shell, was dragging itself across his cheek. He brushed it aside and sat up, wincing. From jaw to ear his cheek was purple and swollen. Finding a pawful of cool wet kelp, he bathed it gingerly as memory flooded back. The *Sayna*, her crew, Luke, the red ship looming out of the fog!

Vurg leaped up. Sloshing through the shallows, he climbed up on his ship's wrecked hull, looking desperately this way and that. Far off out to sea, sailing north by east, he saw the *Goreleech* ploughing the main. Scrambling down into the wreckage, Vurg ignored the splitting ache in his face and head and shouted aloud, "Luke! Cordle! Denno! Ahoy, mates, anybeast aboard? Coll! Dulam! Where are you?"

Ripping away broken spars and dragging damp canvas out of his way, Vurg forced an entrance to the shattered main cabin. Coll was there, pierced through by a splintered bulkhead spar, his body swaying gently in waist-deep seawater. Yelling in horror, Vurg fled the cabin, flinging himself from the wrecked vessel onto the shore. Cardo was the second one he found, lodged underwater beneath the prow.

Vurg sat on the warm sand, his head in both paws, sobbing uncontrollably. He was alone, all the friends he had sailed with from the northlands shore gone, slain or taken captive aboard the hated red ship.

Sometime towards evening he fell asleep, stretched out above the tideline, numb with grief and aching all over. How long he lay there Vurg had no way of knowing, other than that it was dark when he opened his eyes. But that was not what had wakened him. Somebeast was close by. Vurg did not move. He lay, fully alert now, with his eyes half open, scanning the area around him. He heard noises, a damp scraping sound, coming from behind the *Sayna*'s smashed stern.

Vurg rose until he was on all fours, carefully, silently, making his way to the water's edge. Gritting his teeth with satisfaction, he found a broken spearhead, with half the shaft still attached. Wading quietly into the water, he made his way along the *Sayna*'s hull to the stern. He saw a dark shape on the beach, scraping away at the sand with a chunk of flat wood. Gripping the broken spear tightly, Vurg sneaked up from behind and flung himself upon the creature, yelling as he locked a paw about its neck, "Yaah! You filthy murderin' sum, I'll kill ye stone dead!"

However, killing the creature was not so easy. It lashed out with long hind legs, batted Vurg hard with the chunk of wood, doubled up and sent him sailing over its head. Like a flash his adversary was upon him, forcing his face down into the sand.

A familiar voice rang in Vurg's ears. "I say, steady on there, old lad, wot wot!"

Vurg managed to push his head up and shout, "Beau, it's me, Vurg!"

The hare rolled off him, pulling him upright and dusting sand away from his face.

"Well bless m'paws, so it is. Why didn't y'say so, instead of pouncin' on a chap like that? Didn't hurt you, did I?"

Vurg could not help himself. He hugged Beau and kissed both his cheeks soundly, weeping unashamedly.

"Oh, Beau, Beau, I thought you were drowned long ago!"

The hare managed to extricate himself from the tearful crewmouse and held him off with both paws. "Well, if I wasn't drowned then I soon would be with you jolly well cryin' an' weepin' all over me, wot!"

Vurg stood staring stupidly at Beau. "Then you weren't drowned when you fell overboard?"

Beau could not resist striking a noble pose. "Drowned, me laddie? Pish tush an' fiddledy wotsit! Us Fethringsol Cosfortinghams don't sink that easily, just 'cos some confounded storm chucked me in the briny, an' not for the first time let me remark. Well, says I to m'self, let blinkin' Ma Nature use other fools as fish food, not me, sir! So I struck out for the old terra firma, an' stap me vitals if I didn't land up at Twin Islands. Had t'live on the far isle, of course—pesky little insects on this one would eat a body alive if you let 'em, wot."

Immensely cheered by the fact that he was no longer alone, Vurg smiled and clasped his friend's paw firmly. "But you're alive, that's the main thing!"

The irrepressible hare winked fondly at Vurg. "Pretty much alive, apart from havin' me paw squashed by some hulkin' great mouse. Righto, companion o' mine, come on. We'll cross the channel onto my island an' have a bite to eat whilst we swap yarns. Howzat suit you, ole mousechap?"

Vurg released Beau's paw and turned away. "There's something I've got to do first. My shipmates . . ."

Beau sniffed. One of his long ears flopped down to wipe an eye before he answered, "Say no more, friend. I buried them m'self while you were sleepin'. Just finished the job when you sneaked up an' tried playin' piggyback with me, wot! Don't fret, old fellow, I've put the *Sayna*'s crew t'rest in the shadow of their own ship."

Together they waded into the channel. However, Vurg still had a question to ask. "Was the whole crew slain, Beau?"

"Sadly most of 'em were, Vurg, though I never found Luke or wotsisname an' the other chap, er, Dulam an' Denno, that's 'em. Which means they were certainly taken for slaves aboard that foul vessel *Goreleech*. So, all in all there's four of the old gang left, five countin' yours truly. Hang tight to my paw now, gets rather deep here. We'll have to jolly well swim for it, wot wot. Chin up an' strike out!"

When they reached the far island it was quite a climb to Beau's den. He had made it over the far side of the hill, facing out to the open sea. Because of this, Beau had not known about either the *Goreleech* or the *Sayna* until it was too late. But, as Vurg realized, there was little he could have done anyway against the red ship's crew.

The den was a small cave halfway down the big hill. Beau had made it comfortable and foraged around the island to provide food. Kindling a fire he put dandelion tea on to brew and produced a meal with his own gatherings and a few things they had managed to salvage from the *Sayna*'s galley.

Warming himself by the fire, Vurg allowed Beau to inspect his wounds.

"Hmm, that's a rather attractive shade of purple on your face there, old thing. Have t'make a compound, take out the pain an' swellin'. Cheer up, Vurg, you'll be as good as new in a day or two, my old nautical matey!"

Vurg heaved a sigh and gazed out to sea. "What do we do then, Beau?"

The hare sliced himself a wedge of fruitcake from the *Sayna*'s stores, adding it to his plate of island salad. "What do we do then? Why, we sit here an' chunner whilst we grow old together, like two proper desert isle hermits, m'friend. Huh, an' if y'think that, you're a nincompoop! Do? I'll tell you what we're goin' t'do, laddie buck. Make a boat from the wreckage of our ship *Sayna* an' sail after the red ship. Rescue our friends, an' if we get half a bally chance, we're goin' to put paid to that evil blaggard who calls himself a captain. Disgrace to the blinkin' rank. Right?"

Vurg locked paws with his friend. "Right, Beau. And the sooner we get started the better, mate!'

30

The crew of Vilu Daskar had a special name for the *Goreleech*'s bottom deck: the Death Pit. After two days chained to an oar down there, Luke knew the place was aptly named. In hot weather it was airless and foul; when seas were rough, it was awash with stinking bilgewater. Wretched slaves, chained in pairs at each oar, port and starboard, lived and died there under the lash of Bullflay, the fat sadistic slavemaster, and Fleabitt the drummer, his cruel assistant. Both these creatures delighted in tormenting the helpless oarslaves, withholding drinking water, taunting the sick and generally enjoying the misery they heaped without mercy on their helpless victims.

Luke found himself up at the for'ard end, pulling an oar alone, singled out for special treatment under Bullflay's watchful eye. Before chaining his paws to the oar, Parug shackled the new slave's footpaws to a long running chain, stapled at intervals to the deck. The searat bosun pointed out the reason for this.

"Just in case the oar snaps an' you thinks yore loose to escape, well you ain't. This 'ere chain joins youse all to the ship. If it sinks, you go t'the bottom with 'er!"

If Luke turned his head slightly right, he could see Dulam and Denno, manacled to an oar on the other side of the aisle, about three rows back.

Bullflay's whip cracked, its tip catching Luke's ear. "Git yore eyes front, mouse, or I'll flick 'em out with this whip. Yore down 'ere t'row, not look at the scenery!" He strode off down the center aisle, laying about him. "Bend yer backs, lazy scum, put some energy into it, cummon!"

Fortunately a strong breeze sprang up later in the day. Fleabitt stopped drumming and gave the order to ship oars. A pannikin of brackish water and a hard rye crust was issued to each slave. Bullflay and Fleabitt went up on deck, to eat in the fresh air. Luke tugged at his pawchains, calling across to his neighbour, "Do they often leave us alone like this?"

Norgle the otter, seated behind on the right, answered, "Huh, where are we goin' to run to, matey, or are we fit enough t'bite through these chains?"

Another voice growled, "I'll find a way to break 'em someday!"

Luke could not help himself staring across at the creature who had spoken. Directly opposite, chained singly to an oar, just as Luke was, sat a ferocious black squirrel. Everything about her, from the scars to the savage glowing eyes, bespoke the fact that here was a warrior. He felt an immediate kinship with the dangerous beast. She spoke again.

"Look around. All these poor creatures are defeated, because they are slaves, in chains. But Vilu Daskar could not chain the heart, mind, or blood of Ranguvar Foeseeker. Aye, I'll bite through these chains one day, then I'll slay Vilu Daskar, Bullflay, Fleabitt an' as many of 'em as I can, until they bring me down an' slay me!"

Luke stretched his paw until the chains cut into him. "I am Luke the Warrior and I swear on the memory of my dead wife Sayna that we will break these shackles together, Ranguvar Foeseeker. I will stand beside you when the time comes, and we will take many with us before we fall!"

Ranguvar stretched her paw across to Luke. Where the chains cut the flesh, blood mingled from both creatures' wounds.

"We will do it together, Luke. I have waited long for another warrior to come to the red ship. You are here now!"

Gazing into the fearless dark eyes of Ranguvar, Luke had no doubt that they could accomplish anything together. Murmurings came from all around the bottom deck. Denno spoke for everybeast as he called out, "We'll be with you, to the death!"

Luke smiled grimly. "Good! But we need a plan."

By next morning Vilu Daskar had regained his voice, though he still kept the dark bruises on his neck covered with a white silken scarf. Accompanied by Parug and Akkla, he descended to the lower deck and paid Luke a visit. The stoat captain held the scarf end to his nose as the vile reek of the Death Pit assailed his nostrils. Luke kept his eyes down as Daskar addressed him.

"So, mouse, why does a creature in a small ship follow my *Goreleech*? Surely you must have known you had no chance against the red ship. Why did you do it?"

Luke made no reply. The blade of Vilu's bone-handled scimitar slid along Luke's neck and lifted his chin until he was looking into the stoat's eyes. Still he did not speak. Daskar raised his eyebrows and nodded. "Speak or I'll slit your gizzard. Why were you following me?" Though the sharp blade was pressing on his neck, Luke closed his eyes and held the silence. "I warn you, mouse, talk, or you're a deadbeast!" To add weight to the threat, Vilu swung the blade high over Luke's head, bracing himself for the strike.

"No, wait! Don't kill our cap'n. I'll tell ye, sire!"

All eyes turned on Denno, who was waving his paws agitatedly. "Please spare the cap'n, please, sire. I'll tell you all!"

Vilu strode over to Denno, chuckling. "Loyalty to one's captain, a wonderful thing. I wish that my crew of sea scrapings showed that faith in me. But then they wouldn't be Sea Rogues, would they? So, loyal mouse, save your captain's life. Tell me why your silly little tub was pursuing the mighty *Goreleech*?"

Denno's face was a picture of simple honesty as he explained, "Do you recall the northland shore, sire? We followed you from there to avenge our families."

Vilu's paw tapped the bone scimitar handle pensively. "Northland shore, hmmm. Ah yes, I remember now. Bunch of mice, fools, burning a fire like a signal beacon on the beach. Aye, they were all either too young, too old, or too weak to make oarslaves of. We slew them for fun and ate their food. Oh dear, were they your families? Well, never mind, they provided a bit of amusement for my crew. By the way, where were you and all the able-bodied ones whilst this was going on, eh? Probably hiding somewhere to save your own skins, I shouldn't wonder."

Seated next to Denno, Dulam's fetters clanked as he struggled to rise, tears streaming down his cheeks. "That's a lie! If we'd've been there we would have fought you murderers down to the last beast!"

Vilu smiled condescendingly. "But instead you chose to go off and gather daisies."

Dulam's whole body was shaking with rage. "No we never!" he blurted out. "We were up the coast by the tall rocks, keepin' lookout while Luke and the others buried our tre—"

"Shut yore mouth, idiot!" Luke shouted.

Vilu turned to Parug and Akkla, smiling triumphantly. "Unchain these two and their captain. Bring them to my cabin."

As they unshackled Luke, he glanced across to Ranguvar and winked. The plan was beginning to work.

The three mice were hustled roughly into Vilu Daskar's cabin, where they were lined up in front of an ornate table. Lounging behind it in a magnificent carved chair, Vilu watched as his servants laid out wine, baked fish, preserved fruits and bread, fresh from the ovens. He picked at the feast, whilst Luke and his friends stood dull-eyed and hungry, trying to ignore the wonderful food. Akkla, Parug and Bullflay stood by awaiting orders.

Vilu dabbed the silken scarf across his lips, weighing the three slaves up carefully. He addressed Denno.

"You, tell me what it is you were hiding up the coast in the tall rocks. But take care. One false word, one little lie, and I will hang both your friend and your captain from the mainmast, where their bodies will stay until they rot and seabirds pick at their bones. But speak truly and I will give you all your freedom, once I have what you hid in the tall rocks. That is your choice. Now speak."

Denno glanced apologetically in Luke's direction, then said, "It was the treasure of our tribe, sire. We had traveled many seasons, guarding it from foebeasts. Havin' chosen the northland shore as our new home, we searched out a safe place to hide it. Among the tall rocks, further north."

Luke was glaring angrily at Denno. Vilu smiled at the Warrior mouse in mock surprise.

"Now now, don't pull faces at your friend. He's just saved your life and bought your freedom. Let's hear you speak your piece now. Tell us about this treasure, or I'll hang both of these mice in your place and you can watch them dangle!"

An expression of defeat replaced Luke's glare, and he sighed. "Only if you promise to spare our lives and set us free once you have the treasure."

Vilu spread his paws disarmingly. "Akkla, Parug, Bullflay, tell this mouse about my word."

The three vermin nodded vigorously.

"Oh aye, the cap'n never lies!"

"You can rely on that, mouse!"

"I'll take me oath on it!"

Vilu took a sip of wine and dabbed his lips. "See?"

Luke told him what he wanted to hear. "'Tis a great treasure, plates, chalices, daggers an' swords, all wrought of gold'n'silver, studded with many jewels."

The pirate stoat nodded approvingly. "Just as I thought. Now tell me the exact location. Where did you hide it?"

Luke stared levelly at Vilu Daskar.

"Only three creatures went among the tall rocks to hide that treasure, myself, Vurg and Cardo. I am the only one you left alive out of the three, so only I know the true location. But I am not a fool, Vilu Daskar. I do not trust the word of a murderer, so I will not tell you, no matter what you do to me or my friends. However, I have a proposition for you. Set sail for the northland shore, and when we reach there I will pilot your red ship up the coast and steer you to the spot. That way you will have to keep us alive, at least until you have the treasure. Agreed?"

Bullflay grabbed Luke and raised a belaying pin, but Vilu held up a paw and stopped him.

"Release him, Bullflay. I like this mouse. It will be a change to do business with a creature who has a brain. Good enough. I agree to your proposition, mouse."

Luke could not resist a parting dig at his enemy. "You have no choice but to agree. Dead mice cannot find the treasure for you."

Vilu popped a piece of preserved fruit into his mouth. "How wise of you. Of course I must keep you alive. Meanwhile, days and nights spent in the Death Pit will make you realize how wonderful freedom will be when you eventually gain it. Bullflay, you can be as hard on them as you please, as long as you keep them alive. Go now!"

That night, as Bullflay lay snoring on a heap of old fenders and Fleabitt dozed with his head resting on the drum, Luke winked at his two friends. "Well done, mateys. You played yore parts well!"

Ranguvar Foeseeker whispered across to Luke, "I think I can feel this staple startin' to move!" The black squirrel had wrapped a piece of rag around her pawchains, and had been silently heaving and levering for many hours. Only after much strain and effort was the heavy iron staple, which held the running chain that connected all the footpaw shackles to it, beginning to move in the damp solid deck timbers. For the first time since he had been aboard the *Goreleech*, Luke smiled.

"Keep at it, Ranguvar. Once you've got the staple out pass it over to me, mate!"

The *Goreleech* dipped her high bows into the trackless waste of the main, bound north into the night, the red sails bellied to the wind. On she went, like a giant blood-coloured bird of ill omen, sated on a cargo of misery.

Vurg was sweating in the sun, prying timbers loose from the wreckage of the *Sayna*. Beau was sawing away at some sail canvas with a rusty dagger. Beside them on the sand a mish-mashed pile of timber and cordage was bound together in the rough shape of a raft.

"I say, old thing," the hare called up to his companion, "we'll need somethin' a bit straighter than that rib plank t'make a blinkin' mast, wot?"

Vurg wiped his brow in exasperation. "Well it's the straightest piece I can find. I'm a farmer, not a boat builder. If'n you can find a better bit o' wood, matey, then yore wel-come t'try!"

As he hacked away at the canvas, Beau nicked his ear when the dagger point tore free and shot upward.

"Well keep your fur on there, mousey, I thought the flip-pin' agreement was that I built the perishin' raft an' you sup-plied the bally materials. Hold y'temper in the ranks, wot wot, I nearly chopped my ear off there whilst you were yam-merin' on at me like an old frogwife!"

Vurg left off prying loose timbers. Sucking at a splinter in his paw, he climbed down to join Beau.

"Owch! There's so many splinters in me I'd float if'n I fell into the sea, mate. How's our raft comin' along?"

The hare stood paws akimbo, surveying his work. "Oh, splendid, absojollylutely spiffin'! All she needs is a jib boom, spanker, top royal gallants an' mizzen shrouds!"

Vurg peered at him questioningly. "D'you know wot yore talkin' about?"

Beau leaned against the raft. It collapsed. "No, d'you?"

"Yeeeehawhawhaw! Y'ain't figgerin' on goin' ter sea on that thing, are yer, mates? Yukyukyukyuk, worra mess!"

Beau and Vurg were astonished to see a large fat sea lion basking in the channel, watching them. Patting a bulging stomach with both flippers, he snorted a cloud of droplets from his bristling whiskers and chortled heartily.

"Yukyukyukyuk! Looks more like a mad seagull's nest than a raft. Only place you'd go on that termites' brekkist is straight t'the bottom. Yukyukyuk!"

Vurg stood open-mouthed, but Beau recovered his compo-sure smartly, twitching his ears disdainfully at the creature.

"Mad seagull's nest? Termites' breakfast? Have a care

there, chubbychops, wot wot! My old auntie used t'say, don't criticise what y'can't do y'self. Pity you never met her!"

Floating flat on his back, the sea lion blew a jet of water onto his stomach and watched it evaporate in the sun. "Aye, more's the pity, flop-ears. I 'ad an ole auntie once, got 'erself et by a shark, cheered my ole uncle up no end. She was a grouchy beast at best o' times."

Beau drew himself up to his full lanky height. "Call me flop-ears once more an' I'll wade out there an' chastise you severely, m'good feller. Name's Beauclair Fethringsol Cosfortingham, Beau f'short. Now, what appellation d'you answer to? Speak up, wot?"

Paddling into the shallows, the sea lion beached himself like a glistening grey rock on the sand. He grinned as he extended a flipper the size of a small table.

"Ain't got a h'allepation. They calls me Bolwag. Pleased t'meet ye, Beau, an' yore liddle mouseymate there."

Vurg shook the proffered flipper. "My name's Vurg!"

Bolwag heaved his bulk further up, and galumphed around the raft, inspecting it.

"Seen a lot better, an' one or two worse. Not much of a craft t'go chasin' after the red ship, though, is she?"

Vurg looked up curiously at the gigantic sea lion. "How did you know we were goin' after the red ship?"

Bolwag sorted through the mess of timbers with flipper and muzzle, sending planks flying. "Watched it come'n'go fer many a season, Vurg. Saw what happened to your mates. That ole cap'n, Vilu Daskar, he's worse'n any shark, evil beast!"

Beau began picking up the planking. "I say there, Bolwag, d'you mind not chuckin' our raft around like that? Took us long enough t'put it together, wot. Of course we'll be sailin' blind, haven't a bally clue where old Vilu wotsischops has sailed off to."

Bolwag nodded his great head wisely. "I know which way the red ship's bound. Always goes the same course when it leaves 'ere. North'n'west two points, to Wood Isle. Takes on water'n'provisions there."

Vurg peered upchannel to the open sea. "Wood Isle? Have

you been there, Bolwag? Will you show us the way to this place?"

Bolwag frowned, then his whiskers split into a huge grin. "Suppose I'll 'ave to, matey. Couldn't let a pair o' liddle sardines like you two go twiddlin' round alone out there. Beau's ole auntie might never clap eyes on 'im agin, and we can't 'ave that now, can we? But first let's git yore raft built proper'n'seaworthy. You lay out a good crisscross of timbers on a big piece o' canvas, I'll go an' fetch some bladderwrack—grows big in these warm waters. Git t'work, an' I'll be back afore you knows it, mates!"

Neither Beau nor Vurg had the least idea what bladderwrack was. They stretched the biggest canvas sail on the sand and began laying a grid shape of ship's timbers on it. Bolwag returned, though at first it was hard to tell whether it was he, because a huge clump of seaweed surrounded the sea lion's body as he swam, towing it with him. With a powerful heave he flung it ashore.

"Bladderwrack, buckoes. Nothin' like it fer keepin' afloat!"

It was slimy, slippery seaweed, but studded with big inflated air bubbles.

Bolwag winked at them. "Cover those timbers with it, an' lay on more timber atop o' the bladderwrack. I'll go an' get some more."

The process was repeated three more times, after which they cloaked the lot with the sailcloth ends. Under Bolwag's directions, Vurg and Beau laced the canvas casing tight with rope until the sea lion was satisfied with the job. It looked an ungainly bundle.

Vurg bounced up and down on it. "Haha, 'tis springy enough. Will we need a sail, Bolwag?"

"Nah, I'll be either pushin' or pullin' all the way. Well, it don't look like much, me 'earties, but 'tis tight'n'strong an' 'twill get you to Wood Isle without sinkin'.'"

Afternoon was well advanced when they loaded the last provisions aboard and launched the odd-looking raft into the channel. Bolwag grabbed a trailing line in his mouth and went off like a fish. At first Beau and Vurg clung to one another on the skimming, bobbing raft as it bounced and cavorted across the wavetops. However, after a while they became used to the momentum and sat sharing some bread and cheese. Heading north and west, they sped onward, creating a small bow wave of spray, though it was hard to tell exactly where the raft's bows were located, as it swivelled from side to side. Bolwag kept the sunset in the corner of his left eye as he pulled them effortlessly along.

Beau waxed lyrical at approaching evening. "Does somethin' to a chap, the old sunset, rather jolly, wot. Sky goes the color of meadowcream when y'stir it into a plate of damson pudden, sea's as dark as blackcurrant cordial, an' the sun looks like a rosy apple covered with honey. I say, Vurg old lad, rather poetic, wot wot?"

Vurg hid a smile. "Did you compose that with your stomach?"

Beau grinned. "Yes, it did sound rather gutsy, didn't it! Oh I say, nothin' to ruin a perfect evenin' like a great pack o' sharks. Just look at that lot!"

Vurg saw the ominous fins cutting through the water until they surrounded the raft. Suddenly the whole craft swayed threateningly as Bolwag flopped aboard. Beau threw himself on top of the sea lion, grabbing at his slippery hide with all paws and roaring heroically.

"I've got you, old fellow. They'll have t'deal with me before I'll let 'em get to you. Ahoy an' belay, you slab-sided swabs. Scuttle me bilges an' other nautical terms, show me a shark an' I'll show you a coward! Take one bite out of our raft, just one munch, I dare you! I'll leap into the briny an' give you a sound drubbin'! Hah, y'dealin' with a Cosfortingham now, wot wot!"

Bolwag shrugged his huge bulk, sending Beau toppling into the sea. The hare yelled out in panic.

"Didn't mean it, only jokin' you chaps, there, there, nice sharky, good sharky. Yowoops!"

One of the big fishes flicked his tail, catching Beau and sending him sailing back onto the raft.

Bolwag chuckled. "Yukyukyukyuk! Don't yer know a bottlenose when y'sees one?"

Beau clung to Bolwag's flipper, shivering. "Keep mum, old chap. Don't go callin' 'em names like bottlenose—you'll get 'em mad an' they'll scoff the raft. Nice sharks, good sharks. I say, aren't sharks handsome chaps?"

Bolwag's stomach shook as he laughed. "Yukyukyukyuk! Those aren't sharks, ye great booby, they're pals o' mine, bottlenosed dolphins. They offered t'push awhile an' let me 'ave a rest!"

Vurg smiled at his irrepressible friend. Beau regained his composure quickly in any situation.

"Pish tush, sah, I knew that all along, what d'ye take me for, wot? Sharks indeed. What gave y'that idea?" He leaned over the raft's edge and patted the strange beak-shaped snout of the nearest dolphin, which stuck its permanently smiling face out of the sea as Beau nodded to it. "Ahoy there, you jolly bottlenosed rogue, what d'you mean by impersonatin' a flippin' shark? Wipe that smile off your face an' answer me, laddie!"

The big fish gave an earsplittin' squeak and shot a jet of water into Beau's astonished face. He sat back wiping water from his eyes, remarking to Vurg, "Pity that chap never had an auntie to teach him a few manners, wot. Spittin' seawater into a feller's fizzog, huh, very nice, I don't think!"

Bolwag flapped Beau's ears gently with his huge flipper. "Don't you go talkin' about my pals like that, matey. Kweekum an' his school 'ave been friends o' mine since I was a pup!"

Whilst Bolwag held an unintelligible conversation, which consisted of exchanging varying degrees of squeaks with Kweekum, Beau whispered to Vurg, "Tchah! School indeed. Only school that chap ever attended was the school of spittin'. I'd give him detention or a few whacks of the cane if I was his schoolmaster, wot! Blighter can't even speak without squeakin' like a confounded seagull. I'll bet all the baby bottlenoses are a right shower of yahoos. Still, y'can't expect any better if you're brought up with a name like bottlenose, I suppose, wot wot?"

Over a score of dolphins were around the raft, propelling it along at an alarming rate. Every so often, an extra frisky one would jump out of the sea and leap clear over the raft. Vurg sat awake, excited and astounded by it all. Beau tried to sleep, stuffing a piece of bladderwrack in both ears, muttering to himself, "Fat chance of shuteye a chap's got round here. Great lump of a Bolwag, snorin' away like a thousand frogs on concert night, an' those pesky bottlenoses squeakin' like a pile o' rusty gates. Not the sort o' thing a Cosfortingham's used to at all. Indeed not. Good job auntie's not here!"

However, despite the intrusions, Beauclair Fethringsol Cosfortingham was soon adding to the din, snoring uproariously and chunnering on in his dreams through the night watches as the strange craft hurtled towards its destination over the sprawling main.

"Hmm, mm, wot? Pass the salad there, auntie, an' tell the cap'n to stop the boat rockin', will you? Mmm, mm. No thanks, old chap, couldn't touch another bowl of that bladderwrack pudden, foul stuff. Give it to old bottlenose for school lunch, will you? Sharks like that sort o' thing. Mmm mm, wot!"

31

Bullflay cracked his whip over the heads of the wretched rowers chained to the decks of the Death Pit.

"Back water an' ship oars, you idle bunch o' landspawn! Sit still there, not a word or a move, or I'll 'ave the hide off yore backs 'til yer bones shows through!"

Luke heard the anchor splash as he drew his oar inboard. Placing a cheek flat on the oarshaft, he tried looking through the rowing port, but it was a very limited view. Shallow clear water, a white sand beach and just a glimpse of heavily wooded rocks. Norgle the otter, who had his head bent in similar fashion, murmured to Luke, "I always hate makin' landfall. Makes me sick t'me stummick, thinkin' of green growin' things, firm ground under me paws, an' livin' free like I once was."

The otter flinched numbly as the lash descended across his back. Fleabitt the rat stood wielding his own personal whip, sneering at the chained Norgle.

"Then don't think, oarscum. Mister Bullflay told yer not to move or speak, now I'm tellin' yer not to think, see!" He turned as chains rattled nearby. Ranguvar was sitting up straight, her mad eyes boring into the rat.

"Try that on me, ratface. I'm thinkin'—aye, *thinkin'* I'd like to get just one paw round your louse-ridden throat. Go on, swing that lash, see if y'can stop me thinkin'!"

Fleabitt wilted under the black squirrel's gaze and fled the bottom deck, following Bullflay without a word.

Vilu Daskar came out of his cabin, the silken scarf still bound around his neck, which was permanently marked from Luke's attack upon him. He cleared his throat painfully and beckoned to the two ferrets, Akkla and Ringpatch. They hurried to his side for orders.

"Break out the neckchains. We need watercask carriers and food gatherers. Choose a party, but only from the top deck. Take enough crew with you, so that you have two to each one slave. We'll lay over here two nights for provisioning. If any slave escapes you'll answer to me with your lives."

Vilu stood waiting whilst two searats set up a chair and table on the stern deck. When a canopy had been rigged over the chair and food put on the table, he sat down. "Willag, Grigg, Bullflay, bring the mouse Luke to me."

Luke was freed from his oar shackles and fitted with a neckchain attached to paw manacles. Bullflay raised his whip. "Up on deck, mouse, move yerself!"

Luke smiled contemptuously at the slavemaster. "Bring that whip down on me an' I'll strangle ye with it!"

Bullflay's paw faltered, and he let the whip fall to his side. Sometimes he was not sure who he feared the most, the black squirrel, or the Warrior mouse. Luke strode past him, head held high, giving a broad wink to Dulam and Denno as he passed them on his way to the stairs.

Vilu Daskar popped a wild grape into his mouth, chewing it slowly as he looked Luke up and down. "Willag, bring a chair for our guest."

The Warrior dismissed the offer with two words. "I'll stand."

Indicating the roast seabird, fruit and wine, Vilu said, "Suit yourself, Luke. Here, you must be hungry. Have some food and drink. It's good—I'm only served the best."

Though Luke's mouth was watering at the sight of the victuals on the table, he shook his head. "I don't eat food from the table of a murderer."

Vilu shrugged. "Have it your own way. I brought you up here because I want to hear more about this treasure you have hidden. Where did you come by it?"

The reply Vilu received was flat and harsh. "I've told you all, I'll take you to it, there's nothing more to say."

Vilu's bone-handled scimitar was out, its tip under Luke's chin.

"There are many ways to die: quickly, with a single stroke, or slowly, painfully, bit by bit. Now talk!"

Luke's chained paws rose, and he pushed the blade aside. "If I die swift or slow, you will never find the hiding place. Remember, murderer, I am the only beast alive who knows where it is. Kill me or my friends and you will never possess a single piece of my tribe's treasure."

Vilu stuck the bladepoint down into the deck timbers, and the scimitar stood quivering. He nodded and smiled. "You're a strange and reckless creature, Luke, different from the rest. A brave beast like you would go far in my crew, maybe even standing at my side, second in command."

Luke smiled back at him. "Aye, Daskar, then you could make me a real warrior, teach me how to plunder defenseless ones, murder innocent creatures and run away to hide aboard this red ship. You and your Sea Rogues would never stand up to real warriors in combat. Cowards, assassins and the scum of oceans, that's all the captain of the *Goreleech* and his crew are!"

A burly weasel named Clubface was working nearby and heard Luke's words. Thinking to gain the admiration of Daskar, he drew his dagger and leaped upon the manacled slave, roaring, "Nobeast talks to our cap'n like that an' lives. I'll gut ye!" The weasel was big and strong, but he did not possess Luke's speed. The Warrior mouse's pawchains rapped him hard between his eyes, and Luke grabbed the paw holding the dagger, twisting it inward. Clubface felt himself tripped, and fell backward. Luke slammed his weight down on top of the weasel, falling with him and driving the dagger deep into his attacker's heart. Like a flash, Luke was upright, the dripping blade in his paw, facing the pirate stoat. Daskar laughed aloud, thumping the tabletop with his scimitar handle, applauding.

"Neatly done, Luke, you are a real warrior. Come on now, you've got the dagger, try to kill me!"

Sea Rogues had come running to surround Luke. He relaxed and stood with the blade hanging loosely from one paw. Vilu Daskar stood and bowed slightly. Motioning his crew to stand off, he pointed the scimitar at Luke. "My compliments. You are not only brave, but wise also."

Luke nodded towards the vermin all around him. "The numbers are a bit one-sided, Daskar. I'll slay you one day, but I'll pick the time and place!"

Smiling and shaking his head, the pirate stoat replied, "Well said. I like an enemy who uses his brains. Take him below and chain him back to the oars."

Zzzzipthunk!

Before anybeast could move, Luke had thrown the dagger, embedding it deep in the mast alongside Daskar's head.

"Sometimes a knife can reach further than a sword. Remember that, stoat!"

Luke went down under the press of crewbeasts. Vilu Daskar stood over him, shaking with rage. He raised the sword, holding it trembling over the fearless slave, then, thinking better of his actions, he snarled, "Get him below, out of my sight!"

Sea Rogues hoisted Luke upright and dragged him off, back to the Death Pit of the lower deck.

Bolwag's flipper, damp and heavy, touched Vurg's face, wakening him. The sea lion was back in the water; it was midnight of the second day since leaving Twin Islands. The dolphins were gone.

"Vurg, wake up, liddle friend. Give Beau a shake. Look yonder. Wood Isle an' the red ship!"

Moonbeams danced on the phosphorescent sea. No more than an hour's sailing time away, the *Goreleech* could be seen, riding at anchor, close to the shore of the island, which looked for all the world like a chunk of forest sticking out of the main.

Beau rubbed his eyes drowsily. "I say, does look jolly pretty in the moonlight, wot!"

Bolwag drifted off from the raft. "Aye, pretty dangerous too, mate. Well, shipmates, this's where we parts comp'ny. I wouldn't be of much use to ye on land or aboard a vessel. But I got ye here."

Vurg waved at the friendly giant. "So you did, Bolwag, an' our thanks to ye for that. You've done more'n enough for us. Good fortune to you an' those bottlenoses—give 'em our thanks if'n you see 'em again!"

Beau added his farewells to those of his friend. "Toodle-oo and farewell, you old rascal, wot. I'd watch out for sharks if I were you. Remember how they scoffed your ole auntie, bit careless that, keep your eyes peeled, sir. Oh, an' give my regards t'those bottlenose chaps, not bad types really, except for all that pesky spittin' an' squeakin'. G'bye now!"

Bolwag sank beneath the surface and was gone.

Now they were alone, with only their wits to rely on. Lying flat on the raft, they paddled with their paws, discussing the situation, whilst they were still out of earshot of the *Goreleech*.

"Well, Beau, we've got this far. What's the next move?"

"Patently obvious, m'dear feller. Got to free our friends from durance vile, wot!"

"Huh, I know that, but we won't get very far jumpin' aboard the *Goreleech* an' challengin' 'er crew now, will we?"

"Of course not, we'd need at least three of us t'do that. We need a scheme, a plan, an idea, or a combination of all three. C'mon now, Vurg, get the old mousey thinkin' cap on. I'm more a leader than a planner, don't y'know."

As they drew closer to the monstrous red ship, Vurg weighed it up carefully, an idea forming in his mind.

"Beau, d'you see those rope'n'canvas fenders hangin' over the sides to protect the *Goreleech* from rocks?"

"Indeed I do, whackin' great things they are too, some of 'em, bigger than our little raft. Why d'you ask?"

"Because I been thinkin', we could be a fender, too!"

"The deuce y'say, an' what good'll that do, pray?"

"Well, I notice that the stern fenders hang a bit low. S'pose

we was to cut one loose an' let it float off. Then we ties our
own up in its place an' hides there."

Suddenly Beau was thinking along the same lines as Vurg.
"Rather! Spiffin' wheeze, wot. From there we could contact
the oarslave chaps at night, when nobeast's about!"

"Aye, get word to them we're here, see if we can't pinch a
few weapons t'help Luke an' the others!"

"By the left, I'm glad I thought o' that little plan. Don't
slack, Vurg, paddle harder. Please. Hmph! It's one thing
strainin' m'brain t'think up these plans, but it's a bit much to
expect me t'do all the paddlin', old chap!"

"Oh, button up, Beau, y'make more noise than a squeakin'
bottlenose!"

"I beg y'pardon, sah! Confounded nerve o' the mouse,
wot?"

"Stop natterin' an' keep paddlin'!"

"Pish tush, I could say the same for you, whiskerface!"

"No you couldn't, floppylugs!"

"Yes I could, bottlenose!"

"Bottlenose y'self, gabbyguts!"

Glaring at one another and arguing heatedly, they ran
smack into the *Goreleech*'s stern. Thud!

High up near the afterdeck a window swung open. Poking
his head out, a searat, blinking from the cabin lanterns,
called, "Ahoy, who's out there? C'mon, show yerself!"

The two friends grasped the bottom of a fender, pulling the
raft close in beneath the stern. Huddled together, they held
their breath, listening as somebeast joined the searat.

"Aye aye, wot's goin' on 'ere, mate?"

"Thought I 'eard a noise out there. Sounded like two
beasts arguin', then summat struck the ship."

A third voice joined the conversation angrily. "Somethin'
will strike you if'n yer don't shut that winder. Can't a beast
gerra bit o' rest without bein' blown outer the bunk by
draughts from the seas at night!"

The window slammed amid sounds of muffled argument.
Both friends gave a quiet sigh of relief. Vurg whispered,
"Better wait until later, when they're all asleep. Then we'll
see what can be done. What's the funny face for, Beau?"

"Funny face nothin', old lad, I'm blinkin' well famished!"

"Wot, y'mean the vittles are all gone?"

"Exactly, an' the water too. We'll starve t'death!"

"Don't talk rubbish. You could live off'n yore fat for ages."

"Yukk, urroogh, blaaaah!"

"Don't make so much noise. What're you up to now, Beau?"

"Yurkk, this bally bladderwrack tastes absolutely foul!"

"I ain't surprised, matey. Bet even the sharks turn their noses up at that stuff. Beau, where are ye goin'? Come back!" But Beau was shinning up the stern gallery with the alacrity that only a hungry hare could muster.

"Won't be a tick, old thing. Hold the fort 'til I get back."

A moment later the gluttonous creature had vanished into the darkness. Vurg perched on the raft, nibbling anxiously at his paw, wondering where his friend had gone to.

A ferret and a searat were working in the galley. The ferret laid out loaves of hot bread to cool at the open serving hatch, whilst the rat was occupied chopping up fruit, which he mixed in a bowl with honey.

"Good fresh fruit they got from the island t'day, cullie. Cap'n doesn't go much fer it, but it'll look nice on 'is table fer brekkist."

Sampling a slice of apple, the ferret licked honey from his paws and winked at the rat. "We'll 'ave it fer lunch, after we clears the cap'n's table."

Wiping his paws on a rag, the rat took down a dead pigeon from a hook. "Lend a paw ter pluck this willyer, mate?"

They both bent to the task until the bird was plucked. Shuffling to the cupboard for a roasting spit, the rat stopped, looked at the empty space on the table, just inside the window ledge, and turned angrily on his mate.

"Think yore funny, don't yer? Cummon, put it back!"

"Put wot back? Wot's up, matey?"

"Hah, don't you matey me, y'fat robber. Where's me fruit salad got to? Now give it back 'ere."

"I never touched no fruit sal— Hoi! Where's me bread gone? It was laid out there t'cool a moment ago."

"Lissen, slopchops, never mind usin' yore bread as an

excuse. I saw yer pinchin' slices of apple outta that fruit salad. I'll chop yer thievin' paws off wid me cleaver!"

"Ho, thief is it? Well you kin explain t'the crew where the bread's gone when there's none fer brekkist, so there!"

"Don't you accuse me o' stealin' yore lousy bread. Take that!" Swinging the dead pigeon, the rat caught the ferret a smack.

"Ooff! That wuz a foul blow. 'Ere, you 'ave some o' this!" The ferret dealt the rat a stinging blow to his rear with a wooden rolling pin, and they fell to fighting in earnest.

Beau watched from his hiding place on the deck, munching on a hot loaf. The sound of approaching paws caused him to slide into the shadows of the galley bulkhead. As he did, a loaf of bread fell to the deck. Fleabitt stopped in passing, noticed the loaf and grabbed it. Gnawing away happily, he went to see what all the noise was about in the galley. Poking his head around the door, he said, "Nice bread this is, mates. 'Ope you got plenny more fer brekkist tomorrer. Likes good bread I does!"

Instantly he was dragged into the galley and set upon by the two cooks, who pounded him mercilessly.

"So yore the one, yer scringin' liddle thief!"

"Owow! Yowch! Murder! 'Elp, they're killin' me!"

The ferret swung his rolling pin with relish. "Kill yer, y'durty grubswiper, I'll murder ye. Take that!"

Brandishing a copper ladle, the rat leaped on the hapless Fleabitt, pounding him severely. "Aye, an' after he's killed an' murdered yer, I'm goin' to slay yer, yew filthy vittle plunderer!"

A sound overhead caused Vurg to look up. Beau's muted whisper came out of the darkness. "Stand by the raft there. Here, catch these!"

Two long hot loaves dropped down on Vurg, then Beau was alongside him, placing a bowl between them both. "Nothin' like fresh fruit salad'n'honey to keep a chap's chin up, wot. Don't hog all the bread, there's a good chap, chuck a loaf over here. Oh, I found a flask an' filled it from the water cask, better than nothin' I suppose, wot wot."

Vurg was glad of the food, though he lectured Beau

severely. "Your stomach could've got us both caught and killed. That was a foolish risk you took, Beau, don't ever do it again!"

The garrulous hare twiddled both his ears carelessly. "Oh, fiddle de dee, mouseymate, what d'you expect a bod t'do, sit here and jolly well starve? Fat chance!"

Vurg could not help smiling at the devil-may-care Beau. "Oh, all right, but be careful. Great seasons, lookit the size of these loaves. There's enough here t'feed most of the crew. Did you have to take so much bread?"

Beau tore off a chunk and dipped it in the honey. "Waste not want not, old bean. Bet Luke an' company'll be glad of fresh bread. Don't imagine they get it too often, wot wot. When we've had a nap we'll go an' seek 'em out!"

It was still some hours to dawn. Luke sat shackled to his bench, head bent as he slumbered over his oar. Bullflay lay snoring on his makeshift bed. All was quiet amid the smouldering lanterns of the lower deck, save for the odd whimper of some wretched oarslave, dreaming of home and happier times. Ranguvar was dozing, too. She flicked at something tickling her ear. It was a dried stem of bladderwrack. It tickled again, and this time she caught it in her paw, opening her eyes as somebeast whispered, "What ho, old thing, y'don't happen to have a chap down there named Luke, do you? Warrior type like y'self?"

Ranguvar immediately became alert. She looked to the oar port and saw a bewhiskered hare smiling in at her, holding a paw to his lips as a caution to silence. Ranguvar nodded. Pointing across to Luke, she murmured quietly, "Over there, first oar port on t'other side. Who are you?"

"Formal introductions later, friend. Here, chew on this." Completely mystified, but grateful, Ranguvar accepted the big chunk of fresh bread packed with fruit salad. "Don't eat so fast, marm, twenty chews to each mouthful now. Bye bye!" With a wave the hare vanished.

Ranguvar shook Luke awake by waggling the end of his oar. "Ssshhh! You've got a visitor, Luke. Look to your oar port."

Beau peeped in at Luke, his face a mask of mock accusation. "Why aren't you dead, sah?"

Luke shook his head in disbelief. "Why aren't you?"

"Far too hungry to let things like dyin' interfere with my plans, old feller. Vurg's alive too, y'know. Listen, I can't stop t'chat. Here's some food, share it about. Be back tomorrow night, keep y'chin up. I'll see what I can do about bringin' somethin' to deal with those chains. Meanwhile, sit tight an' smile, the rescue party's arrived at last, wot!"

When Beau was gone, Luke and Ranguvar took the hare's advice. They sat tight and smiled, sleep forgotten, now that the first bright rays of hope had started to glimmer.

32

The voyage to the northern coast was well under way. Fortunately, the weather remained fair with favorable winds. Parug, the rat bosun, however, was not a happy Sea Rogue. Vilu Daskar had sent a command, through Akkla, that he was to report to the captain's cabin. Parug was all of a tremble as he rapped hesitantly on the door. Vilu Daskar was sly and unpredictable—who could tell what he wanted to see his bosun about? Whip in paw, the slavemaster Bullflay opened the door to admit Parug. It did not bode well by the look on Bullflay's ugly face.

"Get in 'ere. Cap'n wants to see you."

Vilu was seated at a table, his wicked bone-handled scimitar before him. Parug came to attention in front of the pirate stoat, shaking visibly. Vilu Daskar sat in silence, his face betraying nothing as he stared levelly at the dithering bosun, who managed to gulp out a word. "Sire?"

Vilu touched the silken scarf at his neck, extending the silence until it became almost unbearable, before he spoke. "There is a thief aboard my ship."

"A th-thief, sire?"

"Yes, Parug, a thief. I have a dagger to match this sword, bone-handled, with a curved silver blade. Last night it was on this table, where it usually is. This morning it is gone."

"G-gone, sire?"

Vilu got up and walked round the table. Halting behind Parug, he dug his claws hard into the bosun's shoulder. Parug whimpered in pain and terror as the stoat hissed viciously in his ear. "Stop repeating everything I say, or I'll slice the foolish tongue from your slobbering mouth. Have you been walking 'round this ship with your eyes shut? Other things are being stolen. Food, water, equipment, ship's gear. Now I want to know the names of those who are robbing me. Do you understand, Parug? Speak!"

The bosun knew his life was at stake. Words babbled from him like water pouring from a barrel. "Sire, cap'n, I've noticed it meself, all kinds o' things are disappearin', 'specially vittles an' drink, sire. But on me oath, cap'n, I'm keepin' a sharp weather eye out fer the villains, I swear I am, sire, day'n'night!"

Vilu released him and went to sit back in his chair. "But you haven't a clue who the thieves are, right?"

Parug nodded miserably, unable to stop his head from bobbing up and down. Vilu glanced across at Bullflay. "I don't suppose you've any ideas about the culprits?"

Shuffling awkwardly, the gargantuan weasel shrugged. "Can't think o' none, cap'n, unless 'tis like the crew sez, the Sea Bogle! Some of 'em even sez that—"

Bullflay got no further. Vilu Daskar moved like lightning. Clearing the table at a bound, grabbing his scimitar as he did, the stoat laid Bullflay low with a resounding blow to his face from the flat of the glittering blade.

"Enough! Do you suppose I am as big a fool as the idiots who serve me? Don't dare speak to me of Bogles or phantoms! What need would ghosts have of food? You addle-witted moron, the thieves are living breathing beasts, with the same need for food and drink anybeast has! Out! Get out of my sight, both of you. Search the *Goreleech* from stem to stern!"

Lined up on deck, the crew of the red ship were made to stand fast all morning as a search was made of their living quarters. Vilu Daskar sat beneath an awning, watching as each one was called out to accompany Akkla, Parug and Bullflay below decks.

"Foulscale, yore next, step forward, lively now!" The weasel Foulscale went with the searchers into the crew's accommodation. They searched his hammock and the area around it, and he was then made to gather up his belongings and taken up on deck. Bullflay ordered him to unroll his bundle and display the contents. Then the slavemaster called out, "Righto, crew, take a look at this gear. Is it all the property of Foulscale?"

A brass-earringed searat stepped forward, pointing. "No it ain't, that belt's mine. I'd know it anywheres, sharkskin, wid a green stone in a round brass buckle!"

"I found it lyin' by me bunk!" Foulscale protested.

Vilu Daskar strode over to Foulscale's belongings. With his swordpoint he flicked the belt to its owner, then addressed Foulscale.

"You stole the belt. Get over there with the others!"

Ashen-faced, the weasel walked over to join an ever growing band of Sea Rogues who had been caught with the property of fellow shipmates among their gear.

It was high noon by the time the search ended. Those who were innocent stood in line, looking greatly relieved. More than a score of vermin, who had been caught in possession of stolen property, huddled miserably around the mainmast, awaiting the consequences.

Vilu Daskar delivered his judgement for all to hear. "I know you are not the thieves I seek. Somebeasts are plundering wholesale from this ship. Make no mistake, I will find them and punish them slowly to the death. There will be an end to thieving aboard my *Goreleech*. But you who have been caught, you are still guilty of stealing from your shipmates and must be punished. Thank your lucky stars I am in a lenient mood, and keep your paws to yourselves in future. Akkla, Parug, Bullflay, hoist them up by their tails and give them twenty lashes apiece, sluice them with salt water, let them hang there until sunset, then cut them down. The rest of you will witness the floggings as a reminder never to steal whilst aboard the red ship!"

• • •

Vurg and Beau perched on their raft, well hidden by the over-hang of the high carved stern. They could not avoid hearing the screams and wails of the miscreants as they were sub-jected to the whipping. Neither had any pity for Sea Rogues.

"Makin' more noise than a school of confounded bottle-noses, wot. That'll teach 'em honesty's the best policy!"

"Aye, there's only one thing worse'n a thief, Beau."

"Indeed, an' what is that, pray?"

"Two thieves!"

"Haw haw, rather good that, Vurg."

"We'll 'ave t'be more careful of a night from now on, mate. They'll be watchin' for us, y'know."

"Of course they jolly well will, so you do the stealin' an' I'll keep 'em diverted in me Sea Bogle costume, eh?"

Vurg chuckled. "Sea Bogle, wot a load of ole nonsense!"

Beau fixed two horns he had made from dried bladder-wrack to his ears. He waggled them and scowled fiercely. "Talk not like that of ye Sea Bogle, old lad, or I'll put a spell from the dark murky deeps upon thee!"

Vurg closed his eyes, enjoying the warm noon sun. "Pity you can't put a spell on yore stummick, stop it needin' so much food, y'great fat fraud!"

"Steady on there, m'good mouse, us Sea Bogles need nourishment if we're to perform properly. No self-respectin' Sea Rogue'd be scared of a half-starved skinny Bogle. Er, any more of that skilly'n'duff left?"

"There's some in the bowl. Help yoreself, I imagine you'll spirit it away without too much trouble. What are you writin' there? The ship's log of our raft, the *Floatin' Fender*? Put me down as mouse mate, an' you c'n be cap'n Bogle."

Beau was scraping away with a charcoal stick on a strip of canvas, his tongue sticking out at the side of his mouth. "Actually it's a poem I'm composin' about Bogles. Some of those ignorant vermin may be unaware of the tale, so I'm doin' a bit of publicity for meself, doncha know."

Vurg winced as they heard the splash of water, followed by more agonised wailing from the upper decks. "Ooh! Must sting somethin' awful, bein' flogged an' gettin' salt water chucked on the cuts."

The hare was unmoved as he continued writing. "Prob'ly the only decent wash they've had since their dear old mothers used to scrub 'em in the tub when they were babes. There's a thought, can you imagine a filthy beastly little pirate babe bein' scrubbed in a tub? I'll wager his language would frazzle his auntie's slippers, wot?"

In the crew's accommodation that night, the vermin who had been released sat nursing their hurts, whilst others swaggered about, displaying the treasured gear they had thought lost. The rest huddled around the mess table, playing an old searat game with shells and fruit pips. The entire crew jumped with fright as the cabin door slammed open. Parug staggered in as if his paws were made of jelly, grasping a long strip of sailcloth.

The searat Willag helped him to a seat at the table. "Wot's the matter, bosun? Y'look as if y've seen a ghost."

Somebeast passed him a •tankard of barnacle grog. He drank the fiery liquor in one long swallow, and it was dribbling down his chin as he stared wildly about.

"'Twas the Sea Bogle, mates. I saw the Sea Bogle wid me own two eyes, on me affydavit I did!"

A chilled silence fell over the crew. Parug was quite a stolid rat, not given to silly imaginings. The tankard was refilled and Parug took a deep swig before continuing, "I jus' came out to patrol the deck, searchin' for a sign of any thieves. Before I could blink a glim it 'ad me by the throat. Long long arms it 'ad, like steel, I couldn't move! I tell ye, shipmates, I'll never be the same agin after seein' the Bogle. It 'ad great big horns, three eyes, an' a face that was all lit up, glowin'! Covered it was, wid 'orrible flowin' weeds from the bed o' the seas, all wet an' drippin'. Ugh! 'Twas too terrifyin' to describe!"

Willag took a gulp from the tankard Parug had put down. "Why didn't yer run an' tell the cap'n?"

Parug shot him a haunted glance, whispering dementedly, "Cap'n won't 'ear of it, 'e don't believe in Bogles. I couldn't tell 'im, mate, 'e would've slayed me!"

Foulscale temporarily forgot his stinging back. "Did the Bogle speak to ye, Parug? Wot did it say?"

The bosun held up the canvas strip. "It never said nothin', jus' growled an' gave an awful squeak, like a bottlenose dolphin. Then it pressed this sailcloth inter me paw, let go of me neck an' stood there."

Foulscale shook his head in amazement. "So wot did you do?"

"Do? Wotjer think I did? I ran off, fast as I could!"

"Is it still out there, d'ye think?"

"I don't know. Go an' look fer yoreself!"

"Wot? Lissen, mate, I ain't movin' out o' this cabin 'til it's daylight an' the sun's shinin', so there!"

The crew nodded their heads vigorously in agreement.

Willag picked the sailcloth from Parug's shaking paws. "See, there's writin' on it. Wot does it say, Parug?"

"I don't know, I can't read letters or words."

Grigg the searat beckoned to Willag. "Give it 'ere. I can read. Let's see wot it sez."

Grigg read it out in halting tones. He could read, but only just. His voice echoed out in the awed silence.

"From the dark and icy deeps,
Where the dreaded Bogle sleeps,
He'll rise one night and climb aboard your ship,
Bringing fear and deathlike doom,
To your very cabin room,
Beware the Bogle's clammy vicelike grip!

Aye, woe betide that crew,
Sailing on the main so blue,
And to those who don't believe me double grief,
When the Bogle takes a meal,
You will hear a dreadful squeal,
He strikes when nighttime falls, just like a thief!

Aye, who of you can tell,
Give him gifts and feed him well,
Then the Bogle may slide back into the sea,
But if gifts and food be few,
Hearken now, for it is true,
The Bogle may eat you, or even me!

Crack some ribs or crush a skull,
Stuff down hearts 'til he is full,
Rip paws and tails off any poor seabeast,
Lock your cabin doors this night,
Shake with terror, quake with fright,
For the Bogle may invite you to his feast!"

Grigg was quaking so badly when he finished the poem that he dropped the canvas. Willag was the first to move. He dashed to the cabin door and locked it, calling down the long smoky cabin to his mates, "Bar those skylights, batten 'em down tight! Trim the lamps an' clean 'em, we need it good'n'bright in 'ere!"

Fleabitt and the ferret Ringpatch were on duty in the Death Pit. The slaves were sleeping, draped across their oars. Ringpatch, who generally worked on top deck of the trireme, took a quick glance around.

"Hoi, Fleabitt, this lot won't be no trouble fer the rest o' the night. Come on, mate. Let's go up to top deck, it stinks down 'ere. Walloper an' Ching from middle deck'll be up there, my mate Flanjear, too. Top deck ain't like this pest'ole—we got a liddle oven up there. Bet they're makin' skilly'n'duff an' suppin' grog."

Fleabitt coiled his whip over one narrow shoulder. "Skilly'n'duff! Why didn't yer say, matey? Lead on, I'm right be'ind yer. Nothin' like a bowl o' the ole skilly'n'duff!"

The moment they were gone, Luke and Ranguvar sat up. All through the bottom deck, oarslaves became alert. Luke's orders were relayed from one to another.

"Those closest to the steps, keep watch. Give the warning if y'hear anybeast comin'!"

"Dulam, Denno, look to your oarports. Vurg will be along with food soon."

"Ranguvar, how's that big staple coming along, nearly out?"

The black squirrel looked up from her labors. "'Tis a big 'un, set deep an' well rusted, but I've got it on the move, Luke."

"Good, but be careful you don't splinter the wood too much. Bullflay usually stands near there, an' we don't want him to spot anything suspicious."

Norgle the otter tossed something across to Ranguvar. "All taken care of, matey. I'm mixin' tallow with dirt from the deck, that'll disguise it good."

Luke nodded his approval. "Great stuff, matey. See if y'can get more o' that tallow, we'll need it for the oarchains."

As Luke talked he was busy with his own oarshackles, filing a deep groove into a link close to his paw. "Gricca, have you got those weapons stowed safe?"

An old female hedgehog several rows back answered, "Aye, Luke, all safe'n'sound, they're jammed in slits I cut on the undersides of these benches. Here, you have this'n. 'Tis a fancy liddle toy that Beau found. Duck yore nut, mate, comin' over!"

Luke bent his head as something whizzed by and stuck in the upraised oarshaft. It was a fine curved silver dagger with a bone handle. He plucked it from the oar. "Well, this is a fine sharp gizzard slitter!"

Ranguvar sniffed the air, shaking her head in disbelief. "I can smell hot scones dipped in honey."

Denno confirmed the squirrel's statement. "So you can, friend. Vurg's here!"

"Ahoy, Vurg, where'd you get these?"

"Ooh, they're still hot from the oven!"

"Pass that bag along, mates, share 'em out!"

Shaking with laughter, Vurg passed another flourbag loaded with hot scones through the oarport. "Go easy, mates, don't crush 'em. Pass the empty bags back an' I'll fill 'em agin. Luke, how's it goin' down here?"

"Fine, Vurg, just fine. Where did all these scones come from? They're delicious. I didn't know vermin could bake as good as this. Did you'n'Beau steal all these? How in the name o' seasons did you get away with 'em?"

Vurg managed to poke his head partly through the oarport. He was grinning from ear to ear. "We never stole 'em, Luke, we baked the scones ourselves. Ole Beau the Bogle has the crew frightened out o' their wits, an' they battened themselves up tight in the crew's accommodation, terrified. So, seein' there wasn't anybeast on deckwatch, we found the galley empty, stoked up the ovens an' went to work. Beau sends his compliments!"

The entire deck of oarslaves, conscious of the need for silence, shook with suppressed mirth until tears popped from their eyes and ribs began to ache. There was a scrabbling from the bulkhead and Beau appeared at the opposite oarport, still in Bogle garb, but with his face covered in flour and honey.

"What ho, chaps, Beau the Bogle baker here. I say, I hope you oarslave types aren't laughin' at my cookin', wot?"

A young vole, closest to the oarport, took Beau's paw and shook it heartily. "No sir, even my ole mum couldn't cook a scone like you do. They're the best anybeast ever tasted. If we're laughin' 'tis because you've taught us how to. Some of us have been down 'ere for long seasons, treated harsh, too, with no reason t'smile. We're 'appy 'cos you've given us back a reason t'live, with yore bravery an' kindness, both you an' mister Vurg, may fortune bless yer both!"

The young vole was so overcome that his tears of merriment turned to real tears, which flowed onto the hare's paw. Beau the Bogle tried to make light of things, though his long ear dipped to wipe moisture from his own eye.

"There, there, young feller m'bucko, 'twas the least we could do, wot? Though if you want more scones I suggest you release my jolly old paw. You've washed it quite clean thank you, but all that oar pullin' has given you a rather powerful grip, an' you seem t'be crushin' me paw t'pulp!"

Ranguvar Foeseeker began to tremble with rage. Her voice shook as it echoed around the deck known as the Death Pit. "All the prisoners aboard this red ship have strong paws through pulling long oars across heavy seas. But those same paws won't always be pulling oars. One day soon they'll be shaking off their chains an' taking up arms against Vilu Daskar and his Sea Rogues. Then we will take vengeance for ourselves, our families and friends and all the lost seasons of our lives. I give you my word!"

Beau took one look at the black squirrel's eyes, and said, "I don't doubt it, marm, not one word!"

33

The *Goreleech* ploughed the seas, hours became days and days turned to weeks, the waters grew more tempestuous and the weather changed as the red ship sailed into wintry latitudes. Swathed in a soft cloak of light green wool, head protected by a purple silk turban, Vilu Daskar rested a paw on the scimitar thrust into his waist sash. Bracing himself against the for'ard rail, he gazed north over the grey spume-topped waves, narrowing his eyes against a keening wind. Akkla the ferret stood to one side, awaiting orders from his captain.

It had not been a good trip. Despite the whippings and beatings given to the crew, thievery on a grand scale had prevailed. Both Vilu and Akkla hoped it was not the Sea Rogues who were responsible, but the red ship's vermin were growing sullen, muttering among themselves about the floggings and the shortage of food. The pirate stoat knew that discipline and order had to be retained aboard ship, if he were to stay master, so he had enforced his will. Still superstitious murmurings continued, dark tales of a Sea Bogle haunting the *Goreleech*. Even though he threatened, ranted and rea-

soned, Vilu knew he was helpless against the ignorant beliefs
held by seagoing vermin. However, with the scent of treasure
in his nostrils, he was not about to give up. One idea he
pounded into the thick skulls of his crew was that they would
follow orders or die. Knowing they were on a ship at sea,
with nowhere to run, that and the fear of their murderous captain kept the crew in line.

Vilu spoke to Akkla without looking at him. "I'm going to
my cabin. Have the mouse Warrior Luke brought there, then
return here and let me know the moment you sight land. Oh,
and tell Parug to keep the crew busy. I want the mess deck,
galley and accommodation scrubbed and cleaned from bulkheads to deckheads."

Willag dipped a chunk of pumice stone into a wooden pail of
cold seawater and began scrubbing half-heartedly at the mess
tabletop, complaining, "Huh, clean the mess deck agin. I've
wore me paws t'the bone scrubbin' at this stupid table,
must've scoured it more'n ten times o'er the past few days!"

Foulscale was on all fours, toiling away at the mess deck
flooring, slopping icy seawater everywhere. "Aye, an' it ain't
as if there's any vittles t'put on that table, mate. Those
scummy slaves look better fed than us!"

Ringpatch the ferret, who had been rubbing the brasswork
shiny with a mixture of ashes and fine sand, put down his rag
and wiped a filthy paw across his brow thoughtfully. "Yore
right there, bucko. D'you think 'tis the slaves who've been
swipin' our grub?"

Parug the bosun swung a length of rope, knotted at one end
and stiff with pitch and resin. "Oh aye, it has t'be the slaves,"
he sneered scornfully. "I can just see 'em, cookin' up pans o'
skilly'n'duff in the galley, carryin' their oars over their shoulders o' course, wid their footpaws chained to large chunks of
deck. You great blitherin' nit! 'Ow could slaves manage that?
'Ave yew got mud fer brains? Now get on wid shinin' those
brasses. I wants ter see me face in 'em, or I'll feed yer a taste
o' this rope's end!"

Luke's paws were bound behind him, and he had a rope halter around his neck. Vilu Daskar sat on the edge of his cabin

table, questioning the prisoner. "So, my friend, do you know where we are?"

The Warrior met his captor's eyes fearlessly. "I'm not your friend, but I do know where we are—in the northland seas."

"Oh indeed? I know that, too, but where precisely in the northland seas are we?"

Luke shrugged. "Your guess is as good as mine. One wave looks the same as another out there."

Daskar shook his head, a thin humorless smile on his lips. "Still the Warrior, eh? Listen well, mouse, I did not bring you here to play games with me. How soon will I know exactly where we are? Tell me or I will stop all oarslaves' water rations. That would be easy—there's little enough left for me and my crew. So tell me."

As if ignoring the stoat, Luke shuffled past him and looked out of the cabin window at the icy heaving seas. "Take a course east until you sight land, then steer north again. No doubt you will remember a rocky headland—that's where you massacred my tribe. Once you see that headland, send for me. I will steer your ship from then on, because only I know the route."

The bone-handled scimitar flashed skilfully, grazing Luke's ear. There was no mistaking the menace in Vilu's voice. "Sure enough, you will steer the *Goreleech*, chained to the wheel, with this blade at your throat!"

Luke's smile was wintry as the weather outside. "I'll look forward to it, but don't make it too easy for me, will you?"

Vilu's teeth ground audibly as he snarled to the guards, "Get this defiant fool out of my sight!"

As he was hustled from the cabin, Luke managed to put a chuckle in his voice. "Defiant yes, but a fool . . . never!"

When they had chained Luke back to his oar, Ranguvar murmured out of the side of her mouth, "When do we make our move? Everything's ready. I got word that the top deck cut their last chain whilst you were gone."

Luke pondered the question before replying. "Sometime tomorrow, maybe evenin', I've a feeling we may sight the headland by my old home. I'll be up on deck with Daskar probably. If my tribe see the red ship, they'll be ready for trouble, so we can count on help from them."

Ranguvar had to wait whilst Bullflay walked past down the aisle, towards the oarslaves at the stern end.

"So, if yore on deck, how will we know, Luke?"

"Hmm, good question, mate. I know, we'll have Beau or Vurg make their way up near the prow. If they hear me shout 'Dead ahead,' that'll be the signal to take over the ship. But if I shout 'Veer north,' you must do nothing. I'll be chained to the ship's wheel by then. Sit tight an' wait until I get word to you."

Ranguvar paused as Fleabitt strode sternward.

"Got it. If Vurg or Beau tells us 'Dead ahead,' the attack is on, but if the message is 'Veer north,' we wait!"

The two messengers in question were undergoing severe hardships. Beau and Vurg were freezing and soaking from the cold weather and pounding seas. Huddled together beneath layers of stolen blanket and sail canvas, they clung grimly to the raft, which was lashed to the *Goreleech*'s lower stern. The hare poked his head out of the wet jumble, catching the backlash of a big wave. He retreated back down, wiping his face on the damp blankets.

"By the bally cringe, old lad, can't last much longer in these inclement latitudes, wot?"

Vurg closed his eyes and tried to sleep, but Beau persisted. "My jolly old auntie'd say it's cold enough to whip the whiskers off a mole an' wet enough t'drown a lobster. Cold'n'wet wouldn't be so blinkin' bad if I wasn't flippin' well starvin' t'death. What would you sooner do, Vurg, freeze t'death, drown t'death, or starve t'death?"

The mouse opened one eye and murmured, "You didn't say wot wot."

"Wot wot? Why the deuce should I say wot wot?"

Vurg smiled sleepily. "'Cos you always say wot wot!"

Beau's ears stood rigid with indignation. "I beg your very pardon, sir, I do not. Wot wot? I was merely speculatin' on our demise. I said, would you rather freeze t'death, or drown t'd—"

Vurg interrupted him rudely. "I heard what you said first time. Hmph! Freezin' drownin' or starvin' wouldn't be so bad if I wasn't already bein' nattered t'death. Don't you ever stop natterin', mate?"

Beau's indignation switched to injured innocence. "Well, chop off m'tongue, pull out m'teeth an' sew up m'lips. I'll put a cork right in it an' quit assaultin' your dainty shell-like lugholes, old bean. Far be it from me to try an' make companionly conversation with a friend facin' adversity. Not another word, m'lips are sealed!"

Vurg immediately felt sorry for his garrulous companion. "Take no notice of me, Beau, I'm just feelin' sorry for myself. You carry on, wot wot!"

The hare chuckled and ruffled his friend's ears. "Well of course you are, old mouseymate, that's why fate threw us t'gether like this, so I could jolly you up whenever y'feel down in the dumps. My dear old auntie taught me a song about such situations. I say, shall I sing it for you? Cheer you up no end, wot?"

Vurg turned his head aside and pulled a wry face. "Oh well, seein' as I can't escape the sound of yore voice I s'pose I'll have to listen. At least it'll scare any sharks away if they're hangin' about. Sing on, Beau."

Needing no second bidding, Beau launched into his auntie's song, ears clasped in traditional hare manner.

"When you're feelin' down an' glum,
Don't just sit round lookin' dumb,
Sing tickety boo a fig for you, wot ho fol lah!
'Cos there's time for all that gloom,
When you're dead an' in the tomb,
Sing tickety boo a fig for you, wot ho fol lah!
When 'tis rainin' all the day,
An' the skies are dirty grey,
An' you've ate the last plum pudden off the shelf,
Jig an' caper in the wet,
You'll be better off I bet,
Than pullin' faces, feelin' sorry for yourself.
Oh tickety boo a fig for you, wot ho fol lah!
These few words will cheer you up an' take you far,
Not like that old frumpy duck,

Or a frog who's out of luck,
Or the little maggot who has lost his ma, ah ah ah ah
    aaaah!
If you laugh there'll be no rain,
An' the sun'll shine again,
Then your dear old aunt will bake you apple pie,
So when hedgehogs learn to fly,
Fish will quack an' wonder why?
Tickety boo a fig for you, never say die aye aye,
Aye aye, aye aye, aye aaaaaaaaaaaaaye!"

Vurg threw himself on Beau, stifling his efforts. "What are
you tryin' to do, attract the attention of the entire ship's
crew?"

That put Beau into a sulk. He wrenched himself away from
Vurg, working himself into a huff and muttering, "Huh,
bouncin' on a chap just as he's reachin' top note, jolly dangerous thing t'do, wot? An unexploded phrase might've
backfired down m'neck an' fractured me warbler. Little
you'd care, though. An' I still had another three verses t'sing.
There was the line in the second verse about a toad losin' his
trousers up a tree, very movin' an' profound part o' the ditty.
But I ain't goin' to sing it now. What's the use of one chap
singin' to cheer another chap up, if the other chap keeps
jumpin' on the first chap's head? Bad form I'd say, ungrateful
wretch!"

All that evening and throughout the night, the slaves were
forced to row, though only at quarter speed in the wild northern seas, whose tides, rocks and currents had sent many a
vessel to its doom. Fleabitt pounded his drum slowly, with a
monotonous regular cadence, and Bullflay dozed fitfully,
only striding the aisle when he felt the need to stretch his
paws. Luke pulled the heavy oar alone, spray whipping
through the oarport at odd intervals to wet his face. Sleep was
the farthest thing from his mind, now that he was near to his
old home.

Thoughts of his son Martin raced through the Warrior's
imagination. He would be tall now, quick and strong, with
the blood of a leader and a fighter flowing in his veins. Mar-

tin would know what to do, the moment the *Goreleech* was sighted. He would get the old and feeble, together with those too young to do battle, together. Having hidden them safely, Luke's son would do as he had been taught by his father: gather together the strong ones, arm them and come to his father's aid, wielding the very sword Luke had passed on to him. As the slaves broke loose and fought to gain control of the red ship, Luke would run her into the coastal shallows, causing the vessel to heel over. He would hail his son from the ship's wheel. Once Martin heard the voice of his father, he would come hurtling through the shallows at the head of his fighters to board the *Goreleech*. Then Vilu Daskar and his murderers would pay dearly for their monstrous crimes.

Ranguvar Foeseeker's whisper reached Luke, and he looked across at the fierce creature.

"Are we close to the place where you left your son?"

"Not too far now," Luke murmured as he pulled at the oar, "I feel it in my bones, friend."

Grigg the searat gripped the edge of the crow's nest. Leaning forward, he peered into the leaden rainswept dawn at a rocky point in the blurred distance. With all the agility of a searat, he clambered down from the rigging to the deck.

Vilu Daskar was slumbering on a window seat, a charcoal brazier glowing nearby to warm the cabin. Parug the bosun gave a perfunctory rap at the door and entered. "Headland's been sighted, cap'n, dead ahead!"

Daskar leaped from the seat. Grabbing his wool cloak and scimitar he dashed from the cabin, with Parug at his heels, bellowing to rouse the crew.

"Land ho, all paws on deck!"

Daskar raced for'ard, wind whipping the cloak straight out behind him, calling to Parug as he went, "Get Luke up on deck here, quick!"

Wind thrummed the rigging ropes like harp strings. Daskar perched high in the bows, his eyes shielded by a paw as he noted the headland's position. Jumping down, he gathered his cloak around him and hurried to the stern. Luke was standing by the wheel, bound and surrounded by six vermin. The pirate stoat smiled triumphantly at his oarslave.

"So, 'twas as you said, the point lies dead ahead. A wise decision, mouse, for if you had played me false, then your head would be on the deck for sure! Bind him to the wheel, make sure the ropes are tight!"

Rough paws dragged Luke to the big steering wheel. He was tied to it securely by both paws, and a rope halter was placed about his neck. Vilu held the other end.

"Right, sing out, Luke, give us the course!"

Knowing it was too early to give the signal, the Warrior murmured, keeping his voice low, "Steady as she goes."

Swinging on ropes, just below the stern gallery, Beau and Vurg strained their ears.

"Wot wot, did y'hear what he said, Vurg?"

"No, mate, but I'm sure he didn't shout 'Dead ahead!' "

Groaning, the hare slid down his rope. "Oh fiddlesticks, that means the attack ain't on yet. I'll go an' let Ranguvar an' the others know."

Vilu tugged viciously at Luke's halter. "Looks as if you're sailing her close in to land. Why?"

Moving the wheel a touch north, Luke kept his eyes ahead. "Got to get my bearings. I'm not quite sure that's the right headland. Don't worry, Daskar, your ship's safe. I'm not going to try anything with all those poor slaves chained below. Give the order to ship oars and take her to half sail. We'll go forward nice an' easy if you're afraid."

Vilu gave the halter another savage jerk. "I'm not afraid, mouse, just cautious. I've sailed northern seas before—they can be treacherous."

Luke smiled fearlessly. "As treacherous as you?"

Vilu Daskar returned the smile. "Not quite."

At midday the rain cleared, though the skies still remained dull and wintry. Luke was close enough to see the shore plainly now. His heart sank, as if a great boulder was forcing it down, causing a heavy ache in his chest. Before him the shoreline lay deserted, only seagrass and some tattered rags fluttering in the wind. Charred wood and broken implements, hoes and rakes, were half buried in the shifting sand. The caves, where once he had settled his tribe, had had the protective shields of driftwood and vegetation ripped from their fronts. They stood empty, like the eyeless sockets of a corpse staring out to sea. Martin his son, Windred and the rest of the tribe were gone from the place.

Sick with grief, he slumped across the wheel. Vilu Daskar was grinning slyly as he brought his face close to Luke's.

"What a shame, my friend. Has your plan gone wrong? What sort of fool did you think you were playing me for? I would have been stupid to let you sail my ship inshore where the creatures of your tribe could have helped you." Luke stared dully as his enemy laughed in his face. "Fool! I am captain of the greatest ship that ever sailed the seas. How do you think I did it? I learned to read the minds of others, to out-think those who thought they were smarter than me. I knew all along that you yearned for vengeance after the slaying of your tribe. All you have lived for is a chance to kill me!"

Luke nodded. "Then you must know there is no treasure?" He felt hot rage sweep through him as Vilu patted his cheek, almost fondly. The stoat's voice was wheedling.

"The old double bluff, eh, Luke. Don't try to pull the wool over my eyes. I know that every tribe, no matter how poor and lowly, has some kind of treasure. Right?"

Luke bit his lip, lowering his head as if defeated. "What beast could hide anything from you. But I hold you to your promise. If I show you the way to my tribe's treasure, you must set me and my two friends free."

Vilu leaned upon Luke's shoulder, happily surveying the empty shore. "But of course, I am a creature of my word, all three of you will have your freedom. Now set a true course."

Awkwardly the Warrior mouse maneuvered the wheel round. "It's further north up the coast. The cross-currents shouldn't give us much trouble if you pile all sail on and put the oars to a steady half pace."

Ranguvar waited until Bullflay lumbered by before turning to the oarport. Vurg popped his head into view, spray dashing at his face.

"Luke's not given the word yet, friend. But I'd stay ready tonight if I were you. That's when we should be further upcoast, amid the high rocks and deep water!'

34

Ringpatch the ferret came in from watch and slumped down on a pile of old rope and sailcloth, glad to be back in the big smoky crew's cabin, mopping water from his fur.

"Bad night out there, mates. Weather's rough as a toad's back an' cold as a cap'n's 'eart. Any vittles left?"

Foulscale pointed to the empty pan on the table. "Take a look in there, mate. If'n there's anythin' left then save 'arf fer me. Why'n the name o' fishguts aren't we down south somewheres in the warm sun, pickin' ripe fruit offa trees an' plunderin' birds' nests? Wot's to be 'ad up 'ere, apart from yer death o' cold an' starvation, that's wot I'd like ter know?"

Akkla snuggled up to the smoking stove, shaking his head. "Did the ice git down yore ears, Foulscale? We're in the northern waters fer treasure, or 'aven't yew 'eard?"

"Treasure?" Ringpatch crawled over to sit by the stove.

Akkla tossed some old rope into the stove and watched it burn bright as flames licked round the tarry strands. "Aye, treasure. Y'know that Warrior mouse Luke? Well 'e's

280

steerin' the ship up t'where he stowed 'is tribe's booty. Vilu 'ad a word with 'im, promised t'set Luke an' his two mates free if'n they let the cap'n git 'is paws on the treasure they 'id."

Foulscale showed his blackened teeth in a knowing grin. "Set 'em free, eh? Remember the last lot Vilu Daskar set free, those four 'edge'ogs, d'yer recall that, Willag?"

The searat chuckled with wicked glee. "Oh, I remember it awright. They were 'oldin' back a supply of grain they'd 'arvested. Ole Vilu promises t'set 'em free once he's got 'is claws on the stuff. So they showed 'im where they'd 'idden it. Hawhawhaw!"

One rat had not been a crew member at the time, so he had to ask. "An' did Daskar set 'em free?"

Akkla looked about for more rope to feed the stove. "Course the cap'n did. He 'ad 'em sewed up in the grain sacks with some good 'eavy rocks an' dropped overboard. Vilu's last words to the 'edge'ogs were, 'You leave my ship alive, free t'go where ye will'!"

The Sea Rogues pounded each other's backs and laughed aloud.

"Never tole a lie in 'is life 'as our cap'n. Hohoho!"

"Wonder wot 'e'll think up fer this mouse Luke an' 'is mates?"

"Heehee, bet 'e'll take 'em up ter some clifftop an' set 'em free as birds. Heeheehee!"

"Or introduce 'em t'some new friends, the sharks. Hahahaha!"

"Wotever it is, the cap'n's shore t'give us all a good laugh, mates. Then we can sail south'ard t'the sun an' prime vittles fer a while. Widout Luke an' 'is two mateys though."

Parug the bosun gestured to Foulscale with his knotted rope. "Oi yew, stir yer stumps there, 'tis yore turn t'relieve Ringpatch on watch. Never mind sittin' 'round 'ere laughin' an' jokin', git out on deck wid yer, go on!"

Foulscale shot the bosun a hateful glance. Wrapping a piece of sailcloth around him he lumbered reluctantly out. Akkla called after him, "Don't let the Sea Bogle git yer!"

Foulscale spat out of the cabin door, and it blew back in his face. "Tchah! Sea Bogle, that'n deserted ship as soon as there wasn't enough grub left t'feed a fly. Sea Bogle only brought bad luck ter this ship, just's well 'tis gone."

He ducked as Parug flung an old seaboot at him, calling, "It won't be Sea Bogles you'll 'ave ter worry about if'n yew stands wid that door open much longer, freezin' us all into our graves. Gerrout on watch, yew idle lump, an' shut that door after yer!"

Beau and Vurg had climbed aboard the red ship, being unable to endure further cold and hardship hanging onto the raft at the stern. Gripping any protrusions available, they made their way along the outside of the *Goreleech*, avoiding being seen from the after peak, where Luke was tied to the wheel, guarded by ten crew and Vilu Daskar, who had a canvas awning to protect them and a brazier to warm their paws upon. The two friends made it to the foredeck and hid behind a sail-draped hatch cover. From their hideout they could see the shoreline: white sand backed by sheer cliffs which reared into the night.

Beau snuggled down. "Well, it ain't much, Vurgy, but as my old auntie used t'say, somethin's better'n nothin' when y've got nothin', wot?"

Vurg threw an affectionate paw about his comrade. "Shall I tell you wot my ole auntie used t'say, Beau? Well, she always said t'me, if yore hidin' under a hatch cover with a sailcloth over it, an' there's a hare with you, then don't let the hare talk about how 'ungry he is an' don't let 'im sing. There, that's wot my ole auntie used t'say!"

Beau was still in a fine old huff with Vurg. "Food? Who said I was goin' to talk about food, eh, wot? Far too hungry to talk about food. An' I ain't goin' to sing to you no more, after you jumped on my head an' damaged me warbler. Savage mousewretch, that's what y'are. Oh, great seasons of stones, take a look up ahead, Vurg!"

The mouse poked his head from the sailcloth, his gaze following the bowsprit to judge the ship's course.

"'Tis the tall rocks, Beau, we're headed straight for the tall rocks!"

Rearing like prehistoric giants to the stormy night skies, hundreds of the monolithic stone pinnacles stood out from the coast for leagues. Waves crashed into white foam at their bases, sending white spume flying high into the air. A peculiar effect, like screaming tortured animals, assaulted their ears, as the gale force winds tore between the awesome columns, whose tops seemed to touch the tempest-driven clouds.

For the first time in his life Beauclair Fethringsol Cosfortingham was robbed of the power of speech. He sat there with his mouth hanging open.

Vurg was the first to recover and do something. "Luke's goin' to smash this ship into the tall rocks! Quick, Beau, climb down to Ranguvar. I think Luke will give the signal very soon now. I'll go astern an' listen out for it. The moment I hear Luke's voice I'll make my way along the ship's side an' yell at the top of my voice. Go now!"

Vilu Daskar was also feeling something for the first time in his life. Fear! He had seen the tall rocks, once many seasons back when he was younger. However, he had not sailed remotely near them and had vowed never to do so. But now he was in the midst of a storm, his vaunted *Goreleech* headed straight for the tall rocks, relying only on the skill of a mouse oarslave, bound to the steering wheel. Daskar stood dry-mouthed, sweating despite the cold, paws atremble and stomach churning. Tugging hard on the rope halter about Luke's neck, he yelled shrilly, "Watch what you're doing, go careful with my ship, pull her away from those rocks. Away I say!"

Luke kept his head bent, resisting the rope's tug. "How does it feel, murderer, to have death starin' you in the face?" he gritted out from between clenched teeth. "Think of all the innocent creatures you've sent to their deaths. Go on, tell me how it feels?"

Vilu reached past Luke and managed to get a paw on the wheel. The Warrior mouse sank his teeth into the paw, and with a yelp the pirate stoat withdrew. Vilu's guards drew their weapons. Luke shouted at them without turning his head.

"One move from you, murderer, or any of your scum, and I spin this wheel and send her side onto the rocks!"

Vilu's big mistake had been in binding Luke to the wheel. He was fully in control of steering the ship. The stoat signalled his crew to stay clear. Luke decided then to make his move. Throwing back his head, he roared at the top of his lungs, loud and long, "Dead ahead! Dead ahead! Dead aheeeeaaaaadddd!"

Slipping half in, half out of the lashing churning sea, Vurg scrabbled and clawed his way along the port side until he was amidships. Ahead of him he could see Beau, balancing perilously on Ranguvar's oarshaft as it stuck out from the bowside, waiting for the signal. Vurg clambered up onto the rail, shouting, "Dead ahead! Free the slaves, take the ship!"

In his excitement he had forgotten all else. Next instant Parug and Akkla came rushing from the crew's quarters.

"What's happenin', who's takin' the ship?"

"Somebeast's tryin' to free the slaves! Call to arms! All paws on deck!"

Slaves began pouring from the companionways of the three oardecks, some armed with what they could find, lengths of chain, pieces of timber and pitifully few daggers. Unsure how to proceed, they milled about on the deck, some weeping openly, not knowing what to do with their new-found freedom. These slaves, all from the upper and middle decks, soon found themselves set upon by masses of heavily armed Sea Rogues, veterans in the business of bloodshed. Vurg and Beau rushed to their aid. Laying two searats low with savage kicks from his long hindlegs, the hare grabbed the vermin's cutlasses and tossed one to Vurg, bellowing, "Rally to us, you chaps, don't sit 'round blubberin'. Fight!"

Several of the younger and bolder spirits obeyed, but there were others, too weak and frightened, who were thoroughly intimidated by the fierce horde of the *Goreleech*'s crew. These wretched creatures ran and hid, and a lot of them tried to push their way back down to the oardecks, to the benches and chains where they had lived for long seasons.

Then Ranguvar Foeseeker arrived upon the scene.

Battering slaves aside like ninepins, Bullflay came screaming out of the companionway, terror stamped upon his ugly features. Behind him, like the shadow of death, was Ranguvar. Laying into the slavemaster with his own whip, the black squirrel was a sight to strike fear into the heart of anybeast now that she was on the loose. The long whip cracked around Bullflay's ears as Ranguvar Foeseeker went after him, the stormy night echoing to her battle cries.

"Yayalaho! I am the Foeseeker, born in moondark to the crash of thunder! Sing your deathsongs! Yayalahooooo!"

In his panic Bullflay fled straight up the rigging, with Ranguvar hard on his heels, her eyes red with bloodwrath, laughing madly as she closed on her hated foe.

Vilu Daskar felt himself gripped by the icy claws of panic. Never in his wildest imaginings had he dreamt this could happen aboard his red ship.

"Akkla! Parug! Bring the crew astern! Gather to me!"

As the Sea Rogues crowded round, Luke called to his enemy above the din of storm and battle, "What are you goin' to do now, coward? Yore slaves are free and fightin', the *Goreleech* is bein' driven to the rocks. 'Twas a bad day for you when you murdered my wife!"

As if to emphasize the dilemma, Bullflay's body, choked by his own whiplash, came flying down from aloft and crashed through the afterdeck stairs, taking with it two vermin who were making their way aft. Ranguvar Foeseeker climbed halfway down the rigging, then, with a bloodcurdling yell, hurled herself on a group of Sea Rogues who were hacking at helpless slaves on the main deck.

The pirate stoat turned on Luke, his voice a venomous hiss as he slashed at the bound Warrior with his sword.

"You were the cause of all this, but I will end it here!"

Luke could not protect himself from the wild, vicious onslaught, even though the swinging blade chopped the ropes free from one of his paws. Dulam and Denno were battling their way to the afterdeck when they saw Luke being attacked.

Beau and Vurg saw it too, and fought their way to the shattered stairs, Vurg crying out, "Luke! No! Hang on, mate, we're comin'!"

But Luke was not finished. Fighting his way up through waves of pain, he put all his strength into a single blow. His paw chopped down on that of Vilu Daskar, sending the bone-handled scimitar skimming off into the sea. Then Luke had Daskar in a death grip, crushing him tight against the ship's wheel. Sea Rogues hurled themselves upon the Warrior, trying to free their captain, who was screeching with fright. Pounding willy-nilly at the Warrior, they were about to break the awful grip he had on Vilu Daskar when suddenly Ranguvar Foeseeker was in their midst, armed with two swords. The black squirrel was like a berserk tornado, dealing out death and fearsome wounds, laughing madly into the stricken faces of her foes.

"Yaylaho! 'Tis a fine night to die! Yaylahooooo! Take a deep breath, buckoes, it'll be yore last! I'll hold 'em off, Luke, you hold Daskar tight! Yayalahoooooo!"

Looming up to the red ship was a towering rock, ten times the girth of any craft, with waves riding high up its sides and smashing in foamy cascades. Luke had Daskar's paws twined through the wheel spokes like a captive upon a rack, and the pirate stoat, his back pressed hard against the wheel, began begging and pleading hoarsely for his life as the *Goreleech* rode side on towards the monstrous column of wave-lashed stone.

"Spare me, Luke. You can have the treasure and freedom for all the slaves. Take the red ship too, but let me go. I speak truly, my word is my bond. Spare my life!"

Luke the Warrior pressed his face close to that of his mortal enemy, crushing him tighter and whispering, "Cowards die a thousand times, a warrior dies only once. The spirits of all you have slain are watching you, Vilu Daskar, and they will rest in peace now that your time has come. You must die as you have lived, a coward to the last!"

When the red ship struck the rock it reverberated from stem to stern. There was a noise like an overhead peal of thunder, then it was shorn in two halves upon the mighty pin-

nacle of stone. The *Goreleech* hung there for one awful
moment, then the whole stern, from afterdeck to midships,
fell. With a huge creaking of sundered timbers it hit the water
and sank instantly. Far far below the seas, never to be seen
again.

BOOK THREE

A Warrior's Legacy

35

Sunlight lanced through into the cabin of the *Arfship*, dust-motes swirled lazily about the still lit lanterns. Denno took the rock crystal glasses from his nose end and placed them on the closed book in front of him. Yawning and rubbing his eyes gently, he leaned back and stared up at the noon sky.

"So now you know everythin', Martin of Redwall, that's the whole story, as best as we could remember."

All eyes were on the stonefaced warrior, awaiting his reaction. After what seemed an interminable silence, he spoke.

"Am I to understand then that my father wrecked the *Goreleech* on the big column, knowing that he would die?"

Beau wiped a paw across his eyes and sniffed.

"Aye, that's what he did, old lad, wounded almost t'death, with Ranguvar Foeseeker holdin' off almost an entire vermin crew so Luke an' her could have their revenge on Vilu Daskar, the red ship, an' all that had caused 'em to lose their loved ones. By the fur, blood, tooth an' sword! Two braver warriors never lived!"

Vurg grasped the Warrior mouse's paw tightly. "They did it for you—for all of us, Martin. Everybeast who'd ever suf-

fered by the wickedness of Daskar an' his red ship. Luke was
past carin' about what happened to himself—Ranguvar, too.
Between them their final sacrifice was to rid the land an' seas
of a great evil!"

Martin's eyes were like chips of ice.

"I would have done exactly the same in my father's place!"

Dulam felt the hairs rise on his nape as he watched Martin.
"I believe you would've, too. That sounded just like yore dad
talkin' then. We all would, but for the fact we were at the
for'ard end when the ship broke in two."

Martin stared keenly from one to the other.

"Is there anything else I should know? Vurg, you knew
him better than most. Tell me."

The old mouse shook his head wistfully. "He gave you all
he could, vengeance for your mother an' our tribe, freedom
from a terror that the coastlands an' seas lived in fear of. But
I remember that day we sailed off from the northlands, he
gave you his sword. That blade had never left his paw, or that
of his father an' his father before him. It was the most precious thing Luke ever owned! But there was something else,
Martin, not from your father alone. When you discovered me
in the old cave back there, I had found something buried in
the sand. Here!"

Vurg passed the beaded linen bag to Martin. It was the sort
of container a mother would use to keep her baby's things in,
together with the small possessions she held dear. Martin's
paw traced the beautiful pattern of tiny threaded beads
worked onto the linen. He eased himself slowly away from
the table and left the cabin.

Gonff called after him, "You all right, matey? Need any
help or company?" There was no answer from the Warrior.
Gonff settled back against a bulkhead. "Best leave him alone
awhile. Get some shuteye, mates. I've a feelin' that when he
comes back through yon door we'll be leavin' this place. You
an' yore pals better pack, Vurg. We ain't leavin' you stranded
up in these rocks on a broken ship. You'll have t'keep
pinchin' yoreselves to make sure yore not dreamin' when you
see Redwall Abbey, mates!"

• • •

Martin climbed down the front of the huge main column and sat on a ledge, with the sea almost lapping his footpaws, gazing down into the fathomless deeps. Somewhere far below lay the stern of the *Goreleech*, with his father, Luke the Warrior, pinning Vilu Daskar against the steering wheel, holding his enemy in an eternal embrace. Around them would be strewn the pirate stoat's vermin guard, and Luke's berserk friend Ranguvar Foeseeker. Pride surged through Martin. His father and the black squirrel had kept their vows, they were the bravest of the brave, true warriors.

Martin sat there a long time, staring at the spot where sunlight ended in seagreen haze. From that beaded bag he took a stone, a rounded, medium-sized pebble, banded with various colors. The sort his father might have picked up from the beach, long ago, and brought back to the cave for his wife or little son. Martin held it awhile, until the stone took on warmth from his paws. Then he dropped it gently into the sea, watching it sink rapidly from sight into the depths.

"This is for you, my father, from Sayna, the wife you lost, and Martin, the son you strove to return to. But I have made good your promise, I returned to find you. Ranguvar Foeseeker, I know not if you had any family, but you have two friends forever. Luke the Warrior and Martin of Redwall. I will carry your memories in my heart."

Martin left the tall rock then, with the seas still booming in his ears as they broke against it. In all his life he never went back to that place. On the next ebb tide the skiff *Honeysuckle* sailed away from Tall Rocks, bound south for Redwall.

Skipper of Otters craned his head back, staring up into the pale blue summer morn. Bella the Badgermother of Redwall waited patiently, already knowing what her burly friend's question would be.

"Of course I can tell the squirrels to set up more scaffoldin' at the south end, marm, but why, pray?"

Bella spread her paws wide, as if the answer were obvious. "Because summer is nearly done and autumn will soon be here."

Sitting back on his powerful tail, the big otter shrugged. "Huh, 'fraid you've lost me, marm. What difference will that make? Autumn always follered summer, 'tis the way o' the seasons. What's that got t'do with scaffoldin'?"

Bella sat beside him, fiddling with the strings of her apron. "Mayhap 'tis just a foolish fancy of mine, Skip, but I'd like to see the south gable built right up as far as it will reach. According to Abbess Germaine and Martin's plans, that's where the weather vane will be, at the highest point."

Columbine approached them and sat down, unfolding a clean white linen cloth to reveal a scone still warm from the window ledge where it had lain to cool. "Taste that and tell me what you think?"

Breaking it in two, she gave them a piece each. Bella inspected the pastry, sniffing it appreciatively.

"Smells wonderful. I can see chopped nuts and bits of crystallized honey in there, but tell me, why is the scone pink?"

"Because it's a Redwall Abbeyscone," the pretty mousewife explained. "I used wild cherry juice in the mix, to give it the color of our walls. I plan on making them in the shape of the sandstone blocks we've used to build our Abbey with. D'you like them, Skip?"

The otter had bolted his piece in one great mouthful, and now he picked crumbs from his whiskers and nibbled them.

"Very tasty, Columbine marm, exceedin' nice! But yore goin' t'need a big oven to bake 'em big as sandstone blocks."

Columbine gave Skipper a playful shove. "Oh, you great puddenheaded riverdog, they'll only be little scones, baked in the shape of the big stones!"

The otter Chieftain scratched his head. "Aye, marm, seems I can't get a thing right t'day. D'you know why autumn follows summer, an' that's why the squirrels must build more scaffoldin', so that we can build the south gable end up to its peak with a weather vane atop? 'Cos I'm blowed if'n I do, ole pudden'ead that I am!"

Columbine hugged Bella's huge paw. "Oh, what a lovely, wonderful idea! Our south gable built high, with a weather vane sticking up on it. When my Gonff comes marching down the path with Martin and Dinny and Trimp, why, they'll be able to see it from a great distance. How nice!"

A slow smile spread across Skipper's face as the reason for Bella's request dawned upon him.

"Haharr, so that's it! Swoggle me rudder, why didn't I think o' that?"

He fell backward as Bella and Columbine tugged his footpaws, chuckling aloud as they chorused together, "'Cos you're a great puddenheaded old riverdog!"

Bella made the announcement right after breakfast. It was wholeheartedly supported by all the creatures of Redwall.

Lady Amber added to the excitement. "An excellent idea. I'll get my squirrels to work straight away on the scaffolding. Though 'twill take most of the day erecting it up on the south end, so here's what I suggest. Friends, you've worked hard and long all summer, why not have a day's rest? Perhaps a picnic by the pond can be arranged for early evening. We'll have finished the scaffolding by then, so we'll be able to join you. First thing tomorrow everybeast can pitch in and we'll really go to work and top off that south gable. How's that?" Rousing cheers greeted the Squirrelqueen's scheme.

Ferdy and Coggs, the hedgehog Cellarkeepers, trundled barrels, kegs and casks out of the main Abbey door onto the lawn. Baby Gonflet was waiting with his gang of Dibbuns, all armed with wedge stones and prodding sticks. Coggs narrowed his eyes. "Wot are you up to, Gonflet, ye liddle wretch?"

Gonflet waved his barrel-prodding stick dismissively. "You'n'Ferd go now, Cogg. Us take these barrels down to a pond. Not wurry, us good barrel rollers!"

Coggs exchanged glances with his twin brother. "Wot d'ye reckon, Ferdy, shall we let 'em?"

Ferdy smiled at the Dibbuns, who were dancing about and waving their sticks eagerly.

"Aye, they got to learn sometime, I s'pose. But roll that big barrel o' strawberry fizz slow now, Gonflet, an' go easy with those firkins o' elderberry wine. An' the rest of ye, stay be'ind the barrels all the way, don't go runnin' in front. We

don't want yore mammas after our blood 'cos you've been
run down by some keg or cask!"

Bella walked by, followed by a group of Redwallers carrying canvas and poles.

"We'll make a good leanto," the Badgermother was saying. "It'll provide shade for the food and the elders can rest
there. Mayberry, will you and Catkin get a trolley, line it with
blankets and fetch Abbess Germaine down to the pond? Go
easy with her, please—remember, she's very old and frail."

Mayberry and Catkin, the two ottermaids, bobbed curtsies
to Bella and trotted off, feeling very important.

Columbine supervised the kitchens, bringing order and
calm to the bustle of cooks and helpers. "Clear those window
ledges of scones now. We need room for the turnip and parsley flans to cool. Miz Woodspike, would you like to top those
blackberry tarts off with meadowcream? I don't know anybeast who does it as neat as you do. Mister Pitclaw, could you
help me to get the oatloaves out of the ovens, please? Oh, and
tell your moles we need more charcoal to heat that back oven
for cheese and mushroom flans. No, don't worry about your
deeper'n ever pie, I'll watch it whilst you are gone. Now, let
me see, strawberry shortcake, rhubarb crumble, leek and
onion turnovers, deep apple pie, is that everything? Oh dearie
me, I've forgotten the salad!"

A fat bewhiskered bankvole broke in on Columbine's mus-
ings. "Never fret, missus, I been choppin' salad an' mixin' it
since hard after brekkist. 'Tis just about made. Gurbee, did
we remember to pick some fennel?"

A jolly-looking mole dug both claws into his apron pocket,
rocking back and forth as he announced, "Hurr, you'm may
'ave furgitted ee fennyel, zurr, but oi bain't. Oi gurtly loiks
moi salad well fennyelled. Burr aye!" Beamingly he pointed
to a sizeable pile of fennel.

Lady Amber stood high up on the south gable, heading the
line of squirrels passing up thick yew scaffolding poles to
others, with knives held in their teeth and lengths of stout
cord draped over their shoulders. They chatted away nonchalantly, clinging by tails and paws from their perilous positions. Below them the lawns of Redwall Abbey looked like a
series of green kerchiefs.

"Chuck me that big 'un with the forked top, Barko. Aye, that's the one. Ashtwig, grab this end while I tie it off to the main platform. Pass more cords up, will ye!"

Swift and sure they toiled away, with a clear blue sky above and a breathtaking void beneath them.

"Looks nice'n'cool down by that pond, they're puttin' a leanto up, see."

"Aye, an' lookit, there's miz Columbine an' the others, carryin' trays o' vittles from the Abbey. What's that noise?"

"My tummy, mate. Mmmm, I can almost smell cheese'n'-mushroom flans from up here. Hope they don't start afore we get down."

"If you don't cut the gab an' tie off that pole we'll be up here come this time t'morrow. Shape yoreself, matey!"

Mayberry and Catkin delivered Abbess Germaine to Bella, who was waiting beneath the canvas awning. Both the young ottermaids bobbed another curtsy together.

"Here she is, safe'n'sound, miz Bell!"

"Snug as a bug in a rug with all those cushions an' blankets, miz Bell. We was very very careful with 'er, marm."

Twinkle-eyed, the ancient Abbess peered out of the trolley. "Mm, mm, if they'd pushed me any slower we would've stopped. Two snails passed us on the way, would y'believe!"

Both ottermaids' lower lips began to tremble. Abbess Germaine chuckled, nodding fondly at them. "Mmm, mm, now don't fret, little maids, I was jesting. An old fogey like me couldn't ask for more gentle or better care than you two showed to me. Cheer up now!"

Bella ruffled the ears of both affectionately. "That's why I sent them. Mayberry and Catkin are my two best and most trusted helpers. Run along now, you two."

Smiling and curtsying, they prepared to skip off.

"Thankee, miz Bell. Nice t'be of service to ye!"

"An' you too, Mother Abbess, just call if'n you needs us!"

Germaine was a bit warm. She shrugged off the blankets as she watched the two ottermaids looking for others to assist.

"Such good little things, Bella, a credit to Redwall, eh?"

"I'll say they are. They're both Skipper's granddaughters, y'know. I was only saying to him the other day— Yaaaah! Look out! Everybeast out of the waaaaaay!"

Amid squeaks of dismay and a great bumping and rumbling, Bella seized both Abbess and trolley. Heaving them up in her strong paws, she dashed from the leanto, not a moment too soon. Gonflet and his Dibbuns had let Coggs and Ferdy's cellar stock get away from them. Down the slope a thundering stampede of kegs, barrels, firkins and casks leaped, bounced and spun. In their wake came Gonflet and his gang of little Abbey creatures, hallooing and whooping wildly.

Bella ducked, covering the Abbess with her body as a keg of pennycloud cordial bounced and whizzed by overhead, missing the badger's ears by a whisker. In a trice the leanto was levelled, flattened to the ground. In a resounding boom of splashes the picnic drinks in their oaken containers hit the pond's surface, drenching everybeast within range in a cascade of pondwater.

Dripping from ears to tail, Bella turned to the saturated gang of Dibbuns. Gonflet grinned from ear to ear, pointing with his stick at the array of floating barrels bobbing about in the pond.

"All go'd too fast t'stop, miz Bell. But pond keep d'drinks nice an' cool, I fink!"

Bella could not be angry in the face of the little fellow's irresistible charm, though she hid a smile and tried to sound stern.

"I knew a young mouse one time who was just like you, a scamp, a rascal and a complete pickle!"

Gonflet pawed water from his eye, wrinkling his nose as he stared up at the big Badgermother. "Wot was him name, miz Bell?"

The huge striped muzzle lowered, until it was level with Gonflet's face. "If I recall rightly, his name was Gonff!"

This sent the tiny mouse off into tucks of laughter. Waving his stick, he raced off with his Dibbun gang, shouting, "Heeheehee! Jus' wait I tell my daddy. You a scamp! Raskill! Pickler! That wot miz Bell call you. Heeheehee!"

Creakily Abbess Germaine emerged from the swathe of blankets and cushions in her trolley. She began sorting out poles from the pile of collapsed canvas.

"Hmm, mmm, 'tis some long seasons since I built a leanto. Lend a paw here, Bella, come on!"

The Badgermother sighed as she dragged the canvas aside.

"Gonflet was right, though, the pond will keep those barrels nice and cool on a day like this, Mother Abbess!"

That evening the picnic was a huge success. Lady Amber and her squirrels skipped nimbly down the scaffolding, navigating the sheer walls as if they were on level ground, singing as they descended.

"The dull old ground is not for me,
I can't stand it somehow,
Leave me in a good stout tree,
Upon a knotty bough!

'Tis hey ho and up we go,
Above the ground we dwell,
Where every leaf'n'twig we know,
And every branch right well!

A squirrel a squirrel so nimble,
Can climb most anywhere,
A tail in a tree is a symbol,
That I'm at home up there!

So ash, oak, rowan or pine,
Stately elm or beech,
They're all fine, they're all mine,
They're all within my reach!"

Whilst the Redwallers made merry, otters fished the barrels of drink from the pond. Gonflet and his Dibbun gang had everybeast roaring with laughter as they performed a dramatic re-enactment of the barrel incident. Skipper held his sides to stop them aching, tears of helpless merriment streaming from his eyes, as a small mole, acting a barrel of dandelion and burdock cordial, tumbled downhill into the pond. Columbine hauled him out and attempted to give the tiny creature a strict lecture, but was unable to do so because she collapsed laughing.

Lanterns were lit at the pond's edge when evening shadows deepened, the still water reflecting their glow. Mayberry and Catkin performed a graceful dance to the accompaniment of Ferdy and Coggs on drum and fiddle, playing a time-honored favorite called "Bide in the Rushes." Columbine left off serving drinks, and sat eating pensively. Abbess Germaine watched her closely.

"An acorn for your thoughts, my dear."

Columbine recovered herself as Gonflet hurled himself into her lap. "What? Oh, er, sorry, Mother Abbess, I was in a bit of a daze. I was just thinking how much I miss Gonff—Martin and Dinny, too, of course. I wish autumn would hurry and they'd return to Redwall."

Gonflet yawned and looked up at his mother. "I want my daddy. When it be h'autumn, mamma?"

The dancing had stopped, and all eyes turned on Columbine. Gonflet's lids began drooping as she stroked his head and softly recited an old poem.

" 'Round the seasons slowly turning,
Faithful as the stars and moon,
Summer fades, the earth is yearning,
Softly whisp'ring, autumn soon.

Drape the woods in mist one morning,
Now small birds have learned to fly,
Mother Nature's gentle warning,
See green leaves turn brown, and die.

In old orchards on the bough,
Fruit hangs russet, red and gold,
Purple scarlet berries now,
All the rambling hedgerows hold.

Hazel, beech and chestnut too,
Each displays its burden fair,
They will shed them, all for you,
Ere winter lays their branches bare.

Fields of ripened grain and corn,
Swaying to a murm'ring breeze,

Shaking off the dew of dawn,
When the eye sees signs like these.

Summer's long hot days are ended,
Harvest moons o'er stream and mere,
Tell the tale, as 'twas intended,
Autumn's peaceful dream is here."

Columbine shifted slightly, trying not to disturb her sleeping babe. "Ooh, this fellow's getting heavy these days."

Bella relieved her friend of the burden, scooping Gonflet neatly up in one huge paw. She nodded knowingly. "Little wonder. See, the pockets of his smock are full of wedgestones to use on the barrels. Pity the scamp never bothered to use 'em!"

Abbess Germaine could not help remarking, "Think of the fun we'd have missed if he did. That one'll grow up a bigger rascal than his father. But you're right, Columbine. Redwall isn't the same without Martin, Dinny and your Gonff. Let's hope they'll make it back safely."

Skipper paused, a cheese and mushroom flan halfway to his mouth. "Only beasts I'd be worried about, beggin' yore pardon, marm, are those foolish enough to try an' stop 'em returnin' to our Abbey. Huh, I'd sure enough feel sorry for those!"

Columbine topped the otter's beaker up with October Ale. "I suppose you're right, Skip, but my Gonff attracts trouble no matter where he is. I think he enjoys it."

Abbess Germaine patted the mousewife's paw. "That's why he has two good friends—Martin, who has never been defeated by anybeast, and Dinny, full of caution and sensible mole logic. Don't fret yourself over those three, my dear, they could overcome anything!"

Bella winked at Skipper, to lighten the evening's end and take Columbine's mind off worries about Gonff and his friends.

"Getting late, Skip. Come on, you haven't sung tonight. Send us all off to our beds with one of your funny ditties."

The burly otter was only too willing to oblige.

"Good night, sleep tight!
Don't forget t'close the door,
Good night, sleep tight!
Use the bed an' not the floor,
Good night, sleep tight!
Now don't let me hear you snore,
Good night, sleep tight!
An' don't sleepwalk any more.
Blow out the candle,
Turn down the bed,
Stop yore yawnin' sleepyhead.

Good night, sleep tight!
Up the wooden stairs y'creep,
Good night, sleep tight!
Put on yore nightie, go t'sleep,
Good night, sleep tight!
Stop that talkin' in yore dreams,
Good night, sleep tight!
Don't rip y'sheets to smithereens,
If a nightmare starts t'show,
An' you wake me up, oho,
Out the window you will go . . . good night!"

Leaving the pondside, they trooped slowly back to the
Abbey—Bella in the lead carrying the sleeping Gonflet,
Columbine linking paws with the ottermaids, Ferdy and
Coggs pulling the trolley in which the Abbess slumbered,
followed by all the other beasts. Skipper brought up the rear
of the procession, singing as quietly as his big gruff voice
would allow. Everybeast joined in, keeping their voices low,
the catchy melody acting as a gentle march, echoing softly
over moonlit Abbey lawns.

As they entered the main Abbey door a vagrant breeze ruffled Bella's fur. She shuddered lightly and whispered to
Columbine, "Bit of a chill in the air just then."

Gonflet, who was supposed to be fast asleep, opened one
eye and grinned cheekily.

"Soon be's h'autumn now, miz Bell!'

36

The *Honeysuckle* skimmed southward like a playful swallow, Log a Log Furmo proudly showing off her prowess as a skiff to the four creatures from the *Arfship*. Martin sat in the prow, enjoying the sun, seaspray and breeze, with his faithful friend Gonff alongside him. Together they listened to Trimp attempting to chide Chugger for his lack of respect to the elders.

"I'll not tell you again, Chugg, please stop calling our friends old granpas, 'tis not very good manners!"

"Tchah! You don't know noffink, they good ole granpas for Chugg. We makin' lorra skillyduffs for 'em!"

Folgrim and Dinny had been appointed assistant cooks, helping Chugger to cook skilly 'n' duff. They were on his side.

"Maister Chugg bain't doin' no 'arm, missie, bain't that so, zurr Fol?"

"Aye, let the liddle tyke be, miss, he ain't never 'ad a granpa. Haharr, now he's got four of 'em!"

Trimp appealed to Vurg and his friends. "Please forgive Chugger. I hope he hasn't offended you."

"There there, don't fret, young gel, wot! He can call us
blather-faced bloaters as long as he keeps feedin' us. Jolly little rip, ain't he, Vurg?"

"Aye, an' seein' as we've got no families of our own, 'tis
nice t'be chosen as grandsires by him. Ahoy there, cap'n
Chugg, is our skilly'n'duff ready yet?"

The small squirrel gave his concoction a final stir and
licked the ladle. Nodding brusquely he issued orders.

"Skillyduff cookered now. Mista Fol, Mista Din, give ole
granpas some first. Miz Trimp, you serve a rest o' my crew!"

Martin and Gonff had difficulty keeping straight faces as
they accepted their bowls from Trimp. The hedgehog maid
was quietly seething. "Bushtailed little villain, who does he
think he is? Issuing orders to me as if I were some sort of
lackey!"

Martin blew upon his spoon as he tasted the food. "Mmm,
he does make great skilly'n'duff, though. What d'you think,
Gonff?"

"Never tasted better, matey. D'you reckon Chugg'd adopt
us as ole granpas?"

"No, we're a bit young for that. Why don't we apply to be
uncles, like Folgrim and Dinny."

Trimp stamped off to serve the Guosim shrews, muttering,
"I don't know, everybeast aboard this boat has got that
cheeky-faced villain spoiled rotten!"

Chugger's latest order interrupted her rebellious musing.

"Find more bowls for the sh'ews, miz Trimp!"

Trimp turned on Chugger, paws akimbo, shouting shrilly,
"Yes sir, no sir, three bags full sir! Perhaps you'd like me to
scrub the decks and polish the oars!"

Chugger's reply left her speechless. "No no, do that later,
jus' stop shoutin' for now, my ole granpas're gonna take
naps. Hush y'noise now!"

It was some days later, and the weather was getting noticeably warmer. Furmo steered the *Honeysuckle* closer inshore,
hallooing the creatures standing paw deep in the shallows.

"Dunespike, old mate, how are ye?"

Splashing about joyfully, the fat old Dunehog Chieftain

hailed the boat. "Sure an' I'm all the better for yore askin', Furmo. Come ashore now an' rest yer ould fur!"

Willing paws helped haul the *Honeysuckle* above the tide-line. Murfo and a gang of young male hedgehogs fell over each other assisting Trimp ashore.

"Faith an' fortunes, missie, but yore lookin' grand, grand. Prettier'n ever, though I says so meself!"

Trimp grabbed an oar and vaulted over them onto the sand. "Aye, and still well able to take care of myself, thank ye!"

Martin seized Dunespike's paw and pumped it heartily. "Greetings, Chief, you're looking very well!"

"True, true, I'm gettin' younger by the day, plump as a pear an' brisk as a bumblebee. Well now, c'mon up t'the dwellin' an' loosen off yore belt. We've been watchin' out each day for a glimpse of y'grand little boat. Sure an' the cooks are roastin' the paws off themselves to make ye a grand ould supper. I think we'll even be able to fill Gonff's belly tonight. How are ye doodlin' there, Mousethief?"

Gonff fell into the Dunehogs' speech mode. "Sure an' if'n I look half as grand as yerself, then I'm twice the mouse I used to be, sir!"

Linking paws and chattering away happily, crew and Dune-hogs made their way into the sandhills and entered the cunningly disguised dwelling house. Beau and his friends were quite impressed by it all, and the hare expressed his admiration to all the young hedgehogs, whilst shielding Trimp from them.

"I say, what a super wheeze, a jolly great place like this inside a sand dune, wot! Well done, you chaps, top marks!"

One of the young males was winking slyly at Trimp. "Sure an' I'd forgotten how pretty ye are. A hog'd travel ten rough country leagues an' not see the likes o' ye. I'll wager y'could charm the stars out o' the skies with just a flutter of those eyelashes!"

Beau pretended to think the Dunehog was talking to him. He tweaked the creature's ear sharply.

"Mind y'manners, sir, we haven't even been introduced, wot. Though you seem jolly perceptive for a hedgehog. Mind you, I do strike quite a handsome impression on most creatures."

The *Honeysuckle*'s crew found that the Dunehog hospitality was not lacking. For supper they dined on a fine leek and potato soup, followed by mushroom, radish and seafood stew, with an enormous fruit trifle for dessert. After that they sat about drinking cordials and Seafoam Ale whilst they were entertained to a Spinetussling exhibition, some lively Dunehog reels and jigs, and various poems, recitations and ballads. Trimp sat with a group of hogmaids and they all flirted outrageously with the young males, who danced and Spinetussled to vie for their attention. Martin sat with Dunespike and Furmo, watching them with amusement.

Furmo gestured towards them with his tankard. "Don't you wish y'were their age again, Chief?"

Dunespike shook his great head until the spikes rattled. "Away with ye, indeed I do not. They're completely mad, all of 'em! I'd sooner have vittles'n'drink any day!"

Martin gave Dunespike a friendly shove. "You old fogey, look at them. They're young and happy, with not a care on earth. Good luck to them I say, eh, Furmo?"

The Guosim Chieftain nodded his agreement. "They don't have our problems, mate. We've got to figure how t'get a boat of the *Honeysuckle*'s size up a waterfall and past a pine wood full o' painted savages. Aye, an' even when we get by that lot we'll still be battlin' upstream, against the current. 'Tis goin' t'be difficult t'say the least!"

Dunespike poured himself some cordial. "Then why d'ye not find another route?"

"Huh, easy said, Chief, but is there another route?"

"Hmm, let me think. Ah now! What about Northfork!"

Furmo stared over the rim of his tankard at Dunespike. "Northfork? Does it run up this far?"

"Sure it does an' all, two days of a good pawslog from here."

Furmo called across to Folgrim. "Ahoy, mate, d'you know the Northfork stream?"

The scarred otter left off contending for the remains of the trifle with Beau.

"Aye, I know Northfork stream right enough, though I never traveled right up it. I was reared at the southern end of that stream, 'tis where my holt is at."

Furmo thumped the rush mat they were seated on. "Of course! It joins up to the stream we sailed here on, about three days down from my tribe's summer camp. Just one thing, though. How're we goin' to get the *Honeysuckle* overland to the Northfork stream?"

Dunespike shrugged his powerful shoulders. "An' how else but to carry it? Sure, me an' the Dunehogs will lend a paw t'do the job. A fine lot we'd be if'n we couldn't help out. That's what friends are for!"

Martin clasped paws with the good old Hogchief. "And you surely are a great friend to us, sir!"

Dunespike's huge frame shook with merriment. "Sure an' I wouldn't risk bein' anythin' else to a warrior who can wield a sword like you, Martin of Redwall!"

By first light next morning they were all down on the beach. Dunespike had slept on the idea and awakened with a brilliant solution. Martin and the crew stood on one side, watching as the hedgehog Chieftain put his scheme into action. Two sets of wheels on axles were trundled out from somewhere in the dunes. Dunespike called out orders.

"Here now, Murfo, you an' the lads attend to them wheels. Martin, get that grand ould crew o' yores on the starboard side, an' I'll take the portside with my crowd."

Paddles and stout poles were thrust beneath the skiff's flat bottom to emerge the other side. Everybeast took firm hold of them. Dunespike roared out, "Are y'fit now. Lift!"

The *Honeysuckle* rose clear of the sand as they lifted. Murfo and the young ones rolled the wheels in for'ard and aft.

"Ah that's grand, let her down now, easy!"

Two Dunehogs with big staples and mallets fixed the axles in position beneath the boat. Dinny whispered to Trimp, "Hurr hurr, ee boat wot doan't sail on ee seas, oi loiks et. Yon Dunespiker be a gurtly h'intelligent 'og, burr aye!"

There was some minor trouble getting the wheeled vessel through the dunes and off the soft sand. However, once they hauled her up through a low gap in the clifftop, the going was good. It was fairly flat scrubland, grass and hardpacked earth, and there was no call to use the pulling ropes. With her sail up, the *Honeysuckle* caught the wind and rolled along unaided. Beau and the other three elders were aboard her, with Dunespike, Trimp and Chugger. The rest trotted along-side, sometimes even having to tug on the towropes to slow the *Honeysuckle*'s progress.

Gonff laughed. "Just think, if'n there was no woodlands 'twixt here an' Redwall, we could've sailed home by land!"

Later in the afternoon, the land began a mild uphill slope and the breeze died completely. They split into two parties, one for'ard, pulling on the towropes, the rest at the stern, pushing. But the skiff still ran fairly smooth on its wheels, so it would have been no great effort were it not for Chugger. The little squirrel had attached a gull feather to a pole, and he dashed back and forth, tickling the pullers and pushers mer-cilessly and haranguing them.

"Cummon! Cummon! Run, make 'er go plenny faster, or cap'n Chugg tickle you tails off!"

Trimp decided she had put up with enough. Looping a line about the tormentor, she relieved him of the pole and tied him to the mast. Chugger set up an immediate clamour.

"I a cap'n, lemme go! 'Elp me, ole granpas, mista Din, mista Fol, 'elp Chugg!"

But no help was forthcoming. Quite the opposite, in fact. Beau took hold of the feathered pole and began tickling his adopted grandsquirrel.

"See how you like it, sah, wot! Silence now, or I'll jolly well tickle the tip of y'nose an' make you sneeze all season. Now, what d'ye say t'that, cap'n Chugg?"

"Choppa you tail off, Beau, an' Chugg not make you any no more skillyduff!"

Beau slumped down beside Vurg, nodding sadly. "No skil-ly'n'duff eh wot. Ah well, such is the fate of a blinkin' muti-neer, old chap!"

That night they set up camp in the lee of a wide stone out-crop at the base of a hill. Log a Log Furmo sat looking at the *Honeysuckle* speculatively.

"Y'know, Gonff, I think I'll leave those wheels on 'er. Won't do no 'arm to a flat-bottomed craft like the *Honey-suckle*. Hah, wait'll my missus sees our new boat. She'll be proud as a toad with a top hat!"

Folgrim had been to the top of the hill, to see what the

going would be like next day. On his return, the otter called Martin and Dunespike to one side.

"I think I just spotted trouble the other side o' this hill."

The Warrior mouse became instantly alert. "What sort of trouble, Folgrim?"

"Bunch o' ragtag vermin, foxes, stoats an' the like."

Martin was away uphill swiftly, sword in paw. "Let's go and take a look!"

Bellying down, the three friends crawled over the hilltop. Below them on the gorse-strewn plain, several small fires were burning. There was little need to investigate further, for by the light of a half-moon they could estimate the numbers of foebeast below. Dunespike had seen the same band before.

"They were sniffin' round in our dunes last winter, but we covered our tracks well an' got the young 'uns safe inside the ould dwellin'. Sure, meself an' some others put on our sheets and stilts an' scared the blaggards off. What d'ye think we should do about 'em, Martin?"

Without hesitation the Warrior answered, "We could defeat them in a fight, but there's no sense in that. I want everybeast to reach their homes safe. Listen now, I think I've got a solution to the problem."

Skipper perched high up on the south gable, his footpaws firmly lodged in a roofbeam gap. From where he stood, the otter Chieftain could see out over the countless acres of Mossflower Wood to the east. He turned slowly, looking across the vast plain to the west.

"Rap me rudder, wot a sight! Now I know why birds are singin' happily. Everythin' looks so different from up 'ere." He shut his eyes momentarily as he caught sight of Lady Amber walking along the topmost scaffold pole as if it were a broad roadway. "Marm, I beg ye, would y'mind not doin' that 'til I'm back on the ground. Somethin' inside me just did a somersault."

The Squirrelqueen leaped lightly down beside him. "Sorry, Skip, I forgot there was a land dweller up here. Is the weather vane ready yet?"

"Nearly. Ole Ferdy'n'Coggs are doin' as fine a job of smithyin' as I ever saw, marm. Though miz Columbine says there won't be a scrap o' charcoal left in the kitchens t'cook with. They're usin' the open hearth fire to heat the iron an' beatin' it out on the stone floor. I came up 'ere 'cos I couldn't abide the noise. Ding! Bang! Ding! Bang! Me pore ole head's still ringin' inside."

Lady Amber's manner was more practical than sympathetic. "Don't tell me, Skip, you can't abide noise? Hah, 'tis usually you who creates most of the noise 'round here with your big foghorn voice. As for heights, if you haven't got a head for them I don't advise hanging 'round up here, you'll only make yourself ill. Why not pop down to the orchard and help the carpenters. That's far more peaceful."

Skipper tugged on the pulley rope of the hoist. "Good idea, marm, the orchard it is!"

The hoist was merely a system of counterweights. Skipper stepped aboard a small platform and it descended slowly. On the way down he was passed by the other platform, on which stood a squirrel with two blocks of sandstone going up. They waved to each other as the platforms passed.

"Where are ye bound, Skip?"

"Down to the orchard, matey, t'lend a paw with the beams."

"Tell Gurdle to load mortar on that platform when y'get down. I'll leave one o' these blocks on as a counterweight."

A mole and four mice were waiting at the bottom, and they locked off the platform against a log protruding from the wall. The mole touched his snout in greeting. "They'm needin' more blocks oop thurr, Skip?"

The otter stepped from the platform. "Not at present, Gurdle, 'tis mortar they want."

Gurdle and the mice began shovelling a mixture of sand, crushed limestone and water onto the platform. It would enable the builders to cement the heavy sandstone blocks firmly into place.

At the far corner of Redwall's orchard the carpenters had set up shop. A pit had been dug so that they could cut planking with long double-pawed saws, and there was a bench with vice, chisels and mallets, as well as a fire with augers and pokers resting in it. These would be used to bore holes, so the wood could be jointed with pegs. Seasoned trunks of elm, oak, beech, pine and sycamore were stacked against the wall in piles. Skipper loved the fragrant smells of fresh wood and heaps of bark shavings. A fat whiskery old bankvole with a charcoal stick behind one ear and a long canvas apron glanced up from a pine log he was working on and nodded at the otter Chieftain.

"Afternoon, Skip. D'ye fancy helpin' me strip the bark off'n this timber? It'll make good skirtin' boards for the upper dormitories. I like pine, got a fragrance all of its own."

Skipper found a spokeshave and began working on the other side of the log. Long pine slivers ran curling from his sharp blade, and Skipper sniffed fondly.

"Yore right, Migglo, 'tis a clean fresh smell. I can feel it clearin' me head up nicely."

A dormouse popped her head up from the sawpit. "Hello, Skip. How's it goin' on the south gable? I spotted you up there earlier. Huh, y'wouldn't get me anywhere that high, not for all the nuts in Mossflower, matey!"

Skipper blew off a shaving that had stuck to his nose. "Aye, leave that to the squirrels an' a gang of crazy mice'n'hedgehogs who likes that sort o' thing. Well, I tell ye, marm, I was surprised 'ow far they'd gotten along. Lady Amber says another couple o' days should bring it to a peak. Then they can set up the weather vane."

Migglo chuckled gruffly through his bushy whiskers. "Amber's squirrels ain't settin' up no weather vane—'tis Ferdy'n'Coggs who'll be doin' that job. Hohoho! Wait'll ye see those two bulky ole Cellar'ogs wobblin' about up there. They ain't lookin' forward to it, I can tell ye!"

Skipper smiled at the thought of Redwall's twin Cellarhogs high on the south gable. "No, nor would I fancy it!"

Carrying a big earthenware jug and beakers on a tray between them, Mayberry and Catkin the ottermaids awkwardly bobbed curtsies to all the workers.

"Miz Bella said to bring you a cool drink, mint leaf an' rosehip cordial from the cellars."

"She said it'd wash the sawdust down, sir."

Migglo swigged off a full beaker in one go. "Just the stuff, colder'n ice an' very refreshin'. Thank ye."

Skipper sipped his drink slowly, relishing it. The ottermaids topped up his beaker.

"We didn't know you were a carpenter, Grandpa?"

He winked at them. "Just shows yer, me pretties, you don't know half the things yore ole grandpa can do."

"Oh yes we do, we know lots of things you can do."

"Do you now? Like wot?"

"We know you can hide underwater in the pond when 'tis your turn to wash pots'n'dishes."

"Yes, an' we know you can wake everybeast when you talk in your sleep with your big loud voice."

"And we know you can sup more hotroot soup than anybeast, and drink more October Ale and scoff more damson pudden . . ."

The otter Chieftain squinted fiercely at his two young granddaughters as he advanced on them. "Haharr, me pretties, an' did ye know that I can clip the noses of liddle ottermaids with me spokeshave?"

They fled squealing and giggling from the orchard.

That evening it went cool suddenly. Standing on the outer wall ramparts of the Abbey, Bella and Columbine watched the enchanting sight of summer's last evening. Streaked to the west with slim dark cloud tails, the sunset was awesome. In the final moments the skies turned deep scarlet on the horizon, ranging up through crimson and rose to a delicate pink. Above this it faded to a broad band of buttery amber with soft dark blue pierced by the faint twinkle of early stars. Columbine let her breath out in a long wistful sigh.

"I hope my Gonff can see all of this beauty."

Bella placed a paw gently on her friend's shoulder. "I'm sure he can. I know he'll be thinking of you and the little one here at Redwall, awaiting his return."

A random thought caused the mousewife to cover her mouth, stifling a chuckle. "Unless there's food to be had, of course. Gonff would sooner gaze at a fruit puddin' than a sunset!"

Bella joined in her laughter. "Then I suggest we post a daily lookout on this wall from now on. No doubt we can accommodate his sense of beauty with a big apple pie."

37

A lively breeze stopped autumn's first day starting with a gentle mist. The *Honeysuckle* was positioned just below the brow of the hill, armed with slings and oars, and the crew and their Dunehog allies stood waiting.

Furmo tested the wind direction with a damp paw. "Couldn't ask for a fairer breeze, Martin!"

The Warrior signalled to Folgrim. "Off you go, mate, and don't forget to raise a shout at the right moment."

The smallest of the Guosim shrews was bent double, wearing a cape which Trimp had made for Chugger. He grasped Folgrim's paw and toddled off over the hilltop, with the scarred otter adopting his old hunched hunting pose. Together they looked like a grandsire and his grandchild.

A stringy-looking weasel was arguing with a ferret, disputing over a wooden skewer festooned with insect and moth carcasses, which had been spiked there to roast over the fire. A motley collection of rats and assorted vermin watched them, knowing a fight was inevitable. As the weasel reached for the skewer, the ferret kicked him.

"Getcher dirty paws offa me vittles, longnose!"

The weasel was knocked forward, scorching his paw in the flames. He turned snarling at his tormentor.

"Half o' them are mine. Lift yer paw t'me agin an' I'll chop it off, greedyguts!"

Like a flash, a broad evil-looking blade appeared in the ferret's paw. He aimed another kick at the weasel.

"Yew couldn't chop yer way outta a daisy patch. Back off from those vittles, they're mine!"

The weasel shrugged, as if admitting defeat. Picking up the sharpened skewer, whose end was on fire, he turned to the ferret.

"Ah, wot's a pile o' squashed bugs t'me. You 'ave 'em!"

Bounding forward, he thrust the skewer hard into the ferret's gut. A shriek of agony rang out, and the ferret fell backward dying, stabbed through his stomach.

Callous laughter and coarse remarks greeted the cruel act.

"Haw haw haw! Somethin' upset 'is stummick!"

"Heeheehee! Ole Brango looks jus' like a bug on that skewer, lookit 'im wriggle!"

A fox who had lost interest in the gruesome spectacle happened to turn and look uphill. He caught sight of the two pitiful figures hobbling side by side.

"Oh lucky day, look wot's comin' this way, mates!"

Paws grasped blades as most of the vermin began inching towards the two unfortunate creatures, calling mockingly, "Come an' join us fer dinner, friends."

"Aye, don't be scared, you'll 'ave nought t'be worried about soon, ain't that right, mates?"

The two creatures halted, as if noticing the evil crew for the first time. Slowly they backed off uphill, crying piteously, "Please don't hurt us, we're only poor travelers!"

Speeding up their advance, the vermin began to spread in an arc, trying to cut their quarry off. The poor travelers ran then, scampering uphill and yelling aloud, "Help! Oh, help us somebeast! Help!"

Pulling a rusty axe from his belt, the fox ran after them. "I saw 'em first!"

The skinny weasel dashed past him, snarling. "First there, first served, brushtail!"

As Folgrim and the Guosim shrew reached the ridgecrest,

they were yanked aboard the *Honeysuckle*. Down the hill she thundered, the breeze billowing her sail full out. War cries rang round the hillside.

"Eulaliaaaaa! Redwaaaaaalll! Gorramahoggorraaaaa!"

The vermin were taken completely by surprise. Dinny whacked out with an oar, laying the skinny weasel out cold. Hard round slingstones cracked against skulls, ribs, paws and tails, filling the air like angry hornets in swarm. Heedless of the stupidity of their retreat, the vermin fled off downhill, with the *Honeysuckle* skimming behind them. Vurg caught the fox by his tail and dragged him along, whilst Beau hung over the side belaboring him with an oar. "You thoroughly"—Whack!—"despicable"—Thwack whack!—"cad!"

A rat who was tripped by one of the for'ard oars leaped smartly up, only to be felled by Furmo, who from his position at the stern walloped him over the head. Onward plunged the vermin in their rout, hotly pursued by a skiff on wheels, leaving in its wake a trail of wounded and senseless creatures.

Finally the remnants of the ragtag vermin band broke, running off in separate directions, but not before Dunespike lassoed one. The terrified ferret was dragged aboard. He lay quivering on the deck of the still traveling craft, staring up into the fearsome scarred face of Folgrim.

Resting his axeblade between the ferret's eyes, the otter growled in a menacing voice, "I see I've got yore attention, scumbrain, so lissen hard. We'll be sailin' these regions for the next couple o' seasons, huntin' down vermin an' cleanin' up the land. Yore lot are the first—ain't you the lucky ones. We're lettin' you live, so you an' yore cronies can spread the word 'round that we've arrived. Y'see that warrior with the nice sharp sword? He's our leader. Name o' Martin of Redwall, a very fair beast. He believes in givin' vermin a sportin' chance . . . then slayin' 'em!"

Martin prodded the ferret with his bladetip. "Up on your paws, bully, come on!"

Trembling uncontrollably the ferret rose. The *Honeysuckle* had slowed down minimally, breasting another rise, then she picked up speed, skimming downhill. Martin swung his sword up high. "Jump or die?"

"Eeyaaaaagh!"

With a pitiful wail the ferret flung himself overboard. They watched him bounce and spin as he rolled downhill until a rock halted his progress with a juicy thud.

The breeze made a hissing sound as it ran through Dunespike's stickles, and he clapped his paws happily.

"An' isn't this the grand ould way t'be travellin'. Sure I've not had this much fun since I caught a jellyfish on me spikes. Cap'n Chugg sir, do we throw out the anchor at lunchtime, or does eatin' on the move sound like a grand ould idea to ye?"

Chugger gave Dunespike his captain's scowl. "Wot a jellyfish is?"

The hedgehog Chieftain caught him and tickled Chugger until he broke down laughing.

"Yore a jellyfish, ye liddle omadorm, a fat wee jellyfish!"

Chugger rolled about, unable to escape. "Heeheehee 'elp me, mista Fol! Heeheehee, I norra jellyfish, I on'y a likkle Chugg. Heeheehee, 'elp 'elp!"

The *Honeysuckle* did not stop for lunch; they kept on whilst the breezes favored progress. During the afternoon the wind deserted the sails, and the skiff rolled to an easy halt, at the fringe of a copse.

Guosim cooks discovered a small spring among the trees, where the water was cool and sweet. Apples, pears and wild berries were plentiful. Lounging in the tree shade, the crew ate and drank their fill.

Dunespike looked about admiringly. "Murfo, me son, does this place not look grand t'ye?"

"Aye, grand, da, grand 'tis!"

"An' a whole lot better'n livin' midst ould sand dunes?"

"Aye, 'twould be, da, 'twould be so!"

"Sure we've got fruit t'pick from the bough an' berries t'gather as we please. What would y'say to livin' here?"

"Oh, grand t'be sure, da. We'd want for nothin'!"

Dunespike cuffed his son's ear fondly. "Well spoken. Take ten o' the lads an' start diggin' a good ould cave beneath these trees. I'll send the rest back t'the dunes for the babies an' the elders. Would that be all right with you, Martin of Redwall?"

Martin was looking up at the sky, and replied absently,

'Yes, of course it will, Chief, providing you show us where Northfork stream lies."

"Sure, of course I will. What're ye starin' up at the sky for? Don't worry, it won't fall, it's been up there a long time."

Martin spoke to Dunespike, though he was looking at Gonff. "Birds are starting to fly south, the autumn has come."

The Mousethief watched until the birds were out of sight. "We must remember our word, mate. Time for us to fly home."

Following breakfast in the Great Hall of Redwall Abbey, all the creatures sat awaiting the allotment of daily chores. Bella, whose duty it was to apportion the work, was deep in conversation with Abbess Germaine. Eager eyes watched the Badgermother as Redwallers speculated on which way the roster would go for them.

"Hope I'm helpin' Ferdy'n'Coggs in the cellars again!"

"Cellars are closed today; they've got to raise the weather vane on south gable. I'm not goin' up there!"

"Hurr, you'm wuddent be h'allowed oop thurr, zurr. On'y ee squirr'ls be on sou' gable to 'elp with ee vane."

"Hope I don't get picked as cook's helper again. Huh, they had me scrubbin' pots all day last time."

All talk ceased instantly when Bella rapped the table. "Lady Amber and her squirrels will be assisting Ferdy and Coggs to raise the weather vane on the top of south gable."

"Thurr see, jus' loik oi tole ee!"

Bella paused, looking in the direction of the interruption. There was a muffled giggle, followed by respectful silence. She waited a moment before continuing.

"All other building work today will be suspended. Migglo, Mayberry and Catkin, you are today's duty cooks."

The whiskery old bankvole winked at both ottermaids, who wriggled and tittered excitedly, before realizing the importance of their position and sitting up primly.

Bella nodded to the three Redwallers. "Forget any cooking or baking for today. There's enough bread, scones and pastry been readied overnight. Concentrate on a cold buffet, salads, fruitcups and such. Skipper will take watch on the battlements for signs of our returning travelers. Without exception, every otherbeast within our walls is to go to the storerooms for sacks and baskets. Columbine, will you and Gurdle see that ladders and sticks are available, please?"

Some of the elders began smiling and nudging one another, but the younger element looked puzzled. Abbess Germaine allowed Bella to help her up onto the table; then she waved her paws in the air and called out in a reedy quaver, "Then 'tis all to the orchard for fruit harvest!"

Gleeful cheers greeted this announcement, followed by chaos. Redwallers dashed to the storerooms, where Columbine was issuing sacks and baskets as fast as she could.

"Form a line there, don't push, there's plenty for all. Gonflet, take that sack off your head! Gurdle, will you see that all Dibbuns are given berry trugs, thank you!"

Passing out the small baskets to the little ones, the mole chuckled at their antics. "They'm be barskets, not sandals, take 'em off'n ee futtpaws."

Columbine was settling Abbess Germaine down in a wheelbarrow full of soft moss, beneath the shade of a spreading horse chestnut tree. Both of them broke down laughing at the sight of Bella leading the band of pickers in a harvest dance, singing as she went. Clutching Columbine's paw, the ancient Abbess chuckled. "Oh dearie me an' preserve m'paws! It's like seeing a great boulder roll down a mountainside, watching our Bella dance! Heeheehee!"

Columbine skipped aside as Bella hurtled by. "Hahahaha! Maybe so, but there's those not even half Bella's age who can't keep up with her!"

Winding its way through trees and around bushes, the merry dance went on, with everybeast singing their hearts out.

"Now go good son and daughter,
Haste to our orchard fair,
And gather in the harvest,
Which lies a-waiting there.
Ripe apples, ripe apples, are falling to the ground,
As pears so sweet and juicy are lying all around!

Keep singing pretty daughter,
Until the work is done,
So you don't eat the berries,
And leave your mother none.
Blackberries, ripe cherries, don't bruise or break
    them miss,
For sweetness can be lost, like a faithless lover's kiss!

The gooseberry and greengage,
Are bittersweet my son,
And damson has a heart stone,
You'll find before you're done.
Enchanting, enticing, like wild grape on the vine,
The maidens want to help you, to let their paws
    entwine!

So pick a berry, sing so merry,
Harvest time is here,
Go skipping 'round our orchard,
My son and daughter dear!"

Bella stood tall. Reaching a high branch, she pulled it
down to her face and sniffed deep. "Aaahhh! Nought so
sweet as the smell of a good russet apple on the bough.
Mmmmm! I could sniff 'em all day!"

Beneath her, a hogwife stood tapping her footpaw, sack
held wide open and waiting. "Beg pardon, miz Bell, but
could y'leave off sniffin' an' start shakin' afore it goes dark?"

"Oops, silly old me. Sorry!"

The badger gave the bough a mighty shake, releasing ripe
russets in a shower. When she looked down, the hogwife was
still tapping her footpaws, two apples impaled on her headspikes, another two on her back.

"Tch tch! Miz Bell marm, 'twould be a help if'n you
shook 'em into the sack!"

Columbine and Germaine were picking redcurrants, the
Abbess keeping a curious eye on Gonflet.

"My dear, what is that little son of yours up to? He's supposed to be gathering raspberries, isn't he?"

Columbine could not help smiling as she watched the little

mouse. He would fill both his smock pants with fruit, take a
furtive glance left and right, then scurry off to empty his load
into a trug hidden beneath the berry hedge.

"Hmm, just like his father, a real mousethief. He's not
happy unless he thinks he's stealing something, Mother
Abbess. I'll have to turn him upside down and shake him
before he goes to bed tonight. Otherwise there'll be raspberries squashed around the dormitory for the rest of the season.
Little pickle. He's a good worker though!"

The harvesting was going well, moles trundling off to the
storerooms with laden trollies as the fruit was picked and
basketed or bagged up. At midday the cooks borrowed three
trollies to bring lunch for the pickers. Mayberry and Catkin
repulsed any advances on the food with frosty glances and
severe words.

"Not a single bite until you've washed at the pond!"

"Gracious me, look at those sticky paws. Away with you!"

Migglo gave them a whiskery grin. "That's the stuff,
missies! You tell 'em! Go on, yore the cooks, 'tis up to you!"

Emboldened, the ottermaids spared nobeast from censure.

"Miz Bella, have you been pickin' apples with yore nose?
You can just go an' wash y'face, this instant!"

"Hmph, shame on you, Mother Abbess. 'Tis up t'you to set
an example. Look at yourself, redcurrant juice from tail to
ears. Gurdle, help her to get washed, please!"

Columbine's giggles were cut short as they turned their
attentions upon her.

"'Tis no laughin' matter, miz Columbine. Shame on you!"

"Aye, woe 'pon you if'n mister Gonff was to see y'now.
We'll inspect those paws after you've washed 'em!"

It was a simple and satisfying lunch which had been prepared for the harvesters. Sliced apples, cheese and fresh
crusty bread, with new cider or cold mint tea to sip and
strawberries with meadowcream for dessert. Columbine sat
beneath the chestnut tree with her friends, still shaking her
head and smiling over the bossy cooks.

"Honestly, I felt just like a naughty Dibbun, the way those
two young snips ordered me off to the pond!"

The Abbess sandwiched a wedge of cheese with bread.
"Me too, bless their hearts. They meant well, though."

Bella snorted. "Meant well? The little tyrants—they sent me back to the pond twice to wash my snout properly!"

Migglo had been eavesdropping, and he called across to them, "Aye, but they're a credit to ole Skipper, that they are!"

Suddenly, everybeast started with fright as a loud cry rent the air.

"Redwaaaaaaaaaaalll!"

Bella was on her paws in a flash, pointing upward. "Look! They've raised the weather vane on south gable!"

Everybeast in the orchard raised their paws and returned the shout to the tiny figures high up on the Abbey building.

"Redwaaaaaaaaaaallll!"

Cheering broke out as the Squirrelqueen, Lady Amber, stood out, balancing on the crosspieces of the iron vane, swaying as a light breeze turned its metal arrow topspike. Ferdy and Coggs clung to the North and South struts, waving jubilantly to their friends below. As Columbine gazed up at the completed south wall, she hugged the Abbess. "Oh, they've done it, Mother Abbess. Isn't it beautiful!"

Germaine looked for as long as she could, then shut her eyes tight to stem the tears.

"At last! My Redwall Abbey. I never thought I'd live to see the dream become reality!"

Bella picked the Abbess up as though she weighed nothing, sitting the ancient mouse upon her shoulder to allow her a better view. Whilst Germaine was up there, Bella took advantage of her robe hem to wipe her own eyes.

"Three cheers for Redwall Abbey. May it stand as long as seasons change and the sun rises, my friends!"

Never were three cheers raised so joyously.

"Hurrah! Hurrah! Hurrah!"

38

On a rare boisterous autumn morn, two otters stood waist deep in the waters where Northfork stream merged with the main flow seaward. It was here in the swirl of currents that the finest watershrimp were to be found. Unstaking a long tubular reed net, they hauled it carefully to the bank. The elder of the pair, a sleek tough otterwife, instructed her half-grown son in the rudiments of his tribe's fishing tradition.

"Always haul the net in slow'n'easy, Jiddy. I seen silly beasts lose all their catch many a time, from rushin' things. There now, lookit our net, son, bulgin' with the liddle beauties. Tie the end off good'n'tight, that's it!"

Grinning from ear to ear, Jiddy patted the well-packed net. "Haharr, wait'll Chief Tungro claps eyes on this lot! I bet by next season he'll let me come 'ere alone—"

The young otter had no time for further conversation. His mother knocked him flat into the cover of hanging willow fronds. Stifling his mouth with a swift paw, she lay beside him, peering upstream at the strange craft in the distance.

"Strike me rudder, will y'look at that thing. I ain't never seen nothin' like it in these waters. Wait! I'd know that beast standin' in the bows if'n he was the last otter on earth. C'mon, Jid, let's get the bad news back to Tungro!"

They hurried off southward along the bank, toting the loaded net between them, with Jiddy, like most youngsters, besieging his mother with questions.

"It was an otter on that boat, I saw 'im too. But why's it bad news for Tungro? Does he know the otter?"

"Hah, know 'im? I'll say he does. That's Folgrim, his mad brother. I thought we'd seen the last o' that 'un."

"Mad? Why's he mad? What did he do?"

"Well he used t'go huntin' vermin, an' when he caught up with 'em he'd, er, he'd . . . Never you mind what he did. Now keep up, an' don't drop that net or 'twill burst!"

The day was rather overcast, though the sun showed at intervals, between masses of grey-white cloud, which the playful wind chased to the south-east. The *Honeysuckle* rode at half sail, Furmo steering her into the bank, which was crowded with otters. Trimp stood alongside Folgrim, watching him closely.

"My goodness, Fol, they've all turned out to welcome you home. See, there's your brother Tungro!"

Chugger launched himself from the mast onto his friend Folgrim's shoulders. "Tchah! Otters not welcome you, mista Fol, nobeast laugh or shout 'ello t'you, big long faces on 'em."

Folgrim settled the little squirrel on his strong shoulders. "They got good cause not t'be cheery, mate. My tribe fears me. I was nought but a load o' trouble to 'em."

Chugger growled. "Gurrr! You not t'ubble, mista Fol, you my matey. I choppa they tails off for ya!"

Folgrim slid over the side, still carrying Chugger. "You sit up there an' be'ave yoreself now. Leave this t'me."

Otters parted ranks, fearing to be near the returning warrior. But Tungro waded swiftly forward. Clasping Folgrim's paws tightly he smiled into the heavily scarred face with great fondness.

"My brother, welcome back to the holt! Come on, matey, bring y'liddle friend, bring all yore friends. Rest and eat!"

The holt was an enlarged bank cave, old and very com-

fortable, filled with beautifully carved furniture, which was
the speciality of Tungro's tribe, who were master craftsbeasts, proud of their carpentry skills. Most of the tribe were
still wary of Folgrim, so he kept to the company of the *Honeysuckle*'s crew. They sat on elaborately carved benches by
the fire, dining on fresh hotroot and watershrimp soup, oat-
farls and a riverbank salad.

Martin and Gonff sat at a highly polished table with Tungro, who poured steaming blackberry and sage cordial for
them whilst the cooks served their food.

"You and your friends have worked wonders with my
brother. He is not the same savage beast, thanks to you,
Martin."

The Warrior sipped his cordial gratefully. "Don't give me
the credit, friend. It was young Trimp and little Chugger who
wrought the change in Folgrim."

Turning to Gonff, the otter enquired, "Why do you keep
staring at me, Mousethief?"

The irrepressible Gonff shrugged. "The more I look at
you, the stronger you remind me of somebeast. Martin,
would you say Tungro resembles Skipper?"

"Aye, mate, now you come to mention it, he does, very
much!"

Tungro sat up at the mention of the name. "Skipper? Is he
an otter about old enough to be my father?"

Gonff slapped the table. "I knew it, yore related to him!"

A faraway look entered Tungro's eyes as he unfolded the
tale.

"My grandmother gave birth to three sons on the same
day—Bargud, my father, and his two brothers, Riverwyte
and Warthorn. Riverwyte was much like my brother Folgrim,
a great fighter and slayer of vermin. Everybeast thought him
sick in the head because of his love for battle. He left our holt
to go roving, and they say his tail was severed by foebeasts.
An otter without a rudder, as you know, is like a fish without
water. Riverwyte became a woodland dweller, a master of
disguises, and he called himself Mask because of this. Travelers told my father that he had been slain, though where,
when an' how it all happened we never got t'know. The other
brother, Warthorn, was the biggest an' strongest of all three.

He left the holt when he was scarce half grown, because he couldn't ever buckle down to my grandfather's strict rule. Warthorn was such a natural leader that nobeast used his given name, they nicknamed him Skipper, which is a title we give to otter Chieftains. Anyhow, he went off to found his own tribe an' hasn't been heard of since. When Bargud, my father, was alive, he'd look at me an' say that I was the image of his lost brother Skipper. Then he'd turn to Folgrim an' say that he was the double of Riverwyte, his other brother."

Martin leaned across the table and held Tungro's paw. "Would you like to meet your uncle Warthorn?"

Tungro nodded wistfully. "I'd love to, I've heard so many tales about him, but he'd left this holt long afore I was born. Do y'think I ever could meet Warthorn?"

"Certainly, my friend. Journey to Redwall with us, and you will."

A few days later, Log a Log Furmo's large fierce wife, Honeysuckle, was coping with her brood on the streambank of their summer camp. Energetically she scrubbed at the wriggling body of her eldest.

"Be still, you liddle worm. I'll teach ye to roll about in that midden of a water margin, filthy shrew!" Flicking out with a wet rag she caught another young one a stinging slap across the tail. "Git yore paws away from those scones, or I'll chop y'tail off an' bake ye in a pie. Go on, be off with you!"

Four tiny shrewmaids came dashing along the bank, squeaking, "Mamma mamma, daddy's comin' in a big boat wiv a sail!"

Honeysuckle grabbed the nearest one. "Just lookit the bankmud on that smock, an' it was clean on this very morn. Go an' git a fresh one off'n yore granma, not one of those off the rock ledge, they ain't dry yet. So, the great rovin' Log a Log's decided to come home again, has he?"

Furmo's deep rich voice hailed her from upriver. "Honeysuckle, me precious, I'm back, O dew of me life!"

She scowled at Furmo, standing heroically in the prow of the skiff as it sailed inshore. Twirling the corner of a face cloth she wiggled it down the ear of the little shrew she was attempting to clean up. "Back at the end o' summer, my dar-

lin'; I'll return on the first autumn mist, O jewel o' the woodlands. What time d'ye call this t'be gettin' back, you great
useless lump o' Guosimfur, eh?"

Gonff sprinted ashore, with two shrews in his wake, carrying a carved otter footstool and several strings of Dunehog
quills and beads in various gaudy colors. He pointed to the
name plate on the skiff's bow, planting a genteel kiss on the
shrew wife's sud-covered paw.

"O beauteous beast, yore spouse brings ye gifts from afar,
an' all borne on a fine vessel that carries yore own fair name.
He has done nought but pine f'you night'n'day!"

Honeysuckle melted immediately in the face of Gonff's
gallantry. Fluttering her eyelids, she gave him a playful
shove, which sent him sprawling in the shallows.

"Oh, mister Gonff, you ole flatterer, fancy callin' that luvly
ship after me. Wotever gave you the idea?"

The Prince of Mousethieves stood up, shaking water from
his rear end, still spouting eloquently. "'Twas all your good
Furmo's idea, m'lady. We wanted to call the boat *Gul-
lywacker*, but he wouldn't hear of it. No no, sez he, we must
call it *Honeysuckle* after my beloved!"

Furmo gasped as Honeysuckle grabbed him from the prow
and squeezed the air from his lungs in a mighty embrace.

"Ow ow, I wronged you, me dear one, forgive me. All
these wunnerful things you brought back for yore wife. Ow
ow, I could cut out me tongue for wot I said about you!"

Furmo managed to gasp out in a stifled mutter, "Cut yore
tongue out? No such luck, more's the pity!"

She dropped him in the shallows. "Wot was that you
said?"

Furmo scrambled up, thinking quickly. "I said, 'Cut yore
tongue out? No no, my duck, yore far too pretty!'"

Vurg and his friends were greatly taken with the shrewbabes, but none more so than Beau. The gluttonous hare
allowed the tiny creatures to feed him vast amounts of food at
the noontide meal.

"Can you eat more plum pudden, sir?"

"Just try me, laddie. Shove it this way, wot!"

"My mamma maked this salad, sir, d'you like it?"

"Rather! What a clever lady your mamma is. Fill m'bowl up again, there's a good little tyke!"

"D'you like apple'n'pear turnover, sir?"

"Like it? Steer it in my direction, y'young tailwagger, an' I'll show you whether I like it!"

Honeysuckle perched gingerly on the footstool, which she thought was a small chair, casting a jaundiced eye in Beau's direction.

"I'd hate t'be standin' next to that long-eared rabbit in a famine season. Where does he put it all? No thanks to you, Gonff, you fetched 'im 'ere, an' that tribe o' starvin' otters too. We'll soon be eaten out o' house'n'home!"

Gonff tweaked the shrew wife's cheek slyly.

"Well, me beauty, you don't want vittles goin' stale in the larder. Not whilst yore away on the nice trip that Furmo's planned for you!"

"Trip? Furmo never told me about no trip?"

"Aha, that's 'cos he wants to surprise you, pretty one. How d'you fancy a nice boat trip to Redwall Abbey?"

"Ow ow, bless 'is good 'eart, is there nothin' Furmo wouldn't do fer me? Wot a wunnerful thoughtful beast 'e is!"

Furmo waggled a paw in his numbed ear. "Oh, give yore wailin' a rest an' pass the beer."

"Wot was that you said, Furmo Log a Log?"

"I said, 'My love's unfailin', nothin' but the best for you, my dear!' "

Squeaks of fright from the little ones caused Martin to leap up, sword in paw. A dark shadow circled overhead, suddenly dropping like a stone into their midst. The great goshawk, Krar Woodwatcher, folded his wings and bowed courteously.

"Oh joyous day, thou hast returned to my fiefdom, Prince of Mousethieves, and thou, too, Martin Warrior of Redwall."

Gonff nodded formally, with appropriate regal disdain. "Lackaday, sirrah, have thou a care, landing in such manner 'mongst the babes of Furmo, our faithful vassal!"

Krar lowered his beak to the ground in the face of such royal displeasure from the Prince of Mousethieves.

"Alas, 'twas not my intention to affright the babes thus,

Prince. My hasty landing was prompted by a desire to be in
company with thee an' thy noblebeasts once more."

Martin allowed his footpaw to touch the lethal beak. Krar
did not see him exchange a wink with Gonff.

"I pray you, Prince Gonff, be not wrathful with our friend
Woodwatcher. For we know him to be a good an' honest bird.
Tarry with us, Krar, there are victuals aplenty here."

The huge fierce goshawk awaited Gonff's decision. Sensing he had pushed his luck far enough with the dangerous
bird, Gonff smiled magnanimously, patting the ground at his
side.

"I spoke in haste. Come, sit thee beside me, my faithful
friend. It comes to my mind that one who battled with a swan
in our defense must surely be worthy of our hospitality!"

Honeysuckle nudged Furmo, almost knocking him over.
"D'ye hear that? Why don't you learn to speak like Gonff an'
Martin? Proper gentlebeasts they are!"

Beau sat watching in open-mouthed admiration as food
vanished down Krar's beak at an alarming rate.

"Great seasons o' starvation, d'you suppose that chap'll be
able to fly when he's finished scoffin', wot wot?"

Trimp could not help teasing the hare with a wry comment. "I wonder if the Redwall Abbey kitchens will have
enough food to keep up with the both of you?"

Dinny shook his head at the hedgehog maid's observation.
"Burr aye, miz, oi 'adn't thought o' that. They'm two'll keep
ee cooks gurtly busy, oi'm surrting o' that!"

Traveling upstream was not difficult as they traced back their
original path. Tungro's tribe were strong swimmers, and they
weaved in and out of the growing flotilla of shrew logboats
surrounding the *Honeysuckle*, lending strong paws wherever
they were needed. On a lazy golden afternoon, Gonff lay
stretched out beneath the stern awning, tossing hazelnut
pieces in the air and catching them in his mouth. Martin was
napping nearby, whiskers gently twitching against a curious
midge, bent on investigating his face. A fragment of nut,
which Gonff had missed, bounced off Martin's nose, and he
opened one eye slowly.

"D'you mind not disturbing me? It's not often I get the chance of an odd snooze."

Gonff aimed another piece of nut at his companion. "Snooze? How can you talk about snoozin', mate? We're nearly home! I'll be seein' my Columbine soon, haha, an' that Gonflet o' mine. Wonder if he's grown at all?"

Martin stared up at the changing leaf patterns, blinking as the sun traced through, blurring the edges.

"Oh, I imagine Gonflet will be tall enough to cause us more trouble, young scamp! Hope the work on our Abbey has progressed without too much bother. I bet Bella's missed us, though the kitchen crew will probably be glad you're gone. Pies can lie cooling on windowsills in safety."

"Hah! Not with my Gonflet runnin' loose they won't!"

In one smooth motion, Tungro slid aboard the skiff. He whispered urgently to Martin, "We're due to run into trouble, I think!"

The Warrior lay still, though his paw was seeking his blade. "What makes you think that, friend?"

"Well I can 'ear a waterfall somewheres up ahead, but that ain't really it. Somebeasts are followin' us. I saw movement in the trees, ripples in our wake, an' I think they're up ahead of us too!"

Immediately Martin arose, sword in paw. "Sounds like they've got us surrounded, eh, Gonff?"

"You two stop here. I'll go an' take a peek."

Gonff crawled out on deck and took stock of the situation. Tungro's otters were in the water, guarding the shrew logboats, which Furmo had grouped around the *Honeysuckle*. Only the streamsounds and the distant waterfall broke the ominous silence. Suddenly the soft autumn noontide had grown dangerous. Krar perched upon the *Honeysuckle*'s prow, watching keenly. Folgrim had his axe out, and was standing in the stern of the back logboat. Furmo and his Guosim crouched, rapiers drawn. Gonff held up his paws, signalling everybeast to wait. His eye caught a movement in a tree-shaded shallow.

Then the Mousethief relaxed, waving his paws for the crew to stand down. He shouted then, his voice cutting the stillness. "Haharr, I'll bite y'tail off an' stuff it down yore ear!"

A gruff voice responded from the shallows. "Surrender, mousey, yer surrounded, mate!"

Gonff gave a broad wink to the Guosim shrews. "Surrounded? Y'great lard barrel, stay there. I'm comin' to surround you, ye forty-faced frogflusher!"

Hurling himself from the deck, Gonff hit the water with a loud splash and threw himself onto the creature which sped out from the bank. Streamwater boiled in chaos as the pair met, roaring and bellowing.

"Garraway Bullow, ye bangtailed riverdog, I knowed it was you all along. Take that!"

"Whupperyhoo, Gonffo, don't try t'fool me. You was scared out o'yore mousey wits, admit it!"

"Scared? I been scareder of dead logs floatin' in the water. Only thing I'm scared of is that you won't 'ave supper ready, ye whiskery waterwet puddenwalloper!"

Yelling with delight, Folgrim and Tungro dived into the water. "Auntie Garraway, 'tis us, yore nephews!"

"Oh no, lock the larders, it's Bargud's brats. Lookit the size of 'em. My pore sister must've starved t'death tryin' to feed 'em. Gonffo, get 'em off me!"

Otters of Garraway's tribe began popping up everywhere, shouting to the otters from Tungro's crew, who yelled back at them. Trimp looked to Martin, who was chuckling and shaking his head at their antics.

"It looks like the two tribes are related. We're surrounded by aunts, uncles, nieces and nephews. Yugggh!"

A large pawful of soggy bankmud caught Martin full on the nose. Both groups of otters were so happy to see each other that they had started a mud fight. The remainder of the *Honeysuckle*'s crew and Furmo's shrews did not hesitate. Laughing madly they leaped into the water, joining in the fun. Right along the bank they fought, slinging heaps of sludgy brown mud at one another, slipping, sliding and splashing as they pelted away furiously. Mud was everywhere! Swiftly aimed globs of the sticky goo splattered, sticking to fur, spikes, muzzles, paws and tails. A practically unrecognisable hedgehog maid stumbled into what appeared to be a small moving mud mound.

"Heehee, is dat you, miz Trimp?"

"Hahaha, of course it is, who're you?"

"On'y a likkle Chugg, take dat!"

"Yutch! You filthy imp, don't chuck mud at me. Throw it at those otters, they started it!"

"Heehee, I frow muds at everybeast, here some more f'you!"

Whizz! Splat! Splotch! Whopp!

Only Krar remained aloof, perched on the skiff's prow, shaking his head in disgust at the undignified spectacle.

"Zounds, 'tis surely a day of fools' delight. These river-dogs are a mad species methinks. Yawch!"

A mud-covered Beau stooped to gather more. "Oh, well hit, Fethringsol. Maybe that'll spoil the great pompous feath-erbag's appetite, wot!"

Evening had fallen by the time both sides had wearied of mud throwing and washed themselves off in the stream. Queen Garraway Bullow took a last chance to grab her nephews and duck them soundly.

Gonff waded over. "Ahoy, what's goin' on here? Tryin' to drown off yore kin?"

"That's right, Gonffo. Disrespectful rascals, I'll teach 'em to address me as Yore Majesty, not auntie Garraway. Well, friend, we'd best rest up awhile, then I'll have my crew rig blocks'n'tackles to pull yore pretty boat over the waterfall. 'Tis the least I can do for such fighters!"

Folgrim broke the surface, blowing water. "Aye, 'cos if you don't yore name'll be mud for ever!'

39

Milk-white mist covered the land up to the height of a tall elm tree. Early dawn silence lay over Redwall Abbey, disturbed only by muted birdsong from afar. It was an hour after dawn. Skipper and Bella leaned on the north battlements, with Gonflet between them. Keeping a paw behind the little mouse, Bella cautioned him, "Stay away from the battlement edge. Your mum'll have a word or two to say if I let you fall."

Gonflet stamped his paws in frustration, peering into the blanket of mist. "When'll my daddy be's comin' back, Skip?"

Skipper sat the tiny fellow on his shoulder, out of harm.

"Oh, don't you fret, mate, he'll come back soon now. Maybe later on, when the mist lifts."

Gonflet tugged the otter's ear. "Phwaw! You say that alla time, every day, Skip!"

Columbine's voice sounded from the lawn below. "Hello, Bella, Skip, where are you?"

"Up 'ere, marm, west corner o' north wall!"

Columbine came up the wallsteps, carrying a tray, which she placed on the wall.

"Gracious, you three are up here early today. Surely there's not much point yet, with all this autumn mist about. Gonflet, shouldn't you still be in your bed?"

"No no, it my turn to watch for daddy. Miz Bell an' Skip 'elpin' me. My daddy come soon, you see!"

Columbine stroked her son's head fondly. "Yes, I'm sure he will. Oh, look, the mist is turning gold! Come and have some breakfast now. The sun will burn all this mist away before long."

Columbine stayed on the ramparts with them. Still surrounded by the cocoon of golden autumnal mist, they ate bowls of hot oatmeal with fresh berries and honey.

With otters hauling and shrews pushing, the skiff *Honeysuckle* slid over the ditch and out of west Mossflower's trees onto the path. It was the same spot where Trimp had met Ferdy and Coggs a season before.

Gonff called through the mist to Martin, "Hoist the sail, matey!"

Furmo shook his head at the Mousethief. "Wot d'you want the sail spread for, matey? We're in a fog, there ain't a feather o' breeze nowheres to stir her sail."

Taking a brightly colored Guosim headband, Gonff bound it about his brow. He climbed to the prow and struck a pose. "You an' the breeze can do what you like, Log a Log, but if I'm comin' home then I'm goin' to arrive in style, eh, Martin?"

His friend joined him on the prow, drawing his sword and pointing forward in an equally heroic pose. "Right, mate. Let's go home!"

Furmo nodded admiringly at the pair. "That's the way, crewmates. Come on, everybeast, we'll grease the wheels, comb our whiskers, haul the ropes an' sing our friends home every bit o' the way. You all know 'Journey's End.' Trimp, you take the top harmony, I'll do the baritone, an' Garraway the bass. One two three . . ."

Away the *Honeysuckle* rolled down the path, with her crew pulling the headropes, two tribes of otters and a tribe of Guosim crowding around to push; Martin, Gonff, Dinny and Trimp, the original four who had set out from the Abbey, all standing in the prow. Krar perched on the masthead, keeping a firm grip on Chugger, who still considered himself captain.

Now the sun was beginning to thin the mist, they could see through it. As they rounded a bend by a grove of oaks, the singing suddenly died, and the *Honeysuckle* rolled to a halt. Everybeast looked up and saw Redwall.

Floating above the golden mist like a vision from some wondrous dream, south gable reared to the soft blue skies, with the weather vane standing proud atop the dusty rose-colored sandstone buttresses. It was a magical, breathtaking sight. For one awestruck moment they all stood, gazing dumbly, then a mighty cheer broke out. Dinny chuckled proudly, through tears he was unable to check, "Yonder be moi 'ome!"

Gonflet sprang from Skipper's shoulders onto the northwest corner battlement, which was higher than the rest. Skipper held out his paws for the little mouse to jump back down again.

"Come offa there, matey. You can't see anythin' yet in this mist."

Columbine sensed something. She looked up at her son. "Gonflet, what is it?"

"I 'ear 'em, mamma! Lissen! Daddy comes 'ome! Lissen!"

Faintly at first, but growing in volume, the sound of many-beasts singing reached the walltops. Bella scrambled up onto the battlement and laughed aloud with joy.

"There's a ship coming down the path! A ship! Would you believe it, friends, I see them! I see them!"

High into the sunny morning the song rang out.

"Marching home! Marching home!
Jolly friend! Jolly friend!
Trav'lling on, until our journey's end,
So away with all your fears,
Smile with me, forget those tears,
Though the road was long an' dusty we survived.
And arrived!
Tramp tramp tramp tramp,
Lay your head down where you camp,

It ain't your home or fireside.
Tramp tramp tramp tramp,
Moorlands dry or forests damp,
Sharing together side by side.

Marching home! Marching home!
Jolly friend! Jolly friend!
O'er each highland, around each river's bend,
Keep your chin up in the rain,
Soon we'll be back home again,
Though my paws are worn an' weary never fear.
Oh my dear!
Left right left right,
Onward mate by day or night,
Lean on my shoulder now old friend,
Left right left right,
Grey the day or sunlight bright,
Until we reach our journey's end.
Marching home! Marching home!"

Bella's shouts boomed like thunder over the lawns.
"Rouse yourselves, Redwallers, they're back! Turn out the cooks! Open the gates! They've come back home!"
As Ferdy and Coggs flung the outer gates wide, Columbine allowed Gonflet to dash off and meet the ship. He was swept aboard and lifted onto his father's shoulders. Ferdy and Coggs, still in their nightshirts, held the outer wall gates wide open. With all the creatures of Redwall pushing it, the skiff *Honeysuckle* sailed regally inside, halting in the center of the main lawn. Gonff leaped down with Gonflet still on his shoulders, swept Columbine up and hugged her tight. "Yore Prince o' Mousethieves is returned, milady!"
Chaotic greetings broke out everywhere.
"Oh, Dinny, our faithful Foremole, how we missed you, my friend. Welcome home, welcome home!"
"Hurr, thankee, miz Bell, oi missed ee too, aye, so gurtly that oi be lostened furr wurds, marm!"
"Uncle Warthorn, it is you, ain't it?"
"Well rip me rudder, so 'tis. Don't tell me yore Bargud's sons? Lookit the size o' you both. Wot were ye fed on, boul-

ders'n'logs? Fergit Warthorn, call me Skip. 'Ere, come an'
meet Mayberry an' Catkin. I thinks they're yore cousins, but
I'll let ye know when I works it out!"

"Ferdy, Coggs, hello there, 'tis me!"

"Why so 'tis, miz Trimp, y'look taller, I think!"

"Aye, an' pretty as ever. Good to 'ave ye back, me dear!"

"H'i name Chugg, only a likkle squiggle, but lotsa t'ubble!"

"Me called Gonflet, I lotsa t'ubble too, Chugg!"

"Ahoy there, Skip, whupperyhoo to ye. Let go o' those two
bullies an' shake yore otterkin's paw, ye ole rascal!"

"Haharr, Garraway Bullow, me ole heart's delight.
C'mere, me second cousin twice removed an' longtailed on
yore granma's side!"

Amid the shouting and laughing as old friends were
reunited and new ones made, a small stooped figure, leaning
on a blackthorn stick, shuffled across the lawn. Everybeast
made way for Abbess Germaine. Mayberry and Catkin hurried forward, assisting her to the *Honeysuckle*'s prow, where
Martin stood waiting to meet her. Drawing his sword he
knelt, laying it at the old mouse's footpaws. She smiled.

"Martin of Redwall, you have returned to us, my friend."

"Aye, Mother Abbess. It was a good journey, a long and
eventful summer. I am happy to be back at Redwall."

The Abbess Germaine waved her stick at the strange craft
standing in the middle of the lawn, with a great goshawk
perched on its prow.

"An eventful summer indeed, Martin. What is all this?"

"That is Log a Log Furmo's skiff *Honeysuckle*, named
after his goodwife, marm. Yonder noble bird is Krar Woodwatcher, a valiant fighter and a great friend to us. These
shrews are Guosim, and we have with us two tribes of
otters—the tribes of Queen Garraway Bullow and the brothers Folgrim and Tungro."

Abbess Germaine silenced Martin by raising her paw.

"Enough. You will confuse my old mind if you carry on
further, Martin. Welcome, welcome to you all, peace be with
you, may you find happiness and joy within Redwall Abbey.
If there is anything you need from me or my Redwallers,
please do not hesitate to ask for it."

In the brief silence which followed this announcement, the

old hare confronted the Abbess with a courteous, though slightly creaky, bow.

"Beauclair Fethringsol Cosfortingham at y'service, marm. I was, er, wonderin', wot, er, if perchance, you maybe had, er, a slight, hmmmmm, beggin' y'pardon of course, er, er . . ."

Germaine nodded. She understood him completely. "I take it you are hungry, mister Cosfortingham?"

Beau nodded eagerly, still stammering. "Quite, er ah, thank ye, marm, I am mayhap a little, er, shall we say, er, peckish?"

Smiling broadly, the old Abbess took his paw. "I never knew a hare who was not hungry, sir. We have been preparing since the back end of summer for such an event, and we have plenty enough for everybeast including you, sir. Is everything ready, Bella?"

The Badgermother nodded, pointing towards the orchard. "By the time the mist has risen completely. Cooks, servers, cellarhogs, helpers, to your stations for the feast!"

A mighty cheer arose into the autumn morn as the Redwall helpers hurried off to the kitchens for their trolleys. Paw in paw, all the guests strolled off behind them, chatting animatedly at the prospect of Redwall hospitality.

"A feast eh wot, hope there's enough for all this lot, wot?"

"Burr, zurr, you'm bain't never been to ee Redwall feast. Thurr be enuff gudd vittles to keep twice this yurr number a-goin' furr ee full season. Hurr aye!"

"Ahoy, Ferdy, wait'll you see ole Krar take to the vittles. That bird could make you look like a Dibbun at table!"

"We'll see about that, Gonff. What about yon hare?"

"Hoho, don't even ask, matey. His name should've been Famine, not Fethringsol. Don't sit next to him!"

"I sit by you, Gonflet, we eats everyfink all up, eh?"

"Ho yiss, but later, Chugg, come wiv me, we pincha pies off the windowsills, they still coolin'. Heehee!"

"Looks like you've got double trouble there, miz Columbine."

"You could be right, Skip, treble trouble if you count Gonff. But better the trouble that we know, and at least they're home safe and sound!"

"Gurr, 'ome, marm, bain't et a wunnerful word!"

Epilogue

Extract from the journal of Germaine, Mother Abbess of Redwall Abbey.

It is winter now, a time for sitting 'round the fire in Cavern Hole and storytelling on long dark evenings. By the time next winter arrives our Abbey will be completely built. Never have we had so many welcome and useful guests. This beautiful desk I am sitting at was made by the tribe of Tungro, as is all our furniture—what wonderfully skilled craftsbeasts those otters are. His brother Folgrim is to stay here and live with us; he and Skipper have become inseparable. Many of our guests will stay permanently. It gives me great joy, they are good hardworking creatures. Trimp and Chugger are now part of Gonff's family. How could they not be happy with two such as our Prince of Mousethieves and his lovely wife, Columbine. Everybeast here says that I still have many seasons in front of me. I hope so, Redwall is such a joyous place to be. I look forward each morning to breakfast with my close companions, Vurg and Beau. I wish I could have gone sea roving with them in my younger seasons. What adventures they have had!

Martin seems to have regained his old zest for life. He is not the troubled Warrior any more. It was a wondrous tale he had to tell, both of himself and his brave father, Luke. It was also very sad at times, but does not sadness mingle with joy, to make us grow fully into the creatures we are? Strangest of all, though, he showed me something from a beaded linen bag, which belonged to his poor mother. It was a woven tapestry of his grandsire, who was also called Martin. The picture is of a mouse in armour, bearing a great sword. I was amazed, it looked like Martin himself, to the very life. Though he said to me that it reminded him greatly of Luke, his father. Columbine has had a lovely idea: she thinks that the picture might form a centrepiece for a big tapestry, which would someday hang in Great Hall. When I look at the picture, I know it is our Martin. I think that he and his ancestors have always been warriors, champions, whose spirit exists to inspire good honest creatures.

Martin has also done a remarkable thing. He has decided to give up his sword and live a life of peace. He has done so much to help found our Abbey that no creature could deny him the right to do this. The goshawk, Krar Woodwatcher, has hidden the sword where Martin directed him to put it. The only hint he gave of the great sword's location was to me and no other. These are his words.

Above where autumn's mists do rise,
Where I beheld with mine own eyes,
My dream, my vision, hov'ring there,
One morn upon old Mossflower's air.

Then he said a strange thing to me which I will tell to you.

I stand here in this world alone,
No kin of mine to take the sword,
No son or daughter of my own,
A bitter and a sad reward,

But Redwall in its hour of need,
Will bring forth one to follow me,
To that one, valiant in deed,
I leave a Warrior's legacy.

Then he would talk no more of such matters. Now if I want to find him, I have only to follow the sound of our Abbey babes, the Dibbuns, laughing and playing. Martin will be there, joining in with them; Gonff too. They are both enjoying a new-found happiness, though I doubt that our Prince of Mousethieves ever really grew up. Perhaps Martin is making up for the lost seasons of his youth, who knows? It does every Redwaller's heart good to see him thus.

Well, my friends, I am tired now, that is the privilege of an old Abbess, burdened with so many long seasons. I will go down to Cavern Hole and sit in my big chair by the fire, with a blanket on my lap. There I can listen to the songs and the stories, watch the young ones dance and play, drink some hot cordial and drift off into a warm sleep, whilst winter reigns outside in the night. I won't say good-bye to you, because one evening you may drop by to share this good life with us. You know you are always welcome at Redwall Abbey. All you need to bring with you is a ready smile and an open heart.

Germaine, Abbess of Redwall.

New in Hardcover
from Philomel Books

A TALE FROM REDWALL

BRIAN JACQUES

Rakkety Tam

MathCAD®
FOR INTRODUCTORY PHYSICS

Denis Donnelly

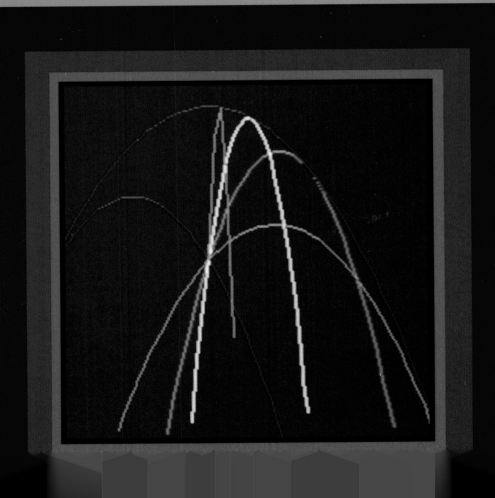

MathCAD®
for Introductory Physics

Denis Donnelly
Siena College

Addison-Wesley Publishing Company

Reading, Massachusetts • Menlo Park, California • New York • Don Mills,
Ontario • Wokingham, England • Amsterdam • Bonn • Sydney
Singapore • Tokyo • Madrid • San Juan • Milan • Paris

MathCAD is a registered trademark of MathSoft, Inc.

Library of Congress Cataloging-in-Publication Data

Donnelly, Denis P., 1937–
    MathCAD for introductory physics / Denis Donnelly.
       p.   cm.
    Includes index.
    ISBN 0-201-54736-8
    1. Physics–Data processing. 2. MathCAD. I. Title.
  QC52.D66   1992
  530'.0285'5369–dc20   92-7768
                                                CIP

1 2 3 4 5 6 7 8 9 10 HA 95949392

Preface

Physics is the most basic, the most fundamental of the sciences. It is a study of matter and energy and their interactions. To a beginner, that may sound deep and powerful (which it is) and perhaps even a bit frightening (which it needn't be) but surely something you want to be in on (which is right on). Beginner or not, you can get in on the action right away. Our goal is this; we want you to get a feeling for what physics is about, how it works, what it can do. Our approach to attaining that goal requires three things: an active learner, this book, and a computer running MathCAD. With these tools available, we can attack a wide range of problems and think about lots of different phenomena, get a sense of physical behavior, and let the computer do most of the work. We have at our fingertips a means to explore aspects of physics that would be very cumbersome (and in a number of cases virtually impossible) to do any other way. With MathCAD, it is easy to calculate, check units, plot, change, redo, try this, try that, see what happens, get a feel for the process. That's what you need to do. That's what I hope you will be doing.

You should use this book in a different way than you would a typical text. A textbook may be loaded with information but it's not interactive the way a computer is with you at the controls. This book is not just meant to be read; it is meant to be alongside you as you sit at your computer running MathCAD. When you access one of the files on the disk, it is in an active state, ready for you to change, process, and/or extend as the need requires.

The code for a number of documents is included in the text (a number of the documents are in two parts on separate pages). This material is to be read just as is the text. Follow the development; first imitate and then create your own documents. Once you get used to moving regions, it is fun to arrange a document so that the regions are in a form that you enjoy. Some of the documents near the beginning are demonstrations, designed for you to enter values and observe outcomes (e.g., the summation of vectors). There may be some advanced features in these documents that are necessary to create the figure(s) or to solve some equations. You are not expected to write things this complex, although by the time you have finished the book, you will have gained enough experience to do so.

The book is designed primarily for students taking college-level physics who have access to either a PC, a PC clone, or a Macintosh computer that runs MathCAD. An adept high school physics student could make good use of this book as well. Of course, individuals not officially enrolled in a course but interested in learning physics on their own would find this book's approach to physics very useful, as well.

This book is meant to accompany any general physics text. Topics from both semesters of a typical course are included. Some of the discussion makes use of the calculus but the actual computations are performed by MathCAD. So don't run when you see an integral or a deriative. You only need to know what to take the derivative or integral of, you do not need to know how to take the derivative or how to perform the integration.

The phenomena described in general physics are so rich and so varied, that it is possible to direct one's attention to almost any problem or phenomenon and discover something surprising. On several occasions in the text, we explore the transition between a discrete and a continous system. For example, we consider the motion of a rocket as the fuel is expelled in different states; at one extreme, the fuel is ejected in one large discrete chunk, at the other extreme the fuel is a gas ejected over a period of time. Or we compare the pressure in a wall constructed from a series of blocks. Such a simple model hardly seems like a model of either compressible or incompressible fluids.

For such problems, to appreciate the outcomes, first you must understand the model, then see how the model is expressed in equations, and finally you must explore a number of different cases. As you vary parameters or change models and consider a variety of cases, then you begin to understand the system. One-answer calculator problems appear rather limited from this perspective.

I'm willing to make you a bet. If you spend a sufficient amount of time with MathCAD to get some facility with the language, enough so that you are comfortable with it, you will change. The more you work with the computer, the less you will want to do by hand. A typewriter is a terrific device but once you understand how to use a word processor, a typewriter has a somewhat archaic aura. A pocket scientific calculator is essential for modest computations but if you want to explore a problem in more detail and with greater generality, a more powerful approach is essential. Learn, explore, and gain insight. The opportunity is yours for the taking.

Acknowledgments

Many colleagues and students have generously taken time from their busy schedules to comment on preliminary drafts of sections of the manuscript. I particularly wish to thank Shamshad Ahmad, Burt Brody, Josh Diamond, Harvey Gould, Leonard Merrill, and Ed Rogers. Clearly, the errors, omissions, and limitations are my own.

Thanks, too, are due to members of Siena College's administration for their support of this project. In particular, I thank David Rice, former Vice President for Academic Affairs; Ken Wittig, Dean, Division of Science; and Josh Diamond, Head, Department of Physics. I also thank Stuart Johnson, the physics editor of Addison-Wesley for his interest and support, Lorraine Ferrier for the careful copy editing, and Mona Zeftel for her production work. The text was produced using TeXtures. The figures showing the documents were produced directly from MathCAD.

To   Jacqueline

Jane
Philip
Stephen
Peter

and

Lulu

Contents

List of Programs

MathCAD Fundamentals

MathCAD, an equation-solving software package, provides a convenient direct method for handling numbers, equations, graphs, and text. A unique feature of MathCAD is that it allows the computer to be used like a notepad. Equations appear on the screen as equations do when written on a pad of paper. Such equations or any other information entered into the computer are contained within regions. These regions can be arranged on the screen in any desired nonoverlapping form. The only constraint in placement is that processing proceeds from left to right and from top to bottom.

Any information entered into a MathCAD document is in one of three types of regions: equation, plot, or text. Equation is the default mode. That is, unless a text or plot region is specified, any entry will appear in an equation region. The symbols to initiate text and plot regions are " and @, respectively.

MathCAD has many built-in functions so that any calculations done on a calculator are easily performed with MathCAD. MathCAD's advantage is that, once information is on the screen, it is easy to review and modify what has been done, to extend the calculation, to explore ideas that come to mind as the process unfolds, to save the work for recall at a later time, and to print out the contents of the document. Computational possibilities with MathCAD are extensive. They include solving equations, plotting graphs, curve fitting, performing numerical integration and differentiation, and matrix operations. MathCAD provides a rich environment in which to deal with numerical questions and models.

"Central Services . . . . We do the work, you do the pleasure."

Brazil

1.1   Prelude: A Glance at MathCAD

An example gives tooth to the words. In Fig. 1.1, a series of calculations demonstrate various MathCAD capabilities and give an indication of the kinds of things that can be done quite readily. There are regions of text, equations, and plots. The equations, whether or not they are familiar, at least appear in a familiar form.

Follow the document from left to right and from top to bottom. There is text. There are examples of arithmetic operations, with units and the use of variable names. Note the different equality signs used when defining a quantity and when evaluating a quantity. Observe the use of the place marker to express a result in terms of a particular quantity (the π in asin (1)). We then see trigonometric and arctrigonometric functions; a user-defined function, $y(x)$; a range variable, x; a plot region; subscripted variables, xx_i, yy_i; derivative and integral operations; finding a zero of a function using the root function; using subscripted variables in an iterative procedure; and finally solving simultaneous equations using a solve block.

The point of this example is to see the general layout of a document and to see the kinds of things that can be done with only a few steps. The details of MathCAD and many additional examples follow. In short order, you will be performing all of these operations and others as well.

1.2   Getting Started

The most sensible way to learn to use MathCAD is to sit down at the console and perform some operations. Start out by imitating examples that you know work. As you gain experience, the overall process as well

Some examples of basic Mathcad operations.

Note that when values are assigned, the sign is `:=`; when values are calculated the sign is `=`.

Define a unit of length $m := 1L$

The circumference of a circle $2 \cdot \pi \cdot 3 \cdot m = 18.85 \cdot length$ $2 \cdot \pi \cdot 3 \cdot m = 18.85 \cdot m$

or with variable names $r := 3 \cdot m$ $c := 2 \cdot \pi \cdot r$ $c = 18.85 \cdot m$

The advantage of using variable names is that they can be used again.

$A := \pi \cdot r^2$ $A = 28.274 \cdot m^2$ $ratio := \dfrac{A}{c}$ $ratio = 1.5 \cdot length$

The use of trigonometric functions is straight forward.   Angles in radians.

$\sin\left[\dfrac{\pi}{4}\right] = 0.707$ $\cos(2 \cdot \pi) = 1$ $asin(1) = 0.5 \cdot \pi$

To plot a function, there are two possible methods, a user defined function or a vector.

A parabola $y(x) := x^2$ $x := -2, -1.9 ..2$

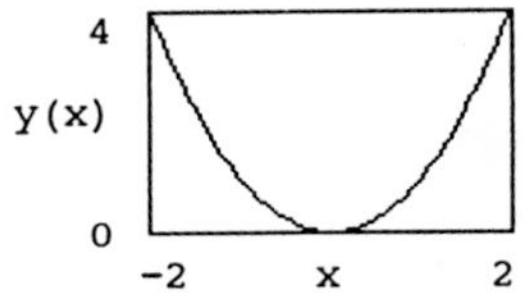

$n := 20$

$i := 0 ..n$ $xx_i := \dfrac{i}{n} \cdot 4 - 2$ $yy_i := xx_i^2$

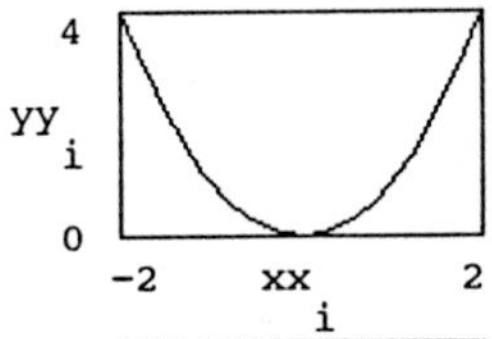

Each method has its advantages.

Some more advanced functions.

Differentiation. $y'(x) := \dfrac{d}{dx} y(x)$

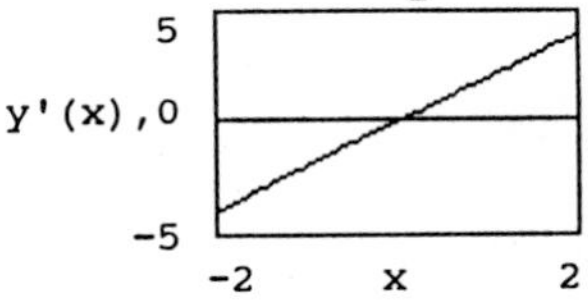

Integration $I := \int_0^2 y(x)\ dx$

$I = 2.667$

Find the zero, the root, of the y curve.

guess value $z := 1$ $rt := root(y(z), z)$ $rt = 0.029$

The value for y is within the default tolerance. $y(rt) = 8.661 \cdot 10^{-4}$

Solve two simultaneous equations.

$c1 := 2$ $c2 := 3$ $g := 1$ $f1(x) := c1 \cdot x$ $f2(x) := c2 \cdot x^2$

given $f1(g) \approx f2(g)$ $g := find(g)$ $g = 0.667$

check results $f1(g) = 1.333$ $f2(g) = 1.333$

Figure 1.1 MathCAD examples.

as the details will become clear and, generally, straightforward. When you see a double bullet, ••, that is a sign for you to do something. The more active you are, the more quickly you will learn.

There are implementations of MathCAD on PC and on Macintosh computers. The computer-specific comments that follow apply to the PC version; Macintosh users will have little difficulty adapting the concepts.

To begin, you need a computer, a monitor, DOS, and some implementation of MathCAD. There is more space to work if the computer has 640K of memory. A coprocessor will speed the calculations. Of course, use the fastest machines available.

Make a backup copy of MathCAD. Save the original copy, and work with the backup. See your manual for instructions.

Getting the Machine Ready.   These directions are for a hard disk system in which MathCAD has already been stored in a separate directory titled MCAD.

Turn on the power for the computer and monitor.

After DOS is loaded, change the directory to the MCAD directory. To change directories, type, following the prompt:
C:\ > cd\ mcad

On the screen will appear the new prompt: C:\ MCAD >

To load MathCAD, type following the prompt: mcad/m. (Note, in one case a backslash was used and in the other a slash.) The /m directs MathCAD to load in manual mode. This means that processing takes place only when requested. Automatic mode is a nuisance because reprocessing takes place every time a change is made. This is a waste of time.

• •   If you haven't already done so, turn on the power and load MathCAD into the machine.

On occasion, the machine will crash. To restart, hold down [Ctrl][Alt] and press [Del]. Then release all three buttons. This will bring the system back up under DOS control. You must reload MathCAD.

It is a good idea to keep a notebook of MathCAD information. When you discover or are told something useful, write it down. Later, when you are alone with the machine, and that question — Now, how did I do that? — occurs, you will be prepared.

The startup screen, a space of 24 lines and 80 columns, includes a flashing underscore cursor, the message line at the very top of the screen, and the Mathsoft logo. The logo disappears with the first operation. Toward the right of the message line, there are two zeros. These numbers provide the line and column location of the cursor. If a file were loaded, the file name would appear at the left of the message line. Commands are also entered on this line.

The information about MathCAD in the rest of this chapter is intended as a brief introduction to MathCAD. It is not intended to tell you everything there is to know about MathCAD. The point is to get you started quickly. Keep the MathCAD manual handy and refer to it as necessary. The professional manual provides a more extensive coverage of the MathCAD language than does the student manual. However, the student manual in combination with this text should cover all the essentials and then some. For on-line help press [F1].

Before starting, it is useful to know **how to quit**. It is always best to exit from a program by the proper means; don't just turn off the machine (although nothing will blow up if you do). The command to quit is [Ctrl]Q; hold down the [Ctrl] key and press Q. This command tells MathCAD to end the session. If there is information on the screen that has not been saved, the following statement appears on the command line: "Changes not saved. OK to discard?" If you press return without typing anything, you are returned to your existing MathCAD document. If you type y (for yes, it is OK to discard the current document) and then press return, the document is discarded, MathCAD is removed from RAM, and control is returned to DOS. If you do want to save the document, you must do so before quitting. Press [F6] and provide a name for the file where the document is to be saved; see the section on files, below, for more details. After saving the document, press [Ctrl]Q.

1.3 The MathCAD Language

The information in the rest of this chapter falls roughly into two main categories, general operations and coding. The general operations, which include processing and printing documents and loading and saving files, will be treated last. We do this in order to start right out going over the basic MathCAD moves. (Of course, those who feel more comfortable proceeding in the other order can jump ahead to the next section, and then return.)

Beginning any language is a bit awkward. The thing to keep in mind as you go is the final result. Even if things get frustrating and you get angry, remember

"Never hate your enemies, it clouds your judgment."

The Godfather III

Many features of the MathCAD language are described in the following sections. They provide the basis for the work that follows. No document is being designed. Rather, the features are described one by one, and brief exercises are suggested. There is probably too much for one session. Get as far as is reasonable for you, stop, and come back later. Working with a friend is a good idea.

Regions.   MathCAD permits the user to enter information essentially anywhere on the screen. All information is one of three types: text, equation, or plot. Equation is the default mode; that is, unless text or plot is specified, entries are considered as equations.

To create a **text** region, type a single quotation mark. A pair of quotation marks will appear. As long as the cursor is within the text region, these quotation marks will remain visible. When the cursor exits the region, the quotation marks disappear. To exit a text region use the arrow keys, not the return or enter key.

To create a **plot** region, type the at sign @, shift 2. A rectangle will appear bordered with six place markers. These place markers are to identify what is to be plotted and the ranges for each. The text and plot regions will be discussed more fully later in this chapter. However, we see examples in Fig. 1.2.

• •   Type a quotation mark and then enter some text. The backspace can be use to delete characters to the left of the cursor. The delete key deletes characters at the cursor.

• •   Now create a plot region. There is nothing to plot yet, but the region and the markers can be observed. Move the cursor within the plot rectangle and press the letter f, for format. Observe the possible features that can be changed. Press [Esc] to return.

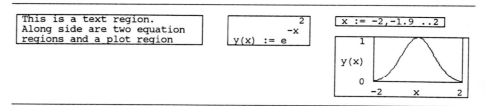

Figure 1.2 Text, equation, and plot regions, outlined.

• • Enter something in equation mode. Type 2+3= and press [F9]. Do not attempt to enter spaces; MathCAD takes care of spacing automatically.

When creating a document, keep some space between regions. Often, it is necessary to go back and change things. This may result in regions expanding and overlapping if new material is included.

Avoid putting all regions in a vertical pattern. Get used to placing regions horizontally.

Viewing Regions/Outline/Refresh.   To see the space assigned to each region, press [Ctrl]V (hold down [Ctrl], next, press V, and then release both). This is a toggling operation. For each [Ctrl]V operation, the outlines are either drawn or removed.

• • Press [Ctrl]V several times. In general, it is preferable to omit the outlines as it slows the screen refresh.

When a MathCAD document is processed, the processing moves from left to right and from top to bottom. Regions with the top edges aligned will be processed from left to right. For processing order, the top of the region is what counts; do not go by alignment of equality signs.

If the screen display becomes corrupted for any reason, it can be refreshed or rewritten by pressing [Ctrl]R.

• • Press [Ctrl]R.

Cut, Copy, and Paste.   Any region can be cut (that is, removed from the document), copied, and if desired pasted elsewhere in the document. When a region is cut or copied, it is stored in a buffer. There is only one buffer; only the last region cut or copied is saved.

To cut a region, move the cursor to that region and press [F3]. To copy a region, move the cursor to that region and press [F2]; note, on the command line, the statement, region copied. To paste a region, move the cursor to the desired location of the upper left corner of the region and press [F4].

If you cut or copy a region, move to a new empty location and press [F3], for example, instead of [F4], the region in the buffer is not lost. Press [F4] and it will be pasted.

• • Copy the regions on the screen and paste them elsewhere. Cut a region and paste it elsewhere. (You could, of course, paste it right back where it was, which is useful when you cut the wrong region.) Attempt to paste one region on top of another.

There are also commands referred to as incut, incopy, and inpaste. These will be discussed later.

Insert or Delete Blank Lines.   As a document is developed, frequent changes in the layout of the document may be very useful. In addition to the cut, copy, and paste operations, blank lines can be inserted or deleted.

The command to add a blank line is [Ctrl][F9]. The command to remove a blank line is [Ctrl][F10]. The operations can be repeated by holding down the [Ctrl] key and pressing [F9] or [F10] as many times as required. The screen takes a moment to refresh.

• •   Add and delete lines between the regions on the screen.

Reset.   To clear the screen without saving what is present, press [Esc], type reset, and press return. If the document has been changed since it was last saved, the comment "Changes not saved, OK to discard?" will appear. Type y for yes and press return.

• •   Clear the screen.

Separate.   If regions overlap, one region may obscure another. Regions can be separated. Press [Esc], type sep(arate), and press return. Curious errors can occur because regions were overlapped and one is invisible or only partly visible.

• •   Move the cursor five spaces to the right using the arrow key. Type x:2. Move the cursor left five spaces so that it is back where it started (keep the cursor on the same line as the $x := 2$ region). Type y:3.141592654. The y region now completely covers the x region. Even though it is not visible, the x region is still there and still active. Move several spaces to the right, type $x =$, and evaluate. Now separate the groups using the above procedure. If you keep the regions separated, there will be no surprises.

1.3.1   Equation Regions

Equality Signs.   MathCAD has four different kinds of equality. Ultimately, we will need them all. The two types that we need immediately are for definitions or assignments and for calculations. The other two kinds of equality are for global assignment (as opposed to local) and for relational equality. We will encounter the global assignment when discussing units and for convenience in processing some documents. We will encounter the relational equality when using solve blocks.

The local assignment uses the colon, as in x:2. The value 2 is assigned to x. Whenever x is used, it carries with it that value, unless it is reassigned a different value.

The calculational equality, as in $x=$, when processed, returns the value assigned to x.

The global equality, as in $k\tilde{}\ 2$, which appears as $k \equiv 2$, is an assignment equality, as is the colon. However, in processing a document, MathCAD takes two passes through the document, the first time processing all global equalities and the second time everything else. This provides a mechanism whereby the code can be placed at the end of a document and plot regions, for example, that depend on the code can be placed first.

The relational equality is used in given-find and given-minerr solve blocks. It is called by typing [Alt]=, as in $2 \cdot x \approx 3 \cdot y$.

• •   Assign 2 to k with a global equality. Evaluate k by typing $k=$ and pressing [F9]. Reset the screen.

Processing or Evaluating.   We make some brief comments on processing now. More will be given in the general features section.

To process a document — that is, to evaluate the various quantities within the document — press [F9]. MathCAD will process the document to the bottom of the present screen. If more regions exist below the bottom of the screen they will not be processed. To process everything, press [Esc], type pro(cess), and press return.

Variable Name.   A value can be assigned to a variable name. The local assignment symbol, as we have already noted, is the colon. To assign the value 4 to the name x, one would type $x{:}4$. Leave no spaces; they are handled automatically.

Variable names must start with a letter (Roman or Greek) and can include numerals, the underscore, and the percent sign. A variable name can include up to 64 characters. Let the name describe the quantity it is to represent.

Warning. Never use the same name for two different things in the same document. Two common errors are using m for meters and also for mass, and using N for Newtons and also for normal force or the upper limit of an index.

• •   Enter $hip : 13$ and $be_{bop} : hip$; evaluate by entering $be_{bop} =$ and pressing [F9].

Variable names may include a literal subscript. A literal subscript appears as a subscript when the cursor exits the region. Literal subscripts are implemented by typing variable_name.literal_subscript. The specification for the literal subscript comes after the end of the variable name and is separated by a period. It is strongly suggested that literal subscripts not be integers. If they are integers, they may become confused with active subscripts.

• •   Enter *x.o:e.* Move the cursor in and out of the region. Observe the *o*.

The PC version of MathCAD can display 17 Greek letters, 14 lower-case and 3 uppercase. The general format for displaying these letters is [Alt]letter. For example, θ is [Alt]Q. The Roman letters that, with [Alt], produce the indicated Greek letters are: a (α), b (β), d (δ), e (ϵ), f (ϕ), g (Γ), h (Φ), l (λ), n (ν), o (Ω), p (π), q (θ), r (ρ), s (σ), t (τ), u (μ), and w (ω).

Arithmetic Operations.   The arithmetic operations use the symbols +, –, *, and / for addition, subtraction, multiplication, and division, respectively. The caret, ˆ , is used to raise something to a power, as in xˆ 2, for x^2. The backslash, \, is the symbol for a square root, as in \(4+5).

The order of priority in arithmetic operations is standard. Make sure that parentheses are used to group terms that need to be grouped. A good rule is to use parentheses for grouping whenever there is any question; the MathCAD editor will behave less schizophrenically if you do. Think ahead: Start with a left-hand parenthesis when necessary, rather than saying, "Ah yes," and then having to go back and try to insert one. In an equation region, an apostrophe creates a pair of parentheses. However, where the parentheses go depends on the construction already present. Just try it and see what happens; you can always delete what you don't like.

• •   Reset MathCAD so that you have a blank screen. Type the expression $a + b + c$. Remember, spacing is automatic in equation regions. Move the cursor to the first plus sign (half-surrounding from the right); type an apostrophe. Note the location of the parentheses. Delete the righthand parenthesis. Move the cursor to the second plus sign; type an apostrophe. Again, note the location of the parentheses. The rules are not easily summarized but, in any case, what you see is what you get.

• •   Divide the quantity 17 plus 29 by 2.54. Do this twice, once explicitly using the parentheses and once using the apostrophe. (Ans. 18.11)

• •   Take the square root of the sum of any two or more quantities.

• •   Enter 4+5. Now try to put parentheses around this quantity. Do the right-hand one first; that should be no problem. Now try the left one. Did you get a message "can't edit blank space"?

Note that the cursor in an equation region appears as ⌋, not as an underscore. This is the append cursor. Characters entered are appended

to what has been entered. The insert key toggles the cursor from ⌋ to
⌊ and back. When in ⌊ mode, the cursor is referred to as the insert
cursor. This is a necessary editing feature for approaching from the left.
Press the insert key. The cursor should now appear as ⌊. Now insert the
parenthesis from the left. Note that the cursor must be snuggled up to
and half surrounding the character, not a space away. In general, keep the
cursor in append mode rather than in insert mode.

● ●   Enter 6+4=. Now go back and put a minus sign in front of the 6.
Evaluate.

● ●   Try 87 plus the quantity 16 times 4, the whole thing divided by the
quantity 77 minus 29. (Ans. 3.146)

Format.   The answer to the previous calculation appears with three figures after the decimal point. That can be changed, as can a number of
other features. To see what controls are available, press [Esc], type format,
and press return.

   Six controls are listed: (1) radix — decimal, octal, or hexadecimal; (2)
precision — default 3, possible range 0–15; (3) exponential threshold —
default 3, numbers outside the range 10 to plus or minus the threshold
value are shown in exponential notation; (4) imaginary symbol i or j; (5)
zero tolerance — default 15; numbers less than 10 to the minus default
value are shown as zero (this is frequently not adequate; change as needed,
range 0–308); and (6) complex tolerance — indicating that when the ratio
between larger and smaller values is outside of range, consider the smaller
one to be zero. Of these, the two of most frequent concern are (2) and
(5). Whenever a document is opened, the default values are in place.

Place Marker.   The place marker, an active and useful device, is the solid
box at the end of a region with a standard equality sign (=). See Fig.
1.3. The place marker is visible only if the cursor is in the region. For
example, an evaluated quantity might appear as

$$x = 1024 \ \blacksquare.$$

● ●   Enter x:1024 and evaluate x. Move the cursor to the place marker,
enter 2, and press [F9]. Change the 2 to 2^4 and evaluate.

   This property is a general feature. Any number can be represented
as a multiple of anything. When dealing with angles, frequently useful
quantities to substitute are π or deg (see the section on built-in functions
below).

```
Examples using the place marker.  The result is expressed as a multiple of
the quantity in the place marker.

r := 2      c := 2·π·r       c = 12.566

d := 2·r                     c = 6.283·r      r in place marker

                             c = 4·π           π in place marker

                             c = 3.142·d       d in place marker.
```

Figure 1.3 Example of the functionality of the place marker.

Incutting, Incopying, Inpasting. These operations refer to cutting or copying a portion of a region and pasting that portion either into an existing region or as a new region. There are occasions when an expression needs to be repeated or moved to a different location within an existing region. The in- operations are helpful under such circumstances.

In an exercise in the section on arithmetic operations, we entered parentheses in the expression $a+b+c$ using the apostrophe. The placement of the parentheses is helpful in knowing which portions will be cut or copied.

• • Type $a + b + c$. Place the cursor at the first plus sign and perform an incopy operation. Move to the side and inpaste into a new region. Go back to the original region, place the cursor at the second plus sign, and perform an incut operation. Type a colon. Inpaste the incut information at the right-hand place marker. Try a few examples of your own; include parentheses and other operations.

Built-in Functions. First, let's consider two built-in symbols with values. The symbol π, expressed by pressing [Alt]P, has associated with it the value for π. The letter e has associated with it the value of the base of the natural logarithm.

• • Evaluate π and e. What is the percent error in the approximation $\pi^2 \approx 10$?

MathCAD has built in all the functions one would expect to find on a scientific calculator plus a number of others. (There are approximately 75 built-in functions.) These include the standard trigonometric functions; the angle function, which is often preferable to the arctangent; hyperbolic functions; log and exponential functions; Bessel functions; complex numbers; interpolation; and the fast Fourier transform. Procedures for vector and matrix operations, regression, and statistical, correlation, equation-solving, and other functions are included as well.

The standard format is function_name(argument, argument, ...). Many functions, like the trig functions, have only one argument. Regression and sorting functions, for example, have two; the number of arguments with Find or Minerr depends on the number of unknowns in a solve process.

The arguments for the standard trigonometric functions are in radians. To convert from degrees to radians, the following procedure is suggested. Define the radian as equal to one; then define the degree in terms of the radian:

$$\text{rad} := 1 \qquad\qquad \text{deg} := \frac{\pi}{180} \cdot \text{rad}.$$

If you attach the name deg as a multiplier to any value in degrees, MathCAD will make all necessary conversions, for example, $45 \cdot \text{deg}$.

• •   Enter the statements for rad and deg. Type 45*deg and evaluate.

Evaluate the sine of 90° and of $\pi/2$ radians.

Take the asin of 1. (Ans. 1.571)

Take the tangent of 135° and 225°. Take the arctangent of 1 and −1. This can cause problems if one is not careful. Instead, try the following:

The coordinates of a point at 135° could be (−1,1) and at 225° (−1,−1). Evaluate angle(−1,1) and angle(−1,−1). Enter deg at the place marker and press [F9].

The general form of the angle function is angle(δx, δy). The function returns a value between 0 and 2π. The variables δx and δy are the differences in x and y between the point of interest (x, y) and the reference point (x_r, y_r); $\delta x = x - x_r$ and $\delta y = y - y_r$. If the reference point is the origin, then δx and δy are just the x and y coordinates of the point for which the angle is to be determined. The angle is measured counterclockwise from a line originating at (x_r, y_r) and parallel to the positive x-axis.

• •   The base of the natural log system, e, is available either directly as e or as exp(). Evaluate e, $e\hat{\ }1$, and exp(1). Use the exponential function in a simple radioactive decay problem. If

$$N = N_o \cdot e^{-\lambda \cdot t}$$

calculate the number of nuclei N at time t where $\lambda = 0.2$, $t = 30$, and the number of radioactive nuclei at time $t = 0$ is 10^{12}. Name each of the quantities. Write N in terms of other names, not in terms of numbers. Evaluate N.

Moving the Cursor.   Several useful cursor commands make getting around the screen and around a file quick and easy. They are presented in list form.

The four arrow keys move the cursor one space in the direction of the arrow for each operation of the key. If the key is held down, the stepping repeats automatically.

[Ctrl][Home] moves the cursor to the beginning of the first region in the document.

[Ctrl][End] moves the cursor to the end of the last region in the document.

[Home] moves the cursor to the beginning of the previous region.

[End] moves the cursor to the end of the present region or the beginning of the next. If you are at the last region, the cursor will toggle back and forth between beginning and end with each successive operation.

[PgDn] moves the cursor down five lines.

[PgUp] moves the cursor up five lines.

[Ctrl][PgDn] moves the cursor down 80% of the screen height.

[Ctrl][PgUp] moves the cursor up 80% of the screen height. (If the beginning of the document is showing or is less than 80% of the screen height above the top of the screen, [Ctrl][PgUp] will result in less cursor movement, or no movement at all if the zero line of the document is displayed on the screen.)

[Tab] advances the cursor across the screen, to the right, in ten character steps. [Shift][Tab] moves the cursor to the left in ten character steps. In an equation region, [Tab] moves the cursor within the region.

Two other motion commands are important but do not apply to the student version. These are [Ctrl]G and [Ctrl]E, which move 80 columns to the right and left, respectively.

Spend several minutes trying each one of the movements. Knowledge of these operations makes working within MathCAD much smoother. (Amateurs lean on the arrow keys.)

Range Variables.   Sometimes, it is desirable to perform an operation with a sequence of values. MathCAD can perform such a series of operations using either range variables in combination with some function or vectors.

A range variable takes on a series of values. The values are specified by providing the first, second, and last values of the sequence. The step size is the difference between the second and first values. If no second value is specified, the default step size is one. For example, if θ is to vary over the range from 0 to 2π, in steps of 0.1, the specification is typed [Alt]Q:0,0.1;2*[Alt]P. This would appear as

$$\theta := 0, 0.1 \ldots 2 \cdot \pi.$$

Note the ellipsis, ... , is achieved by typing a semicolon, **not** by typing a sequence of periods.

• •   Enter the above specification for θ and then evaluate it. The results appear in tabular form.

A general method to generate a sequence starting at a and going to b taking N steps is

$$\text{step} := \frac{(b-a)}{N} \qquad x := a, a + \text{step} \ldots b.$$

A function of a range variable, func(range var), will, when processed, evaluate the function for each value of the range variable.

• •   Evaluate $\sin(\theta)$; the above definition for θ must be specified first.

User-Defined Functions.   A user-defined function is expressed as

$$name(variable\ list) = any\ legal\ combination\ of\ terms.$$

A simple example is associated with the free fall of an object near the surface of the earth. A function is desired to express the position of the object as a function of time. We write

$$x(t) = \frac{1}{2} a t^2.$$

Any parameter not in the variable list must be defined before the function is defined. In this case, a value would need to be assigned to a, the acceleration.

• •   Reset the screen. Let $a = 9.81$. Define t as a range variable as described above (let t take on 10 or 15 values). Evaluate $x(t)$. Evaluate $x(2.645)$.

Subscripts.   A variety of operations can be performed on variables with subscripts. By subscript, we mean active subscripts, not the literal subscripts that are part of a variable name. Avoid using both literal and active subscripts in one variable name.

A subscript is called using the left-hand square bracket, [. A subscript must be an integer. A subscript cannot have a value less than the value of ORIGIN.

• •   Evaluate ORIGIN.

The default value is zero. You should not change this quantity without a clear understanding of the implications. Given the default value for ORIGIN, negative subscripts are out of range.

• •   Define a range variable i, i:0;5. Then let $x[i:i\char94 2$. Evaluate x_i and x_2.

Sum all the x-values. The summation operator is called by pressing [Shift]4 (that is, $).

• •   Press [Shift]4, and type $x[i$ at the place marker to the right of the summation sign. Press [Tab] to move the cursor to the place marker beneath the summation sign. Enter the index over which the summation is to take place, i. Evaluate the sum. (Ans. 55)

Vectors.   The variable x_i, above, is a vector; it holds a sequence of values. The subscript is a range variable with integral values. The vector values can be computed according to some function, or they can be entered by hand. Values are entered by hand, by typing, for example, $x[i$:value1, value2, ... , last value. The data appear in tabular form, once the first comma is entered.

• •   Type $y[i$:0,1,2,4,7,8,10. Define i in a region previous to y and then sum the y_i.

To get some sense of what happens if values are not specified over the entire range of the subscript, try the following.

• •   Define i:0;5. Let $z[i$:1,2,3. Sum the $z[i$. Did you get an error message? Cut the region defining the z_i. In its place type $z[5:1$. Evaluate z_i and the sum. Change the $z[5$ in the z-term to $z[6$ and sum.

The vector must be specified for the largest value of its subscript. Values of zero are assigned to all unspecified values of the variable.

Frequently, several different subscripts and ranges are required in one document. If a double subscript is required use parentheses, as in $x[(i,j)$ for $x_{i,j}$.

Disabling an Equation.   Sometimes it is useful to write an equation in a MathCAD document that can be seen but is not to be processed. Equations can be disabled by pressing [Esc], typing eq (equation), and pressing return. When an equation is disabled, a small box, □, resembling an unfilled place marker, ■, appears to the right of the equation. This Esc/eq process is a toggling operation; repeat it to enable a disabled equation. Find regions cannot be disabled.

1.3.2   *Plot Regions*

In MathCAD, plotting is done easily and, generally, quickly. We are going to want to plot many things, so become very familiar with the process.

To create a plot region, press the @ sign. An open rectangle, the plot space, with six place markers appears on the screen. The place markers at the extremes of the abscissa and ordinate specify the plot range. Those at the center of each axis specify the quantities to be plotted.

A quick way to create a plot region and enter the names of the variables to be plotted when plotting $y(t)$ vs. $x(t)$ is to type $y(t)$ @ $x(t)$. This saves some moving around. MathCAD will set limits automatically in all cases. Sometimes, it is convenient to set limits to control the display. If limits are set and one (or more) of the points is outside the defined region, lines will not be drawn to/toward the point(s) or from it (them). This feature has its uses.

There is control over the size of the plot space, the number of subdivisions within the region, whether the plot is linear or log, and the plot type, that is, the plot symbol and whether the points are connected with a line or not.

To select the different plot options, move the cursor inside the plot rectangle and press the letter f (format). On the command line, the following information is displayed (in the student version; the professional version gives the same information in menu form): logs=0,0 subdivs=1,1 size=6,15 type=l. To change any of the values, move the blinking underscore cursor to the point where changes are to be made, delete the undesired values, type in the desired ones, and press return. In the professional version, use the up or down arrow keys to highlight the quantity of interest, press return, enter the new values, press return, highlight and change other areas if desired, and finally press d (for done) and press return once more.

Size.   Size can be changed to suit the character of a particular graph. The first number represents the vertical dimension (equivalent to that number of lines in the document), the second the horizontal (equivalent to that many spaces in the document). Because of the aspect ratio of the screen, equal values do not result in a square plot region. Roughly speaking, one down is equal to two or two and one-half across (for a PC), depending on the monitor. Note that square on the monitor does not necessarily

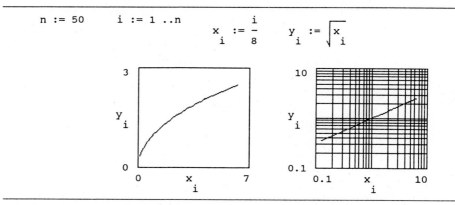

Figure 1.4 A linear and log-log plot of the square root function.

mean square on the printer. If the printed form is important, spend a few minutes and determine what ratio on the screen results in square on the printer. Other ratios can be determined from this.

• •   Reset the screen. Open a plot region. Change the size to 10,20. Change the size to 12,50. Press [Ctrl]V to see the region of the screen that is occupied. Remove the outline.

Linear/Log.   Zero in the log designation means the plot is linear; a positive integer means that the plot is a log plot (see Fig. 1.4). The number has nothing to do with the plot range and nothing to do with the number of log cycles. The number corresponds to the subdivisions. It is not a bad idea simply to use zero for linear and one for log plots. Of course, each axis is designated separately; a semilog plot would be 1,0 (or possibly, 0,1).

MathCAD does not select limits on a log graph to be powers of ten. Note the range of values and then replace them with the appropriate powers of ten. Be sure that the number of cycles you select corresponds to the range; otherwise, some points may be excluded.

Of the values to be plotted, values less than or equal to zero are not permissible with log plots. If a plot that had been linear is changed to a log plot, it may be necessary to delete the limits even though MathCAD specified them. Units cannot be used with log plots.

Subdivisions.   Subdivs, subdivisions, are best left at 1,1 when exploring. Once you have a graph that you want to refine, work with the subdivision possibilities. On a linear graph, choose the range and the number of subdivisions so that they are convenient multiples. For a log graph, of

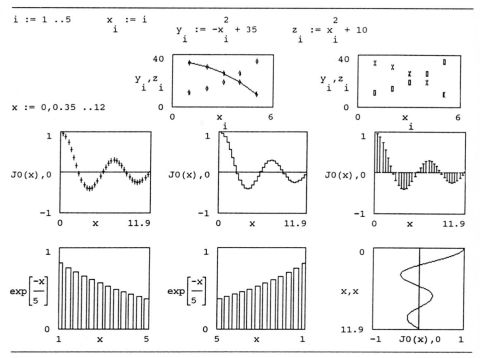

$i := 1 \,..5$ $x_i := i$ $y_i := -x_i^2 + 35$ $z_i := x_i^2 + 10$

$x := 0, 0.35 \,..12$

Figure 1.5 The plot types of the regions are, in order, Vv, xo, pl, sl, e, b, b, and l. In the exponential plot, the abscissa limits were reversed for a different presentation. Similarly, the last plot shows the function rotated from its previous orientation.

the choices 1,2, or 9, choose either one subdivision per cycle or nine. Two subdivisions are of little value.

Plot Types. Graphs are not restricted to lines connecting points. Dots, Xs, pluses, rectangles, or diamonds, can be specified to appear at the plot points. They can be freestanding or connected by lines. In addition, there are some special cases: step, error bars, and bar charts. In a single plot region, different plot types may be used for different curves.

The plot types are l (line), d (dots), s (step), e (error bars), b (bar chart), x (xs), X (xs with lines), p (pluses), P (pluses with lines), o (rectangles), O (rectangles with lines), v (diamonds), and V (diamonds with lines)(see Fig. 1.5).

• •   Clear the screen. Enter specifications so that θ ranges from 0 to 2π in steps of 0.1. Enter θ in the abscissa place marker and $\sin(\theta)$ in the ordinate place marker. Press [F9].

Two curves can be plotted in the same plot region. Move the cursor to the ordinate name. Place the cursor so that it half-surrounds the) in $\sin(\theta)$. Enter a comma followed by the numeral 0. Press [F9]. The second curve is a plot of 0 vs. θ. Remove the 0 and plot $\cos\theta$ together with the sine function.

To gain experience using subscripted variables, let's repeat the sine plot using vectors. Both methods are useful; the subscripted method will be used more frequently. In the subscripted case, it is necessary to write the angle in terms of a range variable that takes on integral values. (See the discussion of vectors above.)

A specific procedure is outlined with possible variable names. The actual code is presented in the next paragraph. Specify the number of points to be plotted (N); assign a range variable (i) integral values that go from zero to the number N. If we wish to plot one cycle of the sine function, the angle should range from 0 to 2π. The quantity i/N will take on equally spaced values between 0 and 1 in N steps as i goes from 0 to N; multiply this quantity by 2π and the range is then scaled to 0 to 2π. Assign these values to the angle variable, ϕ_i. Finally, set the subscripted ordinate, y_i, equal to the sine of the subscripted angle variable, $\sin(\phi_i)$.

• •   Enter $N := 30$ (what equals symbol should be used?). Enter $i := 0 \ldots N$ (how is the ellipsis entered?). Enter $\phi_i := i/N \cdot 2 \cdot \pi$ (which key is used for subscripts?). Enter $y_i := \sin(\phi_i)$. Type @ to create a plot region. Enter ϕ_i and y_i as the labels of the quantities to be plotted. Press [F9]. A zero line could be plotted in the same way as the previous example. Instead, use the format controls described above and change the number of subdivisions.

To plot two curves simultaneously that do not have a variable in common — for example, y vs. x and yy vs. xx (with appropriate subscripts or variable information) — on the same graph, enter x,xx and y,yy at the appropriate place markers. Three or more graphs can be plotted in the same region. How many curves can be successfully plotted may depend on the version of MathCAD that you have. At the present time the PC professional versions have the greatest flexibility.

Histogram.   In a histogram, data (from a data set) that fall within specified intervals are counted and presented in bar form. For example, assume that a number of measurements are performed with outcomes distributed over the range from zero to one. No outcome has a value, for example, of 0.212534796. We can't plot the number of events at a given value on the line. But if we divide the line between zero and one into a series of intervals, then we can count the outcomes that fall within those intervals. The histogram process determines the number of outcomes within a certain interval and displays the outcomes in bar graph form.

Three vectors are involved in creating a histogram: the data, the points defining the edges of the intervals, and the sums determined in the histogram process. A different index is needed for each of these vectors. For example, the data vector is x_i; the interval edge points are y_j; and the counts per interval, z_k. If there are to be M intervals, then j should range from $0, \ldots, M$ and k should range from $0, \ldots, M-1$. The intervals could be determined by taking the difference between the maximum and minimum values of the data and dividing by the number of desired intervals. That always works; however, it may be desirable to refine the range and the number of intervals or, equivalently, the width of the intervals.

The histogram command is $z := \text{hist}(y, x)$; that is, counts per interval equals hist(intervals, data). In the histogram call, no indices are shown. When plotting the histogram, plot z_k vs. y_k. Let the plot type be b for bar. In the histogram plot, the bars are not centered about the interval value but begin at the lower edge and span about two-thirds of the region. A more attractive plot can be obtained by adding half the width of one interval to all the y values. See Fig. 1.6.

1.3.3   Text Regions

In MathCAD, you can place text in regions throughout the document. However, MathCAD is not a word processor. The text ability is principally useful in documenting code. It is well known that undocumented code written by one person is difficult for another to read. In addition, undocumented code returned to after an interim may not be easy reading for the author, either. You should take the time necessary to document your work as you go. In this text, much of the documentation will be in the text, where the file is discussed, rather than in the file itself.

A text region is created by typing a single quotation mark. Type normally. Use the [Backspace] (deletes the character to the left) and [Del] (deletes the character at the cursor location) keys to make changes. Exit the region using the arrow keys or page down, for example. You cannot exit a text region using the return key. In text regions, the cursor is a blinking underline.

• •   Create a text region. A pair of quotation marks should appear on the screen. These quotation marks remain visible as long as the cursor remains within the text region; they disappear when the cursor is removed from the region.

Type the following sentence: "No matter where you go, there you are" (*Buckaroo Banzai*). Exit the region using the [↓]. [PgDn] would also move

Histogram of random data. Values range from 0 to 10. Divide the space into ten intervals.

Generate the data. $n := 199$ $i := 0 .. n$ $x_i := rnd(10)$

Specify the intervals $m := 10$ $j := 0 .. m$ $y_j := j$

(If the data had been in the range from zero to one, y[j would be j/m.)

The interval index $k := 0 .. m - 1$

Sort the data by size. $z := hist(y,x)$

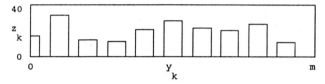

To center the bars in the intervals, add a half interval to each.

$$hlfint := \frac{y_1 - y_0}{2} \qquad y_j := y_j + hlfint$$

Figure 1.6 A histogram plot of randomly generated data.

the cursor out of the text region; however, the cursor moves five lines for each operation of the key, rather than one line for each operation of the [↓] key. Exit and enter by both methods.

Cursor Moves in Text Regions. Move the cursor to the end of the text region. Type the following sentence: "Poltergeists, not pair-production, make up the principal type of spontaneous material manifestation." Press [Home]. This operation moves the cursor to the beginning of the region.

[Ctrl]F and [Ctrl]B result in no cursor movement; they specify the direction of cursor movements that follow, forward or backward.

[Ctrl]W advances the cursor one word (W).

[Ctrl]L advances the cursor one line.

[Ctrl]S advances the cursor one sentence.

[Ctrl]P advances the cursor one paragraph.

Use all the operations; get used to them. They are convenient when editing text.

Incutting, Incopying, and Inpasting.   A section of text can be marked and cut or copied without cutting or copying the entire region. [Ctrl]X marks the beginning or ending of a subregion. [Ctrl][F2] is the incopy command; [Ctrl][F3] is the incut command; [Ctrl][F4] is the inpaste command. Incut or incopied text can be pasted only into an existing text region. One can type a single quote to create a text region and paste the incut text into that empty text region.

• •   Copy a phrase from one of the lines of text and paste it into a new region.

If a text has been edited and the lines are irregular, a rough wrap is obtained with [Ctrl]N (nudge).

If there is to be lots of text, break it up into a series of smaller text regions. Make the regions paragraph sized, no larger. Adjustments are slower with large regions.

1.3.4   *More Equation Features*

Brief descriptions of a number of more advanced features are presented with examples and some exercises.

Solve Blocks: Given Find and Given Minerr.   The given-find solve block can be used to solve simultaneous equations (see Fig. 1.7). The given-minerr procedure is used to minimize the errors in the solution of a set of equations and constraints.

The procedure is as follows:

Define all parameters. Supply guess values for the unknown(s); choose these as carefully as possible. Variables with active subscripts may not be used within a solve block. That is, a value such as x_i, where i is a range variable, may not be used; however, a specific value such as x_1 may be used within the block. No subscripted values can be used in the argument list of a find statement. (A series of values can be obtained using the block as a user-defined function. This is addressed below.)

The solve block begins with the word "given". This word is entered in equation mode, not text mode. The single word is a complete equation region.

Solution of a one-dimensional kinematic equation.

Parameters   g := 9.8   yo := 2   vo := 11   a := -g   y := 8

Guess values   t := 0.5

given
$$y \approx yo + vo \cdot t + \frac{1}{2} \cdot a \cdot t^2 \qquad t := find(t) \qquad t = 0.934$$

check
$$yo + vo \cdot t + \frac{1}{2} \cdot a \cdot t^2 = 8$$

Solution of a two dimensional kinematic problem.   rad := 1

$$deg := \frac{\pi}{180} \cdot rad$$

Parameters   vo := 15   θ := 30·deg

                    vox := vo·cos(θ)   voy := vo·sin(θ)   y := 0

Guess values   x := 10   t := 1

given   x ≈ vox·t
$$y \approx voy \cdot t + \frac{1}{2} \cdot a \cdot t^2 \qquad \begin{bmatrix} x \\ t \end{bmatrix} := find(x,t)$$

x = 19.883   t = 1.531

check
$$voy \cdot t + \frac{1}{2} \cdot a \cdot t^2 = 0 \qquad vox \cdot t = 19.883$$

Figure 1.7 Examples using the given-find solve block.

The equations and constraints to be solved are specified after the given statement, which begins the block, and before the find statement, which ends the block. Equations must use the relational equality ≈, [Alt]=. (In some versions of MathCAD, if a different equality is typed, deleted, and the proper relational equality entered, the solve block will not function. The entire statement must be reentered correctly.) The equations need not be in a vertical pattern. Expressions that are equivalent to 0 = 0 may cause difficulty.

The solve block ends with a find (or minerr) statement.

If there is one unknown, the form is

$$x := find(x) \qquad or \qquad diffname := find(x)$$

If the equation is successfully solved, the find statement returns the solution value and assigns it to x, or as in the second case, the value can be assigned to a different name, for example, diffname, if desired. If a solution is not found, the unknown retains the guess value assigned to it. A minerr statement is of the same form as a find statement: $x := minerr(x)$.

If there is more than one unknown, the form is

$$
\begin{bmatrix} var_1 \\ \vdots \\ var_n \end{bmatrix} := \mathrm{Find}(var_1, var_2, \ldots, var_n)
$$

The left-hand side is a column matrix, created by pressing [Alt]M. Enter the number of variables, n, and press return. Enter the names of the variables at the place markers; move from location to location using the [Tab] key.

Always check your results. Never accept any results blindly.

The procedure is the same whether one uses a find or minerr statement.

• •   The following data are measurements from a free-fall experiment. Find the best value for g, using the given-minerr procedure. Let $k :=$ $1 \ldots 4$. The data are: $s_k := 0.29, 1.8, 3.9, 12.7$; $t_k := 0.25, 0.6, 0.9, 1.6$. Enter the values for s and t; for example, type $s[k:0.29,1.8,\ldots$. Enter a guess value for g. Following the given statement, write the equation, $s \approx 1/2 \, g \, t^2$ four times, with the subscripts on s and t taking on the k-values of $1, \ldots, 4$ (one equation with subscript 1, one equation with subscript 2, and so on). Complete the block with a minerr statement and evaluate g. To check, evaluate the $(1/2) \, g \, t_k^2$ terms and compare with the s_k.

It is possible to use a given-find solve block to determine a set of solutions instead of a single solution. However, subscripts cannot be used in the find statement of a solve block. Instead, the solve block is specified so as to be equivalent to a user-defined function. In particular, the find statement is written in functional form. Once this function is defined, the function can be evaluated for a series of arguments just as any other function.

The procedure to find a set of solutions using a given-find solve block is the same initially as it is to find a single value: (1) specify parameters and guess values for the unknowns; (2) provide the given statement; (3) specify the equations to be solved (so far the same); and (4) write the find statement, not with the unknowns on the left-hand side, but as a function — fcn(*variable*) := find(*unknown*(s)). (The variable must be a variable in the equations.) For example, you might complete a solve block with a statement of the form f(x) := find(y). After the solve block, if you specify a value(s) for x, evaluating f(x) returns the corresponding value(s) for y. A series of values can be obtained using subscripted variables.

The find statement is not restricted to one unknown. For example, with two unknowns, we write

$$f(b) = \text{find}(c, d),$$

where b is a parameter and c and d are the unknowns to be determined, all explicitly shown in the equations within the solve block. When a value(s) for b is specified, $f(b)$ returns the values of the unknowns. The individual values are addressed by the form

$$c = (\text{f}(b))_0 \qquad \text{and} \qquad d = (\text{f}(b))_1.$$

A series of values can be determined by defining parameter values b_i and evaluating $f(b_i)$. A solution must be sought for each parameter value so this may be a slow process.

Root Function.   The root function is designed to determine the roots, the zero points, of an expression. The more carefully you guide it with "good" guess values, the more quickly it will respond with the desired values.

The root function has two arguments:

$$root(expression, variable).$$

The first is the expression for which MathCAD attempts to find a zero. The second is the variable for which a value is sought, a value that, when substituted into the expression, makes it zero.

A good procedure before using the root function is to plot the expression against the variable. Observing the graph is an aid in selecting guess values. Specify a guess value for the variable before evaluating the root function. In many functions, there is more than one root. They can be found sequentially, using different properly selected guess values.

• •   Find the first two roots of $\sin(x)$. Express the results with π in the place marker. Repeat for the cosine. Express results with $\pi/2$ in the place marker. How far off can the guess be and still return the desired root? Describe how far in terms of the shape of the curve.

Derivative.   The derivative operation returns a numerical value for the slope of a curve; it does not return a function. The derivative operation is invoked by pressing the question-mark key. On pressing the key,

$$\frac{d}{d\blacksquare}\blacksquare$$

appears. At the place marker in the denominator, enter the variable name of the differentiation variable. At the expression place marker, enter the expression for which the derivative is to be taken. Specify a value for the differentiation variable and any other variables or parameters included in the expression before taking the derivative.

The acceleration could be defined as

$$a(t) := \frac{d}{dt}\left(\frac{d}{dt}x(t)\right),$$

where $x(t)$ gives the position as a function of time. However, derivatives of derivatives are quite slow and hence are not recommended.

●● Take the derivative of the following functions:

$$y(x) = x^2,$$
$$y(x) = \exp(-x^2),$$
$$y(x) = \sin(x).$$

Plot each function with its derivative as x ranges from 0 to 2 in steps of 0.2.

Finding a Maximum or Minimum.   Use the root function in combination with the derivative operation to locate a maximum or minimum. When successful,

$$\text{root}\left(\frac{d}{dx}y(x), x\right)$$

returns the x-value for which $d/dx\,y(x)$ is zero. If you are sensible about guess values, the process works effectively. Plotting a function, especially if it is unfamiliar, is a useful aid in selecting guess values.

●● For the expression $y(x) = x^2 \cdot \exp(-x^2)$, find the maximum. Try a few different guess values and see how robust the process is for this function.

●● Find the first maximum and first minimum of $\sin(x)$, for $x > 0$. Express results with π in the place marker.

●● Find the maximum of the function $y(t) = 10 \cdot t - 5 \cdot t^2$.

Integration.   The integration process can be considered a method for determining the area under a curve. You do not need to know the methods of calculus to perform these integrations. MathCAD will compute definite integrals numerically. Limits must be specified; a value, not a function, is returned.

The integration operation is called by pressing [Shift]7 (the ampersand, &):

$$\int_{\blacksquare}^{\blacksquare} \blacksquare \, d\blacksquare.$$

Four place markers are shown. The limits of integration must be specified; a variable name that has a defined value is fine. Infinity is *not* an acceptable limit.

Enter the desired expression for the integrand at the place marker after the integral sign. Enter the variable name, over which the integration is to be carried out, in the place marker after the *d*. All variables other than the integration variable must be defined before the integration.

• •   Let $a := 5$. Perform the following integration:

$$xx := \int_0^2 a \cdot t \, dt.$$

• •   Integrate $\sqrt{1 - x^2}$ as x goes from 0 to 1.
Integrate $\sin(x)$ as x goes from 0 to π.
Integrate $\sin^2(x)$ as x goes from 0 to π.

To find the average for some function, simply integrate the function over the region and divide by the size of the region:

$$f_{\text{av}} = \frac{\int_{\text{range}} f(x) \, dx}{\int_{\text{range}} dx}.$$

• •   What is the average value of $\sin(x)$ and $\sin^2(x)$ as x goes from 0 to π?

If and Until.   The if statement is MathCAD's limited form of an if-then-else statement. The form is

$$x = if(condition, \; x - value \; if \; condition \; true,$$
$$x - value \; if \; condition \; false)$$

For example,

$$y(x) := if(\sin(x) > 0, \sin(x), -\sin(x))$$

will return $\sin(x)$ when $\sin(x)$ is greater than zero and will return minus $\sin(x)$ when $\sin(x)$ is less than zero. The net result is than the function $y(x)$ looks like the absolute value of $\sin(x)$.

It is possible to nest if statements:

$$x = if(condition\ I,\ value - condition\ I\ true,$$
$$if(condition\ II,\ value - condition\ I\ false\ II\ true,$$
$$value - condition\ I\ and\ II\ false))$$

For example, for

$$y(x) = if(x > 10,\ x,\ if(x < -10,\ x\ ,0)),$$

if $-10 < x < 10$ the function returns zero; otherwise it returns x.

The until statement permits a process to continue until an expression, not a condition, becomes negative:

$$y = until(expression,\ y - value)$$

For example, for

$$y(x) = until(\sin(x), \sin^2(x)),$$

if x takes on a series of increasing values, $y(x)$ takes on the value of $\sin^2(x)$. However, when x is large enough that $\sin(x)$ becomes negative, the process stops no matter how far x ranges. The values need not be in order; any x value rendering $\sin(x)$ negative stops the process.

Complex Numbers.   Complex numbers are of the form $a + bi$, where $i = \sqrt{-1}$. In MathCAD, when writing the imaginary part of a complex number, do not insert a multiplier between b and i; instead, write bi. If the value desired is just i, write $1i$.

If z is the complex number, $a + bi$:

Re(z) returns the real part of z, a.

Im(z) returns the imaginary part of z, b.

$|z|$ returns the magnitude of z, $\sqrt{a^2 + b^2}$.

$\bar{z}$ returns the complex conjugate of z, $a - bi$. The conjugate is called with a quotation mark, for example, $y"$.

arg(z) returns the angle in the complex plane. The angle is measured from the positive real axis to z. The value returned is in the range from $-\pi$ to π. (Similar to the atan function.)

• •   Enter the complex number $z = 3 + 4i$. Evaluate the real part of z, the imaginary part of z, the complex conjugate, the magnitude, and the argument.

Let $u = 1i$. Observe the 1 as the cursor is moved in and out of the region.

How would one enter the value, when the imaginary part of the complex number has magnitude $5.2 \cdot 10^4$?

Floor, Ceil, and Mod.   These three functions can all be used to modify the value of some quantity. The floor function returns the largest integer less than or equal to some argument. The function call is floor(arg), where the argument is real.

• •   Determine the floor of π, e, -0.7, and 10.

The ceil function returns the smallest integer greater than or equal to some argument. The function call is ceil(arg), where the argument is real.

• •   Determine the ceil of π, e, -0.7, and 10.

Is ceil(floor(π)) the same as floor(ceil(π))?

The mod function has two arguments. The function returns the remainder resulting from dividing the first argument by the second. The function call is mod($arg1, arg2$).

• •   Evaluate mod(1,2), mod(5,3), mod(10,2), mod(11,2), and mod(-5,2).

Let i range from 0 to 15 in steps of 1. Let $s = 4$. What is mod(i, s)? What is floor(i/s)?

Heaviside Function, Φ.   The Heaviside function returns 1 if the argument is greater than or equal to zero. The function returns 0 if the argument is less than zero. The function call is $\Phi(x)$.

The Φ function can be used, for example, to express logic functions such as AND, OR, or XOR. In these logic expressions the arguments are restricted to two values, 0 and 1. For example,

$$\text{OR}(A, B) := \Phi(A + B - 0.5),$$

$$\text{AND}(A, B) := \Phi(A \cdot B - 0.5).$$

• •   If A and B can each be zero or one, there are four possible combinations for the arguments for OR and AND. Evaluate the four outcomes for each.

In logic, a 1 is often referred to as true and a 0 as false. For what values of A and B is the expression OR(A, B) $-$ AND(A, B) true?

Bessel Functions.   These functions are not typically encountered in general physics. They belong to a class of functions known as orthogonal functions. You will have fun meeting them in more advanced courses. In this text, there is only one mention of them, in the optics section. You do not need to know the details of these functions to plot them or make use of them any more than you need to know the details of the integration process to determine the numerical result of an integration.

• •   Plot $J0(x)$ and $J1(x)$ as x goes from 0 to 12.

1.4   General MathCAD Features

1.4.1   Processing

When operating in manual mode, MathCAD does not process anything unless requested. In automatic mode, MathCAD processes everything as the document is assembled. This can often be a nuisance as well as a waste of time. Let MathCAD calculate only when the document is ready, or at least ready to troubleshoot.

MathCAD makes two passes through a document when processing. On the first pass, it processes all global assignments; on the second pass, it processes all local assignments. The order is from left to right and from top to bottom. The topmost edge of the region, not the line on which the equality sign appears, determines its location.

Pressing [F9] is the quickest way to start MathCAD processing a document. The effect of pressing [F9] is to process the document up to and including the present screen. Regions below the bottom of the screen (with higher line numbers) are not processed. When additional regions become visible, pressing [F9] again results in further calculation.

However, pressing [F9] does not always have the desired effect. For example, sometimes after having made corrections to a document, when you press [F9] nothing happens. If this occurs, move the cursor to the next region and try again. Repeat if necessary, each time moving to successive regions. If processing still does not take place, press [Esc], type pro (process), and press return. This sequence always works, but it means recalculating the entire document.

If it is desired to halt a calculation because it is taking too long, or you see an error in the document that must be corrected, or for any other reason, press [Ctrl][Break]. On the command line appears the query, "interrupt calculation?" Type y and press return. The calculation is then halted and the comment "interrupted" descends from the region where processing had been taking place. If it is decided to continue and no changes have been made in the document, place the cursor in the interrupted region and press [F9]. Processing will continue from the point at which it had been interrupted. If the document has been changed, processing starts from the changed regions.

When working with a newly created document, processing may result in a huge string of error messages descending for almost every region in the document. Don't panic. And don't separate the regions. (If the error message is covered up by subsequent regions, press [Ctrl]R, and watch closely.) The number of error messages does not indicate that everything is wrong. If a region contains an error, all subsequent regions depending on the region containing the error will register error messages as well, even though nothing may be wrong with them. Usually, the problem is associated with something at the beginning that, when fixed, will then permit the processing to continue, at least to the next region containing an error.

It is not difficult to exceed the memory addressing capabilities of MathCAD 2.0 or 2.5. The operation [Alt][F2] will show the amount of memory used and the total amount available.

After many changes have been made in a document, the memory may become fragmented. Attempts to process a document may result in the error message "out of memory." If this happens, there are only two choices; quit MathCAD or save the file and then quit MathCAD.

When dealing with large documents, it is not a bad idea to exit Math-CAD, reload, and then bring up the document. Although reset does clear the screen, it does not take care of the memory fragmentation problem.

1.4.2 Files

A number of files are on the disk that accompanies this text. These documents are basic to the text material and are often starting points for further exploration.

Loading a File from the Disk into the Computer. To load a file into the computer from a floppy disk, insert the disk in the drive and press [F5]. To the query on the command line, enter the name of the file including the drive name and press return. For example, if the disk is in drive b and the filename is arith1.mcd, enter b:arith1 and press return. Typing the filename without the extension, .mcd, is proper. MathCAD looks for files with that extension. If the extension is anything else, then it must be entered as part of the filename.

If you are not sure of the filename, after pressing [F5] you can look at a list of all files ending in .mcd on a particular disk by typing the wild card character * when asked for the filename. If you need to specify a path

— that is, if you want to look at a disk other than the default — you would type, for example, b:*, and press return. A list of all files ending in .mcd on the disk in the b drive would then be listed. If the number is large, not all the filenames can be shown at once; use the [↑], [↓], [PgUp], and [PgDn] keys to move through the list. As you move, one file is always highlighted. When the file you wish to load is highlighted, press return. If the file being sought is not on the disk, press [Esc]. This will return control to MathCAD's main shell.

If a document is to be loaded into the computer while another document is still on the screen, the process is similar. Press [F5]. If the document on the screen has not been saved, the command line statement is, "changes not saved. OK to discard?" If it is OK to delete the resident document, type y and press return. This process dumps the present document and loads the file requested. If it is not OK to delete the present document, do not type y, press return; this halts the load request operation. Now save the document in the standard way as described below. Then press [F5] again.

Saving a File: Writing from Computer to Disk.   A document can be written to your disk so that it can be saved and retrieved later for computational purposes or for further development. If the document is new and has not been saved before, press [F6]. On the command line appear the words, "save as:" followed by a blinking cursor. This is a request for a filename. Enter the name without any extension (MathCAD will automatically add .mcd) and press return. For example, type myfile and press return. Math-CAD automatically stores the file under the name myfile.mcd. In general, try to use a descriptive name that suggests the contents. The filename is limited to eight characters.

If the file is to be saved on your personal floppy disk, then, depending on the specific computer arrangement, it may be necessary to precede the filename with a drive name. For example, b:myfile would store the file on a disk in the b drive. Without such a pathname, the file is stored on the disk in the default drive. This means that with a hard disk system, the document would normally be written to the hard disk, the standard default disk.

If a file already exists with the name you have selected, a message will appear saying, "file exists, OK to overwrite?" If you do not want to lose the file previously saved under that name, do not type y; simply press return. Then press [F6] again and choose a different name, one not already used. To respond in the affirmative, type y and press return. The effect is to erase the previously existing file with that name and store the present document under that filename.

"Thirtieth floor, sir. You're expected."
"Er, don't you want to search me?"
"No, sir."
"My ID cards."
"No need, sir."
"But I could be anybody."
"No you couldn't sir. This is Information Retrieval."

Brazil

1.4.3   *Printing*

Before attempting to print a document, be certain that the printer is turned on. Attempting to print with the printer power not on may cause the system to lock up. If this occurs, the system will have to be rebooted. If the document you were attempting to print was not previously saved, it is lost. It is not a bad habit to save a document before printing it.

Before printing, a printer driver must be selected. To select a driver, press [Esc], and type sel . Then, using the [↓] or [↑] keys, highlight the appropriate printer type, and press return. If this is to be the standard printer, the printer selection can be saved and the select process need not be repeated. To save this information, press [Esc], type configsave and press return. The MathCAD disk must not, of course, be write protected when you perform this operation.

Once a printer type has been selected, to print out the document, press [Ctrl]O ("oh", not zero). On the command line will appear the words "Print area" and the range over which the document extends. The cursor is at the command line. If you wish to print the entire document, simply press return twice. The document will start printing right away. If you wish to print only part of a document, change the line and/or column numbers to correspond to the range of interest. (This area can be determined in advance by moving the cursor to the beginning and the end of the area you wish to print and noting the line and column numbers of the cursor.) Then press return.

If something goes wrong, or if for any reason you want to stop the printing process, press [Ctrl][Break] or [Ctrl][Scroll Lock] (these are different names for the same thing) or [Ctrl]A.

1.5   On Processing Documents

Most of the documents on the disk cannot be observed in their entirety at one time on a computer screen. This means that you must move back and forth in the document while you are using it. Therefore, it is essential that you become familiar with the cursor movements so that you can jump about in the document without leaning on the arrow keys.

Frequently, the document is divided into sections. The key parts of a section may fit on a single screen. Be sensitive to which variables or parameters need to be changed and what plot regions or values you want to be able to see. Position the document so that as little movement as possible is needed. Delete lines between regions if that will help; but don't make things so crowded that you have difficulty discriminating between subscripts from one line and superscripts from another.

With each document a number of questions are asked; pursue them. Work out the details. Then step back and ask, "What does this mean?" Your efforts will be rewarded with insight. There is no victory without a struggle.

"Easy, it's an innocent question."

"No question from you is innocent, Mr. Gittes."

Chinatown

Each document is devoted to a particular problem. The techniques are general and you should have no qualms about cannibalizing the documents and restructuring them in any way that will be useful to you.

"I ate his liver with some fava beans and a nice Chianti."

Silence of the Lambs

CHAPTER
2

Curves and Curve Fitting

Visualization is often a key to insight and intuitive understanding. The graphical presentation of either analytic expressions or data — one form of visualization — is essential for taking in quickly large-, medium-, and small-scale features. Such information is crucial in both theoretical and experimental physics. Tables of numbers do not convey their information as readily as does a graphical presentation of data. Even appreciating a curve as basic as that of the sine would be difficult without any graphical representation.

In this chapter, we demonstrate how to plot families of curves, examine some frequently used approximations, consider very briefly the use of interpolation, and finally examine some methods for curve fitting, that is, finding analytic expressions that correspond to data.

2.1 Families of Curves

In this section, you are encouraged to build yourself a library of graphical representations of common mathematical functions. It is one thing to look at a book and see what someone else has plotted; it is rather different to control the process and create your own graphs.

As you go through each case, calculate a sufficient number of examples so that you have a clear understanding of the general form associated with the functions and of the role of the parameters. When data are examined, such knowledge is very useful.

2.1.1 Plotting Families of Curves

We wish to plot sets of curves. To do this we need to examine some features of user-defined functions. In particular, it is important to determine the order in which values are presented when there are two arguments associated with a function.

• • First let's do an exercise. Plot each of the following three functions in three different plot regions (you will have nine plot regions in all). Let the first set of regions be linear, log cycles (0,0), the second set semi-log, log cycles (1,0), and the third set log-log, log cycles (1,1). The three functions to be plotted are (1) $y = 0.9\,x + 1$, (2) $y = 1.2\,e^{-2x}$, and (3) $y = 3\,x^2$.

Plot the functions either as a function, $y(x)$, or as a vector, y_i. Explore the effect of changing coefficients, powers, and sign. Notice especially which functional forms are straight lines among the various plot types. Many functions are not straight lines in any of these representations.

Frequently, it is useful to define a function in MathCAD. The procedure is straightforward: *function-name(variable list) := function* in terms of variables and other parameters previously defined. Quantities in the variable list need not be assigned values before the function is defined. When values are substituted in the variable list and the defined function is evaluated, the results are the same as when those values are substituted into the function itself.

For example, the roots of a quadratic could be written as

$$x(a, b, c) := \frac{-b \pm \sqrt{b^2 - 4\,a\,c}}{2\,a}.$$

Entering values for a, b, and c in x returns the root values. An interesting function that appears in optics is

$$\text{sinc}(x) := \frac{\sin(x)}{x}.$$

The advantage is clear if the function is used more than once. The function need not be rewritten, only the function name with variable list. Note that when a function is defined, identical names on the left- and right-hand sides refer to the same quantities, regardless of the order.

When the function is evaluated, the order in the list, not the name is crucial.

● ●   Explore the effect of the order of variables in the list. Reset MathCAD. Let $n := 1$, $m := 2$, $i := 0\ldots n$, $j := 0\ldots m$, $y(i,j) := (m+1)\cdot i + j$, and $z(j,i) := (m+1)\cdot i + j$. Predict first the sequence of numbers (six in each case; why?) and then evaluate, one by one, $y(i,j)$, $y(j,i)$, $z(j,i)$, $z(i,j)$. Note, in comparing the two sets of y and z values, that the values are not just in a different order; they are different.

Frequently, it is less confusing if functions are defined with variable names not used in the problem. For example, let $w(a,b) := (m+1)\cdot a + b$ and $w'(a,b) := (m+1)\cdot b + a$. This is less confusing when you evaluate the combinations such as $w(j,i)$. How do these functions compare with the expressions for y and z that were just evaluated?

Change the values of n and m to 2 and 4. Plot $y(i, j)$ vs. j and $y(i, j)$ vs. i in two different plot regions. Explain the plots. Reduce the upper limit of the abscissa from 4 to 3.9 in the y vs. j plot. What effect does this have?

The function y contains points that lie along three straight lines with different intercepts. When y vs. j is plotted, we see the three lines, but they are all connected. If you reduce the plot range (from 4 to 3.9), the points at 4 cannot be plotted and MathCAD's plot line is broken, starting again with the next value. In this way, we see the curves independently. Include values slightly beyond the region that is to be plotted, and then plot only the restricted region. The curves will then not show the interconnecting lines.

In describing families of curves, typically, a function (for example, f) is expressed in terms of an independent variable (for example, x) and a set of parameters (for example, a, b, ...). To plot a family of curves, define a function in terms of the independent variable and one of the parameters. A sequence of curves can then be plotted in one plot region by specifying a sequence of values for the parameter. This can be repeated for each parameter simply by changing the parameter name in the definition.

Begin the family of curves with the case of a straight line.

$$y = mx + b \quad \text{can be written} \quad y(m,x) := m\cdot x + b.$$

On plotting $y(m, x)$ vs. x, each curve shows the general functional form; stepping through a sequence of four or five values of m shows the m-dependence for a given b. Another function, $y1(b, x)$, can be defined and plotted showing the b-dependence for a given m.

In each case below, indicate on the printout from your work the parameter values associated with each curve.

•• Load CURV1, a family of straight-line curves (see Fig. 2.1).

Check the programming steps. Process, then change the document so that for a slope of one ($m = 1$), b takes on the values -4, -2, 0, 2, 4.

•• Plot the family of parabolas, $y(a, x) = ax^2$. Let a_i take on the values 0.4, 1, 4. Include positive and negative values for x. Repeat for a_i equal to -0.4, -1, and -4. Could both sets of values of a be plotted simultaneously?

•• Plot the family of parabolas, $y(a, x) = a \cdot (x - x_o)^2 + y_o$. Consider the cases $x_o = 1$, $y_o = 0$, and $x_o = 0$, $y_o = 1$; let a take on the positive values from the previous example.

•• Plot the family of sine curves, $y(\theta, \phi) = \sin(\theta + \phi)$. Let θ range from 0 to 4π. Let ϕ take on values of 0, $\pi/6$, and $\pi/3$ radians. Consider the same values for $\sin(\theta - \phi)$. Examine the cosine similarly.

•• Plot the single curves, x, y, and z vs. α where $x(\alpha) = \sinh(\alpha)$, $y(\alpha) = \cosh(\alpha)$, and $z(\alpha) = \tanh(\alpha)$. Let α take on the values $\alpha = 0, 0.05, \ldots, 2$.

•• Define $r(t) = \sqrt{t^2 - 1}$. Plot $r(t)$ vs. t for $t = 1, 1.05, \ldots, 3$. Plot $x(\alpha)$, $y(\alpha)$ vs. α; set the limits to be the same as for the plot of $r(t)$ vs. t.

```
Family of curves            case - straight line

b := 0           y(m,x) := m· x + b

The i index varies the slope.   The j index controls the position.

i := 0 ..4       m  := -1 + 0.5· i      j := 0 ..14      x  := -7 + j
                  i                                       j

Restrict the x range of the plot to avoid connecting the lines.

xl := 6                    xl
```

```
        y[m ,x ]
           i  j

        -xl
          -xl    x      xl
                 j
```

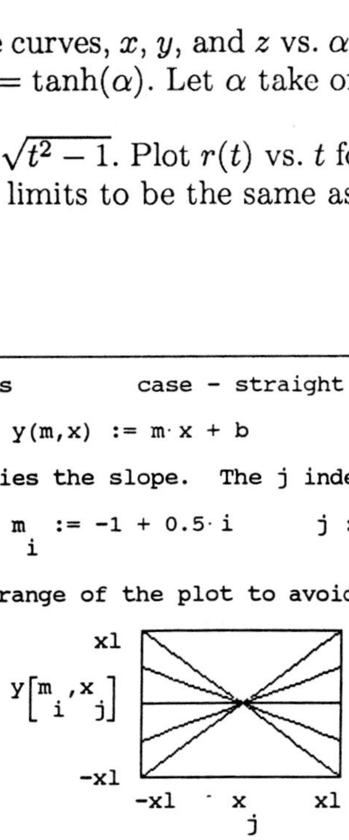

Figure 2.1 CURV1, a family of straight-line curves.

• •   Plot the family of exponentials $y(x, a) = y_o\exp(-ax)$. Let x range from 0 to 4. Let a take on values 1, 2, and 4. Repeat with $\exp(+ax)$.

• •   Plot the family of exponentials rising to a fixed level, $y(x, a) = y_o \cdot (1 - \exp(-ax))$. Use the same ranges for a and x as in the previous example.

• •   Examine the curves $\exp(-x^2/a^2)$ and $\exp(-(x - x_o)^2/a^2)$.

• •   Plot the three curves $\ln(x)$, x, and $\exp(x)$ vs. x in the same plot region. Avoid the singularity at $x = 0$.

2.2   Approximations

For most problems in the real world, exact answers are not possible. Simplifications and approximations are frequently useful and necessary. The criterion is always whether the approximation maintains the accuracy necessary for the problem at hand. Consequently, the practitioner must know the range of validity of the approximations and the range of errors introduced. Misunderstood approximations may lead to incorrect results and false conclusions.

Some commonly encountered approximations are (either for small angle or small x)

$$\sin(\theta) \approx \theta, \tag{2.1}$$

$$\tan(\theta) \approx \theta, \tag{2.2}$$

$$\cos(\theta) \approx 1, \tag{2.3}$$

$$\exp(x) \approx 1 + x, \tag{2.4}$$

$$(1 + x)^n \approx 1 + nx. \tag{2.5}$$

Typically, the value of making an approximation is that the mathematical form of the approximation is simpler than the function, permitting analytic solutions to problems (for some limited range) that might otherwise be far more complicated or even intractable. The motion of the simple pendulum, for example, can be solved easily in the small-angle approximation. The general analytic solution is far more complicated. Numerical techniques also permit a kind of general solution that is readily accessible. The latter will be discussed subsequently.

The approximations shown above all represent the first term of a series expansion. For the case of the sine function, the expansion is

$$\sin(\theta) \simeq \theta - \frac{\theta^3}{3!} + \frac{\theta^5}{5!} + \cdots . \tag{2.6}$$

• •   Load CURV2. Compare of the sine curve with approximations (see Figs. 2.2 and 2.3).

Three different functions are defined which include the first one, two, or three terms of the sine series. The first two approximating functions are plotted together with the sine curve as a function of angle. Observe the quality of fit and the sign of the deviation as the angle increases.

To help see the differences, $d1$ and $d2$ and percent differences $pd1$ and $pd2$ are plotted. To find the angle that corresponds to a given percent error (we consider the $f1$ approximation), it is necessary to solve the transcendental equation

$$\frac{x - \sin(x)}{\sin(x)} \cdot 100 = \text{percent error.}$$

MathCAD's given-find solve block handles this equation readily. Finally, a given-find solve block is used to determine a set of solutions for percent error given a series of values for the angle. (See the section in Chapter 1 on solve-blocks.) In the case at hand, we have fcn(*percent error*) = find(*angle*); specify the percent error, evaluate fcn(*percent error*) and return the corresponding angle. A series of values can be obtained using subscripted variables. See the end of CURV2 for an example.

• •   Using the first given-find (for the function, $pd1(x)$), determine the angles at which the error is 2%, 5%, and 10%. Use the functional form of the solve block at the end of the document to generate the sequence of percent errors vs. angle for the second approximation.

• •   Plot $f3(x)$ and $\sin(x)$ as x goes from 0 to π, just to see what improvement occurs.

• •   For the approximation $\tan(\theta) \approx \theta$ (the expansion starts $\theta + \theta^3/3 + \cdots$), what angles correspond to percent errors 1, 2, 5, and 10? How does the approximation compare with the $\sin(\theta) \approx \theta$ approximation in terms of accuracy?

• •   For the approximation $\cos(\theta) \approx 1$, what angles correspond to percent errors 1, 2, 5, and 10?

Approximations to the sine curve.

rad ≡ 1

Examine the range from 0 to π.   x := 0,.1 ..π

$$\text{deg} \equiv \frac{\pi}{180} \cdot \text{rad}$$

Three approximations.

f1(x) := x

$$f2(x) := x - \frac{x^3}{3!}$$

$$f3(x) := x - \frac{x^3}{3!} + \frac{x^5}{5!}$$

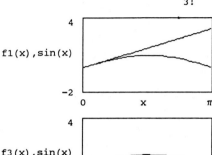

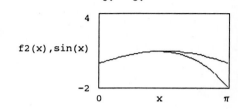

Differences and % differences between the function and the approximations.

d1(x) := f1(x) - sin(x)   d2(x) := f2(x) - sin(x)

$$pd1(x) := \frac{d1(x)}{sin(x)} \cdot 100$$ $$pd2(x) := \frac{d2(x)}{sin(x)} \cdot 100$$

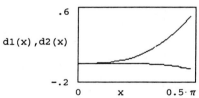

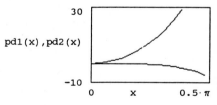

To find where a given value of error occurs, use the given find and solve.

x := 1

Given |pd1(x)| ≈ 1   x := Find(x)   x = 13.986·deg

Given |pd2(x)| ≈ 1   x := Find(x)   x = 57.742·deg

Figure 2.2 CURV2, comparison of the sine curve with approximations. (See the next figure for the rest of the document.)

To compare, find the percent error for approximation 1 at 57.7 deg.

```
pd1(x) = 19.173          Remember at this point approx 2 was off only by 1%.
                         We can use x since the last value assigned to it is
                         the desired one.
```

A series of values is generated by writing the find statement as a function.

The equation in the solve block relates y, the angle, with some percent error, pe. Provide a percent error in the argument for f and the find statement returns the angle. A sequence of value for percent error are provided in pe[i. Ang[i are the returned angles that correspond to those percent errors.

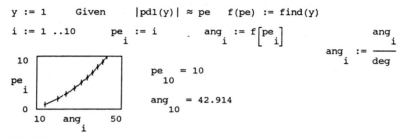

Figure 2.3 CURV2 *continued*.

• •   Find the 1, 2, 5, and 10 percent error points for

$$e^x \approx 1 + x,$$

$$(1 + x)^n \approx 1 + nx,$$

$$ln(1 \pm x) \approx \pm x.$$

• •   Is $\cos(x) + \sin(x)$ a reasonable approximation for e^x, where $0 < x < 1$? Test quantitatively.

2.3   Interpolation

Data are frequently taken at intervals suitable to the measurement at hand. If values are to be obtained from these data, for points intermediate to the sampled data, some kind of interpolation process is required. Math-CAD provides both linear and cubic-spline interpolation. Linear interpolation is, as the name suggests, equivalent to drawing straight lines between adjacent data points and extracting values from those lines. Cubic-spline interpolation, on the other hand, fits a series of smooth curves from one data point to the next. In each case, the first and second derivatives of the fitted curves are continuous.

Besides the obvious application of simply finding an intermediate value, it is frequently useful to determine the area under a curve. This process typically requires integration. However, MathCAD's integration feature requires a functional form, not discrete data values, to integrate. The interpolation process can be used to create a function that can be integrated.

For example, if you had data that were values of velocity at discrete time intervals, it might be of interest to know the corresponding distance travelled. To determine the distance, you would like to integrate the velocity over time to find the area under the curve, which on a $v - t$ curve represents the distance travelled.

The function, linterp, for linear interpolation requires three arguments. They are (1) x-axis data vector with values in ascending order (such as time), (2) y-axis data vector (such as velocity), and (3) an x-value for which the interpolation is to be carried out (for example, a particular time). Linterp returns the y-value (for example, velocity) corresponding to the specified x-value (in this example, time) based on a linear interpolation between adjacent points.

The cubic-spline interpolation process requires two steps: first the creation of a spline vector, and second the interpolation process itself. There are three choices for the creation of a spline vector. The differences between these different spline choices become more evident near the endpoints.

The lspline function generates a spline curve that approaches linearity near the endpoints; pspline approaches a parabola; and cspline approaches a cubic. The functions are lspline(x, y), pspline(x, y), and cspline(x, y), where x and y represent the abscissa and ordinate vectors. The interp function is almost identical to the linterp function already described, except there are four arguments. The first argument is a vector generated by one of the spline functions. The next three arguments are the same as those used in linterp.

• • Load CURV3, examination of linear interpolation (see Fig. 2.4).

The first line of Fig. 2.4 shows three data points. The second shows a call to the linterp function and the interpolated values of two points. The three arguments of the linterp function are the x vector (values in ascending order), the y vector (notice the vectors are called by name and that there are no subscripts), and the variable v, which represents the value of x where the interpolation is to be made.

In the third line, calls are made to each of the spline functions; normally only one would be called. The interp function is called by $z1$, $z2$, and $z3$; each is based on a different spline function. Note that there are four arguments. The first is the spline vector of choice; the rest are as for the linterp case. The plot shows the original data as two straight-line segments. The three curves represent the different spline functions. Between $x = 0$ and $x = 1$ and between $x = 1$ and $x = 2$, the linear interpolation function results in the least curvature. In the range from 0 to 1, the cubic spline has the greatest curvature, but in general it need not. Clearly,

---

Interpolation.   An example demonstrating linear, parabolic and cubic splines.

The data

$x_0 := 0$ $x_1 := 1$ $x_2 := 2$ $y_0 := 0$ $y_1 := 1$ $y_2 := 4$ $i := 0 ..2$

Interpolating using the linear interpolation function, linterp.

$z(v) := linterp(x,y,v)$ $z(.7) = 0.7$ $z(1.5) = 2.5$

Create the spline vectors. Normally, only one would be selected.

s1 := lspline(x,y)   s2 := pspline(x,y)   s3 := cspline(x,y)

$$s1 = \begin{bmatrix} 0 \\ 3 \\ 0 \end{bmatrix} \qquad s2 = \begin{bmatrix} 2 \\ 2 \\ 2 \end{bmatrix} \qquad s3 = \begin{bmatrix} 4 \\ 2 \\ 0 \end{bmatrix} \qquad v := 0,.05\ ..2$$

Interpolate and plot.

z1(v) := interp(s1,x,y,v)   z2(v) := interp(s2,x,y,v)

z3(v) := interp(s3,x,y,v)

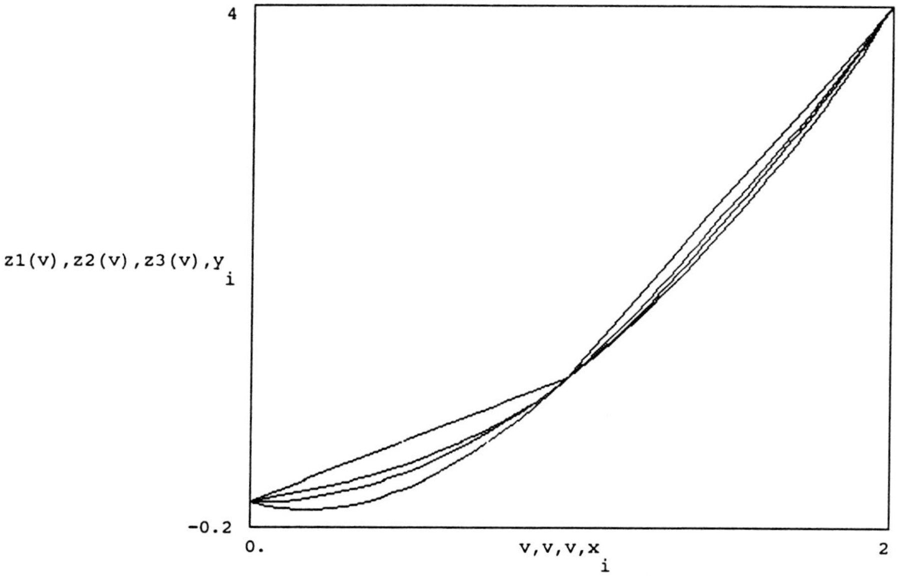

In the 0-1 region. From left to right the curves are y, z1, z2, z3.
In the 1-2 region. From left to right the curves are y, z3, z1, z2.

Figure 2.4 CURV3, examination of linear interpolation.

the interpolation processes can give rather different results depending on the method used. Extrapolation beyond the range where the data exist is more error prone than interpolation between points in the data set.

• •   Load CURV4, the area under a curve (see Figs. 2.5 and 2.6).

The v_j represent any arbitrary data set taken at the corresponding t_j. The area under the curve can be determined by taking the appropriate sums or by integrating.

The area is determined first, in effect by counting the number of rectangles beneath the curve. This can be done by a variety of methods. We

---

Given some arbitrary data, determine the area under the curve.

$$n := 13 \qquad j := 0 \ .. \ n \qquad t_j := j \qquad v_j :=$$

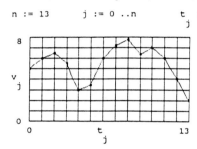

5
6
6.5
5.5
3.
3.5
6
7.2
7.8
6.4
7
6
4
2

The area can be approximated by imagining that the area is constructed from thirteen rectangles of unit width and a height determined by f. Since the width is unity in this case, the area is the sum of the f's for each rectangle.

A sum over all v's would be in error, an overestimate, as it counts both end points and results in one extra rectangle.

$$\sum_j v_j = 75.9 \qquad \text{A sum over all f's, an overestimate.}$$

If the v's are evaluated at the left hand side of the rectangles the area is suma; if the v's are evaluated at the right hand side the area is sumb.

$$k := 0 \ .. \ n - 1 \qquad suma := \sum_k v_k \qquad sumb := \sum_k v_{k+1} \qquad \begin{array}{l} suma = 73.9 \\ sumb = 70.9 \end{array}$$

If the average of v values on either side of the interval is used the result is sumc.

$$sumc := \sum_k \frac{v_k + v_{k+1}}{2} \qquad sumc = 72.4$$

Figure 2.5 CURV4, the area under a curve. (See the next figure for the rest of the document.)

Integration in Mathcad requires a function, not a series of points. A
function based on the points can be created using an interpolation process.

A linear interpolation between points is achieved by calling the linterp
function. The arguments are the abscissa vector, the ordinate vector, and
the position variable specifying where the interpolation is to be evaluated.

vv(x) := linterp(t,v,x)   a := 0   b := 13

$$vint := \int_a^b vv(t') \, dt'$$

vint = 72.4

A smoother interpolation is possible using a cubic spline approximation,
instead of a linear one. Two calls are necessary. The first creates a
spline vector based on the abscissa and ordinate vectors. The second
performs the interpolation; the arguments are the spline, abscissa, and
ordinate vectors, and the position variable specifying where the
interpolation is to be evaluated.

sp := cspline(t,v)   vv'(x) := interp(sp,t,v,x)

$$vint' := \int_a^b vv'(t') \, dt'$$ vint' = 72.63 $\dfrac{vint'}{vint}$ = 1.003

A comparison of results.

suma = 73.9   sumb = 70.9   sumc = 72.4

vint = 72.4   vint' = 72.63

One would expect sumc and vint to be the same, since in this case determining
the average v value is equivalent to a linear interpolation. If one
assumes the data are representative of a smooth curve which does not make
rapid changes relative to the spacing of the v values, then the cubic spline
approximation is the "best" of the values from the set described.

Figure 2.6 CURV4 *continued.*

could say that for each interval of t, we take the value of v at the beginning
of the interval as the representative value. If the curve increases as much
as it decreases, on the average, the overestimates and underestimates will
tend to cancel. Alternatively, we could take the values at the end of the
intervals. Of course, we do not want simply to sum the v values as there
is one more value than there are intervals.

Three sums yield different values, as Figs. 2.5 and 2.6 show. Notice
the use of the index to switch from the beginning of the interval to the
end of the interval. (For $k := 0 \ldots n-1$, the sum for the value at the
beginning of the interval is over v_k, whereas the sum over the final values
is v_{k+1}.) Finally, an average value is used, resulting in an intermediate
value. This provides the most reliable value of these various sums.

To integrate the curve, we must have a functional representation of
the data. The interpolation processes can provide that representation. It
is desirable to define an interpolation function in terms of the variable
to be integrated — for example, $vv(x)$ — and then to integrate that

function. Integration using the linterp process (not lspline) is a straight-line interpolation and gives the same result as did the averaging sum.

Integrating with one of the spline functions is similar. First define the spline vector, then the interpolation function. Finally, integrate the interpolation function. A cubic-spline interpolation provides a smoother fit to the data than does the linterp process and yields a modestly different result. If we assume that the function does not make very rapid variations compared to what is seen, then the cubic-spline interpolation is the more reliable value.

● ●   The area determined by the suma process can be visualized as follows. In the plot region of v vs. t, change the ordinate to read v_j, v_j. Then change the plot type to ls and process.

● ●   A cubic spline was used in the integration. How much different would the results be if the linear or parabolic splines were used instead?

● ●   Since the integrals using the two different splines do not yield identical results, they cannot be the same at all points. Plot $vv(t_j)$ and $vv'(t_j)$ vs. t_j in the same plot region. Are the differences obvious?

Define a new index, m, that ranges from 0 to 39. Define a new abscissa vector $h_m = m/3$. Now plot $vv(h_m)$ and $vv'(h_m)$ vs. h_m. Differences should be more apparent. Locate a range when the integration based on the linear interpolation would be greater than that of the cubic spline interpolation. Change the limits of integration, a and b, to enclose this region. Check the results from the two integrations. Repeat for a different range where the integration of the cubic spline should be greater.

● ●   Extrapolation is dangerous. Let $m = 0, ... ,20$ and $h_m = m$. Plot $vv(h_m)$ and $vv'(h_m)$ vs. h_m. Be sure that MathCAD is able to set all the plot limits (if you are using an existing plot region, delete any limits that may have been entered). Is this extrapolation what you expected? Would it be significantly different if you used pspline or lspline?

2.4   Curve Fitting

A fundamental goal of physics is to describe nature in elegant mathematical form. A concise, elegant theory is more likely to be correct than a complex, messy one (Occam's razor). In the ongoing evolution of understanding, theoreticians attempt to formulate mathematical descriptions of nature; experimentalists attempt to measure the properties of nature. The ideas of each group, of course, influence and direct the other.

Physics and the other natural sciences must be founded on experiment. Observations of the night sky led to many theories of the extraterrestrial world. Plato's theory of homocentric spheres and Ptolemy's theory of epicycles are two such theories. Copernicus put forth still another theory. Still mired in spheres, it was complex and incorrect, yet it contained a key idea of placing the sun near the center of the universe. Kepler seized the idea and, after Herculean labors, solved the age-old problem of the planets, giving for the first time the correct description of planetary motion. Newton's laws of motion and his law of universal gravitation provided a powerful and commensurate mathematical description.

Good data are good data, but in and of themselves are uninterpretable. A theory provides a mechanism for the interpretation of data, yet the theory can be correct only insofar as it agrees with experiment. The cosmic theories of Plato and Ptolemy, and even the sphere-laden theory of Copernicus, were abandoned because they did not correspond sufficiently to the data. Kepler's and Newton's laws do correspond more precisely. In addition, their laws have an overarching simplicity and elegance that suits. Yet the ultimate truth is elusive. For all practical purposes, what is "true" in science is what the community of experts believes to be true.

Do not confuse the last statement with the idea that personal opinion reigns supreme and that we have only pure subjectivity as a guide to the truth. Once the experiments have been performed, the data analyzed, and the theories expounded, judgments are not freely made. The real world is out there whether we approve or not. The universe was evolving long before people appeared on the scene; the universe will continue should we cease to exist. The judgments that we make are about the adequacy of our models to correspond to nature.

> "— but we do at least know that the universe has some shape and order and that you know, trees do not turn into people or goddesses, and there are very good reasons why they don't, and you can't just believe absolutely anything."
>
> *My Dinner with André*

One element in this process of comparing data with a theoretical model is curve fitting. This helps to address the question of how well the suggested mathematical description fits the data. In the following sections, we describe how to perform a linear least squares fit, a polynomial fit, and a general fit.

2.4.1 *Linear Least Squares Fit*

MathCAD includes two built-in functions, slope(x, y) and intercept(x, y), where x and y are subscripted vectors. These functions return the slope and y-intercept of the linear least squares regression line for the data represented by x and y. Note that the index i must start from 0. If the index had started at 1, MathCAD would include the numbers in the zeroth element in the fit. If the zeroth element or any other element is not specified, it is treated as a zero and will skew the results.

• •   Load CURV5, glider on an air track — linear least squares example (see Fig. 2.7).

Velocities of a glider on an air track tilted at 10° are calculated in CURV5 (Fig. 2.7). Random errors are calculated and added to the velocities. Slopes and intercepts are calculated for both cases.

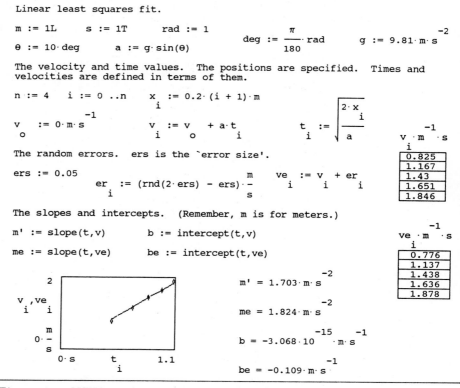

Figure 2.7 CURV5, glider on an air track — linear least squares example.

The error size is represented by *ers*. The errors are randomly distributed over the range $\pm ers$. It is important to include errors. It is one thing to fit to perfect data and another to do the calculation with values closer to what an experimentalist might encounter. Even small errors can have a greater effect on the outcome than one might expect. By examining both cases, one begins to get a sense of the limitations of the curve-fitting process. The errors are uniformly distributed; one could calculate errors with a Gaussian distribution but the extra calculation would gain us little at this stage.

The v_i are the precise values; the ve_i include errors; m' and b are the slope and intercept, respectively, for the ideal data. Why do we use m' and not m?

Move the place marker to the er_i region and press [F9] to recalculate with a new set of random values. Repeat several times. Observe the data in the plot region and the numerical values of slope and intercept.

Change the error size (*ers*) and repeat. In this example, how do error size and uncertainty in slope compare? How small must the random errors be to determine the slope consistently within 1%?

Examine when $v_o \neq 0$.

The linear least squares functions of slope and intercept can be extended to exponentials and one-term polynomials. To apply these functions for the case

$$y = Be^{mx}, \tag{2.7}$$

take the natural log of both sides:

$$\ln(y) = \ln(B) + mx. \tag{2.8}$$

The m-value could be determined by evaluating the equation for two sets of coordinates (x_1, y_1) and (x_2, y_2), subtracting one equation from the other, and solving for m:

$$\ln(y_1) = \ln(B) + m\,x_1, \tag{2.9}$$

$$\ln(y_2) = \ln(B) + m\,x_2, \tag{2.10}$$

$$m = \frac{\ln(y_2) - \ln(y_1)}{x_2 - x_1}. \tag{2.11}$$

However, by identifying $Y = \ln(y)$ and $b = \ln(B)$, equation 2.8 can be rewritten as

$$Y = mx + b.$$

Performing a least squares fit to this equation, using the slope and intercept functions, yields values for m and b based on all the data points rather than just two as in the previous example. Because $B = \exp(b)$, the fit process provides the two parameters, m and B, of the original equation.

A similar method can be applied to expressions of the form

$$x = Bt^m. \tag{2.12}$$

Taking the natural log of both sides yields

$$\ln(x) = \ln(B) + m\ln(t). \tag{2.13}$$

The m-value could be determined by evaluating the equation for two sets of coordinates, (x_1, y_1) and (x_2, y_2), subtracting one equation from the other, and solving for m. The B term drops out as in the previous case, and we have

$$m = \frac{\ln(x_2) - \ln(x_1)}{\ln(t_2) - \ln(t_1)}. \tag{2.14}$$

If we identify $X = \ln(x)$, $b = \ln(B)$, and $T = \ln(t)$, the log form of the equation becomes

$$X = mT + b.$$

Performing a least squares fit to this equation yields values for m and b. Because $B = \exp(b)$, the fit process provides the two parameters, m and B, of the original equation.

• •   Load CURV6, free-fall data with errors (see Fig. 2.8).

The data used here could be from a photograph of a falling ball bearing illuminated with a stroboscope. The expected form of the data is

$$x = \frac{1}{2}at^2.$$

This example is like the case just described, $x = Bt^m$, where $B = a/2$ and $m = 2$. We assume the time data are accurate. Errors are added to the x-data — $\pm ers$.

We take natural logarithms of the xe and t data and fit these data with a linear least squares fit. After $\exp(be)$ is computed, the values are compared with the ideal values.

Place the cursor in the er_i region and process several times. Note that even when the plot seems to fit well, the value for ac may differ significantly from the ideal value. The error is unrealistically large. Reduce it and process several times. How small does the error need to be to determine the value ac with 5% of its ideal value? What is the difference between a linear plot of X_i vs. T_i and a log-log plot of xe_i vs. t_i? (We refer to this problem in the next section.)

```
Linear least squares fit.      Log-log case.

Generate the data.

g := 9.81      a := g

n := 5           i := 0 ..n      t  := 0.05· (i + 3)              1    2
                                  i                          x  := - · a· t
Add in an error signal.                                       i   2    i

ers := .05         er  := rnd(2· ers) - ers    xe  := x  + er
                     i                            i    i    i
```

$$X_i := \ln\left[xe_i\right] \qquad T_i := \ln\left[t_i\right]$$

```
Extract the parameters.

me := slope(T,X)         be := intercept(T,X)        be := exp(be)    ac := 2· be
              me
z  := be· t            me = 2.553                  Ideal me value 2
 i         i           ac = 18.15                  Ideal ac value 9.81
```

Display of the data, data plus errors, and fit. Show the log values, which, if they represent a polynomial, should lie along a straight line.

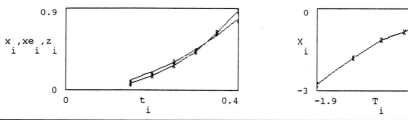

Figure 2.8 CURV6, free-fall data with errors.

2.4.2   *Polynomial Curve Fitting*

Here, we want to extract the coefficients of a polynomial,

$$y = a_0 + a_1 x + a_2 x^2 + \cdots, \tag{2.15}$$

given data sets (x_i, y_i). Matrix methods are helpful in determining the coefficients. An understanding of matrices is *not* necessary to use the results.

Let Y be a vector containing all the y-values; let A be a vector containing all the coefficients; and let X be a matrix whose zeroth column is all 1s (x_i^0), whose first column is the x_i s, whose second column is the x_i^2s, etc. Thus we can write the entire set of conditions (one for each data set)

$$Y \simeq XA \tag{2.16}$$

where $\simeq$ implies a least squares fit. (See Section 2.4.3 on general fit for a discussion of the least squares process.) If we interchange rows and columns, the form would be AX; these two forms are equivalent. We wish to solve for the coefficients.

The solution is given by

$$(X^T X)^{-1}(X^T Y) = A. \qquad (2.17)$$

Thus we have the coefficients in terms of the x and y values. In case matrix operations are unfamiliar to you, these operations will be demonstrated for a small data set.

• •   Load CURV7, quadratic fit (see Figs. 2.9 and 2.10).

```
Demonstration of matrix operations for quadratic fit.

Four data points.
```

$n := 3$ $i := 0 .. n$ $x_i := i$ $y_i := 3 + 2 \cdot x_i + 1 \cdot x_i^2$

x_i	y_i
0	3
1	6
2	11
3	18

```
The equation for y in terms of x, is in effect, four
equations.  One for each i.  The coefficients remain
the same.
```

```
The equations can be written in matrix form as    Y := X·A □  where
```

$X := \begin{bmatrix} 1 & 0 & 0 \\ 1 & 1 & 1 \\ 1 & 2 & 4 \\ 1 & 3 & 9 \end{bmatrix}$ The columns represent x to the zeroth, first, and second power.

$A := \begin{bmatrix} 3 \\ 2 \\ 1 \end{bmatrix}$ The coefficients for the zeroth, first, and second powers of x.

$Y := X \cdot A$ $Y = \begin{bmatrix} 3 \\ 6 \\ 11 \\ 18 \end{bmatrix}$ The same as the y values.

```
So far, all that has been demonstrated is that the equations can be written
in matrix form.

Now let's construct the X matrix more automatically and form the various
products on the way to determining the coefficients.  (If there were lots
of data points, entering them by hand would be a waste of time.)

We wish to use the same names, so set them to zero before we start.
```

$X := 0$ $Y := 0$ $A := 0$

```
The zeroth column of the X matrix is one, x to the zeroth power.  Y is
similarly defined.
```

$X_{i,0} := 1$ $Y_i := y_i$

```
The first column is x to the first power; the x's are already specified.
```

$X^{\langle 1 \rangle} := x$ The column name is called using [Alt]6.

Figure 2.9 CURV7, quadratic fit. (See the next figure for the rest of the document.)

The second column is x squared, that is, each element of x squared.
Calculate them using the vectorize operation. This is a method to do element
by element calculations rapidly. The operation is called with [Alt]-.

$$X^{\overset{\frown}{\langle 2\rangle}} := \begin{bmatrix} 2 \\ x \end{bmatrix}$$

$$X^{\langle 0\rangle} = \begin{bmatrix} 1 \\ 1 \\ 1 \\ 1 \end{bmatrix} \qquad X^{\langle 1\rangle} = \begin{bmatrix} 0 \\ 1 \\ 2 \\ 3 \end{bmatrix} \qquad X^{\langle 2\rangle} = \begin{bmatrix} 0 \\ 1 \\ 4 \\ 9 \end{bmatrix} \qquad X = \begin{bmatrix} 1 & 0 & 0 \\ 1 & 1 & 1 \\ 1 & 2 & 4 \\ 1 & 3 & 9 \end{bmatrix}$$

The transpose is called by [Alt]1.
The transpose interchanges rows
and columns.

$$X^{\mathsf{T}} = \begin{bmatrix} 1 & 1 & 1 & 1 \\ 0 & 1 & 2 & 3 \\ 0 & 1 & 4 & 9 \end{bmatrix}$$

$$A := (X^{\mathsf{T}} \cdot X)^{-1} \cdot (X^{\mathsf{T}} \cdot Y)$$

$$A = \begin{bmatrix} 3 \\ 2 \\ 1 \end{bmatrix}$$

The data are exact, so one would expect a `perfect' fit.

Figure 2.10 CURV7 *continued.*

A quadratic equation, a polynomial, is expressed in CURV7 (Fig. 2.9). A small number of x values are defined. The corresponding y-values are calculated. The x and y values are shown in tabular form. The matrix X has three columns; the values of each column are x to the zeroth, first, and second powers. The values were entered by hand. [Alt]M is the command to create a matrix. The number of rows and columns are requested. Enter the values and press return. The matrix appears filled with place markers; move the cursor to each marker and enter the desired value. The coefficients a_i are listed in the vector A. We perform the matrix multiplication $X \cdot A$ just as if the matrices were numbers. We evaluate Y and see that the values are identical with the y_i.

To construct our matrix more directly from the data, we set

$$X_{i,0} := 1$$

because we want the zeroth column to be all ones. We set the next column equal to the x_i and the next to x_i^2 (type [Alt]^ for a superscript):

$$X^{\langle 1\rangle} = x, \qquad X^{\langle 2\rangle} = x^2.$$

A vectorize operation is used in the document to speed the term by term squaring (the vectorize operation is called by typing [Alt]–).

We examine each column of X and the assembled matrix. We also look at the transpose, which is matrix X with the rows and columns interchanged. Finally, we calculate the values for A in terms of X, its transpose, and Y. The values for A are the ones we seek. Simple examples are useful to make the various steps concrete.

Show that $X^T X$ is a square matrix. Is $(X^T X)^{-1}$ also square? What is the form $X^T Y$?

• •   Load CURV8, free-fall data with errors — as in CURV6/Fig. 2.8. (See Fig. 2.11.)

This procedure is no different from that used in CURV7 (see Figs. 2.9 and 2.10). Without all the details, it can be expressed with only a few statements.

Note that this x and t information is the same as that of CURV6. Errors are defined in the same way but are, of course, random. Does the polyfit procedure yield better, the same, or worse values for ac, on average, than the methods used in CURV6? Provide a semiquantitative answer. How does this document provide information about the value of the exponent of t? Is there a t term in the original expression?

Remove the term linear in t and fit with just a constant and a squared term. Delete $T^{\langle 1 \rangle}$. Rename $T^{\langle 2 \rangle}$ as $T^{\langle 1 \rangle}$ so there are only two columns instead of three. Again examine quality of fit with the same error sizes.

• •   Load CURV9, example with a noninteger exponent (see Fig. 2.12).

Data are created as the square root of x; errors are added. In the first plot region, the exact data and the data with errors are plotted as plot type ℓv. A fit is attempted using the form

$$y = a_0 + a_1 x + a_2 x^{0.5}.$$

Quadratic fit   Free fall data with errors.

$g := 9.81$ $a := g$

$n := 5$ $i := 0 \, ..n$ $t_i := 0.05 \cdot (i + 3)$ $x_i := \dfrac{1}{2} \cdot a \cdot t_i^{\,2}$

$ers := .05$ $er_i := rnd(2 \cdot ers) - ers$ $xe_i := x_i + er_i$

$T_{i,0} := 1$ $T^{\langle 1 \rangle} := t$ $T^{\langle 2 \rangle} := \overrightarrow{\left[t^2\right]}$

$b := (T^T \cdot T)^{-1} \cdot (T^T \cdot xe)$ $b = \begin{bmatrix} -0.244 \\ 1.668 \\ 2.133 \end{bmatrix}$ $ac := 2 \cdot b_2$

$ac = 4.267$

Figure 2.11 CURV8, free-fall data with errors — as in CURV6.

Fit with a **square root term.**

The data   n := 10   i := 0 ..10

$$x_i := \sqrt{i}$$

The error   ers := 1 er_i := rnd(2·ers) - ers

The signal $y_i := x_i + er_i$

The expression to be fitted

$$Y := a_0 + a_1 \cdot x + a_2 \cdot x^{0.5} \quad \square$$

In matrix form   Y := X·a □

$X_{1,0} := 1$ $X^{<1>} := x$

$$X^{<2>} := \overrightarrow{\left[\sqrt{x}\right]}$$

$$a := (X^T \cdot X)^{-1} \cdot (X^T \cdot y)$$

$$a = \begin{bmatrix} -0.624 \\ 0.893 \\ 0.118 \end{bmatrix}$$

$fit0_i := a_0$ $fit1_i := a_1 \cdot x_i$ $fit2_i := a_1 \cdot x_i^{0.5}$

The contribution of each term.

The fitted expression   Y := X·a

A comparison of fit and data

A comparison of the data with the square root term.

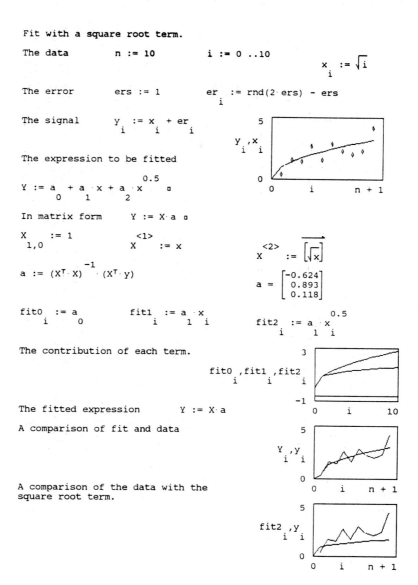

Figure 2.12 CURV9, example with a noninteger exponent.

To examine the fit, we plot each term separately. We plot the data and the fit. We plot the data and the square root term only.

Process several times to get a sense of the fit. Change error size and repeat.

Remove the x term and try to fit the data with the form $a_0 + a_1 x^{0.5}$. How does this change the quality of the fit? Change error size and repeat.

Try fitting the data with $a_0 + a_1 \ln(x)$. Compare the quality of fit with the previous case. Change error size and repeat.

• • The following data are from an accelerator experiment performed by John Davis. Fit energy (as abscissa) and change in energy per thickness (ordinate) with a quartic, $f(x) = a_0 + a_1 x + a_2 x^2 + a_3 x^3 + a_4 x^4$. In matrix form our equations would appear as

$$dEdx = EA.$$

Plot the data and fitted curve vs. energy as energy increases from 0 to 3 in steps of 0.1:

$$E_i = 0.4, 0.6, 0.8, 1.2, 1.3, 1.4, 1.7, \text{ and } 2.3,$$
$$dEdx = 54.4, 61.2, 63.9, 63, 62.9, 62.4, 60, \text{ and } 54.8.$$

2.4.3   *General Fit*

In a least squares fit process, the mean squared error is minimized. You can express the mean squared error for any functional form and ask MathCAD to minimize the quantity.

Values for x and $y(x)$ are known. The analytic expression, $f(x)$, represents the data. Under ideal circumstances, the measured values $y(x)$ and the computed values $f(x)$ would be the same. The function f includes some parameters. The fit process determines the values for the parameters that best fit the data.

The general procedure would be as follows:

Define the functional form for the expression to be fitted, for example, $f(a, b, x) = \cos(ax) \cdot e^{-bx}$.

The functional form, f, defines the function that will be used to fit the data. The parameters, whose values are sought, must be included in the list of arguments together with the variables.

Define the total mean squared error. Take the difference between the data and the function evaluated at the corresponding point (use the same subscripts), for example,

$$sse(a, b) = \sum_i \left[(y_i - f(a, b, x_i)) \right]^2.$$ (2.18)

Use a given-minerr (not a given-find) solve block to determine the parameters that make the sum of the squared errors as close to zero as possible, for example,

$$\text{given} \quad sse(a, b) \approx 0 \quad 1 \approx 1 \quad \begin{bmatrix} a \\ b \end{bmatrix} = \text{minerr}(a, b).$$

The $1 \approx 1$ is required because there must be as many equations in the solve block as there are quantities for which values are sought.

This process can be very slow to converge. Choose the guess values carefully.

Consider a simple example from optics. A beam of light directed toward a smooth surface of water is bent as it passes from the air to the water. Ancient data from Ptolemy give the incident and refracted angles of a beam of light as it passes from air to water. The beam angles are measured from the perpendicular to the surface, the normal. Centuries later a relation, a functional form, between angles and indices of refraction was determined. Snell's law states that

$$\sin(\theta_{\text{inc}}) = n_{\text{ir}} \sin(\theta_{\text{refr}}),$$

where n_{ir} is the index that is sought.

The goal is to fit the data according to Snell's law and determine the best value for the index of refraction, which is a measure of the change in speed of the beam as it passes from air to water. In other words, given the data, what is the value of n_{ir} that makes the mean squared error between the data and the functional form the least?

• • Load CURV10, general fit to determine the index of refraction (see Fig. 2.13).

The data consist of the incident and refracted angles. The values used for the incident angle, θi_i, are every 10 degrees from 10 to 80. The values for the corresponding refracted angles, θr_i, are shown in tabular form.

Snell's law, which you are not expected to know at this point, can be written $\sin(\theta i) = n_{\text{ir}} \sin(\theta r)$.

The procedure is as follows. First, express the functional form and include the unknown in the argument list. For this problem, solve Snell's law for θi; include in the argument list the parameter for which a value is sought. This appears as

$$\theta i'(n_{ir}, \theta r) := \text{asin}(n_{ir}\sin(\theta r)).$$

The prime is used to distinguish the calculated value from the original data (θ' is equivalent to f, above).

Define the sum of the squares of all the errors:

$$sse(n_{ir}) := \sum_i \left[\theta i_i - \theta i'\left[n_{ir}, \theta r_i\right]\right]^2.$$

In a given-minerr solve block, request MathCAD find the value for n_{ir} that makes sse a minimum. Note that sse is set equal to zero, but in general a value of zero is unattainable. In effect, a minimum is determined for sse.

Make comparisons of the fitted values and the data.

What is the average deviation of θi and $\theta i'$? (MathCAD summation is [Shift]4.)

Observe the original data. Plot θr vs. θi. To get some sense of the quality of the fit, plot $n_{ir} \cdot \sin(\theta r)$ vs. $\sin(\theta i)$. Finally, look at the angles

---

Refraction data from Ptolemy

$rad \equiv 1$ $N := 8$ $i := 1 ..8$ $\theta i_i := 10 \cdot i \cdot deg$ $\theta r_i :=$

$deg \equiv \dfrac{\pi}{180} \cdot rad$ $\theta r_i := \theta r_i \cdot deg$

θr_i
8
15.5
22.5
29
35
40.5
45.5
50

Guess value for n.ir $n_{ir} := 1$

The functional form $\theta i'\left[n_{ir}, \theta r\right] := \text{asin}\left[n_{ir} \cdot \sin(\theta r)\right]$

The argument list must include the parameter(s) to be evaluated as well as the variables.

The data $\theta i_i \; \square$

The sum of the squared errors $sse\left[n_{ir}\right] := \sum_i \left[\theta i_i - \theta i'\left[n_{ir}, \theta r_i\right]\right]^2$

The solve block.

given $sse\left[n_{ir}\right] \approx 0$ $n_{ir} := \text{minerr}\left[n_{ir}\right]$ $n_{ir} = 1.293$

Figure 2.13 CURV10, general fit to determine the index of refraction.

themselves. Plot $\theta i'(n_{ir}, \theta r_i), \theta i_i$ vs. θi_i. Set plot types to be vl for this last plot.

• •   It is suggested that the data $y_i = $ 0, 3.4, 8, 11.9, 10.2, 5.5, 3.6, 1.1, 0, 0.2, 0.1, and $v_i = i$ can be fitted with a curve of the form

$$f = av^2 e^{-bv^2}.$$

Plot y_i, f vs. v_i. Try different values for the parameters a and b in the function f until a close fit is obtained. Use the best values for a and b from this process as guess values for a and b in a general fit. Perform a general fit. Plot the final results with the data as a function of v_i. How close were your values of a and b?

• •   In the file TORNADOS are listed the approximate number of tornados that occurred in the United States during the first six months of each year from 1950 to 1990. (April through June is tornado season.) What curve best represents the data? Based on your results, how many tornados will there be in the year 2001?

"I believe I deserve an explanation, Dave."

2001

C H A P T E R

3

Units and Dimensional Analysis

In this chapter you learn how to include units in your calculations, to simplify the fundamental units resulting from a calculation, to determine units of unfamiliar variables in equations, and to consider other systems of units. The choice of units is to some extent arbitrary. The fundamental units of length, mass, time, and current, for example, are the choices of the SI system of units (used almost exclusively in general physics texts today). Among some professional physicists, however, the cgs system of units is still popular. The English system is, of course, in use. Still other systems of units are possible.

Dimensional analysis is then considered. This is a very useful technique that permits you to find dimensionless groups and to learn dependences between variables. Several examples, including Kepler's harmonic law and a nuclear explosion, are considered.

3.1   Units

Every term in an equation must have the same physical units. We cannot equate kilograms and meters or add an acceleration and a velocity and expect anything meaningful. This gives us a very powerful handle. We can look at an equation that we have never seen before and know if it is a possible equation. If every term has the same units, the equation could be true; if the terms do not agree, then we know the equation cannot be correct.

Remember the following points when dealing with units:

1. If there are derivatives or integrals, the ds and integral signs have no units and should be ignored. When thinking units, act as if these symbols did not exist.

2. Similarly, in dimensional analysis, differentials and integrals do not appear. A ratio such as A/T might be dA/dT. This is a limitation of the method.

3. Don't be put off by an equation that you don't know. Units are units. Several equations and quantities in this section may be unfamiliar to you. These procedures provide a means of brushing up against unfamiliar ideas and learning something about them.

In this section, we wish to concentrate on the units, not the numerical values associated with physical quantities. In particular, we will see how to set up a system of units, how to use units in calculations, how to convert units generated by MathCAD in a calculation to a particular form, what happens if we try to combine units improperly. Then we look at some further examples with units.

The general procedure for handling units using MathCAD is straightforward:

1. Define the base units.

2. Define any other needed units in terms of the base units or in terms of any other unit already defined (that is, to the left or above in the document).

3. Assign appropriate units to all variables by attaching them as multipliers or divisors of the numerical values.

4. Perform any MathCAD operations in the standard way. (Some Math-CAD operations must use unitless values; these include logarithms and exponentials.)

Results are given with units attached. Initially, the units are given in terms of the fundamental quantities mass, length, time, and charge. However, these can easily be converted into the particular units that were defined in steps 1 and 2 above. The numerical value of the quantity is automatically adjusted to correspond to the units selected.

There are four basic units in MathCAD. (It would be preferable if there were a fifth so that temperature was automatically included; if you think so too, write Mathsoft a letter.) When defining units, if the global equality, the tilde ˜, which appears as ($\equiv$), is used, then no matter where they are placed, MathCAD notices them first. The global equalities are also read left to right, top to bottom, so that units defined in terms of other units still need to be in the proper order. Examples of definitions of base units are

$$m \equiv 1L \qquad kg \equiv 1M \qquad s \equiv 1T \qquad \text{and} \qquad C \equiv 1Q.$$

Notice that there is no multiplication between the numerical value 1 and the fundamental unit name in the definition process.

• •   Reset MathCAD. Perform the operations in this section as they are discussed in the text. Start by defining the units as described.

Let m represent length in meters, kg mass in kilograms, s time in seconds, and C electric charge in coulombs. In general, define only those units that are needed for a particular application. For example, when treating problems in mechanics, charge is generally not needed.

The name associated with a unit can be changed. For example, one might prefer to change the unit for charge, the coulomb, to the unit of current, the ampere. Or it could be changed to temperature. The name is changed by pressing [Esc], typing dimension, and pressing return. Move to charge, for example, delete the name (backspace over it), and type temperature, current, force, or whatever is desired.

Note that it is not possible to use one variable name to represent two quantities. If m is used for length (meter), then it *cannot* be used later for some generic mass. Similarly, if N is used for the unit of force, the Newton, then it cannot be used later, for example, for normal force or for the upper limit of some index. Instead, use a more complex name, m1, or Nf, or use a literal subscript, m_a, of the $x.x$ variety. For literal subscripts, avoid using numbers for the subscripts; it is difficult to distinguish them from active subscripts.

Once the base units are defined, then any other units to be used are expressed in terms of units already defined. Two commonly used quantities are force (think of it as mass times acceleration; acceleration has units of velocity per time) and energy (think of it as force times distance).

The units of the Newton and the Joule, the SI units of force and energy, respectively, are

$$N := kg \cdot \frac{m}{s^2} \qquad J := N \cdot m.$$

Similarly, cm and gm would be defined cm := $0.01 \cdot m$ and gm := $0.001 \cdot kg$, respectively. To write force equals ten Newtons, use the units as a multiplier. Then evaluate F:

$$F := 10 \cdot N \qquad F = 10 \cdot mass \cdot length \cdot time^{-2}.$$

The result is expressed in terms of the fundamental units, not in terms of the units that were defined. (The numerical value is, however, associated with the base units that were defined.) In general, this is not the desired form for the units. It is necessary to convert the fundamental units into those that have been defined. This process is easy.

Evaluate F (the various different forms which follow are all different expressions of the same F and would occupy only one line in MathCAD):

$$F = 10 \cdot mass \cdot length \cdot time^{-2}.$$

Move the cursor to the place marker, the ■ near the end of the region. The cursor must be in the region for the place marker to be visible. Type kg at the place marker and process. When a quantity is entered at the place marker, press [F9] to process; otherwise, it may appear as if no change occurs:

$$F = 10 \cdot length \cdot time^{-2} \cdot kg.$$

At the place marker, include the unit for length, meter; multiply $kg \cdot m$:

$$F = 10 \cdot time^{-2} \cdot kg \cdot m.$$

At the place marker, include the units for time; multiply $kg \cdot m \cdot s^{-2}$:

$$F = 10 \cdot kg \cdot m \cdot s^{-2}.$$

Finally, at the place marker, remove all the units and replace them with $gm \cdot cm \cdot s^{-2}$:

$$F = 1 \cdot 10^6 \cdot gm \cdot cm \cdot s^{-2}.$$

The numerical value automatically adjusts to correspond to the chosen units. If we try once again, this time typing $m^2 \cdot s^2$ at the place marker (try it), the units are not simplified. But no harm is done. What is wrong can be seen and changed.

Often in problems or in performing measurements, all quantities are not specified in one system of units. For example, some values may be in meters, some in centimeters, and some in microns. However, as long as you follow the procedure of defining and assigning, MathCAD will take care of all the details. For example, you have

$$x1 := m \qquad x2 := cm \qquad x := x1 + x2 \qquad x = 1.01 \cdot length,$$

or, by using the place marker, you have

$$x = 1.01 \cdot m \qquad or \qquad x = 101 \cdot cm.$$

If we try to add quantities of mixed units, MathCAD responds with an error message and will not process any improperly defined quantities, such as the quantity "mess" below:

$$y := m \qquad t := s \qquad mess := y + t.$$

The error message "incompatible units" is displayed. If mess is evaluated after this region (try it), the resulting error message is "undefined". If mess had been defined previously in a legitimate statement in the document, the first assignment would still apply.

If an incompatible-unit problem appears and it is not immediately obvious what the problem is, evaluate the quantities that are incompatible side by side. A comparison will show how the units differ.

No matter how complex or how simple the terms, units must be the same if the quantities are to be added or equated.

• •   If units are mixed in a problem, as long as the proper assignments are made, MathCAD will make the necessary conversions. For example, the velocity of a falling object is to be determined using the equation $v = \sqrt{2\,g\,h}$ with g the acceleration due to gravity and h the height through which the object falls. Calculate the final velocity of a mass that is permitted to fall through a distance of 125 cm, near the surface of the earth. To keep the arithmetic trivial, let $g = 10 \cdot m \cdot s^{-2}$. Perform the calculation in your head or on a scrap of paper. Then perform the calculation using MathCAD and incuding units. Express the results in m/s and in cm/s, using the place marker.

• •   Assume that the equation below relating force, F, electric charges, $q1$ and $q2$, and the distance, r, is valid. The equation is a statement of Coulomb's law and is similar to Newton's law of gravitation. The constant ϵ_o is analogous to the constant G in the law of gravitation:

$$F = \frac{1}{4\,\pi\epsilon_o} \cdot \frac{q1 \cdot q2}{r^2}.$$

Let $q1$ and $q2$ each have a magnitude of one microcoulomb. Let r be one meter. Let the force be 0.009 Newtons. Simplify the units for ϵ_o:

$$\epsilon_o = \frac{q1 \cdot q2}{4 \cdot \pi \cdot r^2 \cdot F}.$$

Use the Newton to simplify the units. Try the Joule. The volt is equal to 1 Joule per coulomb; incorporate it. The farad is expressed in coulombs per volt; incorporate it. (At this point the only units should be farad and meter.)

Don't be afraid to question and test. The computer makes that process easier. These examples help to reinforce the idea that we have another means of thinking about concepts and equations.

• •   Verify that the equation $F = m v^2 / r$ is dimensionally correct. F is force, m is mass, v is velocity and r is a radius.

• •   If the following equation, which relates kinetic energy and absolute temperature, is correct, what are the units of k?

$$\frac{1}{2} m v^2 = \frac{3}{2} k T.$$

A given-find solve block is one way to determine the units.

• •   In cgs units, the unit of force — the counterpart to the SI unit, the Newton — is the dyne, where dyne $:= \text{gm} \cdot \text{cm} \cdot \text{s}^{-2}$. The cgs energy unit — the counterpart to the SI unit, the Joule — is the erg, where erg $:= \text{gm} \cdot \text{cm}^2 \cdot \text{s}^{-2}$.

Define the Newton, Joule, dyne, and erg. Evaluate each and make use of the place markers. In the place marker of the Newton, put dyne; in the place marker of the dyne, put Newton. In the place marker of the Joule, put erg; in the place marker of the erg, put Joule.

It is very simple to go back and forth between any desired sets of units.

• •   The units that we choose are to some degree arbitrary. The SI system uses meter, kilogram, and second; the cgs system uses centimeter, gram, and second; the English system uses foot, something, and second. The most familiar "something" unit is the pound, but in common usage the pound is a unit of force, not mass. Of course, there is the slug as a unit of mass and there is also a pound mass. Would it make any difference if the basic units were length, force, and time, instead of length, mass, and time? If the concern is simply a matter of analytic expression, then the answer is no. In terms of experimentally determining the values, however, it does make a difference.

Let us select for the mechanical units distance, time, and force. Change the unit name associated with M to force. Define X := 1L, T := 1T, F := 1M. Evaluate them so that the names are displayed.

Now define v as X/T, a as X/T^2, m as F/a, ρ as m/X^3, E as $F \cdot X$, and $mmtm$ (momentum) as $m \cdot v$. The expressions for energy and momentum are useful reminders that quantities should be considered in more than one light.

• •   Express the same quantities in a system in which the base units are mass, momentum, and time.

3.2   Dimensional Analysis

We have already seen how useful units are, but now we want to use units in a different way. We want to use them to find how one variable depends on another for some particular set of circumstances. For example, in free fall, starting from rest near the earth's surface, velocity depends on the square root of the distance fallen. This is a very useful relationship. We would like to be able to determine relationships like this using only dimensional analysis.

The basic approach that we are going to use is this: we form a dimensionless group from the essential variables of a problem (dimensionless means that all units of length cancel, all units of time cancel, and so on). We set that dimensionless group equal to a constant of unknown magnitude. Despite the uncertainty with regard to the constant, this grouping tells us the dependence of one variable on another and permits us to see how changing one variable will affect others.

Before we consider specific examples, we provide a more detailed statement of the general procedure:

1. Determine the variables associated with the problem. This is likely to be the most difficult part; it cannot be done blindly. There are no simple rules that tell us when all the necessary variables have been selected. Some physical sense of the nature of the problem is required.

2. Count the number of variables in step 1. Call that number $N(V)$.

3. Count the number of fundamental units associated with the variables in steps 1 and 2. Call that number $N(U)$.

4. Subtract $N(U)$ from $N(V)$. This is the number of independent groups that can be formed. Typically in the problems we deal with, there will be only one group; but that is not always so.

5. Show the variables in each (for us, generally only one) group in a row, one multiplying the other. Set the exponent of the first variable to 1,

the exponent of the second to a, the exponent of the third to b, and so on.

6. Form a similar group, but replace all the variables with their fundmental units. Keep the same exponents.

7. Write $N(U)$ equations, one for each fundamental unit, in which we add all the exponents for the particular fundamental unit and set that sum equal to zero.

8. Solve the equations of the previous step and determine the values of the exponents a, b, ...

9. Form the group with the now known exponents and set it equal to a constant.

10. Examine the interdependence of the variables.

Consider again the free-fall problem, mentioned just before the procedure list. For this case, we will enumerate the steps of the procedure as we go through it.

1. First decide which variables are to be included. The problem explicity mentions velocity and distance fallen. Use h for height and v for velocity. Gravitational forces act on the mass, making it fall with acceleration g. Let's try out this set — h, v, and g — and see what dependence results.

2. The number of variables is three: h, v, and g.

3. The number of fundamental units is two: length and time.

4. There is one group: $3 - 2 = 1$.

5. Group variables in a row, multiplying each other, with exponents 1, a, b, ... Disable the equation:

$$h \cdot v^a \cdot g^b \ \square.$$

6. Form a similar group but replace the variables with the associated fundamental units. Keep exponents the same. Disable the equation. Velocity has units of L/T and acceleration has units of L/T^2:

$$L \cdot \left[\frac{L}{T}\right]^a \cdot \left[\frac{L}{T^2}\right]^b \ \square.$$

7. See step 8.

8. Here we combine two steps into one. Use a given-find structure to determine the values for the exponents.

Enter guess values for the variables: $a := 1,$ $b := 1.$
Given
$1 + a + b \approx 0.$ The L-equation; exponents sum to zero.
$-a - 2 \cdot b \approx 0.$ The T-equation; exponents sum to zero.
$$\begin{bmatrix} a \\ b \end{bmatrix} := \text{Find}(a, b) \qquad a = -2 \qquad b = 1.$$

9. Form the group; show original form; replace a and b with values from step 8:
$$h \cdot v^a \cdot g^b \,\square \qquad \text{or} \qquad h \cdot v^{-2} \cdot g := C1 \,\square.$$

10. Recall that earlier it was suggested that velocity was proportional to the square root of the distance fallen. Could we extract that information from this group? (Constants $C1$, $C2$, and $C3$ are not equal, but they are all constant. At the moment, that is all that is important about them.) Rewrite the equation as follows:
$$v^2 := C2 \cdot h \cdot g \,\square.$$
Since g is a constant near the surface of the earth, we have
$$v := C3 \cdot \sqrt{h} \,\square.$$
The suggested relationship is revealed through dimensional analysis.

• •   Plot linear and log-log plots of v vs. h and, for comparison, h vs. h with h as the independent variable.

• •   If the distance h were fixed and measurements were made at different locations, how would the final velocity depend on g?

3.2.1 Kepler's Harmonic Law

As another example of dimensional analysis, consider the case of what we now refer to as Kepler's third law, or his harmonic law. It relates the period — the time for a satellite to complete one full orbit — with its mean distance from the attracting body about which it orbits. Kepler discovered this law starting with raw data. It required an enormous intellectual struggle on his part to find the law. By assuming that we know the units of G, the universal gravitational constant, we can find his third law — at least the proportionalities — just using dimensional analysis. And it will be vastly easier to do.

First we must decide which variables should be included in the group. Clearly, we want the period, T, and the mean distance, r. Gravity is the attracting force, so include G. The massive central body is essential to all the orbiting bodies, so include M. Group the variables, permitting the first to have an exponent of 1. Disable the group:

$$T \cdot r^A \cdot G^B \cdot M^C \ \square.$$

Then write the same group in terms of fundamental units and disable. This will be our guide for the individual equations for mass, length, and time that must be solved:

$$T \cdot L^A \cdot \left[\frac{L^3}{M \cdot T^2} \right]^B \cdot M^C \ \square.$$

Now determine the exponents, A, B, and C. We solve for them using a given-find procedure. Equations are written for each of the fundamental units, M, L, and T. The equations express the fact that the sum of the exponents for the associated variable must add to zero since the quantity we seek is dimensionless.

$$A := 1 \qquad B := 1 \qquad C := 1 \qquad \text{Guess values for the variables.}$$

$$\text{Given}$$
$$-B + C \approx 0,$$
$$A + 3 \cdot B \approx 0,$$
$$1 - 2 \cdot B \approx 0.$$

These are the equations for M, L, and T, respectively,

$$\begin{pmatrix} A \\ B \\ C \end{pmatrix} := \text{Find}(A, B, C) \qquad A = -1.5 \qquad B = 0.5 \qquad C = 0.5.$$

Since the values of A, B, and C are all multiples of $1/2$, double all exponents. This operation includes the term with exponent 1. We justify this operation by noting that a dimensionless quantity squared is still dimensionless. Write the group:

$$T^2 \cdot r^{-3} \cdot G \cdot M := \text{const} \ \square.$$

Solving for the T term, we get

$$T^2 := \frac{\text{const}}{G \cdot M} \cdot r^3 \ \square.$$

We do not know what the constant is: dimensional analysis will not provide us with that information. But it does provide us with proportionalities, which is very useful information. For example, for a satellite at a given r, if the central mass were to increase by a factor of 4, the period would decrease by a factor of 2.

We've obtained quite a bit of useful information from this exercise. We now know that the square of the period is proportional to the cube of the mean distance. One thing this knowledge will permit us to do is to scale our solar system or any similar system. A procedure would be to measure the periods of the various orbiting bodies and then to calculate all the distances relative to one of them. We can perform some calculations because the constant cancels out when we take the ratio of similar proportionalities.

For example, if we write separate equations, one for the case of the earth and one for Jupiter, we obtain

$$T_e^2 = C \cdot r_e^3 \qquad\qquad T_j^2 = C \cdot r_j^3.$$

Note that the constant is the same in each of the above equations; also note that G and M are now included in the constant. When we take the ratio of the two equations, the constant disappears:

$$\frac{T_e^2}{T_j^2} = \frac{r_e^3}{r_j^3}. \tag{3.1}$$

If we assume that we know the periods of the planets and the distance from the earth to the sun, we can calculate the distances to all the other planets. To do this, we simply use the previous equation relating the period and mean distance for the earth and one of the other planets. Knowing the periods $T1$ and $T2$ and a distance $r1$, we can calculate an unknown mean distance $r2$.

The period of Jupiter's orbit is 11.85 earth years. If we specify the distance from the earth to the sun as one astronomical unit, 1 AU, we calculate the distance from Jupiter to the sun in AU:

$$r_j = r_e \cdot \left(\frac{T_j}{T_e}\right)^{2/3}. \tag{3.2}$$

This yields the value $r_j = 5.198$ AU. Knowing the periods of all the planets, we can calculate the distances to all the planets and, in effect, construct a scale model of the solar system with true relative distances. Of course, if we knew the distance from the earth to the sun from some independent measurement, then we would be able to calculate the actual distances.

One additional useful way to appreciate the relationship of Kepler's third law is to plot a universal curve (see Fig. 3.1). In this case, since r and T are both raised to powers, a log-log curve is appropriate. If the plot is in terms of earth years and astronomical units, r_e and T_e are both 1. This expression then becomes

$$r(T) = T^{2/3}. \tag{3.3}$$

One year implies 1 AU, eight years implies 4 AU, and so on. For Jupiter, $r(11.85) = 5.198$.

```
Planetary orbits           Kepler's Harmonic Law
                                                            B
In compact form               A  B  C                    ⎡   3 ⎤
                            T r  G  M  a            A  ⎢  L   ⎥   C
                                              T L · ⎢ ─── ⎥  · M  a
                                                    ⎢    2 ⎥
A := 1     B := 1           C := 1                  ⎣ M T  ⎦

given      -B + C ≈ 0      A + 3·B ≈ 0          1 - 2·B ≈ 0
⎡A⎤
⎢B⎥ := find(A,B,C)          A = -1.5            B = 0.5            C = 0.5
⎣C⎦

Squaring all terms and solving for the T term          2      const  3
                                                      T  := ─────·r  a
                                                             G·M

or              2          T := 0.2,1 ..100
                -
                3
      r(T) := T
```

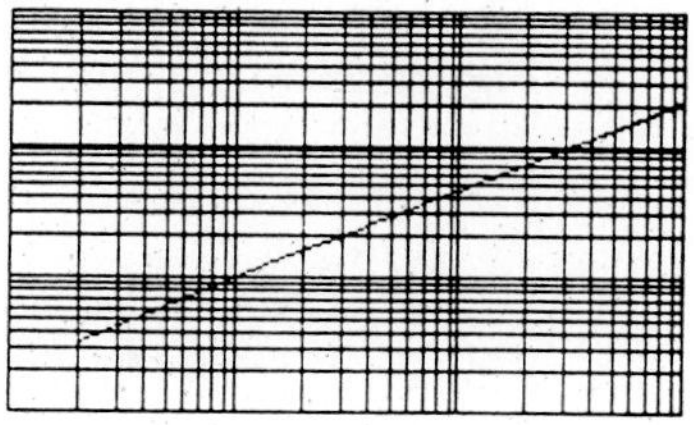

Figure 3.1 DA1, Kepler's third law. Period is in earth years and distance is in astronomical units.

• • Define the function $T(r)$ and plot $T(r)$ vs. r on a log-log plot.

• • Load document PLANET. The periods of the planets and the distances from the sun in AU are included. Using the periods, calculate the distances to the planets and compare with the table. Do you think the distances to the planets are measured or calculated?

3.2.2 Nuclear Explosion

A sequence of 16 photographs were made at intervals of 1/8 ms (millisecond) following the explosion of a nuclear weapon in the atmosphere. Measurements were made from the photographs to determine the size of the shock wave in each case; r_i give the radii in meters. The first photograph corresponds to a time of 1/8 ms after detonation.

• • Load DA2, nuclear explosion (see Fig. 3.2).

Determine whether the relationship between r and t is linear, exponential, or a power law. We plot data in four different ways and determine in which case the plot is closest to a straight line. (In general, curves need not be straight in any of these representations.)

```
Dimensional Analysis - Nuclear Explosion                        r  :=
                                                                 i
A sequence of 16 photographs were made an intervals of 1/8 ms  ┌────┐
following the explosion of a nuclear device in the atmosphere.  │ 31 │
Measurements were made from the photographs to determine the    │ 35 │
size of the shock wave in each case.  r[i gives the radius in    │ 45 │
meters.  The first photograph corresponds to a time 1/8 ms      │ 50 │
after the detonation.                                            │ 52 │
                                                                 │ 55 │
                                                                 │ 61 │
n ≡ 16     i ≡ 1 ..n                           -3               │ 67 │
                            t   := 0.125· 10   · i              │ 70 │
                             i                                   │ 74 │
                                                                 │ 74 │
                                                                 │ 77 │
                                                                 │ 78 │
                                                                 │ 82 │
                                                                 │ 84 │
                                                                 │ 87 │
                                                                 └────┘
```

Figure 3.2 DA2, nuclear explosion.

Determine the slope on a log-log plot by selecting two representative points (for example, #3 and #15); refer, if necessary, to the section on linear least squares fit. Determine the inverse of the slope as well. Repeat with several other points; see how much variation appears in the slope.

Finally, determine the slope and its inverse based on the entire data set rather than on just one pair of points. Use the slope function. See the section on linear least squares fit.

• •   Given the value just determined for the slope, what approximate proportionality is expected between r and t? Express the relationship in such a form that the exponents of both r and t are integers.

• •   Find a dimensionless group that will relate the size of a shock wave from a nuclear detonation as a function of time. Compare this with the results from the previous example.

Four variables are needed. They are the density of air before being affected by the explosion, the radius of the shock wave, the corresponding time, and the energy from the explosion. The four variables and three fundamental units (mass, length, and time) imply one group.

Determine the exponents for the variables. Form the group. Solve for r in terms of the other variables. In this particular case the constant is approximately 1.

Compare the results from the dimensional analysis with those of the exploratory study of the explosion using the time and size measurements.

Using the experimental values for r and t, and taking the density of air to be $1.2 \, \text{kg} \, \text{m}^{-3}$, calculate the energy released in the explosion.

Determine the energy E_i in terms of the r_i and t_i. Then determine the average energy value.

If the energy were available in a controlled manner, how many 100-watt bulbs could be powered for a year? A watt is equal to 1 Joule per second.

If we use the mass-energy relationship, $E = m c^2$, where c is the speed of light, what mass is converted to energy in the process?

Calculate the radius vs. time for the energy associated with the mass conversion of 5 gm of matter.

Double the energy and calculate new radii for the same time intervals. Compare these results with the previous calculations. Plot the two together. Would they be easy to distinguish?

If the lengths, r_i, from the DA2 file were in error by 10%, by how much would the apparent energy of the blast change?

• •   Find the dimensionless group associated with the variables radius, velocity, and acceleration. (Recall this result when dealing with circular motion.)

• •   Find the dimensionless group associated with the variables energy, mass, acceleration, and height. (Recall this result when dealing with gravitational potential energy.)

• •   Investigate, using dimensional analysis, the variation of pressure with depth in water. How many additional variables are needed? What are they? Find the dimensionless group. (Recall this result in the chapter on statics in the section "tower of bricks.")

3.3   Estimation Problems

Estimation problems are just what they sound like, estimations; precision is not the objective. These problems are useful because they encourage the solver to apply basic concepts freely. Often a simple model is required, which you must envision.

You can approximate shapes with spheres or cylinders or other basic geometrical shapes. You should know a few values for density and, of course, the relationship between density, mass, and volume.

• •   How many buckets of water does it take to fill a swimming pool?

• • How many drops of rain fall on an area the size of a football field when an inch of rain falls?

• • Estimate the surface area of your body. (You'll need this later when we discuss wind chill.)

• • What is the mass of all living human beings?

• • What is the volume of the earth's oceans?

• • How many atoms are there in the earth's atmosphere?

• • How many meters of electrical wire are in a typical household?

• • How many kilometers of sidewalk are there in Manhattan?

• • For a one-way commute of 10 miles, over a normal lifetime of work how far would a person drive? Express the result as a multiple of the circumference of the earth?

• • For the same commute, how many days of the worker's life are spent commuting?

• • For the same commute, how many gallons of gas are consumed?

• • For the same commute, how many pounds of tire rubber are worn away?

"Mistake? We don't make mistakes."

"Bloody typical. They've gone back to metric without telling us."

Brazil

CHAPTER

4

Vectors

Many physical quantities can be represented as vectors. Displacement, velocity, acceleration, force, momentum, and electric and magnetic fields are examples of vector quantities. Each has a direction and a magnitude. Temperature, on the other hand, has magnitude but no direction and is not a vector; temperature is a scalar. (Is energy a vector or a scalar?) Other quantites such as the moment of inertia, if treated in complete generality, cannot be described as vectors in the sense referred to above but require a more complex description in terms of tensors. All the physical quantities considered in this text will be treated as scalars or vectors.

4.1   Vector Sums and Components

Vector quantities can be represented with an arrow. The length of the arrow is proportional to the magnitude of the vector. Any vector can be represented as the sum of other vectors. Draw an arrow to represent a displacement vector — a displacement, for example, associated with walking across a field. Now think of this displacement as one side of a triangle, any triangle. From the original point, you could reach the final point by an unlimited number of pairs of vectors. The other two sides lead from the starting point to the final point; the vector sum of the two displacements is the same as the original displacement — same magnitude, same direction.

One especially important case is that of a right triangle, with the legs of the triangle parallel to the x- and y-axes of the coordinate system. The legs, in this case, are referred to as the x and y components of the vector. The hypotenuse is the resultant.

It is important to be able to describe a vector in terms of magnitude and direction — polar coordinates (r, θ) — or in component form — Cartesian coordinates (x, y). The relationships that express one form in terms of the other are

$$(r, \theta) \leftarrow (x, y) \qquad r = \sqrt{x^2 + y^2} \qquad \theta = \tan^{-1}\left(\frac{y}{x}\right). \qquad (4.1)$$

The arctangent operation returns angles within a restricted range. MathCAD's angle function, which returns a value between 0 and 2π, is often preferable:

$$\theta = \text{angle}(x, y). \qquad (4.2)$$

The reverse description giving the x and y components in terms of the magnitude and angle is

$$(x, y) \leftarrow (r, \theta) \qquad x = r\cos(\theta) \qquad y = r\sin(\theta). \qquad (4.3)$$

• •   Load VEC1, the addition of two vectors, V1 and V2, in polar coordinates; paralellogram rule (see Fig. 4.1).

Just above the four plot regions are LV1, LV2 and AV1,AV2, the magnitudes and angles associated with vectors V1 and V2. Displayed in the four plot regions are the two vectors individually, the vector sum in two forms (order exchanged), and (in the last frame) the two sums plus the resultant, exemplifying the parallelogram law of vector addition. Enter values for (LV1, AV1, LV2, AV2). Angles are in degrees; change the numerical value; leave the ·deg. Try data sets (2,30,3,60), (2,210,3,60), (−2,30,3,60), (1,0,1,90), (1,0,1,180), (1,0,1,170). (Sums of vectors with equal magnitude are of interest, for example, in optics when we consider phasors.)

A convenient method for conversion between radians and degrees is to define them as shown near the beginning of the document. Define radians equal to 1 (the radian is not a true unit). Define degrees in terms of radians. Any angle returned by MathCAD will be in radians. Entering

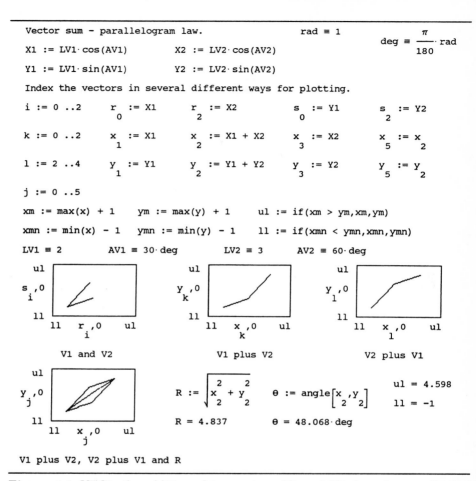

Vector sum - parallelogram law.   rad ≡ 1

$$deg \equiv \frac{\pi}{180} \cdot rad$$

X1 := LV1· cos(AV1)   X2 := LV2· cos(AV2)

Y1 := LV1· sin(AV1)   Y2 := LV2· sin(AV2)

Index the vectors in several different ways for plotting.

i := 0 ..2 r_0 := X1 r_2 := X2 s_0 := Y1 s_2 := Y2

k := 0 ..2 x_1 := X1 x_2 := X1 + X2 x_3 := X2 x_5 := x_2

l := 2 ..4 y_1 := Y1 y_2 := Y1 + Y2 y_3 := Y2 y_5 := y_2

j := 0 ..5

xm := max(x) + 1   ym := max(y) + 1   ul := if(xm > ym,xm,ym)

xmn := min(x) - 1   ymn := min(y) - 1   ll := if(xmn < ymn,xmn,ymn)

LV1 ≡ 2   AV1 ≡ 30· deg   LV2 ≡ 3   AV2 ≡ 60· deg

V1 and V2   V1 plus V2   V2 plus V1

V1 plus V2, V2 plus V1 and R

$$R := \sqrt{x_2^2 + y_2^2}$$ $\theta := angle\begin{bmatrix} x_2 ,y_2 \end{bmatrix}$

R = 4.837   θ = 48.068· deg

ul = 4.598

ll = -1

Figure 4.1 VEC1, the addition of two vectors, V1 and V2, in polar coordinates, paralellogram rule.

deg at the place marker will automatically convert the angle to degrees (press [F9]).

Four different indices, *i*, *j*, *k*, and *l*, are used here. This permits different plotting combinations. Note that each plot region uses a different index. Although MathCAD will automatically set plot limits, on some occasions it is preferable to specify them. Applied to vectors, max and min return the maximum and minimum values. The if statement lets us choose between cases.

• • Load VEC2, practice with components (see Fig. 4.2).

In the first graph, are shown the coordinate axes, a vector randomly choosen, and a marker which shows whether the angle given is measured clockwise or counterclockwise from the x-axis.   The length of the vector is l.v; the angle shown is ang.

Enter values for the x and y components, using sine and cosine functions with angles less than 90 deg.   Do not use lengths greater than lim(it).   To see what you specified, process (F9), and look at the second graph.   In the second graph will be the x and y components specified plus the original vector.

To repeat, press esc, type pro, press return, and press F9 with cursor in x.comp or y.comp region.   You can then enter new values and press [F9] to check as often as needed. Remember trig function arguments are in radians unless otherwise specified.

$l_v = 1.4$ $x_{comp} := 0$ $y_{comp} := 0$

$ang = 340 \cdot deg$ $lim = 1.54$ $x_7 := x_{comp}$ $y_8 := y_{comp}$ $x_8 := x_7$

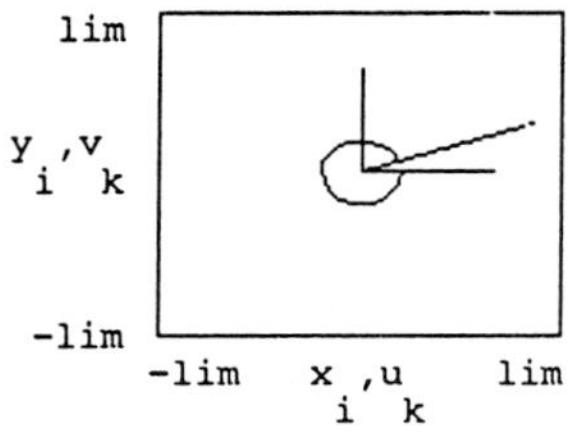

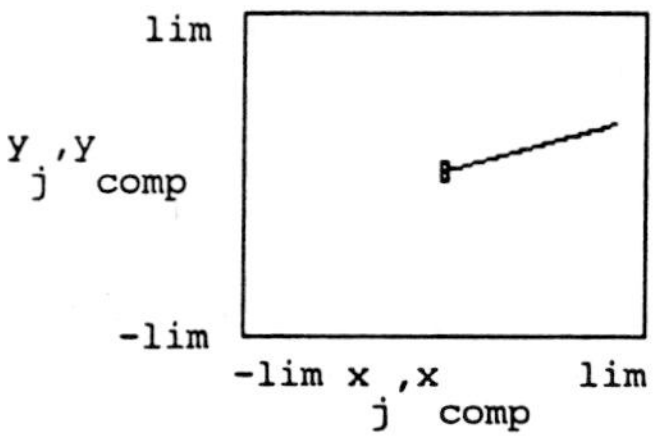

rad ≡ 1   The x,y from 0 to 4 draw the coordinate axes.
$$deg \equiv \frac{\pi}{180} \cdot rad$$ The 5th value is for the randomly directed vector.

$i \equiv 0 ..5$ $x_i \equiv 0$ $y_i \equiv 0$ $\theta_{rng} \equiv 2 \cdot \pi$ $\begin{bmatrix} \theta_v \\ z \\ l_v \end{bmatrix} \equiv \begin{bmatrix} floor(rnd(320)) \cdot deg \\ rnd(1) \\ .1 \cdot floor(rnd(7)) + 1 \end{bmatrix}$

$x_1 \equiv 1$ $y_3 \equiv 1$ $lim \equiv 1.1 \cdot l_v$

$\theta_v \equiv \theta_v + 20 \cdot deg$

$x_5 \equiv l_v \cdot cos[\theta_v]$ $y_5 \equiv l_v \cdot sin[\theta_v]$ $l_v = 1.4$

$ang \equiv if[z > .5, \theta_v, \theta_{rng} - \theta_v]$ $\theta_v = 20 \cdot deg$

$x_6 \equiv 0$ $y_6 \equiv 0$ $y_7 \equiv 0$ $j \equiv 4 ..8$ $ang = 340 \cdot deg$

$N \equiv 23$ $k \equiv 0 ..N$

$$\Phi_k \equiv if\left[z > .5, \theta_v \cdot \frac{k}{N}, -\left[[2 \cdot \pi - \theta_v] \cdot \frac{k}{N}\right]\right]$$

$u_k \equiv .3 \cdot cos[\Phi_k]$ $v_k \equiv .3 \cdot sin[\Phi_k]$

Figure 4.2 VEC2, practice with components.

A vector is selected at random and plotted in the first plot region. The length of the vector is l_v; the angle, ang, may be measured either clockwise or counterclockwise from the x-axis. At x_{comp} and y_{comp}, enter values for the x and y components using the sine and cosine functions and angles less than 90°; for example, $2 \cdot \sin(15 \cdot \deg)$. In the second plot region, the original vector and the vector based on the values supplied for x_{comp} and y_{comp} are plotted. If correctly specified, the two vectors will appear as one. Try several examples. To make sure that the program repeats properly, press [Esc], type pro, press return, move the cursor to either the x or y component region, and press [F9]. Then you can enter new component values repeatedly while the original vector remains unchanged.

A number of statements are required to specify the length, angle, and direction of rotation of the vector, and to draw the axes, the vector, and the arc indicating the direction of rotation. To avoid clutter at the beginning of the document, the code is presented at the end. These statements all require the use of the global equality so that these statements will process before the segment that is shown at the beginning.

• •   Load VEC3, sum from two to six vectors (see Fig. 4.3).

Specify the number of vectors to be summed, N. (Move the cursor to the region; delete the existing value, and enter the new value.) Enter the magnitude and direction of the vectors r_i and θ_i (in degrees). When entering values for r and θ, it is necessary to insert a comma between successive numbers.

In the left-hand plot region shown in Fig. 4.4, the individual vectors are displayed. In the right-hand plot region, the vectors are summed in the order entered. The origin is marked with an open rectangle; the resultant ends in a diamond. The magnitude and direction of the resultant are shown. (We have limited ourselves here to six vectors simply for reasons of space in the document and to keep the graph from getting too muddled. There is no inherent reason for the number.)

Possible data sets include:

$$N = 4; r = 1, 1, 1, 1; \theta = 0, 90, 180, 270;$$

$$N = 5; r = 1, 1, 1, 1, 1; \theta = 0, 90, 180, 270, 360;$$

$$N = 3; r = 1, 1, 1; \theta = 0, 120, 240;$$

$$N = 4; r = 1, 1, 1, 1; \theta = 0, 120, 240, 360.$$

The number of vectors to be summed. $N := 4$ $i := 1 .. N$ $rad \equiv 1$

Enter the values for r and θ.

$$r_i := \begin{array}{|c|} \hline 2 \\ \hline 3 \\ \hline 2.5 \\ \hline 3.5 \\ \hline \end{array} \qquad \theta_i := \begin{array}{|c|} \hline 40 \\ \hline 10 \\ \hline -60 \\ \hline 165 \\ \hline \end{array} \qquad deg \equiv \frac{\pi}{180} \cdot rad$$

$\theta_i := \theta_i \cdot deg$

The vector components.

$$x_i := r_i \cdot \cos[\theta_i] \qquad y_i := r_i \cdot \sin[\theta_i]$$

Select a reference point.   In this case the origin is selected.

$X_0 := 0 \qquad Y_0 := 0 \qquad\qquad j := 1 .. 2 \cdot N$

Vx and Vy represent a means to draw all the vectors starting from the reference point.

$$Vx_{2 \cdot i-1} := X_0 \qquad Vx_{2 \cdot i} := X_0 + x_i \qquad Vy_{2 \cdot i-1} := Y_0 \qquad Vy_{2 \cdot i} := Y_0 + y_i$$

X and Y represent a running sum of the vectors entered in r and θ above.

$$X_i := X_{i-1} + x_i \qquad Y_i := Y_{i-1} + y_i \qquad n := 0 .. N$$

To give the two graphs the same scale, calculate limits.

$xm := max(X) \qquad ym := max(Y) \qquad vxm := max(Vx) \qquad vym := max(Vy)$

$ul := if(xm > ym, xm, ym) \qquad\qquad ul' := if(vxm > vym, vxm, vym)$

$ul := if(ul > ul', ul, ul') + 1 \qquad ul = 6.737$

$xmn := min(X) \qquad ymn := min(Y) \qquad vxmn := min(Vx) \qquad vymn := min(Vy)$

$ll := if(xmn > ymn, ymn, xmn) \qquad\qquad ll' := if(vxmn > vymn, vymn, vxmn)$

$ll := if(ll < ll', ll, ll') - 1 \qquad ll = -4.381$

The resultant $k := 0 .. 1$ $RX_0 := X_0 \quad RY_0 := Y_0 \quad RX_1 := X_N \quad RY_1 := Y_N$

$$\delta RX := X_N - X_0 \qquad \delta RY := Y_N - Y_0 \qquad R := \sqrt{\delta RX^2 + \delta RY^2} \qquad \theta_R := angle(\delta RX, \delta RY)$$

Figure 4.3 VEC3, sum from two to six vectors. (See the next figure for the rest of the document.)

• •   Load VEC4, find the third vector so that the sum is zero (see Fig. 4.5).

Two vectors are selected at random. Specify the third vector, r_3, θ_3, which when added to the others yields a resultant of zero magnitude.

It is necessary to jump back and forth from the r_3, θ_3, regions to the end, where the plots are shown. ([Ctrl]home and [Ctrl]end are useful here.) The two random vectors are shown in the first plot; all three vectors are shown in the second plot. In the final plot, the three vectors are added and the resultant is shown (ending in a diamond). Observe the third vector,

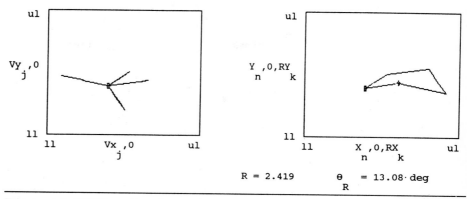

Figure 4.4 VEC3 *continued.*

which you control. Decide what length and angle are needed and jump to the beginning. Then change values and jump back to see how successful you were with your choices. Each time press [F9] to see the results.

To start over with a new set of random vectors, place the cursor in the r_1 region and press [F9].

4.2   Vector Products

Vectors can not only be added and subtracted, but also they can be multiplied. There are two types of products; one results in a scalar and one in a vector. They are known as scalar and vector products, or dot and cross products. The products can be specified in terms of polar or Cartesian coordinates.

The dot (scalar) product is defined as

$$\mathbf{a} \cdot \mathbf{b} = a \cdot b \cdot \cos(\theta_{ab})$$

or

$$\mathbf{a} \cdot \mathbf{b} = a_x \cdot b_x + a_y \cdot b_y + a_z \cdot b_z = \sum_i a_i \cdot b_i.$$

The cross (vector) product is defined as

$$\mathbf{a} \times \mathbf{b} = a \cdot b \cdot \sin(\theta_{ab})$$

or

$$\mathbf{a} \times \mathbf{b} = \begin{pmatrix} i & j & k \\ a_x & a_y & a_z \\ b_x & b_y & b_z \end{pmatrix}.$$

Two vectors are selected at random; magnitudes between 0 and 2, any angle.
The user should enter a magnitude and direction (degrees as measured
counterclockwise from the x-axis for vector C.

$rad \equiv 1$

$$deg \equiv \frac{\pi}{180} \cdot rad$$

$r_1 \equiv rnd(1.5) + 0.5$ $\theta_1 \equiv rnd(2 \cdot \pi)$ $r_2 \equiv rnd(1.5) + 0.5$ $\theta_2 \equiv rnd(2 \cdot \pi)$

Enter magnitude and direction of a third vector r[3 that will result in the
vector sum being zero.

$\theta_3 := 295 \cdot deg$ $r_3 := 1.7$

$r_1 = 0.502$ $\theta_1 = 69.592 \cdot deg$ $r_2 = 1.377$ $\theta_2 = 126.106 \cdot deg$

$X_0 := 0$ $Y_0 := 0$ $N := 3$ $i := 1 .. N$ $j := 1 .. 2 \cdot (N - 1)$

$x_i := r_i \cdot \cos\left[\theta_i\right]$ $y_i := r_i \cdot \sin\left[\theta_i\right]$ $Vx_{2 \cdot i-1} := X_0$ $Vy_{2 \cdot i-1} := Y_0$

$Vx_{2 \cdot i} := x_i + X_0$ $Vy_{2 \cdot i} := y_i + Y_0$ $k := 1 .. 2 \cdot N$

$\begin{bmatrix} X_i \\ Y_i \end{bmatrix} := \begin{bmatrix} X_{i-1} + x_i \\ Y_{i-1} + y_i \end{bmatrix}$ $Rx_0 := X_0$ $Rx_1 := X_N$ $Ry_0 := Y_0$ $Ry_i := Y_N$

$m := 0 .. 1$ $n := 0 .. N$ $\delta Rx := Rx_1 - Rx_0$

$\delta Ry := Ry_1 - Ry_0$ $\theta_R := angle(\delta Rx, \delta Ry)$

$$R := \sqrt{\delta Rx^2 + \delta Ry^2}$$

$R = 0.092$ $\theta_R = 27.521 \cdot deg$

$mVx := max(Vx)$ $mX := max(X)$ $mVy := max(Vy)$ $mY := max(Y)$

$ul1 := if(mVx > mVy, mVx, mVy)$ $ul2 := if(mX > mY, mX, mY)$

$ul := if(ul1 > ul2, ul1, ul2) + 0.2$ $ul = 1.783$

$nVx := min(Vx)$ $nX := min(X)$ $nVy := min(Vy)$ $nY := min(Y)$

$lll := if(nVx < nVy, nVx, nVy)$ $ll2 := if(nX < nY, nX, nY)$

$ll := if(lll < ll2, lll, ll2) - 0.2$ $ll = -1.741$

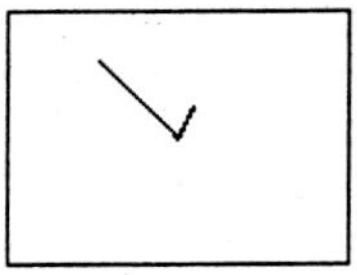

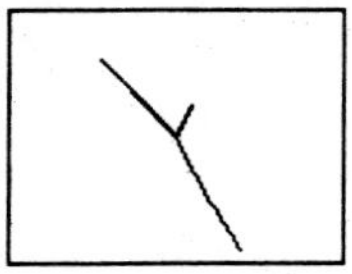

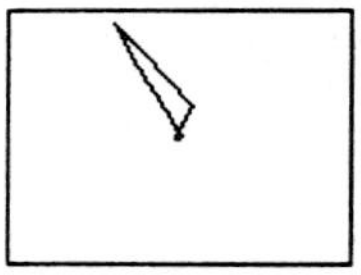

Figure 4.5 VEC4, find the third vector so that the sum is zero.

The angle θ_{ab} is the angle between the vectors **a** and **b**. $a \cdot \cos(\theta_{ab})$ is the component of vector a in the direction of b. Similarly, $b \cdot \cos(\theta_{ab})$ is the component of vector b in the direction of a. Thus the dot product $a \cdot b \cdot \cos(\theta_{ab})$ can be visualized either as the component of a in the direction of b times b or the component of b in the direction of a times a. The dot product is a maximum when the two vectors are aligned. The cross product, on the other hand, is zero when the vectors are aligned and is maximum when the vectors are at right angles.

The cross product as expressed in Cartesian coordinates includes the unit vectors, i, j, k, which have length 1 (unity; hence they are unit vectors) in the x, y, and z directions, respectively. The direction of the resultant is determined by constructing the resultant from the components. The expression for the cross product in polar coordinates does not include the direction. An additional piece of information, such as the right-hand rule, is needed to determine the direction.

It is important to note that the dot product is commutative

$$\mathbf{a} \cdot \mathbf{b} = \mathbf{b} \cdot \mathbf{a}$$

but the cross product is not. Changing the order changes the sign.

$$\mathbf{a} \times \mathbf{b} = -\mathbf{b} \times \mathbf{a}$$

Dot products occur in the formula for work, $F \cdot dl$; in Gauss's law, $E \cdot dA$ and $B \cdot dA$; in Faraday's law, $E \cdot dl$; and in Ampere's law, $B \cdot dl$. Cross products occur in the formulas for torque, $r \times F$; angular momentum, $r \times p$; force on a charged particle in a magnetic field, $q(v \times B)$; and in the Poynting vector (which describes energy flow in terms of electric and magnetic fields, $(1/\mu_o) \cdot (E \times B)$. These examples are noted to indicate that the dot and cross products are used frequently and are necessary tools in our description of the physical world.

• •   Load VEC5, vector products (see Figs. 4.6 and 4.7).

The dot and cross products are defined in two ways. In this example, the two vectors lie in the $x - y$ plane. Note how the vectors are specified in each case (polar and Cartesian). Observe that both forms of the dot and cross products are equal. Regarding the cross product, only the z-component is nonzero. Why is this?

Try several different values of a, b, θ_{ab}, and ϕ. Make sure you understand the role of each. If the r_i and s_i have values (1,1,1); (2,2,2), what is the value of the cross product? If the values are (1,0,0); (0,1,0), what is the cross product?

Now turn to the cross product in determinant form. We define the unit vectors, ii, jj, kk (we use double letters to avoid confusion with

Vector products

$$\text{rad} := 1$$

$$\text{deg} := \frac{\pi}{180} \cdot \text{rad}$$

Polar coordinate forms

dot product $dp(a,b,c) := |a| \cdot |b| \cdot \cos(c)$ a scalar

cross product $cp(a,b,c) := |a| \cdot |b| \cdot \sin(c)$ a vector

Rectangular coordinate forms

dot product $dp'(a,b) := a \cdot b$ Components of a and b must be specified.

cross product $cp'(a,b) := a \times b$ The cross is alt 8.

Example $a := 2$ $b := 3$ $\theta ab := 30 \cdot \text{deg}$ The angle between a & b.

Same vectors in component form.   Vectors in x-y plane.

$i := 0\ ..2$ $\phi := 45 \cdot \text{deg}$ ϕ is any arbitrary angle between vector a and the x-axis.

$$r_i := \begin{array}{|c|} \hline a \cdot \cos(\phi) \\ \hline a \cdot \sin(\phi) \\ \hline 0 \\ \hline \end{array} \qquad s_i := \begin{array}{|c|} \hline b \cdot \cos(\theta ab + \phi) \\ \hline b \cdot \sin(\theta ab + \phi) \\ \hline 0 \\ \hline \end{array}$$

Plot the two vectors. $x_0 := r_0$ $x_2 := s_0$ $y_0 := r_1$ $y_2 := s_1$

Plot limits. $ul := \text{if}(\max(x) > \max(y), \max(x), \max(y)) + 0.4$

$ll := \text{if}(\min(x) < \min(y), \min(x), \min(y)) - 0.4$

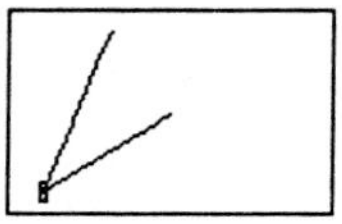

Evaluate the products $dp(a,b,\theta ab) = 5.196$ $dp'(r,s) = 5.196$

$cp(a,b,\theta ab) = 3$

$$cp'(r,s) = \begin{bmatrix} 0 \\ 0 \\ 3 \end{bmatrix}$$

It is not necessary to define functions. $r \cdot s = 5.196$ $r \times s = \begin{bmatrix} 0 \\ 0 \\ 3 \end{bmatrix}$

To appreciate the operations implied by these products, note that for the dot product

$r \cdot s$ is equivalent to $r_0 \cdot s_0 + r_1 \cdot s_1 + r_2 \cdot s_2 = 5.196$

where 0, 1, 2 refer to the x, y, and z components of the vectors.

Figure 4.6 VEC5, vector products. (See the next figure for the rest of the document.)

The individual terms of the cross product can also be expressed.

The cross product requires unit vectors and scalars within the determinant which Mathcad does not allow.

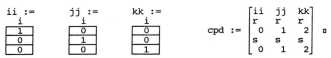

$$ii := \begin{bmatrix} i \\ \hline 1 \\ 0 \\ 0 \end{bmatrix} \qquad jj := \begin{bmatrix} i \\ \hline 0 \\ 1 \\ 0 \end{bmatrix} \qquad kk := \begin{bmatrix} i \\ \hline 0 \\ 0 \\ 1 \end{bmatrix} \qquad cpd := \begin{bmatrix} ii & jj & kk \\ r & r & r \\ 0 & 1 & 2 \\ s & s & s \\ 0 & 1 & 2 \end{bmatrix} \square$$

Write separate determinants for each component and multiply the magnitudes by the corresponding unit vector.

$$cpdx := \begin{bmatrix} 1 & 0 & 0 \\ r & r & r \\ 0 & 1 & 2 \\ s & s & s \\ 0 & 1 & 2 \end{bmatrix} \qquad cpdy := \begin{bmatrix} 0 & 1 & 0 \\ r & r & r \\ 0 & 1 & 2 \\ s & s & s \\ 0 & 1 & 2 \end{bmatrix} \qquad cpdz := \begin{bmatrix} 0 & 0 & 1 \\ r & r & r \\ 0 & 1 & 2 \\ s & s & s \\ 0 & 1 & 2 \end{bmatrix}$$

$$|cpdx| = 0 \qquad\qquad |cpdy| = 0 \qquad\qquad |cpdz| = 3$$

$$cpd := |cpdx| \cdot ii - |cpdy| \cdot jj + |cpdz| \cdot kk$$

$$cpd = \begin{bmatrix} 0 \\ 0 \\ 3 \end{bmatrix}$$

The place markers provide one means of showing the equivalence of the different definitions.

$$r \cdot s = 5.196 \qquad\qquad r \cdot s = 6 \cdot \cos(30 \cdot deg) \qquad\qquad r \cdot s = 1 \cdot a \cdot b \cdot \cos(\theta ab)$$

The two forms are equivalent.

As there is only one component in the cross product, the place marker can easily be used in this case as well. The two product forms are equivalent.

$$r \times s = \begin{bmatrix} 0 \\ 0 \\ 3 \end{bmatrix} \qquad r \times s = \begin{bmatrix} 0 \\ 0 \\ 6 \end{bmatrix} \cdot \sin(30 \cdot deg) \qquad r \times s = \begin{bmatrix} 0 \\ 0 \\ 1 \end{bmatrix} \cdot a \cdot b \cdot \sin(\theta ab)$$

Figure 4.7 VEC5 *continued.*

subscripts). We write each component of the cross product as a separate determinant. Whatever the values of r and s that were specified, they are computed and the final vector is assembled by summing the components.

Finally, the place markers permit displaying the results in a variety of forms.

Form the cross products of $ii \times jj$, $jj \times kk$, $kk \times ii$, and $ii \times kk$. What are the corresponding dot products?

Evaluate an example of $a \times b$ and $b \times a$ to verify that the cross product is not commutative.

• •   Load VEC6, rotating vectors (see Fig. 4.8).

Rotating vectors are often used to describe varying electric and magnetic fields. We observe in Fig. 4.8 a single rotation angle θ. Note that if

---

Vector rotation using complex notation.

The following equation includes 0, 1, π, e, i, plus and minus. That they all combine in such a simple way is marvellous.

$$e^{-i \cdot \pi} + 1 = 0$$

To appreciate this, we must explore the relation exp(i θ). It can be written

$$e^{i \cdot \theta} := \cos(\theta) + i \cdot \sin(\theta) \;\square$$

Observe that this is consistent by plotting the real and imaginary parts of the exponential.

$\theta := 0,.1 \;..2 \cdot \pi$

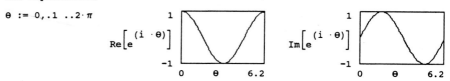

The trigonometric functions cosine and sine should remind you of x and y components. By varying θ, a vector with x-component cos(θ) and y- component sin(θ) is rotated. In the complex plane, complex numbers are plotted with the real part along the x-axis and the imaginary part along the y-axis. The effect of multiplying a vector by exp(i θ) is to rotate it through the angle θ.

Let A be any complex number; A can be represented as a vector in the complex plane by plotting the real part of A along the x-axis and the imaginary part along the y-axis. Multiplying A by exp(i ϕ) rotates the vector A through the angle ϕ. NOTE: the complex part of A, or any complex number in Mathcad, must be of the form numberi, with no multiplier between. If the number is one, it must be written explicity, 1i; the number one will disappear when the cursor leaves the region.

rad := 1

$$deg := \frac{\pi}{180} \cdot rad$$

$n := 0 \;..1$

$A_1 := 3 + i$

$lm := \left| A_1 \right| + 0.5$

$\phi := 30 \cdot deg$

$B := A \cdot e^{i \cdot \phi}$

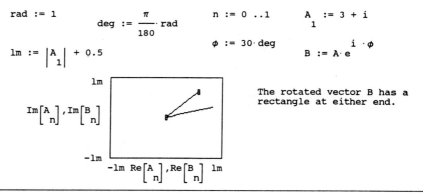

The rotated vector B has a rectangle at either end.

Figure 4.8 VEC6, rotating vectors.

θ were a function of time — ωt, for example — the rotation angle would be continuously increasing. We observe the projection and an example of the wave form generated as the projection varies in time.

As an alternate means of presentation, plots of the real and imaginary parts of $\exp(i\,\theta)$ show that they are indeed $\cos(\theta)$ and $\sin(\theta)$.

Below, we plot two vectors **A** and **B**. We specify the x and y components of **A** by writing them as real and imaginary parts of **A**. **B** is defined as **A** times a complex exponential term.

Let $\phi = 0$. Change the magnitudes and signs of the real and imaginary parts of **A**. Observe the plot region. Can you place **A** in any quadrant? Along any axis?

Let **A** = 1. Let ϕ equal $45°, 90°, 135°, 180°$. Observe vector **B** relative to **A**. Let **A** = $1 + i$. Let ϕ equal $45°$, $90°$, and $135°$.

Multiplying by a complex exponential term is equivalent to a rotation.

"Don't fight it son. Confess quickly. If you hold out too long you could jeopardize your credit rating."

Brazil

CHAPTER
5

Kinematics

The kinematic equations describe how things move. They do not indicate the sources of those motions; they do not answer questions as to why things move as they do. The relationships that we discuss do not have complex forms; yet the equations do not, in general, correspond to the typical intuition. They require experience. A number of exercises are included in this chapter to help you gain that experience and build intuition.

5.1 One-Dimensional Motion

The fundamental kinematic definitions are

$$a = \frac{dv}{dt} \qquad \text{and} \qquad v = \frac{dx}{dt}, \tag{5.1}$$

where a is acceleration, v is velocity, x is displacement, and t is time.

For the case of constant acceleration, the variables are position, velocity, and time; the parameters are initial position, initial velocity, and acceleration. The basic kinematic equations each include two of the variables.

For one-dimensional motion, these equations are

$$x = x_o + v_o t + \frac{1}{2}at^2 \qquad (x, t) \qquad (5.2)$$

$$v = v_o + at \qquad (v, t) \qquad (5.3)$$

$$v^2 - v_o^2 = 2a(x - x_o) \qquad (v, x). \qquad (5.4)$$

Only two of these equations are independent. That is, any two contain all the information that is available.

The variables x and v represent the position and velocity at time t. The values for initial position and velocity are taken at $t = 0$. If the initial velocity and the acceleration were both zero, $x = x_o$ for all time. If the acceleration were zero and v_o were nonzero, the position would increase linearly with time. The units for x, v, a, and t are L, L/T, L/T^2, and T.

• •   Obtain the (x, t) equation by substituting for v from the (v, t) equation into the (v, x) equation.

• •   Load KIN1, an examination of the (x, t) equation (see Fig. 5.1).

In this document, we examine the (x, t) kinematic equation $x = x_o + v_o t + (1/2)at^2$ and consider the role of the individual terms. Each term in the equation is defined separately ($x1(t)$, $x2(t)$, $x3(t)$), so each term can be examined independently from the others. Two sums are defined which incorporate two of the three terms from the (x, t) equation.

Process the document. Examine the graphs; look at each curve and explain to yourself why the curve has the form that it does. Look at the specific values for the parameters and connect those values to the plots. The plot types remain consistent from one plot to the next.

Try various values for x_o, v_o, and a. Before processing, predict the shapes of the curves. Try cases until your predictions are consistently correct. Change both the magnitude and sign of the parameters. Initially, change one value at a time. Try these values (they are in the form (x_o, v_o, a)): (3,0,0), (9,0,0), (–9,0,0), (0,1,0), (0,5,0), (2,5,0), (2,–5,0), (–2,–5,0), (0,0,1), (0,0,5), (0,0,–5), (0,5,5), (0,5,–5), (0,–5,–5).

Let $x_o = 0$. In the second plot region, interchange the order of $x3$ and $x23$, so that the order is $x2$, $x23$, $x3$, 0. Change the plot type to e. The bars then show the difference between $x2$ and $x23$ and between $x3$ and 0. Why are the corresponding bar lengths equal? What does each represent?

Exercises with kinematic curves.

Enter values for the parameters x.o, v.o, and a. There are values already assigned to these names. Run the document with these values, then try values of your own choosing.

$$x_o := 10 \qquad\qquad v_o := 9 \qquad\qquad a := -8 \qquad\qquad t := 0, .3\ ..3$$

The kinematic equation treated here is

$$x := x_o + v_o \cdot t + \frac{1}{2} \cdot a \cdot t^2 \quad \square$$

The terms of this equation are written separately so that the effect of each term can be observed independently from the others.

$$x1(t) := x_o \qquad\qquad x2(t) := v_o \cdot t \qquad\qquad x3(t) := \frac{1}{2} \cdot a \cdot t^2$$

Two sums are also specified.

$$x12(t) := x1(t) + x2(t)$$

$$x23(t) := x2(t) + x3(t)$$

The complete function is x(t).

$$x(t) := x1(t) + x2(t) + x3(t)$$

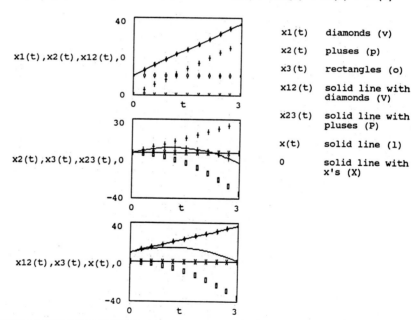

x1(t)	diamonds (v)
x2(t)	pluses (p)
x3(t)	rectangles (o)
x12(t)	solid line with diamonds (V)
x23(t)	solid line with pluses (P)
x(t)	solid line (l)
0	solid line with x's (X)

Figure 5.1 KIN1, an examination of the (x, t) equation.

● ● Load KIN2, pick values and match the given curve (see Fig. 5.2).

Now see how well you can estimate the parameters associated with a kinematic curve just by observing it. We consider the case of constant acceleration.

Two kinematic curves are plotted.   You have control over the parameters in
(h); the function f is fixed.   Select values for x.0, v.0, and a so that
the two curves coincide.   Use integer values for each.

$$x_0 := 0 \cdot m$$

$$v_0 := 0 \cdot \frac{m}{s}$$

$$a := 0 \cdot \frac{m}{s^2}$$

$$h[x_0, v_0, a, t] := x_0 + v_0 \cdot t + \frac{1}{2} \cdot a \cdot t^2$$

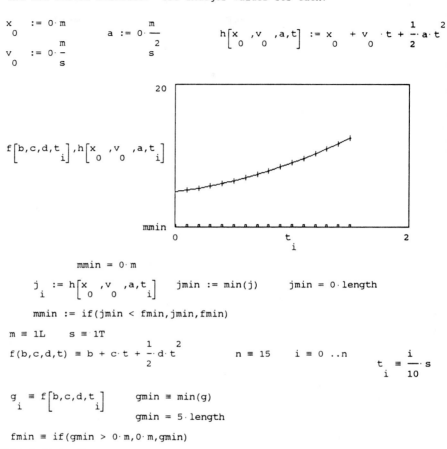

$$f[b,c,d,t_i], h[x_0, v_0, a, t_i]$$

mmin

mmin = 0 · m

$$j_i := h[x_0, v_0, a, t_i] \qquad jmin := min(j) \qquad jmin = 0 \cdot length$$

$$mmin := if(jmin < fmin, jmin, fmin)$$

$$m \equiv 1L \qquad s \equiv 1T$$

$$f(b,c,d,t) \equiv b + c \cdot t + \frac{1}{2} \cdot d \cdot t^2 \qquad n \equiv 15 \qquad i \equiv 0 \ .. \ n \qquad t_i \equiv \frac{i}{10} \cdot s$$

$$g_i \equiv f[b,c,d,t_i] \qquad gmin \equiv min(g)$$

$$gmin = 5 \cdot length$$

$$fmin \equiv if(gmin > 0 \cdot m, 0 \cdot m, gmin)$$

Figure 5.2 KIN2, pick values and match the given curve.

Two kinematic curves (x, t) are plotted. The functions f and h represent position as a function of time. For the function h, the stored values for x_o, v_o, and a are zero; the associated curve is the set of open rectangles. Examine the nonzero kinematic curve f; predict values for x_o, v_o, and a; enter the values and process. All values are integers. The challenge is to cause the two curves to overlap with the smallest number of tries. (1 to 2 tries are excellent, 3 very good, 4 good, 5 fair, 6 go back to KIN1 for more practice.) Repeat for KIN3 and KIN4.

KIN5 is a similar document except that the unknowns x_o, v_o, and a are determined by a random process. In KIN2, KIN3, and KIN4, the values are stored at the end of the document under the names b, c, and d rather than being determined randomly. Set values for your colleagues and let them try them. Have them set values for you. KIN5, of course, selects values at random, but because they are random, you have no control over the sequence in which the cases occur. To repeat KIN5 with new values, press [Esc], type pro, and press return. Place the cursor in the x_o region and press [F9]. Then enter integer values for x_o, v_o, and a; press [F9]. Change x_o, v_o, and a, each time pressing [F9], until a perfect overlap is achieved.

MathCAD's given-find procedure can be used in a general way to solve the kinematic equations. In these equations, there are three variables, position, velocity, and time (x, v, and t) and three parameters, initial position, initial velocity, and acceleration (x_o, v_o, and a). Only two of the three kinematic equations are independent; consequently, two unknowns can be determined.

> "OK. We're a hundred an' six miles from Chicago,
> we've got a full tank of gas, half a pack of cigarettes,
> it's dark, and we're wearing sunglasses."
>
> *The Blues Brothers*

• •   Load KIN6, solve the (x, t) and (v, t) kinematic equations with a given-find procedure (see Fig. 5.3).

Once the kinematic equations are understood, it is helpful to be able to solve them in a general way, a way that is adaptable to a wide variety of cases. Using MathCAD's given-find procedure, we can set up the equations and solve for them in a variety of circumstances. Be aware, though, that equation solvers tend to be a bit fussy; unfortunately, you cannot write down any equations in just any form whatever and expect a solution.

A general procedure is to specify values for all six quantities (variables and parameters). Enter the kinematic equations in a solve block and solve for the unknowns.

You cannot simply enter six values at random. Four of the values must correspond to some possible physical situation. Two values are guess values; it is prudent to choose these values as close to the true values as possible.

General kinematic equation solving routine.

Given x, x.o, v.o and a, solve for v and t.

x := 0   v := -10   t := 2

x_o := 10 v_o := 9   a := -8

$x'(t) := x_o + v_o \cdot t + \dfrac{1}{2} \cdot a \cdot t^2$ $v'(t) := v_o + a \cdot t$ t' := 0,.1 ..3

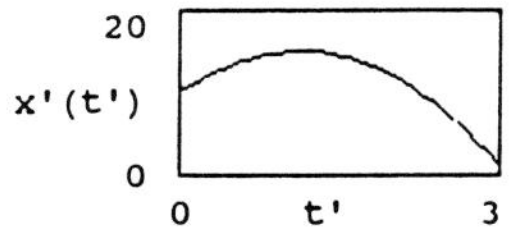

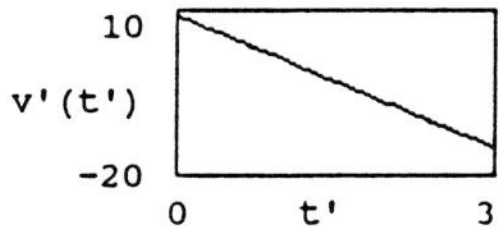

Be sure that the guess value for t is greater than the t where x is a max.

tt := 1 $tmx := root\left[\dfrac{d}{dtt} x'(tt), tt\right]$ tmx = 1.125

t = 2

given $x \approx x_o + v_o \cdot t + \dfrac{1}{2} \cdot a \cdot t^2$ $v \approx v_o + a \cdot t$ t > 0

$\begin{bmatrix} v \\ t \end{bmatrix}$:= find(v,t) x_o = 10

check v_o = 9

$x_o + v_o \cdot t + \dfrac{1}{2} \cdot a \cdot t^2$ = 0   x = 0   a = -8

$v_o + a \cdot t$ = -15.524   v = -15.524   t = 3.066

Figure 5.3 KIN6, solve the (x, t) and (v, t) kinematic equations with a given-find procedure.

Plotting x vs. t or v vs. t may help to indicate appropriate guess values. Keep the names of the functions plotted and the names of the variables distinct; note the use of primes.

If a curve has a maximum or a minimum, the guess value should be on that side of the maximum or minimum which will incline the solver toward the desired solution.

In this example, v and t are the unknowns. For the given parameter values and for $x = 0$ at some time t greater than zero, what are the values of velocity and time?

From the plot of x' vs. t', a value of t when $x = 0$ can be estimated. Using the root function with derivative to determine the time corresponding to the peak of the x vs. t curve, we have a reasonable sense of a guess value for t. A guess value of t less than tmx would not result in the desired solution. Try it.

It is always a good idea to check the results. Check by substituting the new values into the kinematic equations and comparing. Under certain circumstances the solver may return values as if they were solutions, yet the values are not the correct ones. Always think for yourself. Always ask if the results make sense.

Tabular Differences.   In experiments in which position is determined at regular intervals, using, for example, spark tape or photogates, velocity and acceleration information is readily extracted from the position data.

From a series of positions x_i and corresponding times t_i, average velocities over the time interval between measurements are given by

$$v_j = \frac{x_{j+1} - x_j}{t_{j+1} - t_j}. \tag{5.5}$$

Accelerations are similarly defined:

$$a_j = \frac{v_{j+1} - v_j}{t_{j+1} - t_j}. \tag{5.6}$$

If the time intervals between successive measurements are constant,

$$v_j = \frac{x_{j+1} - x_j}{\delta t} \tag{5.7}$$

and

$$a_k = \frac{v_{k+1} - v_k}{\delta t} = \frac{x_{k+2} - 2x_{k+1} + x_k}{\delta t^2}. \tag{5.8}$$

If the range of position measurements is for $i = 1, \ldots, n$, the range of j would be $1, \ldots, n-1$, and the range of k would be $1, \ldots, n-2$.

• •   Verify Eq. 5.8 for acceleration in terms of the various x-values.

• •   Load KIN7, tabular differences (see Fig. 5.4).

This example is performed using "perfect" data. Values for x_i are calculated from the (x, t) kinematic equation. Values for velocity and acceleration are determined according to the method of tabular differences.

Notice that the x-values are calculated using a familiar kinematic equation and the graphs look familiar. You should remind yourself that the velocity and acceleration values are determined in a completely different way than they were before.

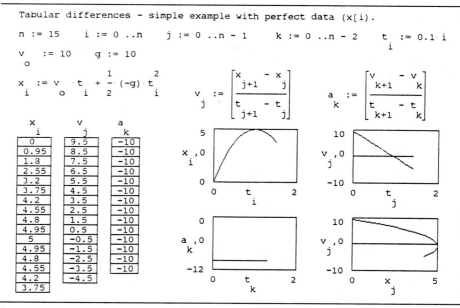

Figure 5.4 KIN7, tabular differences.

The x vs. t, v vs. t, and a vs. t graphs should all look familiar. Interpret the x vs. v curve.

Display the velocity and acceleration values in tabular form.

Calculate the acceleration values directly from the x information.

Calculate

$$J_l = \frac{a_{l+1} - a_l}{t_{l+1} - t_l} \qquad (5.9)$$

where $l = 0, \ldots, n - 3$. If the initial data were not perfect, what would one expect here?

5.2   Simple Numerical Methods

If, instead of knowing the position information and extracting velocity and acceleration information, you knew the accelerations, then the velocity and position information could be constructed.

Consider first a familiar kinematic example:

$$a = \frac{dv}{dt}.$$

If, as in the previous section, we consider finite intervals, then the acceleration is written

$$a = \frac{\delta v}{\delta t} \quad \text{and} \quad \delta v = a\delta t.$$

Substituting $\delta v = v_{i+1} - v_i$ into the previous relation, we obtain

$$v_{i+1} = v_i + a\delta t. \tag{5.10}$$

This is a difference equation for velocity. Similarly,

$$v = \frac{dx}{dt} \quad \text{becomes} \quad v = \frac{\delta x}{\delta t},$$

which yields

$$x_{i+1} = x_i + v_?\delta t.$$

A problem now presents itself (the subscript ? is intentional) which did not occur when we were thinking about constant acceleration. (Remember that constant acceleration is a special case, one that is easily handled analytically. Many interesting applications do not have constant acceleration.) For constant acceleration the difference equation for velocity is correct. However, the difference equation for position, x, cannot have a constant velocity if acceleration is constant.

The question is, if the velocity is not constant then what velocity value should be used? A number of algorithms can be used here. We consider only some basic algorithms. Our goal is not great numerical precision; our goal is to learn how to approach problems numerically and gain insight.

Recall the integration that we performed in Section 2.3. We considered several sums. One took the value at the beginning of the interval, one took the value at the end, and one took the average. The algorithms that we consider make similar choices. The Euler method assumes that the rate of change (for example, of x) is constant over the interval (for example, δt) and evaluates the rate of change (for example, velocity) at the beginning of the interval. The Euler algorithm then indicates

$$x_{i+1} = x_i + v_i\delta t. \tag{5.11}$$

If the acceleration were not constant, the velocity equation would be similar:

$$v_{i+1} = v_i + a_i\delta t. \tag{5.12}$$

If the points are uniformly spaced in time, the values are given by

$$t_{i+1} = t_i + \delta t$$

or more simply

$$t_i = t_0 + i\delta t.$$

For motion that is periodic, such as an orbit, a modification of this algorithm by Cromer is useful. The equations for t and v are the same. The equation for x becomes

$$x_{i+1} = x_i + v_{i+1}\delta t. \tag{5.13}$$

The velocity is taken at the end of the interval rather than at the beginning. This variation by Cromer is sometimes referred to as the last point approximation (as opposed to first point, in the case of the Euler algorithm). We will refer to this variation as the Euler-Cromer algorithm.

When greater precision is required, we list without explanation a third algorithm, the velocity form of the Verlet algorithm:

$$v_{i+1} = v_i + \frac{1}{2}(a_{i+1} + a_i)\delta t, \tag{5.14}$$

$$x_{i+1} = x_i + v_i\delta t + \frac{1}{2}a_i\delta t^2. \tag{5.15}$$

The velocity equation uses for acceleration an average between the accelerations at the beginning and end of the interval. The position equation should have a familiar ring to it.

The size of the accumulated error is related to the size of the time interval. Smaller time intervals, in general, increase accuracy but take longer to compute. There is no general-purpose ideal choice of time interval.

• •   For the case of constant acceleration, does the difference equation for velocity, as expressed in the Euler algorithm, yield results identical to the true values? Calculate a sequence of half a dozen terms and compare the two sets of values. Explain the result.

• •   Load KIN8, Euler algorithm for the case of free fall (see Fig. 5.5).

This is a direct application of the Euler algorithm to the case of constant-acceleration free fall. Values for time, velocity, and position are calculated using the Euler algorithm (t, v, x) and using familiar analytic expressions (T, V, X). The results are presented in tabular form. How do the velocities compare? What did you determine in the previous exercise?

```
Euler algorithm - case of constant acceleration - free fall.

n := 20      i := 0 ..n      t  := 0        v  := 0        x  := 0
                              0              0              0

g := 10     a := g          δt := .02     j := 0 ..10
```

The difference equations. In this case the equations are not coupled.
The v equation, for example, does not depend on x. They can be calculated
independently from each other as long as the v equation is before the x.

$$t_{i+1} := t_i + \delta t \qquad v_{i+1} := v_i + a\cdot\delta t \qquad x_{i+1} := x_i + v_i\cdot\delta t$$

Similar quantities determined by direct application of analytic expressions.

$$T_i := i\cdot\delta t \qquad V_i := v_0 + a\cdot T_i \qquad X_i := x_0 + v_0\cdot T_i + \frac{1}{2}\cdot a\cdot T_i^2$$

t_j	v_j	x_j	V_j	X_j
0	0	0	0	0
0.02	0.2	0	0.2	0.002
0.04	0.4	0.004	0.4	0.008
0.06	0.6	0.012	0.6	0.018
0.08	0.8	0.024	0.8	0.032
0.1	1	0.04	1	0.05
0.12	1.2	0.06	1.2	0.072
0.14	1.4	0.084	1.4	0.098
0.16	1.6	0.112	1.6	0.128
0.18	1.8	0.144	1.8	0.162
0.2	2	0.18	2	0.2

Figure 5.5 KIN8, Euler algorithm for the case of free fall.

Plot the positions as determined according to the two methods. Plot the difference between the two position calculations as a function of the number of iterations. Plot the percent difference between the two methods vs. i.

Determine the dependence of the difference between X_i and x_i as a function of the magnitude of δt. For a specific value of t (not i) determine the dependence. As δt changes, it may be necessary to change n in order to compare identical values of t. After each determination (four or five points) type the values into two tables so the results can be plotted when the sequence is completed. (For example, create two tables $Xdiff_k$ and $tint_k$. After each calculation, enter new values in these tables.) Plot $Xdiff$ vs. $tint$. If a functional form, $Xdiff \propto \delta t^n$, is assumed, what value of n is expressed by these values? The exponent characterizes a numerical method as nth order. What order is the Euler method?

What would happen if the velocity were taken at the end of the interval instead of at the beginning? Try it.

For constant positive acceleration, does taking the velocity at the beginning of the interval overestimate or underestimate the value for position? By taking the value at the end of the interval, is the velocity overestimated or underestimated? In this particular case, how would you modify the difference equation for x to give exact results?

Although we approached the algorithms with a particular kinematic example, the algorithms are general. Any equation of the form

$$\frac{dy}{dx} = f(x) \tag{5.16}$$

can be written in difference form:

$$y_{i+1} = y_i + f(x_i)\delta x. \tag{5.17}$$

5.3   **Two-Dimensional Motion**

The equations for describing two-dimensional motion are essentially the same as those for one dimension, except that there is a set of equations for each dimension:

$$x = x_o + v_{ox}t + \frac{1}{2}a_x t^2, \qquad y = y_o + v_{oy}t + \frac{1}{2}a_y t^2, \tag{5.18}$$

$$v_x = v_{ox} + a_x t, \qquad v_y = v_{oy} + a_y t, \tag{5.19}$$

$$v_x^2 - v_{ox}^2 = 2a_x(x - x_o), \qquad v_y^2 - v_{oy}^2 = 2a_y(y - y_o). \tag{5.20}$$

Velocity and direction must refer to the direction being described.

The two sets of equations appear to be independent, sharing only the variable time. Whether they are independent or not depends on how a_x and a_y are specified. For motion near the surface of the earth and with no air resistance, $a_x = 0$ and $a_y = -g$ (if plus is up). Under these circumstances, the x and y motions are decoupled and each set can be treated independently of the other. However, if the acceleration is velocity dependent, as it is when air resistance is included, the motions are not completely independent. In this case, both a_x and a_y would depend on both v_x and v_y, adding considerable complexity to the problem.

Projectile Motion.   Special cases of projectile motion are worked out in most general physics texts. The range, R — the horizontal distance that the projectile travels when initial and final heights are the same — the maximum height that the projectile reaches, and the general trajectory equation are three particularly useful forms. The initial velocity is v_o; the initial angle with respect to the horizontal is θ_o:

$$R = \frac{v_o^2 \sin(2\theta_o)}{g} \qquad \text{(range)}, \qquad (5.21)$$

$$h = \frac{v_o^2 \sin^2(\theta_o)}{2g} \qquad \text{(maximum height)}, \qquad (5.22)$$

$$y - y_o = \tan(\theta_o)(x - x_o) - \frac{g}{2v_o^2 \cos^2(\theta_o)}(x - x_o)^2 \qquad \text{(trajectory)}. \quad (5.23)$$

The following three MathCAD documents aid in visualizing two-dimensional motion. Each presents the information in a different way.

• • Load KIN9, visualizing projectile motion (1) (see Fig. 5.6).

```
Imagine a projectile fired horizontally in a uniform gravitational field.
The projectile will move in the plus x-direction; it will fall in the negative
y-direction.  The distance fallen in time t is  1/2 * a * t^2.

First, draw vectors which represent the distance fallen.  Space them
uniformly along the x-axis.  The code for y[(3*i+1) represents the distance
fallen.
```

$$n := 4 \qquad i := 0 \,..\,n \qquad g := 9.8 \qquad a := -g$$

$$x_0 := 0 \qquad y_0 := 0 \qquad \delta t := .5 \qquad t_i := i \cdot \delta t$$

$$v_{ox} := 2 \qquad \delta x := v_{ox} \cdot \delta t \qquad j := 0 \,..\, (3 \cdot n + 2) \qquad v_{oy} := 0$$

$$x_{3 \cdot i} := x_0 + i \cdot \delta x \qquad x_{3 \cdot i+1} := x_{3 \cdot i} \qquad x_{3 \cdot i+2} := x_{3 \cdot i}$$

$$y_{3 \cdot i} := 0 \qquad y_{3 \cdot i+1} := v_{oy} \cdot t_i + \frac{1}{2} \cdot a \cdot t_i^2 \qquad y_{3 \cdot i+2} := 0$$

$$xm := \max(x) \cdot 1.1 \qquad ym := \max(y) + (\max(y) - \min(y)) \cdot .1$$

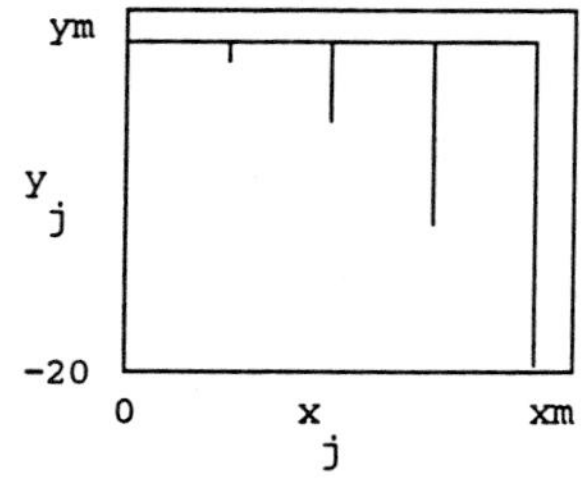

Note the rapidly increasing distance which is proportional to time squared.

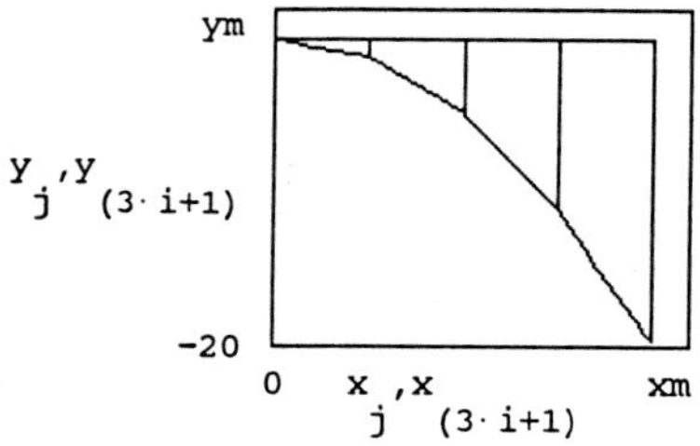

If we connect the tips of these y-displacements, the trajectory is roughly indicated.

Figure 5.6 KIN9, visualizing projectile motion (1).

A particle is fired horizontally in a uniform gravitational field. There is no air resistance; $a_x = 0$. In equal increments of time, the projectile moves equal distances in the x direction. The net y displacement is proportional to t^2. We see the net movement in the x and y directions. We see a rudimentary trajectory. We note that $(1/2)a_y t^2$ is the distance the particle deviates from the path taken were $a_y = 0$.

Try different values for v_{oy} and v_{ox}. (Let v_{ox} be positive.)

Let $n = 8$ and $\delta t = 0.25$. The motion is shown at more points; the trajectory is smoothed. Let v_{oy} take on the values 8, 15, and −8. Observe and interpret the changes.

Compare plots of y vs. t and y vs. x. How are they similar? How are they different?

● ●   How would the Euler method perform in evaluating the x motion? How would the Euler-Cromer method perform in the same case? Try them. Did you predict correctly?

● ●   Load KIN10, visualizing projectile motion (2) (see Fig. 5.7).

The basic motion here is the same as in KIN9: projectile motion with no air resistance. In this case, the total displacement vector is displayed rather than the x and y components of the motion. An additional plot of y velocity vs. x velocity is included. The vectors are displayed at equal time intervals.

How are these graphs related to those in KIN9? Why are the shapes of the vx vs. vy graph and the x vs. y graph so different?

Examine the curves for $\theta_o = \pm 15°$.

● ●   Load KIN11, visualizing projectile motion (3) (see Fig. 5.8).

The trajectory of a projectile is shown. At a series of points along the trajectory, the x and y components of the velocity vector are shown.

In this document and in the previous two, more complicated paths are drawn than are typical of the plots that have been discussed. A vector is created that contains not only the points on the trajectory (this example) but at each point takes a series of other steps. For example, in this case a step is taken in the x direction proportional in size to the x velocity, the same step is taken back to the trajectory point, a step is taken in the y direction proportional to the y velocity, the same step is taken back to the trajectory point, a step is taken to the next trajectory point, and the velocity vector process is repeated.

Velocity and displacement vectors associated with free fall.

$n := 4$ $i := 0 \; .. \; n$ $g := 9.8$ $\delta t := 0.1$ $a := -g$ $\delta vy := a \cdot \delta t$

$v_o := 5$ $\theta := 0 \cdot \dfrac{\pi}{180}$ $v_{ox} := v_o \cdot \cos(\theta)$ $v_{oy} := v_o \cdot \sin(\theta)$

$vx_{3 \cdot i} := 0$ $vx_{3 \cdot i+1} := v_{ox}$ $vx_{3 \cdot i+2} := 0$

$vy_{3 \cdot i} := 0$ $vy_{3 \cdot i+1} := v_{oy} + i \cdot \delta vy$ $vy_{3 \cdot i+2} := 0$

$j := 0 \; .. \; 3 \cdot n + 2$ $vxm := v_{ox} \cdot 1.1$ $xtra := (\max(vy) - \min(vy)) \cdot .1$

$vymx := \max(vy) + xtra$ $vymn := \min(vy) - xtra$

$x_{3 \cdot i} := 0$ $x_{3 \cdot i+1} := v_{ox} \cdot i \cdot \delta t$ $x_{3 \cdot i+2} := 0$

$y_{3 \cdot i} := 0$ $y_{3 \cdot i+1} := v_{oy} \cdot i \cdot \delta t + \dfrac{1}{2} \cdot a \cdot (i \cdot \delta t)^2$ $y_{3 \cdot i+2} := 0$

The velocity vectors at equal time intervals.

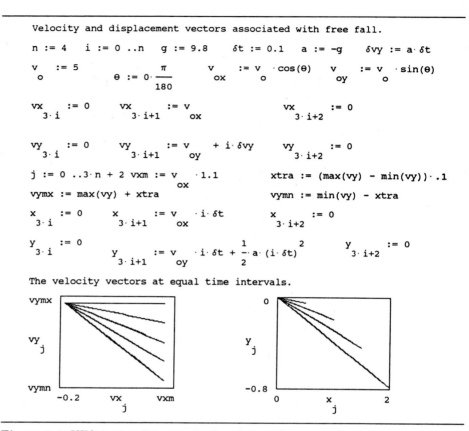

Figure 5.7 KIN10, visualizing projectile motion (2).

Try a number of different values for the initial velocity and angle as well as for a_x and a_y. For example, let $a_y = -g$ and $a_x = \pm g/2$.

• • Load KIN12, properties of a projectile (see Figs. 5.9 and 5.10).

Properties of projectile motion, range, maximum height, and time of flight can be determined in a variety of ways. It is always useful to be able to approach a problem in more than one way.

If the initial and final heights are the same, the range equation can be used. The equations for *xmax* and *ymax* are the range and height equations. Time is specified in terms of the range and the *x* velocity.

Whether or not the initial and final heights are equal, the kinematic equations may be solved directly to determine range, time of flight, and height.

The trajectory equation can be used in a variety of ways. Here we use it to determine the maximum height and in combination with the root-derivative process to find the x and y coordinates of the maximum of the trajectory.

If, instead of v_o, θ_o being known, the known values include v_o and $xmax$, find θ_o. Or given θ_o and $xmax$, find v_o. Will there be more

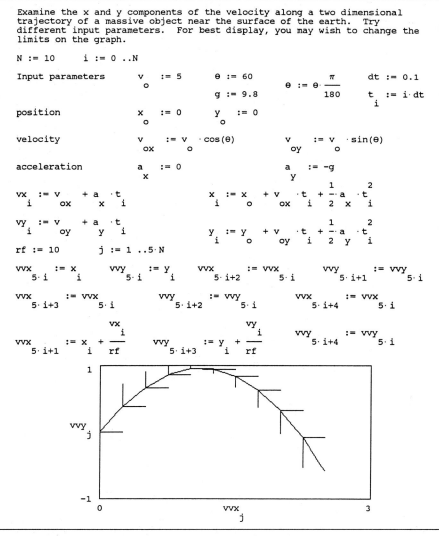

Figure 5.8 KIN11, visualizing projectile motion (3).

than one solution? Plot your results. Given *xmax* and *ymax*, what are v_o and θ_o?

Projectile properties. The time, range, and maximum height are determined in more than one way.

parameters $v_o := 15$ $\theta_o := 30 \cdot deg$ $g := 9.81$ $rad \equiv 1$

$$a := -g$$

$$deg \equiv \frac{\pi}{180} \cdot rad$$

$$v_{ox} := v_o \cdot \cos\left[\theta_o\right]$$ $$v_{oy} := v_o \cdot \sin\left[\theta_o\right]$$

$$v_{ox} = 12.99$$ $$v_{oy} = 7.5$$

If the initial and final heights are the same, the range and height equations can be used. First, the range.

$$x_{max}\left[\theta_o\right] := \left[\frac{\left[v_o\right]^2 \cdot \sin\left[2 \cdot \theta_o\right]}{g}\right]$$ $$x_{max}\left[\theta_o\right] = 19.863$$

The time to cover the range. $$t := \frac{x_{max}\left[\theta_o\right]}{v_{ox}}$$ $$t = 1.529$$

The maximum height. $$y_{max} := \frac{v_o^2 \cdot \sin\left[\theta_o\right]^2}{2 \cdot g}$$ $$y_{max} = 2.867$$

The time and range using a given-find solve block. This method is more general and is not restricted to final and inital heights being equal.

$x := 2$ $y := 0$ $t := 2$

Given $x \approx v_{ox} \cdot t$ $y \approx v_{oy} \cdot t + \frac{1}{2} \cdot a \cdot t^2$ $y \approx 0$

$$\begin{bmatrix} x \\ t \end{bmatrix} := Find(x,t)$$ $x = 19.863$ $t = 1.529$

If the initial and final heights are the same, the maximum height can be determined from the trajectory equation, knowing that maximum height occurs at x/2.

$$y\left[x,\theta_o\right] := x \cdot \tan\left[\theta_o\right] - \frac{g}{2 \cdot v_o^2 \cdot \cos\left[\theta_o\right]^2} \cdot x^2$$ $$y\left[\frac{x}{2},\theta_o\right] = 2.867$$

Figure 5.9 KIN12, properties of a projectile. (See the next figure for the rest of the document.)

Or by using the (y,t) equation and evaluating at t/2.

$$y'(t) := v_{oy} \cdot t + \frac{1}{2} \cdot a \cdot t^2 \qquad\qquad y'\left[\frac{t}{2}\right] = 2.867$$

In general the maximum height can be determined by finding the x-value of the maximum using the root-derivative procedure and then find y-value.

$$x\_ymx := root\left[\frac{d}{dx} y\left[x,\theta_o\right],x\right] \qquad x\_ymx = 9.931 \qquad y\left[x\_ymx,\theta_o\right] = 2.867$$

If the final y-value is zero, the time could be determined using the root function.

$$t := 1.5 \qquad trng := root\left[v_{oy} \cdot t + \frac{1}{2} \cdot a \cdot t^2, t\right] \qquad trng = 1.529$$

A plot of the trajectory is always useful.

$$step := \frac{x_{max}\left[\theta_o\right]}{20} \qquad x := 0, step \,.. \, x_{max}\left[\theta_o\right]$$

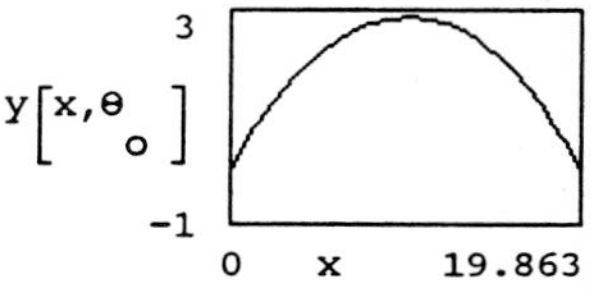

$$y\left[x,\theta_o\right]$$

Figure 5.10 KIN12 *continued.*

Plot the speed ($\sqrt{v_x^2 + v_y^2}$) vs. x, vs. y, and vs. t. (Use three separate plot regions.)

• • A basketball player shoots at a basket (height 10 feet) 20 feet away (horizontally); the ball leaves his hands at a height of seven feet above the floor. (Use $g = 32$.) Let $v_o = 30$. Find the angle θ_o which results in a basket without help from backboard or rim. Solve the problem in two ways using a given-find solve block. First use the two equations $x(x_o, v_o, \theta_o, t)$ and $v(v_o, \theta_o, t)$ and then use the trajectory equation. For a given v_o, is there more than one solution? Plot the trajectories associated with the solution(s). What is the minimum v_o able to reach the basket? What is the corresponding θ_o? Is there a maximum v_o?

• • Load KIN13, trajectory envelope (see Fig. 5.11).

Two trajectories are plotted. The trajectories start from the same point and have the same initial velocity. Only the initial angle is different.

Let $\theta2$ successively take on the values $70°, 60°,$ and $55°$. Note the x location of the intersection as $\theta2$ approaches $\theta1$. Also note that any point on the $50°$ trajectory is reached by two trajectories (the $50°$ trajectory and one other). In general, any point is reached by two trajectories. The two cases correspond to the two solutions of the quadratic equation for the trajectory.

Let $\theta 1 = 45°$, $\theta 2 = 50°$, and $\theta 3 = 70°$ and process. The outer edges of the trajectories begin to define a boundary that separates accessible and inaccessible regions. Recall, in the previous problem (about the basketball), the question about minimum velocity. If the origin in this problem is the point where the ball leaves the shooter's hands, and if the basket were beyond the boundary, then the choice of angle would be irrelevant — the basket is beyond reach.

Let $\theta 1 = 45°$, $\theta 2 = 60°$, and $\theta 3° = 135°$. Add to the plot, the envelope, a second $y(\theta', x, c', x_o')$ having defined the following values $\theta' = \pi/4$ and $v_o' = v_o\sqrt{2}$ so that $c' = 2c$ and $x_o' = -c$. Process.

For a given v_o, plot range as a function of angle and maximum height as a function of angle in the same plot region. For a given v_o, what is the ratio of maximum possible range to maximum possible height?

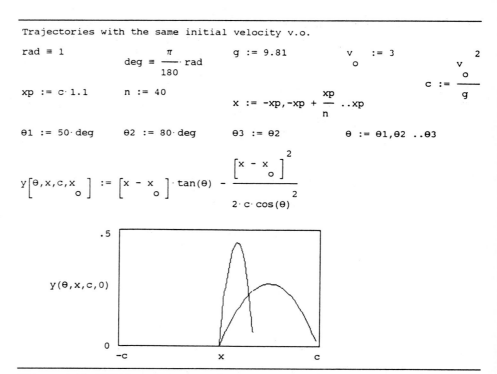

Trajectories with the same initial velocity v.o.

$\text{rad} \equiv 1$

$$\deg \equiv \frac{\pi}{180} \cdot \text{rad}$$

$g := 9.81$

$v_o := 3$

$$c := \frac{v_o^2}{g}$$

$xp := c \cdot 1.1$ $n := 40$

$$x := -xp, -xp + \frac{xp}{n} \, .. xp$$

$\theta 1 := 50 \cdot \deg$ $\theta 2 := 80 \cdot \deg$ $\theta 3 := \theta 2$ $\theta := \theta 1, \theta 2 \, .. \theta 3$

$$y\left[\theta, x, c, x_o\right] := \left[x - x_o\right] \cdot \tan(\theta) - \frac{\left[x - x_o\right]^2}{2 \cdot c \cdot \cos(\theta)^2}$$

Figure 5.11 KIN13, trajectory envelope.

The boundary, an enveloping parabola, is not a trajectory. It is a line that divides the accessible from the inaccessible regions. However, being a parabola, it could be a trajectory, and in the above case it is described as one. What are the properties of the edge trajectory as compared with the trajectories issuing from the origin?

One remaining feature of trajectories is path length. This is not the range but the actual distance the projectile covers during its flight. If a length of arc along the trajectory is

$$ds = \sqrt{dx^2 + dy^2}, \qquad (5.24)$$

then

$$\text{pathlength} = \int ds = \int \sqrt{1 + \left(\frac{dy}{dx}\right)^2} \, dx. \qquad (5.25)$$

MathCAD will perform the integration numerically, freeing us from any worry about how to integrate the specific function.

• • Load KIN14, path length (see Fig. 5.12).

We define the range and the trajectory. The range will be used as the upper limit of integration; x goes from zero to its maximum range. We write the trajectory as a function. In the integrand, we let MathCAD perform the differentiation as well as carry out the integration. This is slow; reduce the number of angle values for a quicker response.

PathLen(θ_o) is a user-defined function. A series of values can be specified for θ_o. The integration will be performed in accordance with those values. We plot the path length as a function of angle (this plot is *not* a trajectory). The root function in combination with the derivative is used to find the maximum of the curve. The maximum path length does not occur at 45°.

Plot together the trajectories for maximum range and maximum path length.

Adapt the process to the case where the initial and final heights are not the same. In the basketball problem above, what is the path length?

Determine the time of flight as a function of angle and plot results; let initial and final heights be the same. One way to do this is to define a function in terms of a given-find solve block. For example,

$$\text{given} \qquad v_o \cdot \sin(\theta) \cdot t + 1/2 \cdot a \cdot t^2 \approx 0, \qquad T(\theta) := \text{find}(t).$$

Then, defining a sequence of angles θ_i, one can plot $T(\theta_i)$ vs. θ_i.

Determine the path length of a trajectory.

$$v_o := 10 \qquad \theta_o := 85 \cdot deg \qquad g := 9.81 \qquad a := -g \qquad rad \equiv 1$$
$$deg \equiv \frac{\pi}{180} \cdot rad$$

$$x_{max}[\theta_o] := \left[\frac{v_o^2 \cdot \sin[2 \cdot \theta_o]}{g} \right]$$

$$y[x, \theta_o] := x \cdot \tan[\theta_o] - \frac{g}{2 \cdot v_o^2 \cdot \cos[\theta_o]^2} \cdot x^2$$

The path length of the trajectory.

$$PathLen[\theta_o] := \int_0^{x_{max}[\theta_o]} \sqrt{1 + \left[\frac{d}{dx} y[x, \theta_o] \right]^2} \, dx \qquad \theta_o := .1, .3 \ ..1.5$$

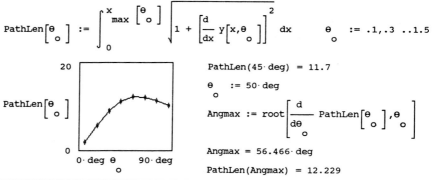

PathLen(45 · deg) = 11.7

$$\theta_o := 50 \cdot deg$$

$$Angmax := root\left[\frac{d}{d\theta_o} PathLen[\theta_o], \theta_o \right]$$

Angmax = 56.466 · deg

PathLen(Angmax) = 12.229

Figure 5.12 KIN14, path length.

5.3.1 *Uniform Circular Motion*

In the term "uniform circular motion", the word "uniform" means that the speed is constant. The acceleration associated with this motion results in the change of direction, not the change in magnitude, of the velocity vector.

• • Load KIN15, centripetal acceleration in uniform circular motion (see Fig. 5.13).

For an object to move in a circle, there must be a force toward the center. If there is force, there is acceleration, and if there is acceleration, there is change in velocity.

Acceleration is given by

$$a = \frac{\delta v}{\delta t} = \frac{v_2 - v_1}{\delta t}.$$

The diagram will help us to visualize the change in velocity, $v_2 - v_1$.

Uniform circular motion - centripetal acceleration.

We show the displacement vectors, the velocity vectors, and the velocity difference. Watch the change in direction of δv as $\delta\theta$ decreases.

$r := 1$ $\quad \theta := 0,.1 ..2\cdot\pi$ $\quad v := 0.5$

$\Phi := \delta\theta + \dfrac{\pi}{2}$

$x_0 := 0$ $\quad x_1 := r$ $\quad x_2 := r$

$y_0 := 0$ $\quad y_1 := 0$ $\quad y_2 := v$ $\quad X(\theta) := r\cdot\cos(\theta)$ $\quad Y(\theta) := r\cdot\sin(\theta)$

$xx_0 := 0$ $\quad xx_1 := r\cdot\cos(\delta\theta)$ $\quad xx_2 := xx_1 + v\cdot\cos(\Phi)$ $\quad xx_3 := xx_2$

$yy_0 := 0$ $\quad yy_1 := r\cdot\sin(\delta\theta)$ $\quad yy_2 := yy_1 + v\cdot\sin(\Phi)$ $\quad yy_3 := yy_2 - v$

$xx_4 := xx_1$ $\quad yy_4 := yy_1$ $\quad i := 0 ..2$ $\quad j := 0 ..4$ $\quad lm := 1.15$

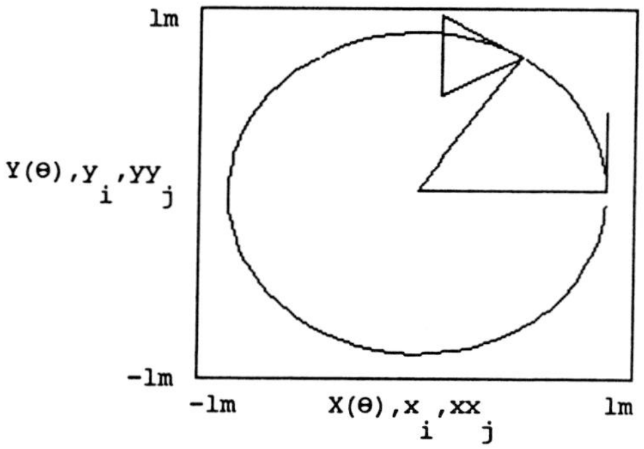

$\delta\theta \equiv 1$

Figure 5.13 KIN15, centripetal acceleration in uniform circular motion.

We want to observe the change in velocity as the object moves about the circle. To do this, we draw two displacement vectors, two radii separated by the angle $\delta\theta$. At the tips of the displacement vectors, we draw the corresponding velocity vectors. The lengths of these vectors are equal because the speed is constant. The angles between the velocity vectors are the same as those between the displacement vectors, the radii. To find the difference in velocity, we subtract the first velocity vector from the second.

We visualize the change by drawing the first velocity vector at the tip of the second. The change in velocity, δv, is represented by the line from the tangent point of the second velocity vector to the lower tip of the first vector (in its new position).

In Fig. 5.13, identify the two displacement vectors, the two velocity vectors, and the velocity difference vector.

Let the angle between successive observations of the particle in motion, $\delta\theta$, equal 1, 0.8, 0.6, 0.4, 0.2 radians successively. Observe that δv approaches the radial direction as $\delta\theta$ becomes smaller. Also note that the velocity and displacement "triangles" are similar and that at small angles the area bounded by the two radii and the short section of arc length does approximate a triangle quite well.

The velocity triangle, and the "triangle" made up of the two radii and adjoining arc δs are similar:

$$\frac{\delta v}{v} = \frac{\delta s}{r} \quad \text{or} \quad \delta v = \frac{v}{r}\delta s.$$

This yields

$$a = \frac{\delta v}{\delta t} = \frac{v}{r}\frac{\delta s}{\delta t} = \frac{v^2}{r}. \tag{5.26}$$

There are many applications involving circular motion. Keep this acceleration in mind.

> he's got all that speed and that power underneath him,
> he's comin' into the stretch and the pressure's on him
> — and he knows. Just feels, when to let go, and how much.
> So he's got everything working for him — timing, touch.
> It's a great feeling boy, it's a really great feeling
> when you're right, and you know you're right.
>
> *The Hustler*

C H A P T E R
6

Mechanics

There are five main areas in physics: mechanics, electricity and magnetism, thermodynamics and statistical mechanics, relativity, and quantum mechanics. The first three are referred to as classical theories, the last two modern. Each of these theories is rich in explanatory and predictive power. They are the cornerstones of modern science.

6.1   Newton's Laws

Mechanics can be summarized in Newton's three laws. His first law, the law of inertia, was known and expressed by Descartes (for whom Cartesian coordinates are named). Newton expressed his first law in words almost identical to those used by Descartes but did not credit their source. The first law states that a body at rest remains at rest and a body in motion continues to move with constant velocity unless acted on by an external force. The reference frame in which we observe this motion must be an inertial reference frame. An accelerating frame is not an inertial reference frame. (An object at rest in an inertial frame would not appear to be at rest or moving with constant velocity in an accelerating frame.)

Newton's second law, relating force and momentum, can be expressed as

$$\mathbf{F} = \frac{d\mathbf{p}}{dt}. \tag{6.1}$$

This law is elegant, simple, and powerful; it is applicable over a vast range.

The third law is a statement of action-reaction force pairs. It states that whenever a body, A, exerts a force on another body, B, then B exerts a force on A of equal magnitude and opposite direction.

Newton's law of universal gravitation,

$$\mathbf{F} = -\frac{Gm_1 m_2}{r_{12}^2}\hat{r}, \tag{6.2}$$

describes the force between two massive objects, m_1 and m_2, separated by a distance r_{12}. In this equation, we have a statement describing an interaction between all massive objects in the universe. We will apply Newton's laws in a variety of circumstances.

Newton's second law is a vector equation. Force and momentum are vectors. In addition, force, as used here, means the net applied external force, the sum of the external forces. So for each component, the law can be expressed as

$$\sum F_{\text{ext}} = \frac{dp}{dt}. \tag{6.3}$$

If the mass of the object remains constant, we have

$$\frac{dp}{dt} = \frac{d}{dt}(mv) = m\frac{dv}{dt} = ma$$

and

$$\sum F_{\text{ext}} = ma. \tag{6.4}$$

Remember that the latter expression is a special case and not a general statement of Newton's second law.

6.2   Constant Force Applications

A general procedure for applying Newton's second law is (1) isolate the body to which the law is to be applied, (2) indicate all applicable external forces, (3) apply the law for each component, and (4) solve for the unknowns.

MathCAD's given-find solve block is frequently useful for such problems. Once the equations are available, as in step 3, where the equations for each component have been expressed, MathCAD can be used to find the solution. Frequently, we can look at a set of solutions rather than a single solution. This feature permits us to obtain a more complete picture of the behavior of a system.

In find statements for more than one unknown, all quantities must have the same units. For example, in the case where we might wish to solve for both tension and acceleration, a solution is not possible if units are included. Either remove the units (the better idea) or temporarily adjust the units of one to match those of the other. An example is included in the following discussion.

6.2.1 Atwood Machine

The Atwood machine is frequently used to demonstrate how to apply Newton's second law. Here we consider the machine to consist of two masses suspended by massless string from a massless, frictionless pulley. Each body experiences two external forces, the gravitational force (weight) and the tension in the string supporting it. We first consider the case where the two masses m_1 and m_2 are known; we solve for the acceleration experienced by the masses and for the tension in the string.

• • Load MECH1, Atwood machine (I) (see Fig. 6.1).

We define the fundamental and derived units, provide values for the parameters, and enter guess values for the unknowns.

As noted earlier, there is a complication involving units and the solve block. Every term in the equations must have the same units. Each quantity in the find statement must have the same units. If they do not, the simplest thing is to delete all references to units. They are included here to show the kinds of adjustments necessary if units are to be maintained.

In this case, we wish to solve for acceleration, a, and tension, T, which do not have the same units. An adjustment must be made if we are to use MathCAD's solve block. The quantity a does not appear in the solve block. Instead, we define a quantity b which has the magnitude of a and the units of T. In the equations, we express a in terms of b. In the find statement, we solve for b (and T). After solving for b, we express a in terms of b, removing the unit that had been inserted.

In this document, there are two solve blocks. In the first, we solve for acceleration and tension, assuming the values for the masses are known. (The general structure can, of course, be applied to many similar problems.) In the second solve block, we solve for the masses, accepting as true the original values for acceleration and tension. The values must,

Atwood machine 1.

$m \equiv 1L \quad s \equiv 1T \quad kg \equiv 1M$

$N \equiv kg \cdot m \cdot s^{-2} \qquad g := 9.8 \cdot m \cdot s^{-2}$

$m1 := 1 \cdot kg \quad m2 := 0.98 \cdot kg \qquad \text{Guess values}$

$a := 1 \cdot m \cdot s^{-2} \qquad T := 1 \cdot N$

$b := a \cdot kg$

Given

$$m1 \cdot g - T \approx m1 \cdot \frac{b}{kg}$$

$$T - m2 \cdot g \approx m2 \cdot \frac{b}{kg} \qquad \begin{bmatrix} b \\ T \end{bmatrix} := Find(b,T)$$

$a := b \cdot kg^{-1}$

$a = 0.099 \cdot m \cdot s^{-2}$

check

$m1 \cdot g - T = 0.099 \cdot N \qquad m1 \cdot a = 0.099 \cdot N \qquad T = 9.701 \cdot N$

$T - m2 \cdot g = 0.097 \cdot N \qquad m2 \cdot a = 0.097 \cdot N$

$a := 1 \cdot m \cdot s^{-2} \qquad T := 1 \cdot N$

Given $\quad m1 \cdot g - T \approx m1 \cdot a$

$$T - m2 \cdot g \approx m2 \cdot a \qquad \begin{bmatrix} m1 \\ m2 \end{bmatrix} := Find(m1,m2)$$

$m1 = 0.114 \cdot mass$

$m2 = 0.093 \cdot mass$

Figure 6.1 MECH1, Atwood machine (I).

of course, correspond to a possible physical situation if there is to be a meaningful solution.

Examine the acceleration and tension as a function of the mass m_2. Change the find statement in the first solve block to a functional form. Let

$$f(m_2) := find(b, T).$$

Then add the statements

$$i := 0 \ldots 20 \qquad \text{and} \qquad m_{2i} := 0.5 \cdot kg + 0.05 \cdot i \cdot kg.$$

Plot $f(m_{2i})_0$ vs. m_{2i} and $f(m_{2i})_1$ vs. m_{2i}. The subscripts 0 and 1 refer to the zeroth and first quantities of the find statement, b and T.

As m_2 goes from $m_1 - 0.5\,kg$ to $m_1 + 0.5\,kg$, why is the acceleration curve not symmetric about zero? Why does the tension curve continue to increase smoothly even as the acceleration changes sign? What is the tension when the acceleration is zero?

Change the find statement to $f(m_1, m_2) := find(b, T)$. Add the statements $M := 2 \cdot kg$ and $m_{1i} := M - m_{2i}$. Plot $f(m_{1i}, m_{2i})_0$ vs. m_{2i}. Similarly, plot the tension curve. Now is the acceleration curve symmetric? Why now? Explain the form of the tension curve.

If it were desired to change the masses in such a way that the acceleration is to be increased while T remains constant, how would the ratio of the masses change? Use the second solve block to examine this question. What is the upper limit on a? Find the ratio m_2/m_1 for a series of accelerations. For a given acceleration, find the ratio m_2/m_1 for a series of tensions. We could, for example, write $f(T) := \text{find}(m_1, m_2)$ and add the statements

$$i := 0 \ldots 5 \qquad T_i := 0.5 \cdot N + 0.2 \cdot i \cdot N \qquad \text{and} \qquad r_i := \frac{f(T_i)_0}{f(T_i)_1}.$$

Plot $f(T_i)_0, f(T_i)_1$ vs. T_i and r_i vs. T_i. Repeat the calculation with $a := 3 \cdot m \cdot s^{-2}$. Be sure all regions process.

• •   A mass m_1 is suspended from a pulley over the edge of a vertical cliff. The supporting string is attached to a unit that moves horizontally with constant speed, v_0. The pulley is a distance y above the plane in which the unit moves. The horizontal distance of the unit from the pulley is x (see Fig. 6.2).

Show that the tension in the string is given by

$$T(v, y, x) := m_1 \cdot g + \frac{m_1 \cdot y^2 \cdot v^2}{(x^2 + y^2)^{3/2}}.$$

For $v = 0$, what is the value of T? Explain.

For $y = 0$ and $v \neq 0$, what is the value of T? Explain.

For $y > 0$ and $x >> y$, explain the limiting value of T.

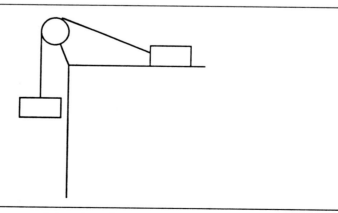

Figure 6.2 Mass, m_1, suspended; unit on horizontal surface moves at constant velocity.

Let $m_1 := 1$ and $y := 1$. Define T as above. Let $x := 0, 0.25\ldots5.25$. Let $v := 1, 3\ldots9$. Plot T vs. x. In the plot region, let the limits of x be 0 and 5 (why not 5.25?); let the lower limit of T be zero.

Which curve corresponds to which velocity? Explain the shape qualitatively.

Let $v := 1$ and $y := 1.5$. Plot T vs. x. In the plot region use the same limits for x, 0 and 5. Let the limits for T be 9.75 and 10.75. Change the dimensions of the plot region to (20,16). (A large vertical scale is needed to distinguish the curves.) Identify specific curves with y values. Explain the pattern qualitatively.

6.2.2 *Friction*

The above procedure can be adapted to a wide range of problems with interconnected masses, accelerations, and tensions. The range of problems amenable to solution can be extended even further by including friction.
The frictional force is expressed in an empirical relation,

$$F_f \leq \mu N, \qquad (6.5)$$

where μ is the coefficient of friction and N is the normal force. The $\leq$ sign reminds us that the frictional force need not be constant, even though μ and N are. This resistive force depends on applied forces and cannot have a magnitude greater than the net applied force.
One procedural approach to solving problems involving frictional forces is first to solve the problem without the frictional force term and determine the sign of the acceleration. Then solve the problem again, including the friction term with its sign so as to resist the motion implied by the first solution. If both solutions yield accelerations in the same direction, then the solution including the frictional force term will yield the correct acceleration and tension. If the signs of the acceleration from the two solutions are opposite, then the acceleration is zero.

• •   Load MECH2, motion of a mass on a plane with friction (I) (see Fig. 6.3).

Mass m_1 rests on a plane tilted at $\theta = 30°$ with respect to the horizontal. A string runs from m_1 over a pulley at the top of the plane to m_2, which is freely suspended (see Fig. 6.3). Assume that the string and pulley are massless and the pulley is frictionless. The coefficient of friction between m_1 and the plane is μ.

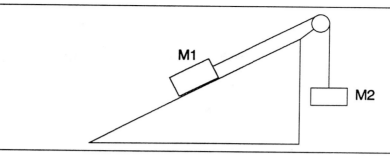

Figure 6.3 One mass on a plane, one suspended.

In the document (see Fig. 6.4), there are two given-find solve blocks. In the first, the friction term is omitted from the calculation; in the second,

One mass on slanted plane; one mass suspended; friction.   rad ≡ 1

Parameters $g := 9.8$

$\theta := 30 \cdot deg$ $m1 := 5 \cdot 10^{0}$ $m2 := 1 \cdot 10^{0}$ $\mu := 0.2$ $deg \equiv \dfrac{\pi}{180} \cdot rad$

Guess values $a := 1$ $T := 1$

First consider problem without friction to get direction of motion.

given $m1 \cdot g \cdot \sin(\theta) - T \approx m1 \cdot a$ $T - m2 \cdot g \approx m2 \cdot a$ $\begin{bmatrix} a \\ T \end{bmatrix} := find(a,T)$

$a = 2.45$ $T = 12.25$ $sgna := if(a > 0, 1, -1)$ $sgna = 1$

Repeat calculation including friction. $N := m1 \cdot g \cdot \cos(\theta)$ $F_f := \mu \cdot N$

given $m1 \cdot g \cdot \sin(\theta) - sgna \cdot F_f - T \approx m1 \cdot a$

          $T - m2 \cdot g \approx m2 \cdot a$ $\begin{bmatrix} a \\ T \end{bmatrix} := find(a,T)$

The frictional force, as expressed in F.f is a maximum. If the sign of `a' in each calculation is not the same, then the acceleration is zero.

$a := if \left[\dfrac{a}{|a|} \approx sgna, a, 0 \right]$ $T := if(a \approx 0, m2 \cdot g, T)$ $a = 1.035$

                                                                    $T = 10.835$

Examine sizes of various terms and check results.

$m1 \cdot g \cdot \sin(\theta) = 24.5$ $sgna \cdot F_f = 8.487$ $T = 10.835$

$m1 \cdot g \cdot \sin(\theta) - sgna \cdot F_f - T = 5.177$ $m1 \cdot a = 5.177$

$m2 \cdot g = 9.8$ $T - m2 \cdot g = 1.035$ $m2 \cdot a = 1.035$

Figure 6.4 MECH2, motion of a mass on a plane with friction (1).

it is included. For this problem, we take the masses and angle as given and solve for acceleration and tension.

Because the sign of the acceleration is needed, we define *sgna* (sign of a). This term is ±1, depending on whether the acceleration is greater or less than zero. *Sgna* is used in the second solve block to assure the proper sign for the frictional term. Locate the equation in the second solve block containing *sgna*. Examine the cases for ±a and convince yourself that the force acts in the desired direction, that is, that it is a resistive and not a driving force. The if statement for a is disabled, initially.

Observe the behavior of the two mass system. Let $\mu = 0$, $m_1 = 5$, and $m_2 = 1$; process. Check the value for the acceleration in each solve block. Note the value of *sgna*. Let m_1 keep its present value and let $m_2 = 10$. Process. Check the values of a and *sgna*.

Let $m_1 = 5$ and $m_2 = 1$. Let $\mu = 0.2$, 0.3, and 0.4. Note the values for a in each case. If the a's have opposite signs, it means that the frictional force is helping to drive rather than to resist the motion — this is an unphysical condition.

Enable the if statement for a and process. Unless the a's have the same sign, no motion is possible or allowed.

Let $\mu = 0$. Let $m_1 = 3.3$ and $m_2 = 1$. Observe the value of a. Now let $m_1 = 6.6$ and process. If $m_1 = 2 \times 6.6$, predict how a will change. Test your prediction. Let m_1 take on the values 5×10^n where $n = 1, \ldots, 5$. Explain the sequence of a values. Let $m_1 = 5$. Let $m_2 = 10^n$ where $n = 0, -1, \ldots, -3$. Explain the sequence of values of a.

• •   Examine the acceleration and tension as a function of μ. In MECH2, in the second solve block, replace the find statement with

$$f(\mu) := \text{find}(a, T).$$

Following the find statement, add the statements

$$n := 6 \quad i := 0 \ldots n \quad \mu_i := 0.2 + 0.03 \cdot i$$

$$a_i := f(\mu_i)_0 \quad T_i := f(\mu_i)_1.$$

Plot a_i vs. μ_i and T_i vs. μ_i. Explain the curves.

• •   Load MECH3, motion of a mass on a plane with friction (2) (see Fig. 6.5).

This problem is the same as that treated in MECH2. We examine the acceleration and tension as a function of m_1. However, in this case, we consider a sequence of values for m_1. The first solve block, written in functional form, is used to generate a sequence of values for the sign of the acceleration, *sgna*. The values are shown using the transpose. Normally, vectors are column vectors and appear as such in tabular form. The transpose interchanges rows and columns; the result is a row vector. Clearly, only a modest number of values can be observed in one screen.

The second solve block is also written in functional form. The arguments are the mass and the sign of the acceleration. Names without subscripts are used in the find statement. The acceleration and tension are then determined for a series of values of m (and the associated *sgna* values).

```
Mass, m1, on slanted plane; mass, m2, suspended; friction.      rad ≡ 1

Parameters
                                                                        π
                                                          deg ≡ ─── rad
m1 := 5      m2 := 1    g := 9.8     θ := 30·deg     μ := 0.22         180

Guess values    a := 1    T := 1

First consider problem without friction to get direction of motion.

given     m1·g·sin(θ) - T ≈ m1·a     T - m2·g ≈ m2·a     f'(m1) := find(a,T)


n := 9     i := 0 ..n     m1'  := 5 - i·.5     sgna  := if⎡f'⎡m1'⎤   > 0,1,-1⎤
                             i                     i    ⎢  ⎣   i⎦           ⎥
                                                        ⎣          0        ⎦

sgnaᵀ = (1  1  1  1  1  1  -1  -1  -1  -1)          sgnaa := 1

Repeat calculation including friction.

given     m1·g·sin(θ) - sgnaa·μ·m1·g·cos(θ) - T ≈ m1·a

          T - m2·g ≈ m2·a          f(m1,sgnaa) := find(a,T)

a  := f⎡m1' ,sgna ⎤    T  := f⎡m1' ,sgna ⎤
 i    ⎣   i      i⎦ 0    i    ⎣   i      i⎦ 1
```

The friction force, as expressed in F.f is a maximum. If the sign of `a` in each calculation is not the same, then the acceleration is zero.

```
                ⎡  a                ⎤     T  := if⎡a  ≈ 0,m2·g,T ⎤
                ⎢   i               ⎥      i      ⎣ i           i⎦
a  := if⎢ ─── ≈ sgna ,a ,0 ⎥
 i      ⎢ |a |      i   i i⎥
        ⎣ | i|              ⎦
```

a_i	m1'_i
0.894	5
0.7	4.5
0.466	4
0.181	3.5
0	3
0	2.5
0	2
0	1.5
-1.516	1
-4.278	0.5

Figure 6.5 MECH3, motion of a mass on a plane with friction (2).

By requiring that the accelerations have the same sign with or without friction, in order that motion occur, we can plot the acceleration and tension, no matter whether the acceleration is positive, zero, or negative.

Interpret the graphs. Why does T take on the values that it does?

Plot the force of friction vs. m'_{1i}.

For each of the following cases, predict how the graphs will change. Let $\theta = 40°$. Let values for (μ, m'_{1i}) equal $(0.3, 10 - i)$, $(1, 10 - i)$, $(0.6, 10 - i)$.

6.3   Velocity-Dependent Forces

The frictional force of a block sliding on a plane was treated as having no dependence on velocity. An object moving through a fluid, however, experiences a force which is dependent on velocity.

It is common practice to consider two distinct cases of velocity dependence. The two cases can be characterized as viscosity dependent and density dependent. Viscosity is associated with the resistance of fluid layers moving past each other. The coefficient of viscosity, η, is the ratio of shear stress, (force per area, F / A) and shear strain per time (change in velocity per thickness, $\delta v / th$):

$$\eta = \frac{F / A}{\delta v / th} = \frac{F\, th}{\delta v A}. \tag{6.6}$$

• •   Use dimensional analysis to find a dimensionless group that will indicate the interdependence of a velocity-dependent force and viscosity. Perform the analysis to find the relationship using the coefficient of viscosity, radius, velocity, and force. Arrange the final result so that $F \propto$ other variables.

• •   Similarly, find the dimensionless group for a velocity-dependent force where the variables are density, radius, velocity, and force. Arrange the final result so that $F \propto$ other variables.

The viscosity dimensional analysis example yields

$$F_\eta \propto \eta r v \qquad \text{or} \qquad F_\eta = C_\eta \eta r v,$$

which, in effect, is Stokes's law:

$$F_s = 6\pi \eta r v. \tag{6.7}$$

The second example yields

$$F_\rho \propto \rho r^2 v^2 \quad \text{or} \quad F_\rho = C_\rho \rho r^2 v^2.$$

The latter is commonly expressed as

$$F_D = \frac{1}{2} C \rho A v^2 \tag{6.8}$$

where A is the cross-sectional area (generalized from r^2 in the dimensional analysis) and C is a dimensionless drag coefficient. The net drag would be the sum of each of these contributions:

$$F_D = C_\eta \eta r v + C_\rho \rho r^2 v^2.$$

At low velocities, the viscosity term dominates; at high velocities, the density term dominates. The velocity at which these two are equal is given by

$$v = \frac{C_\eta \eta}{C_\rho \rho} \frac{1}{r}.$$

For air at standard temperature and pressure, we have

$$\eta \approx 1.8 \times 10^{-5} \frac{\text{Ns}}{\text{m}^2} \quad \text{and} \quad \rho \approx 1.2 \frac{\text{kg}}{\text{m}^3}.$$

The coefficients are roughly

$$C_\eta \approx 17 \quad \text{and} \quad C_\rho \approx 0.73.$$

Thus the velocity at which the forces are equal is given by

$$v_{\rho\eta} = 3.5 \cdot 10^{-4} \cdot \frac{1}{r}.$$

Examine the functionality by performing the following exercises.

• • Plot F_{ρ_i} and F_{η_i} vs. v_i for $i := 0 \ldots 20$ and $v_i := 0.0035 \cdot (i+1)$. Plot the two curves together. Plot both linear and log-log views.

• • Plot F_{ρ_i}/F_{η_i} vs. v_i for $v_i := 0.001 \cdot 2^i$ on a log-log scale.

• • Plot $v_{\rho\eta}$ vs. r as r goes from one micron to one meter.

• • Let $t_{\rho\eta}$ be the time for a particle in free fall, experiencing no resistance, to reach velocity $v_{\rho\eta}$. Plot $t_{\rho\eta}$ vs. r. (Let the initial velocity of the particle be zero.)

• • Plot the free fall time to reach a velocity where the ratio of F_ρ/F_η is 10:1.

These calculations help to indicate where the various contributions are relevant. For many of the velocity ranges encountered in these problems, the neglect of the F_η term is clearly justified.

The region in which the viscosity term is dominant is still of some interest. The equation of motion for a particle falling in a viscous medium is

$$mg - C_\eta \eta r v = ma = m\frac{dv}{dt}. \tag{6.9}$$

As the velocity increases, the resistive force increases. When the gravitational and resistive forces are equal and opposite, the net force is zero, the acceleration is zero, and the object has reached its terminal velocity:

$$v_t := \frac{mg}{C_\eta \eta r}. \tag{6.10}$$

The equation of motion can be rewritten as

$$\frac{dv}{dt} = g\left(1 - \frac{v}{v_t}\right). \tag{6.11}$$

The solution to this equation is

$$v = v_t(1 - e^{-t/\tau}) \tag{6.12}$$

where $\tau = v_t/g$. The constant τ is a characteristic time called the time constant. In this time, if the initial acceleration were maintained, the terminal velocity would be reached.

If the driving force is removed, the velocity decays to zero with the same time constant as did growth toward the terminal velocity. If the mg term is zero, we have

$$\frac{dv}{dt} = \frac{-g}{v_t}v = -v/\tau. \tag{6.13}$$

•• Verify that this form follows if $mg = 0$.

The solution is

$$v = v_t\, e^{-t/\tau}. \tag{6.14}$$

•• Verify that this solution satisfies the previous equation.

•• Plot five time constants of growth toward terminal velocity and five returning toward zero. One way to do this would be by defining the function

$$v(t) = \text{if}\left[t < 5\tau,\; v_t \cdot [1 - e^{-t/\tau}],\; v_t \cdot e^{-(t-5\cdot\tau)/\tau}\right]$$

and letting t go from 0 to 10τ. Note that the velocity is always positive. The object does not return to its initial position.

• • For the motion just described, plot position vs. time.

• • Integrate the function $v(t)$ over time. First integrate from 0 to 5τ, then from 5τ to 10τ. Compare with the plot from the previous exercise.

6.3.1 Sky Diving

In an actual sky diving exercise, with multiple divers, one diver collided with another, hitting her in the head and knocking her unconscious. The group leader saw the woman falling limply, went into a dive, caught up with her, pulled her ripcord, and proceeded to parachute safely to earth himself. The woman sustained only relatively minor injuries (minor at least in comparison with what could have happened).

Let us model this situation approximately. As a simplification, the problem is treated as one dimensional rather than two dimensional. In this case adding the second dimension would only increase complexity and not generate any additional insight.

Before performing the rescue, we need to consider free fall with a retarding force proportional to v^2. The equation of motion is

$$mg - kv^2 = m\frac{dv}{dt} \tag{6.15}$$

where

$$k = \frac{1}{2}C_\rho\rho A.$$

As the velocity increases, kv^2 increases until $kv^2 = mg$ and $dv/dt = 0$. The terminal velocity is given by

$$v_t = \sqrt{\frac{mg}{k}}. \tag{6.16}$$

• • Verify the above equation for the terminal velocity.

• • We now want to make sure that we appreciate the interdependence of the various terms in the expression for terminal velocity. We can do this by looking at sequences of parameter values and looking at the families of related curves.

Examine the relationship between terminal velocity, mass, and cross-sectional area. The initial setup for this problem is in MECH4. Load the document and define two ranges: $A := 0.3 \cdot m^2, 0.5 \cdot m^2 \ldots 1.1\, m^2$ and $m_1 := 20 \cdot kg, 40 \cdot kg \ldots 100 \cdot kg$. Plot $v_t(m_1, A)$ vs. A; set the upper limit of the abscissa at $1 \cdot m^2$.

Define $v'_t(A, m_1) := v_t(m_1, A)$. Plot $v'_t(A, m_1)$ vs. m_1. Set the lower limit on the abscissa to $21 \cdot kg$.

For the plot of $v_t(m_1, A)$ vs. A, which curve corresponds to the largest value for m_1? Which curve corresponds to the smallest? For the plot of $v'_t(A, m_1)$ vs. m_1, which curve corresponds to the largest value for A? Which curve corresponds to the smallest?

The equation of motion

$$\frac{dv}{dt} = g - \frac{k}{m}v^2 \tag{6.17}$$

can be rewritten with finite sized elements as

$$\Delta v \simeq (g - \frac{k}{m}v^2)\,\Delta t \tag{6.18}$$

where Δv and Δt are small incremental changes in velocity and time. We express the velocity difference, Δv (in the document δv), as

$$\Delta v = v_{i+1} - v_i \qquad \text{or} \qquad v_{i+1} = v_i + \Delta v_i. \tag{6.19}$$

The change in velocity for a given v_i is then

$$\Delta v_i = (g - \frac{k}{m}v_i^2) \cdot \delta t. \tag{6.20}$$

This pair of equations (6.19 and 6.20) can then be used to determine the velocity over time. One vector specifies the incremental changes; the other keeps track of the sequence of values. (It is irrelevant whether you specify the acceleration or the change in velocity. They are related by a constant factor; $a_i = v_i\,\delta t$.)

These two equations are iterated simultaneously. Once the values for v_i are known, values of x can be determined, for example, by iterating the equation $x_{i+1} = x_i + v_i\delta t$.

When equations are to be iterated simultaneously, as the v and δv equations are, the left-hand sides and right-hand sides of the equations are grouped together in one-column matrices.

[Alt]M, the create matrix command, brings to the command line a request for the size of the matrix. Enter the number of equations (in the above case, two) and press return. The form

appears. At each place marker, type the left-hand side of the coupled equations — in this case, δv_{i+1} and v_{i+1}. Use the tab button to move between place markers.

When the entries are complete, type the assignment equality, the colon. The cursor then moves to the right-hand side. Press [Alt]M again.

The value entered when the matrix for the left-hand side was created is still present. Press return and enter the corresponding right-hand sides of the equations.

The equations are then ready to be processed. Be aware that as the equations are processed, values calculated on one pass through the equations cannot be used during that pass. For example, in the pass through the equations that calculates a_2 and v_2, the value a_2 cannot be used in the calculation of v_2. The same quantities used to calculate δv_2 would need to be expressed explicitly.

Before continuing with the sky diving problem, it is interesting to note that the equation of motion with a drag force proportional to v^2 does have an analytic solution. The derivation is beyond the scope of this text, but the results can be used and compared with our iterated solution.

For the differential equation

$$m\frac{dv}{dt} = mg - kv^2, \tag{6.21}$$

the velocity is given by

$$v = v_t \tan h\left(K + \sqrt{\frac{K + kg}{m}}t\right), \tag{6.22}$$

and the position is given by

$$x = \frac{m}{k}\ln\left(\cos h(K + \sqrt{\frac{K + kg}{m}}t - \ln(\cos h(K))\right) \tag{6.23}$$

where

$$K = \tan h^{-1}(\frac{v_0}{v_t}) \quad \text{and} \quad v_t = \sqrt{\frac{mg}{k}}.$$

In these expressions, we use the sign convention where plus means down.

• •   Determine the units of each of the following: k, kg/m, $\sqrt{mg/k}$, and K.

• •   Write the position and velocity equations for the case of zero initial velocity. Start with the K equation.

• •   Explore equations 6.18, 6.19, and 6.20. Pick values for m, k, and v_0. Calculate and show v_t before entering a value for v_0. Define expressions for position and velocity and plot both vs. time. Do not use a value of v_0 greater than v_t.

Try different values of m and k. Try some values of v_0 that are negative; remember plus is down; also remember the limitations on the magnitude of v_0. For comparison, include plots of the position and velocity vs. time for similar initial conditions but with zero air resistance.

• • Load MECH4, resisted fall: analytic and numeric solutions (see Fig. 6.6).

We want to calculate the velocity and position of a sky diver starting a fall with zero initial velocity. A density-dependent velocity squared resistive force is included. We approach the problem in two ways. First, we iterate the difference equations as described. Then, we calculate the values using the analytical expressions above.

Plots of velocity vs. time and elevation vs. time are shown for both cases. The last two plots show the difference in velocity and difference in position as determined by the two approaches. The velocity difference, which is never large (the maximum difference is on the order of 1 mi/hr), goes to zero as time increases. The position difference is also relatively small and becomes constant as the velocity difference goes to zero.

Considering the modest algorithm, the agreement between the analytic and numeric approaches is quite good. By examining a problem in different ways and arriving at the same result, you gain confidence in each approach.

• • The agreement that we note is dependent on a particular set of parameters. Vary the area and the mass. Does the shape of the velocity or elevation curve change noticeably? Does the quality of the match between the two approaches change?

Now, let's go back to the rescue. Recall that the drag force is

$$F_D = \frac{1}{2}C\rho Av^2.$$

For the speeds encountered in this problem, we ignore the viscosity-related force. We will assume that C is constant, does not depend on the orientation of the sky diver, and is the same for each diver. A is the cross-sectional area presented to the air flow. For an unconscious person, A would be reduced from the maximum. In the notation below, primes refer to maximum values. Variable names ending in 1 refer to the injured person; those ending in 2 refer to the pursuer.

Let

$A1' = 0.65\text{m}^2$	$A1 = 0.5\text{m}^2$	(injured cross section)
$A2' = 0.7\text{m}^2$	$A2 = 0.35\text{m}^2$	(dive).

A comparison of resisted fall using an analytic and a numerical approach.

units $m := 1L$ $s := 1T$ $kg := 1M$

$$N := kg \cdot m \cdot s^{-2} \qquad ft := \frac{1}{3.28} \cdot m$$

$mi := 5280 \cdot ft \qquad hr := 3600 \cdot s$

parameters

$m1 := 55 \cdot kg \qquad m2 := 75 \cdot kg \qquad g := 9.81 \cdot \dfrac{m}{s^2} \qquad Alt := 5000 \cdot ft$

$m1 \cdot g = 539.55 \cdot N$

$C := 0.7 \qquad \rho := 1.2 \cdot kg \cdot m^{-3} \qquad A := .75 \cdot m^2 \qquad k := \dfrac{1}{2} \cdot C \cdot \rho \cdot A$

$$v_t := \sqrt{\frac{m1 \cdot g}{k}} \qquad v_t = 92.556 \cdot \frac{mi}{hr} \qquad k = 0.315 \cdot \frac{kg}{m}$$

Iterative solution

$N' := 300 \qquad i := 0 \,..\, N' \qquad \delta t := 0.05 \cdot s \qquad t_i := i \cdot \delta t$

$an_0 := g \qquad vn_0 := 0 \cdot m \cdot s^{-1} \qquad xn_0 := 0 \cdot m$

$$\begin{bmatrix} an_{i+1} \\ vn_{i+1} \\ xn_{i+1} \end{bmatrix} := \begin{bmatrix} \left[g - \left[\dfrac{k}{m1} \right] \cdot vn_i^2 \right] \\ vn_i + an_i \cdot \delta t \\ xn_i + vn_i \cdot \delta t \end{bmatrix}$$

Analytic solution

$$kgm := \sqrt{\frac{k \cdot g}{m1}} \qquad va_i := v_t \cdot \tanh\left[kgm \cdot t_i \right] \qquad xa_i := \frac{m1}{k} \cdot \ln\left[\cosh\left[kgm \cdot t_i \right] \right]$$

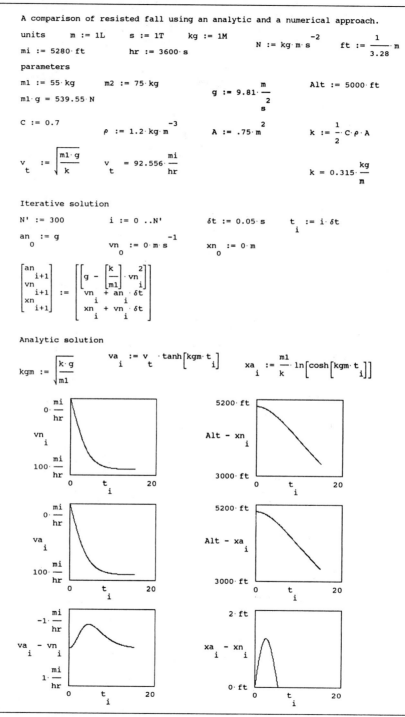

Figure 6.6 MECH4, resisted fall: analytic and numeric solutions.

This information is sufficient to define the k's and terminal velocities for the cases necessary for the problem.

In somewhat arbitrary fashion, the scenario is outlined as

$t = 0$ (diver 1 jumps)

$t = 1$ (collision occurs and diver 2 jumps)

$t = 3$ (diver 2 observes that diver 1 is injured)

$t = 3.5$ (diver 2 goes into dive).

As A changes, so does k. To incorporate those changes automatically, write k as a function of time. An if statement can select between cases. For times before the collision occurs, diver 1 has normal cross section $A1'$. For times before the dive begins, diver 2 has normal cross section $A2'$. These conditions are expressed in the equations

$$k1(t_i) := \text{if}(t_i < t_{\text{coll}}, k1', k1)$$

and

$$k2(t_i) := \text{if}(t_i < t_{\text{div}}, k2', k2).$$

• •   Load MECH5, skydive: the pursuit (see Figs. 6.7 and 6.8).

Observe the sequence of areas, coefficients k, and terminal velocities. Note the numerical values of the terminal velocities. There are two sets of iterated equations; the $k(t)$ in each takes into account the sequence of events described. In this example, we do not model any additional changes in the motion which occur after the pursuer has reached the injured party.

For the pursuer to maintain his own safety, he has to reach the injured woman before she reaches an elevation of 1000 ft. If $A1 := 0.4 \cdot m^2$, could diver 2 still reach diver 1?

What value would t_{div} have, in order that the sky divers meet at an elevation of 1000 ft? Use the original values of A.

The δv curve is telling. For the first second, you see the free fall of diver 1. During the next 2.5 seconds, the velocity of diver 2 is increasing slightly faster than that of diver 1. At $t = 3.5\text{s}$, diver 2 goes into a dive by reducing his cross section. The velocity difference increases more rapidly but is not linear.

The δX curve is also informative. What is the maximum distance of separation? At what time did this maximum separation occur? At what time does diver 2 reach diver 1?

When diver 2 reaches diver 1, what is the elevation?

In a sky diving exercise, one of the sky divers was knocked unconscious. The leader of the group saw the person falling limply, went into a dive, caught up with the unconscious person, pulled that person's rip cord, and then proceeded to parachute safely to ground himself.

Let us see if we can model this problem, approximately. We refer to the falling person as 1 and the instructor as 2.

units $m := 1L$ $s := 1T$ $kg := 1M$

$$mi := 5280 \cdot ft \qquad hr := 3600 \cdot s \qquad\qquad N := kg \cdot m \cdot s^{-2} \qquad ft := \frac{1}{3.28} \cdot m$$

parameters

$$m1 := 65 \cdot kg \qquad\qquad m2 := 80 \cdot kg$$

$$g := 9.81 \cdot \frac{m}{s^2} \qquad C := 0.7$$

$$m1 \cdot g = 637.65 \cdot N \qquad m2 \cdot g = 784.8 \cdot N \qquad\qquad \rho := 1.2 \cdot kg \cdot m^{-3}$$

Cross- sections: A1' normal, A1 injured, A2' normal, A2 dive.

$$A1' := .65 \cdot m^2 \qquad A1 := .5 \cdot m^2 \qquad A2' := .75 \cdot m^2 \qquad A2 := .35 \cdot m^2$$

$$k1' := \frac{1}{2} \cdot C \cdot \rho \cdot A1' \qquad k2' := \frac{1}{2} \cdot C \cdot \rho \cdot A2' \qquad k1 := \frac{1}{2} \cdot C \cdot \rho \cdot A1 \qquad k2 := \frac{1}{2} \cdot C \cdot \rho \cdot A2$$

$$vt1' := \sqrt{\frac{m1 \cdot g}{k1'}} \qquad vt1 := \sqrt{\frac{m1 \cdot g}{k1}} \qquad vt2' := \sqrt{\frac{m2 \cdot g}{k2'}} \qquad vt2 := \sqrt{\frac{m2 \cdot g}{k2}}$$

$$vt1' = 108.082 \cdot \frac{mi}{hr} \qquad vt1 = 123.232 \cdot \frac{mi}{hr} \qquad vt2' = 111.626 \cdot \frac{mi}{hr} \qquad vt2 = 163.404 \cdot \frac{mi}{hr}$$

$$Alt := 3000 \cdot ft \qquad tdiv := 3.5 \cdot s \qquad tcoll := 1 \cdot s$$

$$N' := 300 \qquad i := 0 \,..N' \qquad \delta t := .05 \cdot s \qquad t_i := i \cdot \delta t \qquad N' \cdot \delta t = 15 \cdot s$$

$$k1(t) := if(t < tcoll, k1', k1) \qquad\qquad k2(t) := if(t < tdiv, k2', k2)$$

$$v1_0 := 0 \cdot \frac{m}{s} \qquad a1_0 := g \qquad\qquad v2_{20} := 0 \cdot \frac{m}{s} \qquad a2_{20} := g$$

$$x1_0 := 0 \cdot m \qquad\qquad x2_{20} := 0 \cdot m \qquad j := 20 \,..N'$$

$$\begin{bmatrix} a1_{i+1} \\ v1_{i+1} \\ x1_{i+1} \end{bmatrix} := \begin{bmatrix} g - \left[\dfrac{k1[t_i]}{m1}\right] \cdot v1_i{}^2 \\ v1_i + a1_i \cdot \delta t \\ x1_i + v1_i \cdot \delta t \end{bmatrix} \qquad \begin{bmatrix} a2_{j+1} \\ v2_{j+1} \\ x2_{j+1} \end{bmatrix} := \begin{bmatrix} g - \left[\dfrac{k2[t_j]}{m2}\right] \cdot v2_j{}^2 \\ v2_j + a2_j \cdot \delta t \\ x2_j + v2_j \cdot \delta t \end{bmatrix}$$

Figure 6.7 MECH5, skydive: the pursuit. (See the next figure for the rest of the document.)

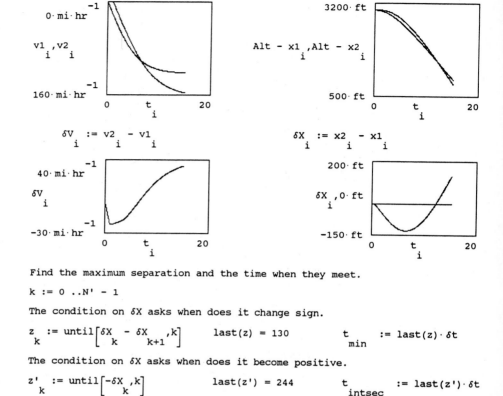

$$\delta V_i := v2_i - v1_i$$

$$\delta X_i := x2_i - x1_i$$

Find the maximum separation and the time when they meet.

k := 0 ..N' - 1

The condition on δX asks when does it change sign.

$$z_k := until\left[\delta X_k - \delta X_{k+1}, k\right] \qquad last(z) = 130 \qquad t_{min} := last(z) \cdot \delta t$$

The condition on δX asks when does it become positive.

$$z'_k := until\left[-\delta X_k, k\right] \qquad last(z') = 244 \qquad t_{intsec} := last(z') \cdot \delta t$$

$$t_{min} = 6.5 \cdot s \qquad\qquad t_{intsec} = 12.2 \cdot s$$

$$\delta X_{130} = -129.389 \cdot ft \qquad \delta X_{244} = 1.284 \cdot ft \qquad \delta X_{243} = -0.745 \cdot ft$$

Figure 6.8 MECH5 *continued.*

6.3.2 *Parachute*

There are records of men in the military falling or jumping from aircraft without parachutes and suffering only minor injuries. (They landed in such a manner, for example, in deep snow, that the deceleration occurred over some distance.) The greatest recorded distance of such a fall is 23,000 ft. Still, most consider it preferable to use a parachute.

We model resisted fall without a parachute, followed by the non-instantaneous opening of the chute, and descent with the chute fully open.

The distance over which the chute opens uniformly is d_{open}. The elevation at which the chute has completely opened is d_p. The height above the earth's surface is ht.

As in the sky diving example, k varies with conditions. Let k_1 be the coefficient without the parachute, and let k_2 be the coefficient with the chute fully deployed. The term $kk(x)$ provides a linear transition between the two values. The expression $k(x)$ includes all the k conditions. These conditions are summarized as follows:

$$ht(x) \geq d_p + d_{\text{open}} \qquad (k_1)$$

$$ht(x) \leq d_p \qquad (k_2)$$

$$d_p < ht(x) < d_p + d_{\text{open}} \qquad (kk(x))$$

The statement for $k(x)$ can be expressed as a nested pair of if statements. The combination permits us to express all the k conditions in one line.

● ●   Plot $k(ht(x))$ vs. $ht(x)$ for the conditions expressed in MECH6. This document contains the parameters but not all the expressions. You must write the equation for $kk(x)$, the k in the transition region. The term $kk(x)$ depends on k_1, k_2, d_{open}, d_p, and $ht(x)$. If $k_2 = 2\text{kg}/\text{m}$, is the change in velocity when the chute opens more gradual or more severe? Why?

● ●   Load MECH7, resisted fall with parachute (see Fig. 6.9).

The initial conditions are the same as in MECH6. The same iteration procedure is used here as was discussed in the sky dive example. We express k as a function of position using nested if statements as described above.

Was your expression for $kk(x)$ in the previous example essentially the same as that shown here? Verify that it is consistent with the conditions given above.

Plot v_1 vs. t. Let the upper limit of the ordinate be 0 mi/hr, and let the lower limit be 130 mi/hr. Plot, directly beneath the previous plot, v_1 vs. $ht(x_1)$. Use the same ordinate limits; let the lower abscissa limit be Altp; let the upper limit be 0 ft. How are the curves similar? Explain the obvious difference.

After the chute has opened, is the final velocity of the iterated solution approximately equal to the expected terminal velocity?

Plot $ht(x_1)$ vs. t. How does the first segment of the curve differ from unresisted motion?

Resisted fall with parachute.

units   m := 1L   s := 1T   kg := 1M

                                                              $ft := 3.28^{-1} \cdot m$

            mi := 5280· ft   hr := 3600· s

parameters

k1 := 0.2   k2 := 14 d_p := 500· ft d_{open} := 250· ft

Alt := 3000· ft $g := 9.81 \cdot m \cdot s^{-2}$ m1 := 55· kg

x – distance fallen, ht – elevation   ht(x) := Alt – x

The parameter, kk(x) is the k-value while the chute is opening

$$kk(x) := k2 + \frac{k1 - k2}{d_{open}} \cdot \left[ht(x) - d_p\right]$$

The general statement for k, for all x.

$$k(x) := if\left[ht(x) \geq \left[d_p + d_{open}\right], k1, if\left[ht(x) \leq d_p, k2, kk(x)\right]\right]$$

$$k(x) := k(x) \cdot kg \cdot m^{-1}$$

The iterated solution.

N := 400   i := 0 ..N δt := .075· s t_i := i· δt

$a1_0$:= g $v1_0 := 0 \cdot m \cdot s^{-1}$ $x1_0$:= 0· m

$$\begin{bmatrix} a1_{i+1} \\ v1_{i+1} \\ x1_{i+1} \end{bmatrix} := \begin{bmatrix} g - \left[\dfrac{k\left[x1_i\right]}{m1}\right] \cdot v1_i^2 \\ v1_i + a1_i \cdot \delta t \\ x1_i + v1_i \cdot \delta t \end{bmatrix}$$

Figure 6.9 MECH7, resisted fall with parachute.

Define the acceleration and plot a_1 vs. t. To see the details of this curve, let the plot region be very wide, with dimensions 10, 60. Explain the plot. Why do the two regions have opposite signs?

Jerk is the rate of change of acceleration. Let $j := 0 \ldots N - 1$ and $jrk_j := a_{1j+1} - a_{1j}/\delta t$. Plot jrk vs. t directly beneath the plot of acceleration. Let the plot dimensions be the same as those of the acceleration region. Explain the shape of the jerk curve in terms of the acceleration. Change the ordinate limits to $-3 \text{ m} \cdot \text{s}^{-3}$ and $1 \text{ m} \cdot \text{s}^{-3}$. Why is the amplitude of the curve so much smaller at the beginning than it is near the center?

6.3.3   *Two-Dimensional Motion with Resistance*

In discussing two-dimensional motion with no resistance, we noted that the kinematic equations describing motion in the x direction were independent from the analogous equations describing motion in the y direction. With velocity-dependent forces, the two sets of equations are no longer independent. The resistive force is directed opposite to the velocity vector, and the magnitude of the resistance is proportional to some function of the velocity. As velocity typically has both x and y components, so does the resistive force. The components of the force depend on the total velocity V, which depends on both Vx and Vy. Consequently, the acceleration in each direction depends on both vx and vy, and the equations in the vertical and horizontal dimensions are not independent.

If the velocity vector v makes an angle, θ, with respect to the horizontal, the oppositely directed resistive force makes the same angle. Applying Newton's second law (constant mass),

$$\sum F_{\text{ext}} = m\frac{dv}{dt},$$

we obtain the equation of motion in the x direction,

$$-kv^2 \cos(\theta) = m\frac{dv_x}{dt} = ma_x. \tag{6.24}$$

The only force in the x direction is due to the component of the resistive force. The equation of motion for the y direction is

$$-mg - kv^2 \sin(\theta) = m\frac{dv_y}{dt} = ma_y. \tag{6.25}$$

The forces are gravitational and resistive.

Knowing that $v_x = v\cos(\theta)$ and $v_y = v\sin(\theta)$, we can eliminate the trigonometric functions from the equations of motion:

$$-kvv_x = ma_x \tag{6.26}$$

$$-mg - kvv_y = ma_y \tag{6.27}$$

or

$$a_x = \frac{-k}{m}vv_x \quad \text{and} \quad a_y = -g\frac{-k}{m}vv_y. \tag{6.28}$$

• •   Load MECH8, trajectory with resistance (see Fig. 6.10).

In the Saturday morning cartoons, the trajectories of objects or characters often seem to make an abrupt transition from motion along one

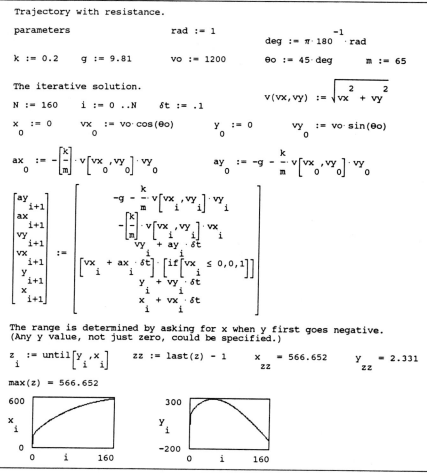

Trajectory with resistance.

parameters   rad := 1

$$deg := \pi \cdot 180^{-1} \cdot rad$$

k := 0.2   g := 9.81   vo := 1200 $\theta o := 45 \cdot deg$ m := 65

The iterative solution.

$$v(vx, vy) := \sqrt{vx^2 + vy^2}$$

N := 160   i := 0 ..N $\delta t := .1$

$x_0 := 0$ $vx_0 := vo \cdot \cos(\theta o)$ $y_0 := 0$ $vy_0 := vo \cdot \sin(\theta o)$

$$ax_0 := -\left[\frac{k}{m}\right] \cdot v\left[vx_0, vy_0\right] \cdot vy_0 \qquad ay_0 := -g - \frac{k}{m} \cdot v\left[vx_0, vy_0\right] \cdot vy_0$$

$$\begin{bmatrix} ay_{i+1} \\ ax_{i+1} \\ vy_{i+1} \\ vx_{i+1} \\ y_{i+1} \\ x_{i+1} \end{bmatrix} := \begin{bmatrix} -g - \frac{k}{m} \cdot v\left[vx_i, vy_i\right] \cdot vy_i \\ -\left[\frac{k}{m}\right] \cdot v\left[vx_i, vy_i\right] \cdot vx_i \\ vy_i + ay_i \cdot \delta t \\ \left[vx_i + ax_i \cdot \delta t\right] \cdot \left[if\left[vx_i \le 0, 0, 1\right]\right] \\ y_i + vy_i \cdot \delta t \\ x_i + vx_i \cdot \delta t \end{bmatrix}$$

The range is determined by asking for x when y first goes negative.
(Any y value, not just zero, could be specified.)

$z_i := until\left[y_i, x_i\right]$ zz := last(z) - 1 x_{zz} = 566.652 y_{zz} = 2.331

max(z) = 566.652

Figure 6.10 MECH8, trajectory with resistance.

path (typically continuing in the original direction) to motion along another path (typically falling). In some medieval works, figures displaying the motion of cannon balls show a similar trajectory. The trajectory does not take the form of a triangle, but the path does trace a fairly rapid transition from motion deviating only slightly from the initial direction to motion with a greatly reduced forward velocity. We might suspect the cartoons of anything, but the medieval texts were serious. How did this point of view arise? Is it totally a misconception, or is there some basis for the trajectories as the medievals conceived them and the cartoonists represent them?

In this document, trajectories are examined where resistance to the motion proportional to the square of the velocity is included. The block of iterated equations includes calculations of acceleration, velocity, and position for both components.

Process the document. The interesting features, once again, are obtained by examining a series of plots. As the plots appear, give a qualitative explanation of each. Compare one plot with another so that all aspects of the motion become clear to you. There may be some mild surprises as you go along. Try all the plots. Keep the plot sizes small, like those included. Plots vs. i are equivalent to plotting against time because i is proportional to time.

If the document becomes too cluttered with plots, print them out and then delete them. There is no reason to keep them all resident at the same time.

Plots of x vs. i and y vs. i are shown. What would these curves look like if there were no resistance?

Plot y vs. x. Find the connections with the previous two plots. Do you find any justification for the medieval depiction of trajectories?

Plot vx vs. i, vy vs. i, vx vs. x, and vy vs. x. First predict the behaviors, then plot.

Plot ax vs. i and ay vs. i. Find the connections to the velocity plots.

Plot v, vx, vy vs. i; increase the width of this plot. Plot v vs. vx and v vs. vy.

Plot $v - vx$ vs. i and $v - vy$ vs. i. (The shape of these plots may surprise you.)

Delete all the plot regions.

For an initial speed of $v_0 = 1200$, what angle yields the maximum range? (To consider larger values for v_0, δt must be reduced proportionately; otherwise, spurious output may occur. Of course, if δt is decreased, then N will have to be increased, leading to more iterations, which means more computer time.)

If trajectories in the atmosphere carry the projectile to very high elevations, the atmospheric pressure is reduced and the resistance to the motion would be reduced as well. The effect can be approximated by permitting the coefficient to be altitude dependent.

• • Load MECH9, trajectory with altitude-dependent resistance (see Fig. 6.11).

Trajectory with resistance. Includes altitude dependent resistance.

parameters   rad := 1

$$\text{deg} := \pi \cdot 180^{-1} \cdot \text{rad}$$

g := 9.81   vo := 1200   θo := 60· deg   m := 65

We compute two solutions   j := 0 ..1

kc := 0.2 $k(y) := \text{if}(j \approx 0, kc, kc \cdot \exp(-a \cdot y))$

$$a := 0.12 \cdot 10^{-3}$$

The iterative solution

N := 160   i := 0 ..N   δt := .1 $v(vx, vy) := \sqrt{vx^2 + vy^2}$

$x_{0,j} := 0$ $vx_{0,j} := vo \cdot \cos(\theta o)$ $y_{0,j} := 0$ $vy_{0,j} := vo \cdot \sin(\theta o)$

$$ax_{0,j} := -\left[\frac{k[y_{0,j}]}{m}\right] \cdot v[vx_{0,j}, vy_{0,j}] \cdot vx_{0,j}$$

$$ay_{0,j} := -g - \frac{k[y_{0,j}]}{m} \cdot v[vx_{0,j}, vy_{0,j}] \cdot vy_{0,j}$$

$$\begin{bmatrix} ay_{i+1,j} \\ ax_{i+1,j} \\ vy_{i+1,j} \\ vx_{i+1,j} \\ y_{i+1,j} \\ x_{i+1,j} \end{bmatrix} := \begin{bmatrix} -g - \frac{k[y_{i,j}]}{m} \cdot v[vx_{i,j}, vy_{i,j}] \cdot vy_{i,j} \\ -\left[\frac{k[y_{i,j}]}{m}\right] \cdot v[vx_{i,j}, vy_{i,j}] \cdot vx_{i,j} \\ vy_{i,j} + ay_{i,j} \cdot \delta t \\ [vx_{i,j} + ax_{i,j} \cdot \delta t] \cdot [\text{if}[vx_{i,j} \le 0, 0, 1]] \\ y_{i,j} + vy_{i,j} \cdot \delta t \\ x_{i,j} + vx_{i,j} \cdot \delta t \end{bmatrix}$$

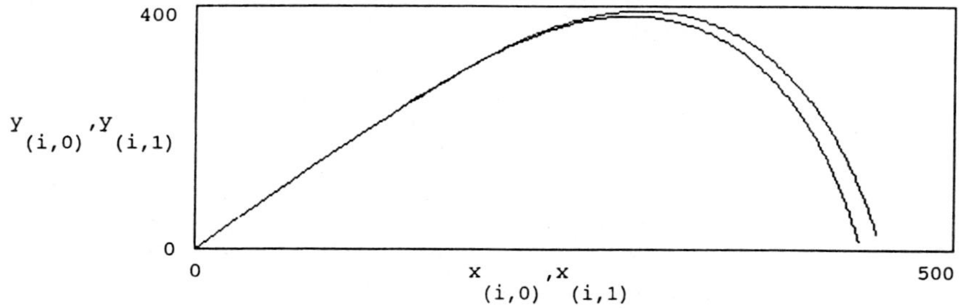

Figure 6.11 MECH9, trajectory with altitude-dependent resistance.

The procedure here is essentially the same as in MECH8. The difference is that k decreases exponentially with y. The value for the constant a is selected so as to reduce k in proportion with the decrease in atmospheric pressure as elevation increases. For modest initial velocities, the difference is not great but is clearly discernible, as you can see from the trajectory plot.

Rather than increasing the initial velocity (for example, the muzzle velocity of a cannon), which would require smaller time intervals and more iterations, increase a. In effect, this increase permits the pressure to decrease more rapidly. How does the range depend on a?

For an increased constant a, observe the trajectory for different angles. Does 45° remain the angle for maximum range (in this model)?

One way to determine the range is to find the value of x for which y first becomes negative. MathCAD's until statement can easily be used in this case. For example,

$$z_i := \text{until}(y_i,\, x_i).$$

For each value of i, z_i is assigned the value x_i until our test expression, y_i, goes negative. The range is approximately equal to the last value of z, which is also the maximum value of x. The value can be obtained in two ways. The statement $\max(z)$ returns the largest value in vector z. The statement $\text{last}(z)$ returns the index of the last value of z. This index corresponds to the first negative value for y. $\text{Last}(z) - 1$ corresponds to the last index when y is positive. The values $x_{\text{last}(z)}$ and $x_{\text{last}(z)-1}$ do not differ by much.

6.3.4   Orbits

A search for the solution to the problem of the planets was central to the development of classical mechanics. Many centuries elapsed between the time when careful observations of the planets were first made and the time when Kepler provided a precise mathematical description of planetary motion by means of his three laws. Kepler spent years performing untold numbers of calculations by hand to arrive at his solution. But now, knowing Newton's laws of motion and his law of gravitation, we can examine in detail, the properties of orbits, in minutes rather than years.

The general approach is the same as that used in the previous section on trajectories. Express the x and y components of the acceleration; write the difference equations for velocity and position. The external force is the gravitational force between the central body and the orbiting body. We shall assume that the mass, m_1, of the central body, located at the origin, is very much larger than that of the mass, m_2, of the orbiting body. The gravitational force is always attractive and along the line connecting the two bodies.

The magnitude of the force is given by

$$|F| = \frac{Gm_1m_2}{r^2}.$$

The components of this attractive force are

$$F_x = \frac{-Gm_1m_2}{r^2}\cos(\theta) \tag{6.29}$$

and

$$F_y = \frac{-Gm_1m_2}{r^2}\sin(\theta). \tag{6.30}$$

As in the case of trajectories, it is convenient to express the forces in terms of Cartesian rather than polar coordinates. Recognizing that $\cos(\theta) = x/r$ and $\sin(\theta) = y/r$, we can write the equations of motion as

$$\frac{-Gm_1m_2}{r^2} \cdot \frac{x}{r} = m_2\,ax \tag{6.31}$$

and

$$\frac{-Gm_1m_2}{r^2} \cdot \frac{y}{r} = m_2\,ay. \tag{6.32}$$

Because of MathCAD's memory limitations, we consider only one or two revolutions in these examples.

To limit the size of the equation block region, user-defined functions for distance, for the x and y components of the acceleration, and for the x and y components of the velocity are specified before the equation block is written. The value for (Gm_1m_2) is taken to be 1. These functions can then be used within the equation block. (As the equation block becomes larger, editing of the block becomes slower. The block we use here is small, so the changes are quick.)

• •   Load MECH10, central force orbits (see Fig. 6.12).

Initial values are specified for the position, velocity, and acceleration. The components of acceleration and velocity are specified in terms of functions. In the equation block, we iterate the acceleration, velocity, and position for each component.

Alongside the equation block, we define the total velocity, the polar coordinates, and the distance. Once again, plots of various parameters help us to appreciate significant aspects of the motion.

Where does the orbital motion originate? Is the orbit circular? To what is i proportional (in other words, of what could i be considered a measure)?

Explain the general shapes of the x vs. i and y vs. i curves.

Examine the vx vs. i and vy vs. i curves. What is the location of the orbiting body when vx is at its minimum? At its maximum? When vy is at its maximum? At its minimum? Why are these curves nonsinusoidal?

In each of the plots for the components of acceleration and velocity that follow, include the origin. For example, plot ff, 0 vs. gg, 0. Let the plot type be lo. This choice of plot types marks the origin with an open rectangle and aids in interpretation.

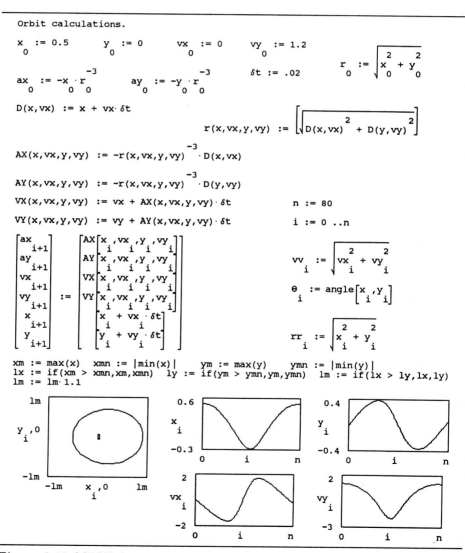

Figure 6.12 MECH10, central force orbits.

Plot vx vs. x and vy vs. y. Do the plots corroborate your answers to the previous questions?

Plot ax vs. x and ay vs. y. For each plot, carefully match where the body is in its orbit with a particular value for the acceleration. Given the initial conditions, you should know the direction in which the curves evolve in time. One quick way to check is to reduce significantly the number of iterations; then only a portion of the curve will be traced out. What is the relationship between the fact that the orbit is not circular and the shape of the ax vs. x curve?

Plot ax vs. y and ay vs. x. Explain the shapes of the curves. In which direction does the motion take them? Check by reducing the number of iterations.

Plot vv, $2 \cdot rr$ vs. i. (The factor of 2 is used to make the curvature of the rr curve more visible.) Explain the shape of this curve and the correlation between these two curves.

Examine the orbit for different initial conditions. For example, let $v_{x0} = 0$ and $v_{y0} = 1$. How would you characterize the orbit? Examine the plot regions and see what changes have occurred. Explain the changes.

Repeat for $v_{x0} = -0.5$ and $v_{y0} = 1$.

Repeat for $v_{x0} = -2$ and $v_{y0} = 1$.

One body orbiting two fixed gravitational centers is another interesting case. Very unusual orbital patterns are possible. The program may yield unphysical results if the orbiting body gets too close to an attracting center. If this happens, just change the initial conditions and try again.

• •   Load MECH11, orbits with two attracting centers (see Figs. 6.13 and 6.14).

The attractive centers are located at $(d, 0)$ and $(-d, 0)$. Observe how the previous document has been adapted. There are two distances and two components to the acceleration. The functions are similarly adapted. The algorithm remains the same.

The plots of x, y, vx, and vy vs. i are more complicated but still worth reading. For the initial case where $x_0 = 0.5$, $y_0 = 0$, $vx_0 = 0$, and $vy_0 = 1.8$, in which the orbit is not too complex, look at plots of ax vs. x and ay vs. y; the origin is included (plot type o). Interpret these plots; compare them with plots associated with a single attracting center.

Orbit.   Two attracting centers.

$x_0 := .5$ $y_0 := 0$ $vx_0 := 0$ $vy_0 := 1.8$ $\delta t := .01$ $d := .25$

$$r1_0 := \sqrt{\left[x_0 - d\right]^2 + y_0^2} \qquad r2_0 := \sqrt{\left[x_0 + d\right]^2 + y_0^2}$$

$$ax_0 := -\left[x_0 - d\right]\cdot r1_0^{-3} - \left[x_0 + d\right]\cdot r2_0^{-3} \qquad ay_0 := -y_0 \cdot r1_0^{-3} - y_0 \cdot r2_0^{-3}$$

$D1(x,vx) := (x - d) + vx\cdot \delta t \qquad D2(x,vx) := (x + d) + vx\cdot \delta t$

$D(y,vy) := y + vy\cdot \delta t$

$$r1(x,vx,y,vy) := \left[\sqrt{D1(x,vx)^2 + D(y,vy)^2}\right]$$

$$r2(x,vx,y,vy) := \left[\sqrt{D2(x,vx)^2 + D(y,vy)^2}\right]$$

$AX(x,vx,y,vy) := -r1(x,vx,y,vy)^{-3}\cdot D1(x,vx) - r2(x,vx,y,vy)^{-3}\cdot D2(x,vx)$

$AY(x,vx,y,vy) := -r1(x,vx,y,vy)^{-3}\cdot D(y,vy) - r2(x,vx,y,vy)^{-3}\cdot D(y,vy)$

$VX(x,vx,y,vy) := vx + AX(x,vx,y,vy)\cdot \delta t$

$VY(x,vx,y,vy) := vy + AY(x,vx,y,vy)\cdot \delta t \qquad n := 200 \qquad i := 0 ..n$

$$\begin{bmatrix} ax_{i+1} \\ ay_{i+1} \\ vx_{i+1} \\ vy_{i+1} \\ x_{i+1} \\ y_{i+1} \end{bmatrix} := \begin{bmatrix} AX\left[x_i,vx_i,y_i,vy_i\right] \\ AY\left[x_i,vx_i,y_i,vy_i\right] \\ VX\left[x_i,vx_i,y_i,vy_i\right] \\ VY\left[x_i,vx_i,y_i,vy_i\right] \\ x_i + vx_i\cdot \delta t \\ y_i + vy_i\cdot \delta t \end{bmatrix} \qquad \begin{aligned} vv_i &:= \sqrt{vx_i^2 + vy_i^2} \\ \theta_i &:= angle\left[x_i,y_i\right] \end{aligned}$$

Figure 6.13 MECH11, orbits with two attracting centers. (See the next figure for the rest of the document.)

Try various initial conditions. You may want to increase the number of iterations.

• •   Adapt MECH8 so that the central body repels instead of attracts. Let the distance dependence remain the same. Create, examine, and interpret a set of plots similar to those in the original document.

"It's not my goddamn planet, monkey boy."

Buckaroo Banzai

```
xm := max(x)   xmn := |min(x)|   ym := max(y)   ymn := |min(y)|
lx := if(xm > xmn,xm,xmn) ly := if(ym > ymn,ym,ymn)
lm := if(lx > ly,lx,ly)·1.1
```

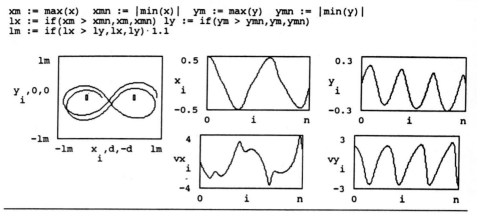

Figure 6.14 MECH11 *continued.*

CHAPTER

7

Momentum and Collisions

The conservation laws lie at the very heart of physics. Quantities that are conserved include energy, linear momentum, angular momentum, and electric charge. For a quantity to be conserved, it means that whatever the amount of that conserved quantity is now, for some system; it will be the same in the future. For conservation to be true, the system must be closed to losses or additions. (See Richard Feynman's amusing story about energy in *The Character of Physical Law.*) Many quantities, of course, are not conserved. Kinetic energy, for example, may be conserved under particular circumstances, but, in general, it is not.

Clearly, an object's linear momentum ($\mathbf{p} = m\,\mathbf{v}$) may change. Newton's second law makes this explicit:

$$\sum \mathbf{F}_{\text{ext}} = \frac{d\mathbf{p}}{dt}.$$

However, if the sum of all external forces is zero, then $d\mathbf{p}/dt = 0$, and the momentum, $\mathbf{p}$, is a constant implying that $p_{\text{init}} = p_{\text{final}}$. For momentum, losses or additions would be in terms of external forces.

When two objects collide, each object exerts a force on the other. The forces comprise an action-reaction pair and are equal and opposite. For each individual object, the force exerted by the other is an external force and the momentum of the object changes. The momentum of neither object is conserved in a collision. However, if we say that our system consists of the two objects, then the forces are internal to the system and the total momentum of the system does not change, even though the momenta of individual parts of the system change.

Two special cases of collision are elastic and completely (or perfectly) inelastic. In an elastic collision, both kinetic energy and momentum are conserved. After a completely inelastic collision, the objects have the same final velocity.

7.1   Collisions in One Dimension

7.1.1   Inelastic Collisions

A perfectly inelastic collision is the easiest case to analyze. Momentum is conserved; initial momentum equals final momentum, and the final velocity of both masses is the same:

$$m_1 v_{1i} + m_2 v_{2i} = (m_1 + m_2)v_f. \tag{7.1}$$

• •   For a completely inelastic collision, with $v_{2i} = 0$, express the final velocity in terms of v_{1i} and the mass ratio $mr = m_2/m_1$. Define a function expressing the final velocity with the mass ratio as its argument, $v_f(mr)$. Plot $v_f(mr)$ as mr takes on the sequence of values $mr_i := 2^{i-5}$, where $i := 1, \ldots, 10$.

Ballistic Pendulum.   The ballistic pendulum is designed to permit the determination of velocities from inelastic collisions. An object such as a bullet is fired at, penetrates, and remains embedded in a pendulum bob. The rather complicated interaction process between the bullet and the pendulum bob (which, for example, could be a block of wood) can be treated as an inelastic collision. Following the collision, the pendulum swings through some angle; the maximum height or angle is determined.

After the collision occurs, mechanical energy — the sum of kinetic and potential energy — is conserved. This can be expressed as

$$KE_i + PE_i = KE_f + PE_f. \tag{7.2}$$

In this example, the potential energy is gravitational and is given by mgh. Let $h = 0$ when the pendulum is at its lowest point. As the pendulum swings following the impact, the elevation of the bob increases and the velocity of the bob decreases. The potential energy of the bob can be expressed in terms of the length, L, of the string supporting the bob and the angle through which the pendulum turns. When the pendulum is at an angle θ, the vertical distance from the pendulum bob to the support point is $L\cos(\theta)$. The height through which the pendulum has risen is the original distance from the support point, L, minus the final distance from the support point, or

$$h = L - L\cos(\theta) = L \cdot (1 - \cos(\theta)). \tag{7.3}$$

In our statement of energy conservation, let the initial state be the instant after the collision occurs and let the final state occur when the bob reaches its maximum elevation (and has zero speed). Given these choices, $PE_i = 0$ and $KE_f = 0$. Thus, $KE_i = PE_f$.

• •   Load COLL1, ballistic pendulum (see Fig. 7.1).

In COLL1, a bullet of mass m_b undergoes an inelastic collision with a ballistic pendulum of mass M. The momentum statement for an inelastic collision is expressed in terms of the final velocity. The final velocity is expressed in functional form; the initial velocity of the bullet, v_{bi}, is the parameter. The final velocity of the two masses immediately after the collision is returned by $v_f(v_{bi})$. Verify that this equation is correct.

In the solve blocks, there is only one equation. The equation is a statement of energy conservation, $KE_i = PE_f$, for the conditions mentioned above — $PE_i = 0$ and $KE_f = 0$. Is this the energy equation (where is the mass)? How can this problem be solved with an energy equation alone? Where is the momentum statement?

The maximum angle through which the pendulum can rotate can be either 90° or 180° depending on the structure of the pendulum. The initial momentum that will result in this angular displacement is a useful parameter of the system. Write an expression for that momentum, for each of the two cases. For a bullet of given mass, this translates into a maximum initial velocity.

Rewrite the equation for v_f in terms of the mass ratio $mr = M/mb$. Express v_f as $v_f(mr)$.

Determine the initial velocity that would result in the maximum possible height of the pendulum, as a function of the mass ratio. In the first solve block, change the find statement to a functional form, $vmx(mr)$. Plot the final velocity as a function of the mass ratio.

In the second solve block, a similar equation is solved. In this case, the final potential energy is not the maximum but that which occurs for a

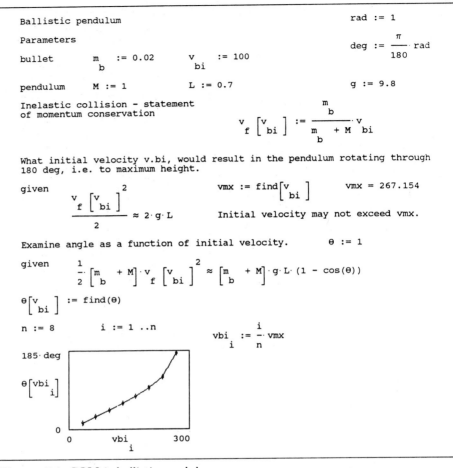

Figure 7.1 COLL1, ballistic pendulum.

given angle θ. The solve block is written in functional form. Given a value for the initial velocity of the bullet, the function returns the maximum angle through which the pendulum swings.

How does the shape of this curve depend on the mass M?

The curve is not smooth near the 180° point. Draw a cubic spline curve through the points to show a smoother fit.

Write an expression for the ratio of kinetic energy just after the collision to the initial kinetic energy of the bullet. Express this ratio as a function of the mass ratio mr: $KEr(mr)$. Plot $KEr(mr)$ vs. mr.

Express the fractional loss in kinetic energy. Plot the fractional loss in kinetic energy as a function of the mass ratio.

• • Tarzan swings down from a tree limb, collides inelastically with Jane (saving her from impending doom), and continues to swing up to the branch of another tree. Consider this problem in three stages: (1) from the starting point to the instant just before the collision — conservation of energy, (2) during the collision — conservation of momentum, and (3) from the instant just after the collision to the final height — conservation of energy. Plot the final angle vs. the initial angle as a function of the mass ratio — $\theta_f(mr)$ vs. θ_i. If $M_T = 1.5\,M_J$, $L = 10\,m$, $\theta_o = 90°$, what is the final angle and final height? What would be the velocity of Tarzan just before the collision with Jane? Would this be a good way to save someone?

7.1.2   Elastic Collisions in One Dimension

In elastic collisions, both momentum and kinetic energy are conserved:

$$m_1\,v_{1i} + m_2\,v_{2i} = m_1\,v_{1f} + m_2\,v_{2f} \tag{7.4}$$

$$\frac{1}{2}m_1\,v_{1i}^2 + \frac{1}{2}m_2\,v_{2i}^2 = \frac{1}{2}m_1\,v_{1f}^2 + \frac{1}{2}m_2\,v_{2f}^2. \tag{7.5}$$

Three relations are commonly extracted from these two equations. One is the statement of relative velocities before and after a collision:

$$v_{1i} - v_{2i} = v_{2f} - v_{1f}. \tag{7.6}$$

This statement is readily determined using the momentum and energy equations. It shows that the rate at which particle one approaches particle two, before the collision, is the same as the rate at which particle two moves away from particle one after the collision. Verify the equation.

The other two relations express final velocities in terms of initial velocities:

$$v_{1f} = \left(\frac{m_1 - m_2}{m_1 + m_2}\right) v_{1i} + \left(\frac{2\,m_2}{m_1 + m_2}\right) v_{2i} \tag{7.7}$$

$$v_{2f} = \left(\frac{2\,m_1}{m_1 + m_2}\right) v_{1i} + \left(\frac{m_2 - m_1}{m_1 + m_2}\right) v_{2i}. \tag{7.8}$$

If $m_1 \gg m_2$ and $v_{2i} = 0$, then $v_{1f} \simeq v_{1i}$ and $v_{2f} \simeq 2\,v_{1i}$.
If $m_2 \gg m_1$ and $v_{2i} = 0$, then $v_{1f} \simeq -v_{1i}$ and $v_{2f} \simeq 0$.

• • When $v_{2i} = 0$, show that the two previous expressions are consistent with the statement about relative velocities before and after a collision.

• •   Consider an elastic collision where $m_1 := 1.5$, $m_2 = 1$, $v_{1i} = 1$, and $v_{2i} = -0.2$. Use a solve block to solve the momentum and energy relations directly for v_{1f} and v_{2f}. Using the results, evaluate the momentum and energy of the individual terms and check that the results are consistent.

Let $m_1 = m_2$. Try several different values of v_{1i} and v_{2i}. Include cases where $v_{1i} > 0$ and $v_{2i} < 0$. In each case evaluate $v_{1i} - v_{2i}$ and $v_{1f} - v_{2f}$. Compare v_{1f} with v_{2i} and v_{2f} with v_{1i}. Do the particles exchange velocities when the masses are equal? Don't base your answer on one example.

In the solve block you set up to solve for v_{1f} and v_{2f}, change the find statement from

$$\begin{bmatrix} v_{1f} \\ v_{2f} \end{bmatrix} = \text{find}((v_{1f}, v_{2f})$$

to

$$f(mr) = \text{find}(v_{1f}, v_{2f})$$

where mr is the mass ratio m_1/m_2. Of course, in this case, $v_{1f} = f(mr)_0$. Plot v_{1f} vs. mr. Plot v_{2f} vs. mr. Plot $(v_{2f} - v_{1f})/(v_{1i} - v_{2i})$ vs. mr, where $mr_i := 0.1 \cdot 2^i$, where $i := 0 \ldots 7$.

Let $v_{2i} = 0$. Plot KE_{2f}/KE_{1f} vs. mr. Plot p_{2f}/p_{1f} vs. mr. Repeat with v_{2i} negative and v_{2i} positive (but for the positive case, less than v_{1i}).

7.1.3   Displaying the Motion

The next document helps us to visualize the one-dimensional collision process in both the laboratory frame (a reference frame, stationary with respect to the laboratory in which the particles are observed) and the center-of-mass frame (a reference frame in which the center of mass is stationary).

For the case of particles of equal mass, where one particle is on a collision course with a second particle which is initially at rest. In the laboratory frame, we see the first mass move toward the second with velocity v, collide, and stop. The second mass, initially at rest, is struck and moves away with the same velocity, v. In the center-of-mass frame, motion is observed relative to the center of mass of the system. Before the collision, both particles approach the center of mass with velocity $v/2$; after the collision both move away from it with the same velocity. The particular velocities depend on the relative mass values.

• •   Load COLL2, elastic collision in one dimension (see Figs. 7.2 and 7.3).

The first plot (plot type s) shows the motion in a sequence at uniform time intervals in the laboratory frame. Time increases from top to bottom. The horizontal width of the steps is proportional to the velocity. Initially, particle one approaches particle two, which is at rest. After the collision, m_1, being larger than m_2, continues to move in the forward direction, and m_2 moves off with a larger velocity than m_1 had before the collision.

In the second plot, the same information is portrayed but in a different manner. The graph is rotated so that time proceeds from left to right, and the format style is changed. The length of the bars is proportional to velocity. The solid line shows the center-of-mass motion. Both before

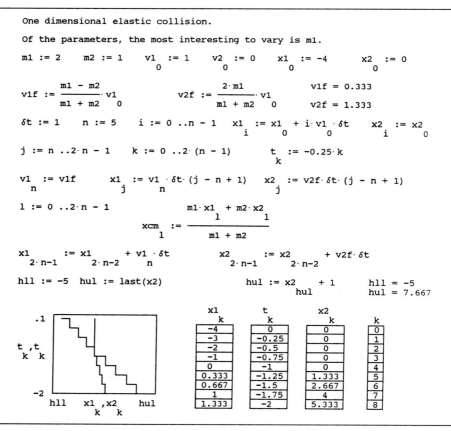

Figure 7.2 COLL2, elastic collision in one dimension. (See the next figure for the rest of the document.)

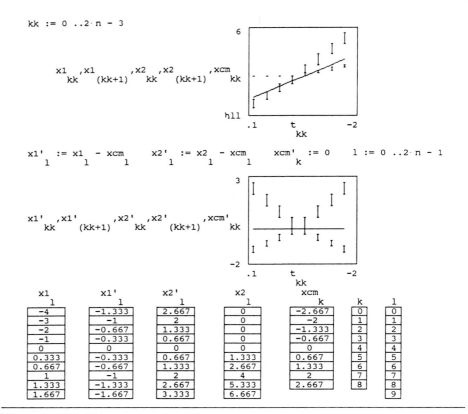

$$kk := 0 \, .. \, 2 \cdot n - 3$$

$$x1_{kk}, x1_{(kk+1)}, x2_{kk}, x2_{(kk+1)}, xcm_{kk}$$

$$x1'_1 := x1_1 - xcm_1 \qquad x2'_1 := x2_1 - xcm_1 \qquad xcm'_k := 0 \qquad l := 0 \, .. \, 2 \cdot n - 1$$

$$x1'_{kk}, x1'_{(kk+1)}, x2'_{kk}, x2'_{(kk+1)}, xcm'_{kk}$$

x1 l	x1' l	x2' l	x2 l	xcm k	k	l
-4	-1.333	2.667	0	-2.667	0	0
-3	-1	2	0	-2	1	1
-2	-0.667	1.333	0	-1.333	2	2
-1	-0.333	0.667	0	-0.667	3	3
0	0	0	0	0	4	4
0.333	-0.333	0.667	1.333	0.667	5	5
0.667	-0.667	1.333	2.667	1.333	6	6
1	-1	2	4	2	7	7
1.333	-1.333	2.667	5.333	2.667	8	8
1.667	-1.667	3.333	6.667			9

Figure 7.3 COLL2 *continued.*

and after the collision, the motions of both m_1 and m_2 are displayed, although, in this case, before the collision the bars have zero length for mass m_2 as it has zero velocity.

The third plot shows the motion from the center-of-mass frame. Again, time increases from left to right. Before the collision, both masses approach the center of mass; after the collision, both move away from the center. The particle of lower mass has the larger velocity in each case.

Try the following values for $(m_1, m_2, v_{10} \, v_{20})$: $(2, 1, 1, 0)$, $(1, 1, 2, -1)$, $(1, 1, 2, 1)$, $(10, 1, 1, 0)$, $(0.1, 1, 1, 0)$. Try values of your own. Keep v_2 small; otherwise the collision may not occur in the region plotted. You can, of course, change the plot parameters.

7.2 Collisions in Two Dimensions

The principle to be applied, that of momentum conservation, is the same for collisions in two dimensions as for collisions in one dimension. However, since momentum is a vector, conservation applies for each component. We consider the case where $v_{2i} = 0$. The momentum statements are

$$m_1 v_{1i} = m_1 v_{1f} \cos(\theta) + m_2 v_{2f} \cos(\phi) \tag{7.9}$$
$$0 = m_1 v_{1f} \sin(\theta) + m_2 v_{2f} \sin(\phi), \tag{7.10}$$

where θ and ϕ are the angles that the paths of particles m_1 and m_2 make with the horizontal. Angles θ and ϕ lie on opposite sides of the horizontal, the direction of the initial path of m_1.

7.2.1 Elastic Collisions

If the collision is elastic then the statement of conservation of kinetic energy applies:

$$m_1 v_{1i}{}^2 = m_1 v_{1f}{}^2 + m_2 v_{2f}{}^2. \tag{7.11}$$

If the masses m_1 and m_2 are equal, the following relationships can be deduced for elastic collisions:

$$\tan(\theta) \cdot \tan(\phi) = 1 \tag{7.12}$$

$$v_{1f} = \frac{\sin(\phi)}{\sin(\theta + \phi)} v_{1i} \tag{7.13}$$

$$v_{2f} = \frac{\sin(\theta)}{\sin(\theta + \phi)} v_{1i} \tag{7.14}$$

• • Examine the relationship between $\tan(\theta)$ and $\tan(\phi)$. Define $\phi(\theta)$, and plot $\phi(\theta)$ vs. θ as $\theta = 1, 5, \ldots, 90$ (degrees). Plot $\phi(\theta) + \theta$ vs. θ. How can you simplify the relationships for v_{1f} and v_{2f}?

In a grazing collision, when only a slight interaction occurs, what are the approximate values for the scattering angles of $m_1(\theta)$ and $m_2(\phi)$? What are the final velocities? In a nearly head-on collision, what are the values of θ and ϕ? What are the final velocities?

Let $v_{1i} = 1$ (we consider the case $v_{2i} = 0$). Define $v_{1f}(\theta)$ and $v_{2f}(\theta)$, and plot both vs. θ. (Note: A function $f(\theta) = \sin(\phi(\theta))$ returns the sine of ϕ, the ϕ selected being that which corresponds to the θ specified.)

Define the momenta, $p_{1fv}(\theta)$ and $p_{1fh}(\theta)$, where v and h refer to vertical/horizontal or transverse/parallel to the initial momentum. Plot the final momentum components as a function of θ. What would the corresponding curves for p_2 look like?

If the masses m_1 and m_2 are not equal, relations analogous to those given above are

$$\tan(\theta) = \frac{\sin(2\,\phi)}{m_1/m_2 - \cos(2\,\phi)} \qquad (7.15)$$

$$v_{1f} = \frac{\sin(\phi)}{\sin(\theta + \phi)}\,v_{1i} \qquad (7.16)$$

$$v_{2f} = \frac{m_1}{m_2} \cdot \frac{\sin(\theta)}{\sin(\theta + \phi)}\,v_{1i} \qquad (7.17)$$

• • Show that these equations reduce to the previous set if $m_1 = m_2$.

One effect of collisions with unequal masses is that the possible range of angles for θ is affected. If $m_1 > m_2$, then θ has a maximum value less than 90°. If $m_1 < m_2$, then θ can range from 0° to 180°. However, ϕ is always restricted to the range from 0° to 90°.

• • Determine the maximum value for θ if $m_1 = 2 \cdot m_2$.

• • Load COLL3, two-dimensional collision: unequal masses (see Fig. 7.4).

Here, θ is written as a function of ϕ. The arctangent function is too restrictive in the range of angles returned and, although shown, is disabled. The angle function is used instead because it returns angles in the desired range.

For simplicity, leave the value for m_2 equal to 1 and change the value of m_1. In this document, do *not* let $m_1 = m_2$: let $m_1 > 1$ or $m_1 < 1$. Because m_1 is assigned its value using a global equality, it can be moved near plot regions farther down in the document when they are examined.

Examine the θ vs. ϕ plot ($m_1 = 0.5$, $m_2 = 1$). Interpret this case. Ask specific questions that direct you to particular cases. For example, if ϕ is approximately zero, what is θ? Why? When ϕ is $\pi/2$, what is θ? Why? How is the plot of $\theta + \phi$ different from the case where the masses are equal?

Let $m_1 = 2$ and process. This curve is quite different. In the plot of θ vs. ϕ, there are two different possible values of ϕ for a given θ. Explain how this is possible. Consider specific cases. Why should there be a maximum? How is the plot of $\theta + \phi$ different from the case where the masses are equal? How is this plot different from the case where $m_1 < m_2$?

Directly beneath the plot regions, two calculations are set up. The first, to locate the maximum of the θ vs. ϕ curve, is valid when $m_1 > m_2$. The second, to find the angle ϕ where m_1 is scattered through an angle of 90°, is valid when $m_1 < m_2$.

Let $m_1 = 1.1, 1.3, 1.5, 2, 4, 10, 50, 10^3, 10^5, 10^8$. Observe the θ vs. ϕ curve and the values of ϕ and θ at which the maximum of the curve occurs. To plot these results, after each calculation enter the values by

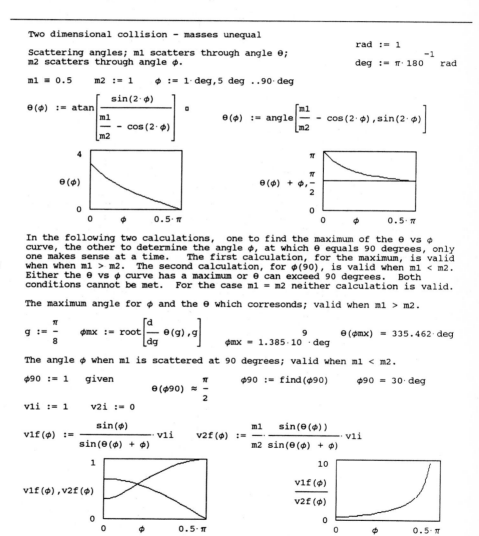

Figure 7.4 COLL3, two-dimensional collision: unequal masses.

hand into tables. There are ten values of m_1. Let $j := 1 \ldots 10$. Insert values into mr_j, ϕp_j, and θp_j. Once the tables are complete, plot ϕp vs. mr and θp vs. mr; a log scale for mr is appropriate.

When the value of m_1 is less than that of m_2, m_1 can be scattered through angles greater than 90°. When m_1 is scattered through 90°, $\phi 90$ is the corresponding ϕ angle.

Let m_1 take on values equal to the inverse of the previous set, that is, $1/1.1$, $1/1.3$, ... Again, put values in a table after each calculation; plot $\phi 90$ vs. mr.

In the next plot region, the final velocities are plotted as a function of the scattering angle, ϕ, of m_2. Examine how these curves change as the relative mass of the two particles change. Does changing the initial velocity change the shape of the curves? Plot the momentum associated with each.

If $v_{1f} = v_{2f}$, how do the angles (θ, ϕ) vary with the mass ratio?

For a given θ $(m_1 > m_2)$, find the two values of ϕ and the corresponding velocities.

For a given mass ratio, for what angles are θ and ϕ the same? Explain.

Plot the energies of the two particles as a function of ϕ. Similarly, plot the momenta.

7.2.2   Displaying the Motion

The next two documents are an aid in visualizing the scattering process. The first provides a laboratory-frame view, the second a center-of-mass frame view. After the previous exercises, you will appreciate their content more.

• •   Load COLL4, two-dimensional elastic scattering: laboratory frame (see Fig. 7.5).

The equations are familiar by now. The values for m_1, m_2, and ϕ use the global equality and are located just above the plot region. The incident mass, m_1, is represented with a series of diamonds; the target, m_2, is represented with open rectangles. The separation between adjacent plot points is a measure of the relative velocity.

For a series of values of m_1, observe the scattering process. Examine the condition of the two different scattering angles ϕ for one θ for $m_1 > m_2$.

What changes would be required to input m_1, m_2, and θ (instead of ϕ)?

• •   Load COLL5, two-dimensional elastic scattering: center-of-mass frame (see Fig. 7.6).

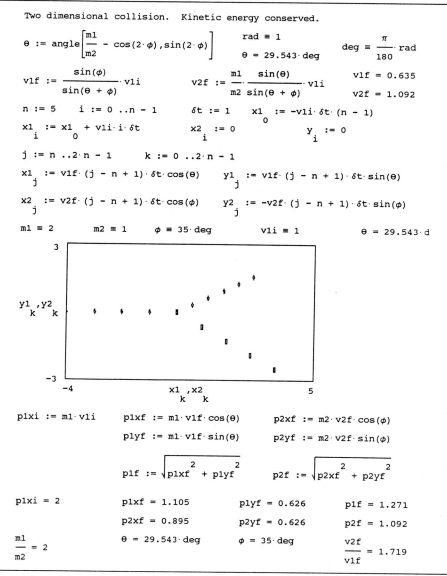

Two dimensional collision.   Kinetic energy conserved.

$$\theta := angle\left[\frac{m1}{m2} - \cos(2 \cdot \phi), \sin(2 \cdot \phi)\right]$$

$rad \equiv 1$

$\theta = 29.543 \cdot deg$

$deg \equiv \frac{\pi}{180} \cdot rad$

$$v1f := \frac{\sin(\phi)}{\sin(\theta + \phi)} \cdot v1i$$

$$v2f := \frac{m1}{m2} \cdot \frac{\sin(\theta)}{\sin(\theta + \phi)} \cdot v1i$$

$v1f = 0.635$

$v2f = 1.092$

$n := 5 \qquad i := 0 ..n - 1 \qquad \delta t := 1 \qquad x1_0 := -v1i \cdot \delta t \cdot (n - 1)$

$x1_i := x1_0 + v1i \cdot i \cdot \delta t \qquad x2_i := 0 \qquad y_i := 0$

$j := n ..2 \cdot n - 1 \qquad k := 0 ..2 \cdot n - 1$

$x1_j := v1f \cdot (j - n + 1) \cdot \delta t \cdot \cos(\theta) \qquad y1_j := v1f \cdot (j - n + 1) \cdot \delta t \cdot \sin(\theta)$

$x2_j := v2f \cdot (j - n + 1) \cdot \delta t \cdot \cos(\phi) \qquad y2_j := -v2f \cdot (j - n + 1) \cdot \delta t \cdot \sin(\phi)$

$m1 \equiv 2 \qquad m2 \equiv 1 \qquad \phi \equiv 35 \cdot deg \qquad v1i \equiv 1 \qquad \theta = 29.543 \cdot d$

$p1xi := m1 \cdot v1i \qquad p1xf := m1 \cdot v1f \cdot \cos(\theta) \qquad p2xf := m2 \cdot v2f \cdot \cos(\phi)$

$p1yf := m1 \cdot v1f \cdot \sin(\theta) \qquad p2yf := m2 \cdot v2f \cdot \sin(\phi)$

$$p1f := \sqrt{p1xf^2 + p1yf^2} \qquad p2f := \sqrt{p2xf^2 + p2yf^2}$$

$p1xi = 2 \qquad p1xf = 1.105 \qquad p1yf = 0.626 \qquad p1f = 1.271$

$p2xf = 0.895 \qquad p2yf = 0.626 \qquad p2f = 1.092$

$\frac{m1}{m2} = 2 \qquad \theta = 29.543 \cdot deg \qquad \phi = 35 \cdot deg \qquad \frac{v2f}{v1f} = 1.719$

Figure 7.5 COLL4, two-dimensional elastic scattering: laboratory frame.

The motion of m_1, the incident particle, is represented with diamonds. The motion of m_2, the target, is represented with open rectangles. The center of mass is represented with plus signs.

In the first plot region, a laboratory-frame view of the motion of the center of mass is included. In the second plot region, the center of mass is located at the origin. Motion is described in relation to this point. The separation between adjacent plot points is a measure of the relative velocity.

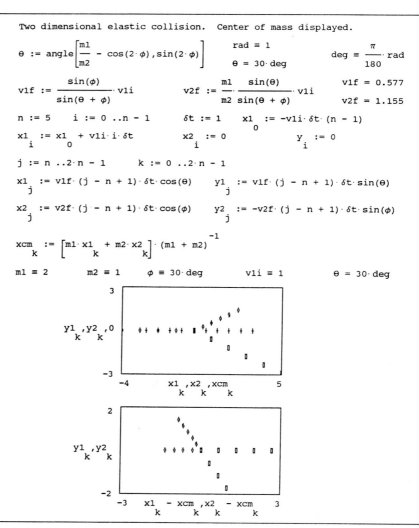

Two dimensional elastic collision. Center of mass displayed.

$$\theta := \text{angle}\left[\frac{m1}{m2} - \cos(2 \cdot \phi), \sin(2 \cdot \phi)\right]$$

$$\text{rad} \equiv 1 \qquad\qquad \deg \equiv \frac{\pi}{180} \cdot \text{rad}$$

$$\theta = 30 \cdot \deg$$

$$v1f := \frac{\sin(\phi)}{\sin(\theta + \phi)} \cdot v1i \qquad v2f := \frac{m1}{m2} \cdot \frac{\sin(\theta)}{\sin(\theta + \phi)} \cdot v1i \qquad \begin{array}{l} v1f = 0.577 \\ v2f = 1.155 \end{array}$$

$$n := 5 \quad i := 0 \,..\, n - 1 \qquad \delta t := 1 \qquad x1_0 := -v1i \cdot \delta t \cdot (n - 1)$$

$$x1_i := x1_0 + v1i \cdot i \cdot \delta t \qquad x2_i := 0 \qquad y_i := 0$$

$$j := n \,..\, 2 \cdot n - 1 \qquad k := 0 \,..\, 2 \cdot n - 1$$

$$x1_j := v1f \cdot (j - n + 1) \cdot \delta t \cdot \cos(\theta) \qquad y1_j := v1f \cdot (j - n + 1) \cdot \delta t \cdot \sin(\theta)$$

$$x2_j := v2f \cdot (j - n + 1) \cdot \delta t \cdot \cos(\phi) \qquad y2_j := -v2f \cdot (j - n + 1) \cdot \delta t \cdot \sin(\phi)$$

$$xcm_k := \left[m1 \cdot x1_k + m2 \cdot x2_k\right] \cdot (m1 + m2)^{-1}$$

$$m1 \equiv 2 \qquad m2 \equiv 1 \qquad \phi \equiv 30 \cdot \deg \qquad v1i \equiv 1 \qquad \theta = 30 \cdot \deg$$

Figure 7.6 COLL5, two-dimensional elastic scattering: center-of-mass frame.

Calculate momenta and energies in the center-of-mass frame. Try various set of values.

We have discussed only the cases of elastic or completely inelastic collisions. These are two extremes. For the case where the kinetic energy is reduced but is greater than that of the totally inelastic case, the restrictions on the scattering angles are still different. It is also possible that during the scattering process, an interaction can occur which will increase the kinetic energy. This, too, changes the relationship for the scattering angles. These cases are worth exploring if time is available.

7.3   Momentum and Rockets

You've probably heard the question about firing a high-powered rifle: which gets more momentum, the bullet or the rifle? The forces arising from the burning of gunpowder are internal, not external, to the gun-bullet system. Momentum is conserved. The momentum of the bullet and the rifle (plus whatever may be coupled to the rifle) are equal and opposite and sum to zero, the momentum before the rifle was fired.

(The problem of gunpowder is a totally separate but interesting problem. The gunpowder should not burn instantaneously; it should continue to burn as the bullet is propelled down the barrel. How should the pellets of gunpowder be shaped so that they burn at a constant rate as they are consumed and do not have a huge peak rate, as they would if they were spherically symmetric? For spherical objects, the ratio of surface area to volume is proportional to $1/r$. As spherical pellets burn, the radius is reduced and the surface area per mass of powder increases rapidly. The resulting huge rise in pressure associated with the end of the burn could be extremely dangerous. Gunpowder pellets are not spherical. One not uncommon design is that of small, hollow cylinders. In this case, the surface area and burn rate remain nearly constant as the pellets burn from both inside and outside.)

The problem of bullet and rifle can be extended to that of a machine gun and to that of a rocket. It is interesting to see how the discrete case (bullets) extends to the continuous case (ejecta from burning rocket fuel).

Consider first a machine gun or device capable of emitting units of mass. Imagine the device to be in interstellar space, far from any massive object and free to move without resistance (or free to move on a frictionless horizontal track in a vacuum). The motion is one-dimensional; there are no rotations. Also, we consider all the mass to be either in the gun or in the bullets.

A central question we would like to consider is: if the total mass of bullets is fixed, will the final velocity of the gun be any different if there is a very small number of large bullets or a large number of small bullets? Other questions can be asked. Each time a bullet is fired, the speed of the gun increases; how does the change in velocity of the rocket vary with each successive firing? Will doubling the velocity of the bullets result in doubling the final velocity of the rocket?

• •   Load COLL6, machine gun/rocket (see Fig. 7.7).

We approach the problem by specifying the mass of the rocket and the total mass and number of the bullets. We then: (1) determine the mass remaining in the rocket after each successive firing (rocket mass plus mass of unfired bullets), (2) calculate the change in velocity due to each succesive firing, (3) determine the velocity as a function of time by summing the changes.

The initial mass, M_0, is the sum of the rocket mass, *mroc*, plus the sum of all the bullets, *mbtot*. The mass of an individual bullet is specified

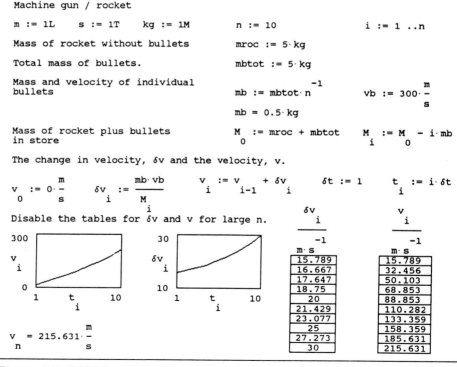

Figure 7.7 COLL6, machine gun/rocket.

in terms of the number of bullets, n, and the total mass of the bullets. The velocity of the bullets, v_b, is also specified. The rocket starts with velocity v_0. The change in velocity of the rocket each time a bullet is fired is δv, determined from the equation for momentum conservation: $m_b v_b = M_i |\delta v_i|$. The mass of the rocket decreases each time a bullet is fired; thus the change in velocity that the rocket experiences increases as each bullet is fired. We plot both the velocity and change in velocity of the rocket as a function of time; we assume the firings are regularly spaced in time.

The document is initially set with the mass of the rocket and the mass of the bullets equal. Keep the total mass constant at 10 kg. Explore the final velocity of the rocket as its mass is a decreasing fraction of the total. Let the final mass be $1/2$, $1/4$, then $1/8$ of the total. What functional form does this suggest?

How does the final velocity depend on the total number of bullets, if the mass of bullets remains constant?

How does the final velocity depend on the velocity of the bullets? Will doubling the velocity of the bullets double the final velocity of the rocket?

If there were 100 bullets, how must *mroc* and *mbtot* be divided so that the final velocity of the rocket is ten times that of the bullet v_b?

Rewrite the document so that you can plot the final velocity as a function of the number of bullets. See COLL7 for a solution.

In COLL7, we calculate the final velocity for a series of cases. When $i = 1$, there is one bullet with a mass of 5 kg. When $i = 2$, there are two bullets with a mass of 2.5 kg; etc. The bullet mass for each successive i is specified by mb_i. The index j is associated with the sequence of firings for a given i; for example, if $i = 4$, then j goes from 1 to 4. $M_{i,j}$ gives the mass remaining after each firing; $\delta v_{i,j}$ give the changes in velocity; $v_{i,j}$ show the sequence of rocket velocities.

The final velocity is $v(i, n)$, where i is related to the number and size of the bullets. The velocity is a maximum when $i = 1$, that is, when there is one huge bullet. However, as the number of bullets increases and the mass per bullet decreases, the velocity decreases — but not indefinitely. It approaches a limit. The tables show some sequences of δv and the velocity sequences.

The equation for change in velocity,

$$\delta v_i = \frac{m_b v_b}{M_i},$$

is for bullets of finite size. Properly taking into account the direction of acceleration of the system, the change in velocity for the infinitesimal case is

$$dv = -v_b \frac{dM}{M}. \tag{7.18}$$

Integrating this expression from the initial conditions of velocity, v_o, and mass, M_o, we get

$$\int_{v_o}^{v} dv = -v_b \int_{M_o}^{M} \frac{dM}{M}. \tag{7.19}$$

The result is

$$v - v_o = v_b \ln\left(\frac{M_o}{M}\right). \tag{7.20}$$

In our example, v_o is zero. Does the final velocity of our calculation approach $v_b \ln(M_o/M)$ as the number of bullets increases and the size decreases? For the case of 10 bullets, what is the percentage difference between the associated final velocity and that determined from the continuous integrated case? A number of variations can be explored here.

"It's alright. They'll fix you. They fix everything."

Robocop

CHAPTER

8

Rotational Motion

The kinematic equations for rotational motion are in one-to-one correspondence with the kinematic equations for linear motion. Linear velocity and linear acceleration are represented by the definitions

$$v = \frac{dx}{dt} \qquad a = \frac{dv}{dt},$$

angular velocity and angular acceleration are similarly defined:

$$\omega = \frac{d\theta}{dt} \qquad \alpha = \frac{d\omega}{dt}. \qquad (8.1)$$

Any linear kinematic equation has its angular analogue. If you know one set, you know the other. For example,

$$x = x_o + v_o t + \frac{1}{2} a t^2$$

and

$$\theta = \theta_o + \omega_o t + \frac{1}{2} \alpha t^2. \qquad (8.2)$$

The linear and angular relations are not independent. Consider a circle of radius r. Measure along the circumference a linear distance, an arc

163

length, s, equal to one radius. The angle subtended by this arc length is, by definition, one radian. That is, when $s = r$, $\theta = 1$. As the arc length increases or decreases, the angle subtended increases or decreases proportionately; $s \propto \theta$. Combining these two concepts, you can see that

$$s = r\,\theta. \tag{8.3}$$

This relation connects linear and angular displacement and indirectly is the link to similar equations for velocity and acceleration.

For constant r, taking a derivative with respect to time yields

$$\frac{ds}{dt} = r\frac{d\theta}{dt}$$

or

$$v = r\omega, \tag{8.4}$$

where $\omega = d\theta/dt$. A second derivative with respect to time yields

$$\frac{d^2s}{dt^2} = r\frac{d^2\theta}{dt^2} \quad \text{or} \quad \frac{dv}{dt} = r\frac{d\omega}{dt}$$

or

$$a = r\,\alpha. \tag{8.5}$$

8.1 Cycloidal Motion

When an object with a circular cross section rolls without slipping, the object translates as it rotates. The distance the center moves and the angle through which the object turns are related by $s = r\,\theta$. For example, if the object (for simplicity, we will refer to it as a cylinder) turns through one revolution as it rolls, the center moves one circumference. The velocity and acceleration of the center of the cylinder are given by $v = r\omega$ and $a = r\,\alpha$, respectively.

If the cylinder rolls with constant angular velocity, the center translates with constant linear velocity. The position of the center is given by

$$x_c = v_c t \quad \text{or} \quad x_c = R\omega t, \tag{8.6}$$

where R is the rolling radius. We note that each revolution corresponds to 2π radians or $\#radians = 2\pi\,\#revs$ and that

$$\omega = 2\pi f, \tag{8.7}$$

where f is the frequency in revolutions or cycles per second (Hz). This permits us to express the motion of the center of our cylinder as

$$x_c = R\,2\pi ft = Cft. \tag{8.8}$$

We describe the motion of any other point on the end face of the cylinder as a combination of translation and rotation. The location of any point on the cylinder, relative to the center, is given by $x = r\cos(\theta)$ and $y = r\sin(\theta)$, where θ is measured counterclockwise from the x-axis and r is the distance from the center. If the cylinder rotates uniformly with constant angular velocity, ω, then relative to the center the locations are written

$$x = r\cos(\omega t + \theta_o) \qquad y = r\sin(\omega t + \theta_o). \qquad (8.9)$$

If the cylinder is not spinning but rolling, the motions relative to the center are unchanged. The net motion is

$$x = R\omega t + r\cos(-\omega t + \theta_o) \qquad y = R + r\sin(-\omega t + \theta_o) \qquad (8.10)$$

The minus sign is present because the rotation due to the rolling motion in the positive x direction is clockwise rather than counterclockwise.

• •   Load ROT1, cycloidal motion (see Fig. 8.1).

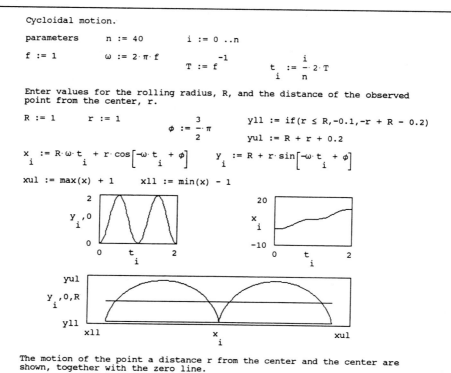

Cycloidal motion.

parameters $n := 40$ $i := 0 \,..\, n$

$f := 1$ $\omega := 2 \cdot \pi \cdot f$

$T := f^{-1}$ $t_i := \dfrac{i}{n} \cdot 2 \cdot T$

Enter values for the rolling radius, R, and the distance of the observed point from the center, r.

$R := 1$ $r := 1$ $\phi := \dfrac{3}{2} \cdot \pi$ $yll := if(r \le R, -0.1, -r + R - 0.2)$

$yul := R + r + 0.2$

$x_i := R \cdot \omega \cdot t_i + r \cdot \cos\left[-\omega \cdot t_i + \phi\right]$ $y_i := R + r \cdot \sin\left[-\omega \cdot t_i + \phi\right]$

$xul := max(x) + 1$ $xll := min(x) - 1$

The motion of the point a distance r from the center and the center are shown, together with the zero line.

Figure 8.1 ROT1, cycloidal motion.

Examine the cycloidal motion of a point on a cylinder with rolling radius R. The distance of the point from the center of the cylinder is r; r is not restricted to values less than R. The angular velocity is ω. The y vs. x plot shows two cycles of the motion; the motion of the center point is also shown. Change the number of cycles if you prefer a different combination.

Why are the plots of the x vs. t and y vs. t motions so different? Is the x motion cyclic?

The case shown is for $r = R$. Examine cases for $r < R$ and $r > R$. Before performing the computations for the different cases, predict what each of the three plots will look like. Then change r and process the document.

The initial phase angle ϕ is $3\pi/2$. Explain why this phase angle was selected. Can you make the motion start anywhere you would like within the cycle?

Imagine that there exist two coordinate systems that have a common origin. One of the systems is at rest; the other rotates with angular velocity ω. At $t = 0$, the two coordinate systems are aligned. At any time t, the relationship between the two sets is given by

$$X_i = x_i \cdot \cos(\omega t_i) + y_i \cdot \sin(\omega t_i) \tag{8.11}$$

$$Y_i = -x_i \cdot \sin(\omega t_i) + y_i \cdot \cos(\omega t_i), \tag{8.12}$$

which is a standard transformation between coordinate systems. The angle between the systems increases linearly with time (ωt).

• • Load ROT2, translation viewed from a rotating frame (see Fig. 8.2).

A simple motion in one frame, when observed from a different frame, can be complex. To appreciate how a particular pattern might develop, it is helpful to approach the final form in a series of small changes from a condition that is readily understood. For example, start with no rotation, followed by a case with a very small rate of rotation, and then continue to increase ω. If the rate becomes too large, the pattern may be unrealistic and a series of straight lines may be drawn. To see the actual pattern at high rotation rates, it is necessary to increase the number of points at which x and y are calculated and decrease the time interval.

Increase ω from 0 to 1 in small steps (for example, 0.1). Observe the development of the pattern. Back up to remind yourself how a pattern developed.

Change $t_i = (i/N) \cdot 1 \cdot \pi$. Observe when $\omega = 1, 2, 3, 4$.

Translation as seen in a rotating frame.

$N := 40$ $i := 0 ..N$ $\omega := 1$ $t_i := \dfrac{i}{N} \cdot 4 \cdot \pi$ $rad := 1$

$x_i := 2 \cdot t_i - 4 \cdot \pi$ $y_i := 1$ $deg := \dfrac{\pi}{180} \cdot rad$

$X_i := x_i \cdot \cos\left[\omega \cdot t_i\right] + y_i \cdot \sin\left[\omega \cdot t_i\right]$ $Y_i := -x_i \cdot \sin\left[\omega \cdot t_i\right] + y_i \cdot \cos\left[\omega \cdot t_i\right]$

$L := 15$

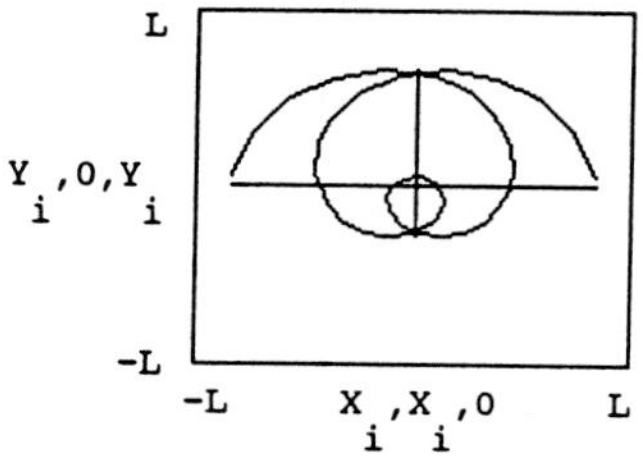

$\omega \cdot t_N = 720 \cdot deg$

$\omega \cdot t_N = 12.566$

$Y_i, 0, Y_i$

$X_i, X_i, 0$

Figure 8.2 ROT2, translation viewed from a rotating frame.

Observing motion from a rotating frame could lead the unsuspecting observer to believe that some force were acting to cause the nonrectilinear motion.

8.2   Moment of Inertia

Although the kinematic relations between linear and rotational motion are in complete correspondence, this is not true of the dynamical relationships. If a net force is applied to a mass, the mass accelerates in proportion to the force no matter how the mass is distributed within the object. If a net torque is applied to a rigid object, the object experiences angular acceleration, the rate depending on both the quantity of mass and how the mass is distributed.

The moment of inertia, I, the angular analogue to mass, includes in its expression both the quantity of mass and its distribution. For a system of discrete parts, the moment of inertia is given by

$$I = \sum_i m_i \, r_i^2, \tag{8.13}$$

where the r_i are measured from the axis about which the motion takes place. If the system is continuous, then the sum becomes an integral:

$$I = \int r^2 \, dm = \int \rho \, r^2 \, dV, \tag{8.14}$$

where ρ is the density and dV is a volume element. Again, r is a measure of the distance from the axis for which the moment is calculated. Choosing a different axis results in a different moment.

• •   An estimation problem. A large icecap at the south pole of a planet melts. Assume that the planet is completely covered with water (or ice). Determine the change in the water level, which rises because of the increased volume of water caused by the melting of the ice. Ignore any change in water volume due to temperature change. How much does the moment of intertia change?

Let the planet have the radius of the earth. You must supply the other quantities, such as the thickness and density of the ice and the extent of the ice sheet. Consider the icecap to be a cylinder. Examine the size of Antarctica for an estimate of the radius of the cylinder.

• •   Examine the moment of inertia of a spherical shell. A spherical shell is a sphere with a spherically symmetric cavity concentric with the outer surface. The moment of inertia of a solid sphere is

$$I_{\text{sph}} = \frac{2}{5} m r^2.$$

The moment of inertia of a spherical shell can be determined by taking the difference in moments between two solid spheres, one with the radius of the sphere and the other with the radius of the cavity.

Load ROT3, moment of inertia of a spherical shell (see Figs. 8.3 and 8.4).

The outer radius is rs; the cavity radius is rc. I_s is the moment of a sphere with radius rs; I_c is the moment of a sphere with radius rc.

Explain the form of I_s and I_c. Why is r raised to the fifth power?

When the radius of the cavity is one-half that of the sphere, by what fraction is the moment of inertia reduced? What cavity radius will result in a shell with a moment 75% of the solid value? 50%? 25%? (Try different values of rc.)

In the second part of the document, the moment of inertia of a solid sphere, $I_{ss}(r)$, is defined in functional form. The function $I(r_1, r_2)$ is the difference between the moments of two solid spheres with radii r_1 and r_2 and gives the moment of a spherical shell with outer radius r_1 and inner radius r_2. For a range of values of r_2, the ratio of the moments of inertia of the shell to that of a solid sphere with the same outer radius is shown.

Now try something slightly different. Calculate the radius of a solid sphere that has the same moment of inertia as that of a spherical shell. Let the outer radius of the shell be $r_1 = 1$. Let the radius of the cavity be r_2 and take on a range of values. Calculate the radii r_3 of solid spheres that have the same moments as the shells. Plot r_3 vs. r_2.

Determine the moment of inertia of a spherical shell. Let the radius of the sphere, rs, equal one. Specify the radius of the cavity, rc, centered about the origin. Compare the moment of inertia of the shell with that of a solid sphere with the same outside radius.

$$rs := 1 \qquad rc := 0.5 \qquad N := 24 \qquad i := 0\ ..N \qquad \theta_i := 2 \cdot \pi \cdot \frac{i}{N}$$

$$xs_i := rs \cdot \cos\left[\theta_i\right] \qquad ys_i := rs \cdot \sin\left[\theta_i\right] \qquad xc_i := rc \cdot \cos\left[\theta_i\right] \qquad yc_i := rc \cdot \sin\left[\theta_i\right]$$

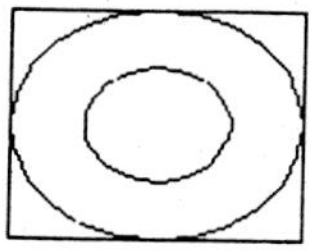

$$\rho := 1$$

$$Is := \frac{2}{5} \cdot \rho \cdot \frac{4}{3} \cdot \pi \cdot rs^5 \qquad Ic := \frac{2}{5} \cdot \rho \cdot \frac{4}{3} \cdot \pi \cdot rc^5$$

$$Is = 1.676 \qquad Ic = 0.052$$

$$\frac{Is - Ic}{Is} = 0.969 \qquad \frac{Ic}{Is} = 0.031$$

The moment of inertia of a sphere with cavity, relative to a solid sphere of the same size, is plotted as a function of the cavity radius.

$$r1 := 1 \qquad r2 := 0,.05 \ ...95 \qquad\qquad Iss(r) := \frac{2}{5} \cdot \rho \cdot \frac{4}{3} \cdot \pi \cdot r^5$$

$$I(r1,r2) := Iss(r1) - Iss(r2)$$

$$Iss(r1) = 1.676$$

$$I(r1,0) = 1.676$$

$$\frac{I(rs,rc)}{Iss(rs)} = 0.969$$

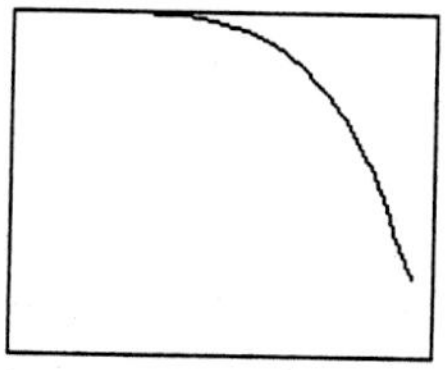

Given the moment of inertia of a shell as a fraction of the moment of a solid sphere of equal radius, find the corresponding cavity radius.

$$f := 0.5 \qquad r := 1 \qquad r' := 0.5$$

given $\qquad I(r,r') \approx f \cdot Iss(r) \qquad\qquad r' := find(r') \qquad\qquad r' = 0.871$

or to find that fraction of the moment of inertia associated with a shell of a particular cavity radius:

$$f := 0.5 \qquad r := 1 \qquad r' := 0.5$$

given $\qquad I(r,r') \approx f \cdot Iss(r) \qquad\qquad f := find(f) \qquad\qquad f = 0.969$

Figure 8.3 ROT3, moment of inertia of a spherical shell. (See the next figure for the rest of the document.)

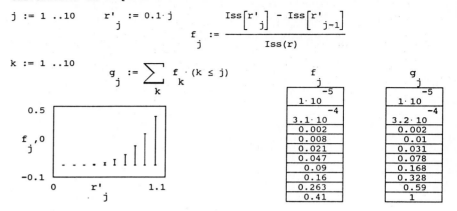

Divide the solid sphere into a set of concentric subshells. Find the contribution of each shell to the total moment of inertia. Perform calculations in steps of 0.1 * r.

$$j := 1 .. 10 \qquad r'_j := 0.1 \cdot j \qquad f_j := \frac{Iss\left[r'_j\right] - Iss\left[r'_{j-1}\right]}{Iss(r)}$$

$$k := 1 .. 10$$

$$g_j := \sum_k f_k \cdot (k \le j)$$

f_j	g_j
$1 \cdot 10^{-5}$	$1 \cdot 10^{-5}$
$3.1 \cdot 10^{-4}$	$3.2 \cdot 10^{-4}$
0.002	0.002
0.008	0.01
0.021	0.031
0.047	0.078
0.09	0.168
0.16	0.328
0.263	0.59
0.41	1

Figure 8.4 ROT3 *continued.*

In the third section of the document are two solve blocks, which provide additional means for extracting numerical information about a shell. In the first solve block, specify what fraction, f, of the total moment of the solid sphere is associated with the shell. The solve block returns the corresponding cavity radius. In the second solve block, enter the radius and return the corresponding fraction.

Start with a sphere of outer radius 1, cavity radius 0.5, and density 1. Fill the cavity with material of density ρ_c. If $\rho_c = 2$, what is the moment of the combination? What density of the core results in equal contributions to the moment from both the core and the shell?

Finally, we imagine the sphere being subdivided into ten subshells (like an onion) each with thickness equal to 10% of the outer radius (see Fig. 8.4). (The innermost shell is actually a solid sphere with radius $0.1\, r$.)

The f_j represent the individual contributions. The g_j represent the sum out to the present radius.

Note the use of the Boolean control in the sum. For each value of k, the sum is calculated for $k \le j$. The multiplication of this condition is equivalent to a logical AND.

● ●   Subdivide a cylinder similar to the manner in which the sphere was subdivided above, and compute the moments of the individual cylindrical shells. For rotation about the cylindrical axis, the moment of inertia of a solid cylinder is $I_{\text{cyl}} = 1/2\, m\, r^2$.

• • Subdivide a thin rod, and compute the moments of the individual contributions. Take the axis through the center of the rod and perpendicular to it. Of the three distributions examined, which has the most extreme dependence on r? Which the least? Why?

If the moment of inertia about an axis through the center of mass, I_{cm}, is known, the moment of inertia about any other parallel axis, I_{pa}, is given by

$$I_{pa} = I_{cm} + Md^2, \tag{8.15}$$

where M is the total mass and d is the distance between the parallel axes.

• • Plot the moment of inertia of a sphere as the distance between the axis of rotation and the axis through the center of mass increases from 0 to $4R$. At what distance is the Md^2 term 99% of the total?

• • As d increases, the details of the object become less important. Given a cylinder and a sphere with the same M and the same R, calculate the moment of inertia about an axis a distance d away from the center-of-mass axis of each. At what distance d do the two moments differ by 1%? Plot the ratio of moments as a function of the distance d.

Torque. A net force is required for masses to accelerate. A net torque is required for an object to undergo angular acceleration. Torque is the angular analogue to force. Just as

$$\sum F_{\text{ext}} = m\,a,$$

the angular analogue is

$$\sum \tau_{\text{ext}} = I\,\alpha. \tag{8.16}$$

Torque is defined in terms of a cross product:

$$\tau = r \times F, \tag{8.17}$$

where r is the displacement from the origin to the point where the force acts. Choose the origin at the axis about which the torque is to be considered.

A massless, frictionless pulley requires no torque to achieve angular acceleration. Tension in the string supporting a mass on either side of such a pulley (as in massless pulley Atwood machine) is the same. The r in $(r \times F)$ for each tension force is the same. Thus the torques have the same magnitude as the r's, the F's (the tensions), and the angles (between the radius vector and the tension) are equal. The torques, however, are oppositely directed; they would accelerate the pulley in opposite directions. The torques sum to zero.

A pulley with mass requires a net torque to achieve angular acceleration. Tensions in the string on either side of the pulley cannot be the same if there is acceleration. For the case of a pulley, the law of motion is, expressing the angular acceleration α in terms of a,

$$T_1 \cdot R - T_2 \cdot R = I \cdot \frac{a}{R}.$$

• • Consider once again the Atwood machine. Before considering the case with a massive pulley, and thus before the necessity to consider torque, quickly review the earlier document, MECH1, on the Atwood machine with a massless pulley. Check the terms in the equations of motion.

Before looking at ROT4, adapt the MECH1 document to include a massive pulley. Delete the units. The tensions need to be different. A third equation is needed for the dynamics of the pulley. Let the pulley mass $M := 3$ kg. Both sides of the find statement need to be adjusted to include b, T_1, and T_2. To add a row to a matrix, move the cursor to the last item in the matrix (in this case T) and press [Alt]M. Enter +1 and press return.

• • Load ROT4, Atwood machine II (see Fig. 8.5).

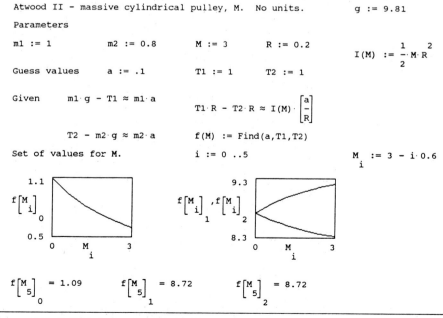

Figure 8.5 ROT4, Atwood machine II.

The suspended masses are m_1 and m_2; the mass of the pulley is M; the radius of the pulley, which is taken to be a cylinder, is R; the tensions in the string on either side of the pulley are T_1 and T_2 .

The given-find solve block is set up in functional form. There are three equations in the solve block, one associated with each of the masses. In this case, we take as the unknowns the acceleration and the tensions T_1 and T_2. In this case the find statement is set up so that on specifying a mass for the pulley, the function returns the values of a, T_1, and T_2.

In the first plot region, the acceleration is plotted as a function of pulley mass. In the second plot region, the two tensions are plotted as a function of pulley mass. Explain the shape of these curves.

Change the functional form of the find statement to depend not on the mass of the pulley but on the radius of the pulley. Let R go from 0.1 to 0.5 in steps of 0.1. It is also necessary to change the moment of inertia to depend on R rather than M. Similarly, in the plot regions, change the arguments. Explain your results.

8.3   Angular Momentum

Angular momentum of a particle relative to some axis is defined as

$$l = r \times p, \tag{8.18}$$

where r is the radius vector from the origin to a particle with momentum p. If we take the derivative of angular momentum with respect to time, we find

$$\frac{dl}{dt} = \frac{dr}{dt} \times p + r \times \frac{dp}{dt}.$$

The first term of the right-hand side is zero because the cross product of any vector with itself is zero:

$$\frac{dr}{dt} \times p = v \times mv = m(v \times v) = 0.$$

The derivative can then be written as

$$\frac{dl}{dt} = r \times \frac{dp}{dt}. \tag{8.19}$$

Identifying first force and then torque, the equation can be expressed as

$$\tau = \frac{dl}{dt}. \tag{8.20}$$

This equation can readily be generalized to a system of particles, and in general

$$\sum \tau_{\text{ext}} = \frac{dl}{dt}. \tag{8.21}$$

This equation is the angular analogue of $\sum F_{\text{ext}} = dp/dt$. Just as linear momentum is conserved in the absence of external forces, so is angular momentum conserved in the absence of external torques.

Angular momentum can be conveniently expressed as the product of the moment of inertia and the angular velocity. When there are no external torques and angular momentum is conserved, we have

$$I_{\text{init}}\, \omega_{\text{init}} = I_{\text{final}}\, \omega_{\text{final}}. \tag{8.22}$$

• • Model the change in rotation rate of a figure skater as she pulls in her arms. Keep the model very simple. Represent the body as a cylinder of mass M and radius R. Represent the arms as point masses, each of mass m, that can be moved in the range $R < r < r_{\text{max}}$.

The skater initially goes into a spin with arms extended and achieves an initial angular velocity, ω_{init}. Plot ω vs. r as the arms are pulled in. Plot rotational kinetic energy vs. r. Is the final velocity more sensitive to a decrease in R or an increase in r_{max}? Plot, for a given r_{max}, ω_{final} vs. R. Plot, for a given R, ω_{final} vs. r_{max}.

• • Model a diver performing a dive from the high board. Keep the model simple. Let the body be a sphere of radius R. Let each of the arms be point masses with a maximum extension of ra_{max} and mass m_a. Let each of the legs have length $r_{l_{\text{max}}}$ and mass m_l.

First determine the time between the leap from the board and the moment of entrance into the water. Include an initial upward velocity in the calculation.

Then decide what is necessary in order to complete a two and one-half somersault dive. The sequence should be: dive with full extension, pull in arms and legs to increase the rotation rate, and finally extend the arms and legs to slow the rotation for a smooth entry into the water.

Plot rotation rate vs. time for the complete dive. Plot angular displacement vs. time for the dive.

> The prize at the other end is a flight education worth one million dollars, but first you have to get past me.
>
> *An Officer and a Gentleman*

9

Statics

An object that remains at rest (or that travels with constant linear and angular velocity) is subject to zero net force and zero net torque. The forces must sum to zero, and the torques about any axis must sum to zero. If we restrict our consideration to the x-y plane, then we reduce the number of conditions from six to three:

$$\sum F_{\text{ext,x}} = 0 \qquad \sum F_{\text{ext,y}} = 0 \qquad \sum \tau_{\text{ext,z}} = 0. \qquad (9.1)$$

(What would the other three be?)

Recall that torque is defined as $\tau = r \times F$; thus the torque is perpendicular to the plane containing the r and F (in this case the x-y plane). The torque vector is directed along axes about which the object might turn subject to the applied torque.

9.1 Simple Truss

The simple truss is a very important element in the design of rigid structures. We examine the forces along the members of a simple truss.

Construct a triangle with all acute angles and a horizontal base. Join the sides of the triangle, the members, at the corners with pins that permit rotation and that exert no torques. Forces are directed along the members. Suspend a weight from the apex of the triangle. Determine the internal forces.

● ●   Load STAT1, simple truss (see Figs. 9.1 and 9.2).

Let the left end of the base of the triangle be referred to as a and the right end as b. The apex of the triangle is c. Let all the forces result from the suspended weight. Ignore the weight of the members.

Specify values for the altitude of the triangle h, the interior angles at the base of the triangle, α at point a and β at point b, and the suspended weight W.

There are no external horizontal forces. External vertical forces support the weighted triangle at the ends of the base. There are internal forces, which are directed along the lengths of the members.

First determine the external forces; there are two, F_{ay} and F_{by}. Two equations are necessary: one, the equation for vertical forces, and the other, the torque equation. An axis must be selected for the torque equation. Whatever axis is selected, any force acting along a line through that axis has no lever arm and is eliminated from consideration. In this case, the apex of the triangle is chosen; W acting along a line through that point is eliminated. The apex is at $x = 0$. In the given-find solve block are the two equations. The values F_{ay} and F_{by} are determined. These values can then be used to determine the internal forces.

The internal forces are determined using simple given-find solve blocks. You could solve these equations directly.

At the end of the document is the code that specifies the drawing of the triangle and the weight. Follow the path drawn. Which coodinates define the weight? Convenient plot limits are also specified.

Verify the equations for F_{ab}, F_{ac}, and F_{bc}.

Change the values of α and β; these values should be less than 90°. Observe the changes in F_{ay} and F_{by}. Also observe the forces F_{ab}, F_{ac}, and F_{bc}.

At corner a, what is the direction of the horizontal component of the force F_{ac}? At corner b, what is the direction of the horizontal component of F_{bc}?

Triangle supporting a weight.   rad $\equiv$ 1

$$\deg \equiv \frac{\pi}{180} \cdot \text{rad}$$

Select values for altitude of triangle, h, acute angles at base, and weight of suspended mass. (Sides of triangle have no weight.)

$h \equiv 1$ $\alpha \equiv 45 \cdot \deg$ $\beta \equiv 45 \cdot \deg$ $W \equiv 10$

$$l_{ac} \equiv \frac{h}{\sin(\alpha)} \qquad l_{bc} \equiv \frac{h}{\sin(\beta)} \qquad x_{ac} \equiv l_{ac} \cdot \cos(\alpha) \qquad x_{bc} \equiv l_{bc} \cdot \cos(\beta)$$

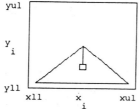

yul

y_i

yll

xll x_i xul

α is the interior angle at lower left
β is the interior angle at lower right.

The lower left corner is referred to as, a
the lower right corner, b,
the peak, c.

The peak is located at x = 0, y = h.

Guess values for the external vertical forces at points a and b, where the triangle is supported.

$F_{ay} := 5$ $F_{by} := 5$

Solve the static force and torque equations for the vertical forces.

Given $F_{ay} + F_{by} - W \approx 0$ $F_{ay} \cdot x_{ac} - F_{by} \cdot x_{bc} \approx 0$

$$\begin{bmatrix} F_{ay} \\ F_{by} \end{bmatrix} := \text{Find}\begin{bmatrix} F_{ay} , F_{by} \end{bmatrix} \qquad \begin{array}{l} F_{ay} = 5 \\[1mm] F_{by} = 5 \end{array}$$

Solve for forces in individual beams.

$$F_{ac} := \frac{F_{ay}}{\sin(\alpha)} \qquad F_{ab} := F_{ac} \cdot \cos(\alpha) \qquad F_{bc} := \frac{F_{by}}{\sin(\beta)}$$

$F_{ac} = 7.071$ $F_{ab} = 5$ $F_{bc} = 7.071$

Figure 9.1 STAT1, simple truss. (See the next figure for the rest of the document.)

Which of the beams, *ab, ac, bc*, are under compression and which under tension (force tending to pull them apart)?

If α equals β, at what angle does F_{ab} have the same magnitude as W?

• •   Invert the triangle, with point *c* beneath the line *ab*. The weight is suspended from *c*. Analyze the forces. Determine which members are under compression and which are under tension.

Details for plot region and limits.

```
i ≡ 1 ..10        z ≡ 0.15

x  ≡ -x        x  ≡ x          -z        z        x  ≡ x      x  ≡ x      x  ≡ 0
 2     ac       3    bc    x ≡ —    x ≡ -       7    6      9    8      10
                           6    2    8   2

y  ≡ h     y  ≡ h          h      y  ≡ y      y  ≡ y - z   y  ≡ y     y  ≡ y
 1          4          y  ≡ -      6    5      7    6       8    7     9    6
                        5   2

y   ≡ y     hr ≡ 1   ·cos(α) + 1   ·cos(β)     vr ≡ h     r ≡ if(vr > hr,vr,hr)
 10    9            ac              bc

xll ≡ -⎡x   + z⎤     xul ≡ r + xll + 2·z    yll ≡ -z    yul ≡ r + z
       ⎣ ac    ⎦
```

Figure 9.2 STAT1 *continued.*

● ●   Extend this concept to a truss structure of three triangles and seven members. Analyze the forces. Determine which members are under compression and which are under tension.

9.2   Center of Mass

The center of mass of an object is, in effect, the average location of the mass. If a massive object is placed in a uniform gravitational field, each element of the object, dm, is acted on by the gravitational force. All those individual forces are equivalent to a single force, equal to Mg, acting at the center of mass of the body.

We can calculate the location of the center of mass of an object by a weighted average calculation. If the masses are discrete, then the location of the center of mass is given by

$$x_{cm} = \frac{\sum m_i x_i}{\sum m_i} \quad \text{and} \quad y_{cm} = \frac{\sum m_i y_i}{\sum m_i}. \tag{9.2}$$

If the distribution is continuous, then the summation goes over to an integration:

$$x_{cm} = \frac{\int x \, dm}{\int dm} \quad \text{and} \quad y_{cm} = \frac{\int y \, dm}{\int dm}, \tag{9.3}$$

where dm could be expressed in terms of a volume density, a surface density, or a line density:

$$dm = \rho dV \quad \text{or} \quad dm = \sigma dA \quad \text{or} \quad dm = \lambda dl,$$

where the units of ρ, σ, and λ are mass per volume, mass per area, and mass per length, respectively.

If we apply these concepts to determining the center of mass of a triangle, the mass elements are those of area (see Fig. 9.3). Let the elements of area be thin rectangles of height y and width dx. The y-location of the center of mass of each of these strips is $y/2$. The area associated with the mass element dm is $y\,dx$, so we integrate:

$$y_{cm} = \frac{\int_0^1 (y(x)/2)\, y(x)\, dx}{\int_0^1 y(x)\, dx}.$$

The corresponding x-value is obtained by replacing the y-value, $y/2$, with x.

• •   Four particles are located at the corners of a square. The masses have the values 1, 2, 3, and 4. Find the center of mass.

• •   Calculate the center of mass of the area enclosed by $y(x) = \sin(x)$ in the range from zero to π. Determine the center of mass of the area enclosed by the cosine curve over the same range.

• •   Determine the center of mass of the semicircular region bounded by $x^2 + y^2 = 2$ with $x > 0$. Try repeating for a hemisphere.

9.3   A Tower of Blocks

The pressure between stacked blocks is similar to the static pressure in a fluid. The process is interesting because we can analyze a simple system consisting of a small number of blocks and describe approximately the pressure in either a compressible or an incompressible fluid.

Construct a tower by neatly stacking one block on top of another. Each block added increases the weight of the column and increases the pressure between the blocks beneath it. The problem is to determine the pressure between the blocks. If we know the density, volume, and cross-sectional area, we can determine the weight per area or pressure.

• •   Load STAT3, incompressible blocks (see Fig. 9.4).

The blocks are 1 m by 1 m by 10 cm. The blocks have the density of aluminum. We calculate the weight of one block and the associated pressure. Descending from the top of the stack, the pressure between successive blocks, P_i, increases in proportion to the number of blocks. The distance from the top of the stack is h_i; the elevation above the ground is el_i.

Center of mass of a triangle by integration.

The triangle is divided into strips with area, y dx. The center of mass of a strip is (x,y/2).

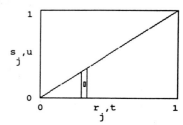

The function. $y(x) := x$

$$ycm := \frac{\displaystyle\int_0^\pi \frac{y(x)}{2} \cdot y(x)\ dx}{\displaystyle\int_0^\pi y(x)\ dx}$$

$$xcm := \frac{\displaystyle\int_0^\pi x \cdot y(x)\ dx}{\displaystyle\int_0^\pi y(x)\ dx}$$

$xcm = 2.094$

$ycm = 1.047$

If the area is divided into rectangles with horizontal orientation, the process is the same.

$xx = 2.094$

$$xx := \frac{\displaystyle\int_0^\pi \left[y + \frac{\pi - y}{2}\right] \cdot (\pi - y)\ dy}{\displaystyle\int_0^\pi (\pi - y)\ dy}$$

$x := 0,0.1\ ..\pi$

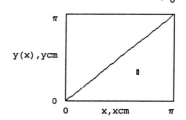

The coordinates to draw the first triangle and show a representative area.

$r_1 \equiv 0$ $s_1 \equiv 0$ $r_2 \equiv 1$ $s_2 \equiv 1$ $r_3 \equiv 1$ $s_3 \equiv 0$

$r_4 \equiv 0$ $s_4 \equiv 0$ $r_5 \equiv 0.3$ $s_5 \equiv 0.3$ $r_6 \equiv 0.3$ $s_6 \equiv 0$

$r_7 \equiv 0.34$ $s_7 \equiv 0$ $r_8 \equiv 0.34$ $s_8 \equiv 0.34$ $t \equiv .32$ $u \equiv \dfrac{t}{2}$

$j \equiv 1\ ..8$

Figure 9.3 STAT2, center of mass of a triangle.

Plots show that the pressure increases linearly as one descends through the pile of blocks, just as the pressure increases linearly as one descends into an incompressible fluid, such as water.

The equation for pressure in a fluid is given by

$$P = \rho g h, \tag{9.4}$$

A tower consists of a series of solid rectangular blocks stacked neatly on top of one another. Let the number of blocks be n. Determine the pressure between each of the blocks. (The lowest index corresponds to the maximum height.

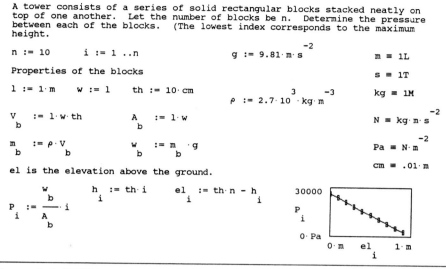

Figure 9.4 STAT3, incompressible blocks.

where h is the depth beneath the surface. Can the equation for P_i be rewritten to resemble this fluid equation?

In fact, the change of pressure with height (we use the same notation as in the document) is

$$\frac{\Delta P}{\Delta h} = \frac{w_b / A_b}{th} = \frac{m_b \cdot g}{A_b \cdot th} = \rho_c \frac{A_b\, th\, g}{A_b\, th} = \rho g.$$

This is identical to the standard expression for the pressure in a fluid, although if y is positive upward, a minus sign is introduced. Upon integration, this yields

$$P = P_{\text{surf}} + \rho g\, h. \tag{9.5}$$

P_{surf} is the pressure at the upper surface of the liquid, which could be atmospheric pressure. This pressure presses down on our tower of bricks as well.

In the previous example, the bricks were incompressible, as was the water in our fluid comparison. Now permit the blocks to be compressible. An effect of compression is that the density is no longer a constant. In the case of the tower of bricks, the density is greater near the ground than at the top of the tower.

Assume that each block has constant density, but different blocks have different densities. The compressibility of each block is proportional to the force applied, a Hooke's law behavior that can be expressed as $(F = -kx)$.

- • Load STAT4, compressible blocks (see Fig. 9.5).

A tower consists of a series of solid rectangular blocks stacked neatly on top of one another. Let the number of blocks be n; what is the pressure between each of the blocks. (Let the lowest index correspond to the maximum height.

$n := 10$ $i := 1 ..n$ $g := 9.81 \cdot m \cdot s^{-2}$ $m \equiv 1L$

Properties of the blocks $s \equiv 1T$

$l := 1 \cdot m$ $w := l$ $th := 10 \cdot cm$ $\rho := 2.7 \cdot 10^{3} \cdot kg \cdot m^{-3}$ $kg \equiv 1M$

$V_b := l \cdot w \cdot th$ $A_b := l \cdot w$ $N \equiv kg \cdot m \cdot s^{-2}$

$m_b := \rho \cdot V_b$ $w_b := m_b \cdot g$ $Pa \equiv N \cdot m^{-2}$

$cm \equiv .01 \cdot m$

Let the blocks be compressible. Let each block have constant density. The density of each block will increase as the distance from the top increases. The compressibility of each block is proportional to the force applied, a Hooke's law behavior. δth is the change in thickness of a block when another block is set on top of it.

$F := w_b$ $k_H := 3 \cdot 10^{5} \cdot \frac{N}{m}$ $\delta th := \frac{-F}{k_H}$ $F = 2.649 \cdot 10^{3} \cdot N$

$\delta V := w \cdot l \cdot \delta th$ $\delta th = -0.883 \cdot cm$

$th'_i := th + (i - 1) \cdot \delta th$ Thickness of individual blocks.

$k := 1 ..n$ $ir_i := n - i + 1$

$el_k := \sum_i th'_i \cdot (i \geq k)$

el - elevation above ground of the tops of individual bricks.

$P_i := \frac{w_b}{A_b} \cdot i$

The pressure as a function of the elevation.

$\frac{el_i}{m}$	$\frac{th'_i}{m}$
0.603	0.1
0.503	0.091
0.412	0.082
0.329	0.074
0.256	0.065
0.191	0.056
0.135	0.047
0.088	0.038
0.05	0.029
0.021	0.021

Figure 9.5 STAT4, compressible blocks.

The density of the top block is the uncompressed density. The block below it is compressed, the change in thickness being determined by Hooke's law. The change in thickness results in a change of volume and a change of density. Descending from the top of the tower, for each successive brick, the density increases and the thickness decreases. The elevation is determined by summing the thickness of the compressed blocks. Pressure between bricks is the same as in the previous case. The mass of the bricks, of course, has not changed.

The thickness of the blocks, th_i', is plotted. The spring constant for the bricks is intentionally made quite small. By the time the bottom of the pile has been reached, a significant change in total thickness has occurred. Summing the individual heights starting from the bottom, the elevation is determined (notice the Boolean condition in the sum) and plotted. The elevation and individual thicknesses are shown in tabular form. Finally the pressure is plotted as a function of the elevation.

Plot the pressure vs. elevation on a semi-log plot. Does this curve resemble (somewhat) an exponential? (Let plot type be V.)

Explore the pressure curve for a variety of values of k. Note that k is very nearly at its lower limit. Why might there be a lower limit? How would it manifest itself? By what factor would k need to increase before the pressure vs. elevation curve begins to look like the incompressible case?

In an analysis of the compression, the previous equation still applies:

$$\frac{dP}{dy} = -\rho\, g. \tag{9.6}$$

In addition, we recognize that a consequence of the compression is that the density is proportional to the pressure, or

$$\frac{\rho}{\rho_o} = \frac{P}{P_o}. \tag{9.7}$$

Solving the second equation for ρ and substituting in the first yields

$$\frac{dP}{dy} = -c\,P \qquad \text{where} \qquad c = \frac{\rho_o}{P_o}\,g.$$

Upon integration, we obtain

$$P = P_o e^{-cy}. \tag{9.8}$$

This relation expresses, for example, the approximate pressure in the earth's atmosphere as a function of elevation.

The ratio ρ/P for an ideal gas, $PV = nRT$, can be expressed in terms of atomic weight, M, and the temperature, T. Thus we have

$$\rho = \frac{m}{V} = \frac{mP}{nRT}$$

and

$$\frac{\rho}{P} = \frac{M}{RT}.$$

In this case,

$$c = \frac{\rho_o}{P_o} g = \frac{Mg}{RT}. \tag{9.9}$$

Plot the pressure associated with the compressible tower together with the pressure associated with a gas, $P' = P'_o \cdot \exp(-c\,el_i)$ vs. el_i. Pick values for P'_o and c. Note that c has units of $1/m$. Two very simple values with P'_o in even thousands and c an integer give an excellent fit. Why would you expect a deviation at the very highest elevation? If k is increased, the curvature diminishes. How are k and c related?

I wanted to tear my teeth out,
I didn't know what I wanted to do.
And I want to remember it, I never want to forget it.
I never want to forget. And then I realized — like I was *shot* ...
like I was *shot* with a diamond ...
a diamond bullet right through my forehead. And I thought,
"My God, the genius of that".

Apocalypse Now

CHAPTER
10

Oscillations

10.1 Simple Harmonic Motion

Motion that repeats in a periodic way is called harmonic. Harmonic motion is called simple harmonic if the motion is described by a sinusoidal function. For example, the equation

$$x = A \sin(\omega t + \phi) \tag{10.1}$$

describes the displacement of a particle as a periodic function of time. The motion is simple harmonic. A is the amplitude of the motion, the maximum displacement; $|x| \leq A$. When the sine function is at its maximum $x = A$. At the time $t = 0$, $x = A \sin(\phi)$. The angular frequency, as noted above, is

$$\omega = 2 \pi f. \tag{10.2}$$

The period is related to the frequency by

$$T = \frac{1}{f}. \tag{10.3}$$

For example, if a motion has a frequency of ten cycles per second (10Hz), the period is one-tenth of a second per cycle. Note that f, T, and ω are interchangeable and all contain the same basic information:

$$\omega = 2\pi f = \frac{2\pi}{T} \qquad f = \frac{1}{T} = \frac{\omega}{2\pi} \qquad T = \frac{1}{f} = \frac{2\pi}{\omega}.$$

The equations for velocity and acceleration are readily obtained by taking derivatives with respect to time:

$$x = A\sin(\omega t + \phi) \qquad\qquad x_{\max} = A \qquad (10.4)$$

$$v = \frac{dx}{dt} = A\omega\cos(\omega t + \phi) \qquad\qquad v_{\max} = A\omega \qquad (10.5)$$

$$a = \frac{dv}{dt} = \frac{d^2 x}{dt^2} = -A\omega^2\sin(\omega t + \phi) \qquad a_{\max} = A\omega^2 \qquad (10.6)$$

• • What is the average velocity? What is the root-mean-squared velocity?

The first two documents in this chapter include these basic expressions, reminding us of the role of the phase angle and relating uniform circular motion with simple harmonic motion.

• • Load HM1, simple harmonic motion (see Fig. 10.1).

The position, velocity, and acceleration are plotted as a function of time. Notice the relative starting point and sign of each curve. Over what portion of the position curve are the signs of position and velocity the same? Are the signs of velocity and acceleration the same?

When the acceleration is at its maximum, what is the position? Process for values of ϕ equal to $0, \pi/4, \pi/2, 3\pi/4$, and π. Express the function $y = A\sin(\omega t + \pi/4)$ in terms of the cosine function. Plot to verify.

Simple harmonic motion and uniform circular motion are interrelated. Consider a radius vector of length A oriented at an angle θ counterclockwise from the positive x-axis. The projection of the vector on the y-axis is $A\sin(\theta)$. If θ increases uniformly in time, $\theta = \omega t$, the tip of the vector traces out a circle. The projection, $A\sin(\omega t)$, executes simple harmonic motion.

In the second part of HM1, we show a radius vector and its projection at $t = 0$. We see the y-projection of the vector as a function of time. We also show the exponential representation with a complex argument to display the radius vector at its initial position. (Refer to Chapter 2.) If the angle increased in time, the vector would rotate.

Let ϕ take on a series of values. Note that the y-component of the vector and the tip of the projection vector give the initial y-value for the

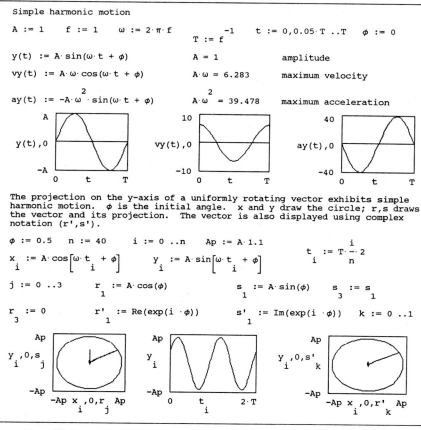

Simple harmonic motion

$A := 1$ $f := 1$ $\omega := 2 \cdot \pi \cdot f$ $T := f^{-1}$ $t := 0, 0.05 \cdot T \; ..T$ $\phi := 0$

$y(t) := A \cdot \sin(\omega \cdot t + \phi)$ $A = 1$ amplitude

$vy(t) := A \cdot \omega \cdot \cos(\omega \cdot t + \phi)$ $A \cdot \omega = 6.283$ maximum velocity

$ay(t) := -A \cdot \omega^2 \cdot \sin(\omega \cdot t + \phi)$ $A \cdot \omega^2 = 39.478$ maximum acceleration

The projection on the y-axis of a uniformly rotating vector exhibits simple harmonic motion. ϕ is the initial angle. x and y draw the circle; r,s draws the vector and its projection. The vector is also displayed using complex notation (r',s').

$\phi := 0.5$ $n := 40$ $i := 0 \;..n$ $Ap := A \cdot 1.1$ $t_i := T \cdot \dfrac{i}{n} \cdot 2$

$x_i := A \cdot \cos\left[\omega \cdot t_i + \phi\right]$ $y_i := A \cdot \sin\left[\omega \cdot t_i + \phi\right]$

$j := 0 \;..3$ $r_1 := A \cdot \cos(\phi)$ $s_1 := A \cdot \sin(\phi)$ $s_3 := s_1$

$r_3 := 0$ $r'_1 := \mathrm{Re}(\exp(i \cdot \phi))$ $s'_1 := \mathrm{Im}(\exp(i \cdot \phi))$ $k := 0 \;..1$

Figure 10.1 HM1, simple harmonic motion.

y vs. t curve. If we could display the rotating vector in time, its projection would always correspond to the y-value in the y vs. t curve.

• •   Load HM2, rotating vector (see Fig. 10.2).

MathCAD cannot display animation, but if several curves are plotted you can see them laid down in time.

In the document, we show four locations of the rotating vector and the four corresponding y vs. t curves. Imagine the radius vector rotating counterclockwise; the four positions lead us through the maximum and most of the way to a minimum. From our fixed vantage point, the y-curve appears to step to the left.

Rotating vector and simple harmonic motion.   Connect the projection of
the rotating vector on the y-axis of the first plot region with the y-t
curves in the second.

$A := 1$ $f := 1$ $\omega := 2 \cdot \pi \cdot f$ $T := f^{-1}$ $t := 0, 0.05 \cdot T \,..T$ $Ap := A \cdot 1.1$

$n := 40$ $i := 0 \,..n$ $m := 3$ $k := 0 \,..m$ $l := 0 \,..2 \cdot m$

$\phi o := \dfrac{\pi}{3}$ $\phi_k := 0.15 \cdot k \cdot 2 \cdot \pi + \phi o$ $t_i := \dfrac{i}{n} \cdot 2 \cdot T$

$y_{k,i} := A \cdot \sin\left[\omega \cdot t_i + \phi_k\right]$ $r_{2 \cdot k} := A \cdot \cos\left[\phi_k\right]$ $s_{2 \cdot k} := A \cdot \sin\left[\phi_k\right]$

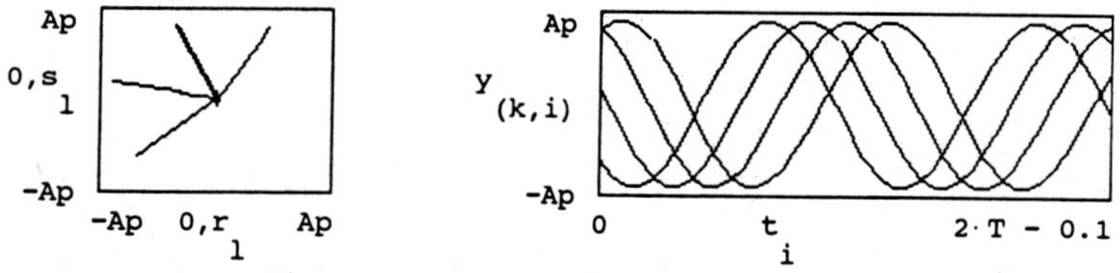

Figure 10.2 HM2, rotating vector.

Try different phase angles; ϕ_0 gives the starting position. In the expression for ϕ_k, changing the value from 0.15 will change the size of the angle between successive pictures. Increasing m will increase the number of snapshots of the motion. However, the y vs. t graph becomes cluttered as m increases.

10.1.1 Spring-Mass Oscillation

The force exerted by a spring that obeys Hooke's law is

$$F = -k\,x. \tag{10.7}$$

The force is a linear (proportional to x), restoring ($-$) force. If x is positive, F is negative; if x is negative, F is positive; thus the tendency is always to return to the equilibrium position. A linear restoring force results in simple harmonic motion.

Attach a mass to the end of a spring, stretch the spring, and release it. Let the force exerted by the spring be the only force acting. On applying Newton's second law, we obtain

$$-k\,x = m\frac{d^2 x}{dt^2}. \tag{10.8}$$

If $x = A\sin(\omega t)$, $d^2x/dt^2 = -\omega^2 x$. After substituting, we obtain an expression relating the angular frequency, the spring constant, and the mass.

$$-kx = -m\omega^2 x \qquad \text{or} \qquad \omega = \sqrt{\frac{k}{m}} \qquad\qquad (10.9)$$

Every frequency equation for oscillatory motion includes a ratio of terms of a similar nature; k is a measure of the restoring force, and m is a measure of inertia. If there is a large restoring force and a small mass, the resulting oscillation will have a high frequency; if there is a small restoring force and a large mass, the resulting oscillation will have a low frequency.

As the spring is stretched, work is performed:

$$W = \int F \cdot dx. \qquad\qquad (10.10)$$

If we stretch the spring, the force we apply is directed opposite to that of the spring, $F_{\text{appl}} = kx$:

$$W = \int_0^x kx\,dx = \frac{1}{2}kx^2. \qquad\qquad (10.11)$$

The energy is stored as potential energy. In an oscillating system the energy flows back and forth between kinetic and potential energy.

• •   Load HM3, simple harmonic motion in a spring-mass system (see Fig. 10.3).

In the specification of parameters, the spring constant, k, and the angular frequency, ω, are defined. Given these choices, the value for the mass is determined. Change the description so that you input k and m, rather than k and ω.

Plot ω vs. k for a mass of 0.1 kg; let successive values of k increase by factors of $10^{n/2}$. Plot a corresponding curve that shows how much the spring would stretch if the mass of 0.1 kg were simply hung from the spring (with no oscillation taking place). At 10^3 Hz, how much does the spring stretch in supporting the mass? At 10^5 Hz?

In the next section, the work done in stretching the spring is calculated. The work is defined as a function and then calculated for a series of x-values and plotted. A comparison is then made with the expression $(1/2)\,kx^2$, which was determined by integrating the Hooke's law force analytically.

Next, we examine the kinetic and potential energy as a function of time. The position is specified as a function of time. The velocity is obtained by taking the derivative of position with respect to time. The

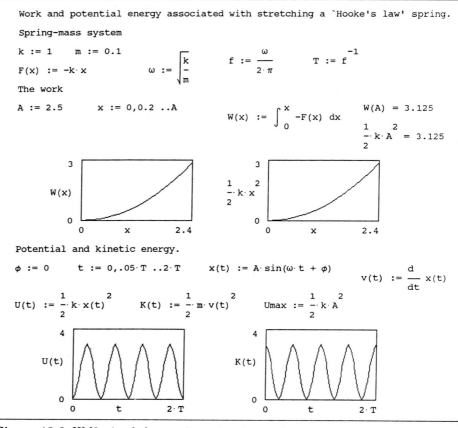

Figure 10.3 HM3, simple harmonic motion in a spring-mass system.

potential energy, $U(t)$, and kinetic energy, $K(t)$, are then defined and plotted. Note that $U(t)$ and $K(t)$ are out of phase. What is the phase difference? Is it the same phase difference as between position and velocity? The maximum value of the potential energy, $U_{\max}$, is given. Determine the maximum value of the kinetic energy, $K_{\max}$.

Plot in one region $U(t), K(t), U(t) + K(t)$ vs. t. Let the upper limit of the ordinate be $1.1 \cdot U_{\max}$.

What information does the constant ϕ supply about the initial division of energy between potential and kinetic? At $t = 0$, what values would ϕ take on to make the energy all kinetic? All potential? Half kinetic and half potential? Verify by plotting. If you know $U_{\max}$ and a specific value of U, do you know the position of the object? Do you know its velocity?

Time in the plots of $U(t)$ and $K(t)$ ranges from zero to $2 \cdot T$. Why are there four cycles of $U(t)$ and $K(t)$? Correlate precisely with the motion. Define $C_1 := (1/2) \cdot k \cdot A$ and $C_2 := (1/2) \cdot m \cdot A \cdot \omega$. Plot $U(t)$, $C_1 \cdot x(t)$ vs. t and plot $K(t)$, $C_2 \cdot v(t)$ vs. t. These plots should assist in the previous question. How are C_1 and C_2 related to maximum potential energy and maximum kinetic energy?

• •   Load HM4, Lissajous figures: phase diagrams and phase differences (see Fig. 10.4).

Lissajous figures provide an amusing way to compare harmonic curves. They are also useful in the interpretation of the phase difference between two signals.

Lissajous figures are created by driving both the x and y motions harmonically. That is, x and y may both vary sinusoidally in time but they are not plotted against time but against each other. For example,

$$x_j := \sin(2 \cdot \pi \cdot f1 \cdot \frac{j}{N}) \qquad y_j := \sin(2 \cdot \pi \cdot f2 \cdot \frac{j}{N} + \phi).$$

Here, time is not specifically mentioned; the curves are simply evaluated at a series of points that could be sequential in time. Both x and y are harmonically driven. Each is driven at its own frequency, f_1 and f_2; these frequencies could be the same or they could be different. A phase shift can be introduced.

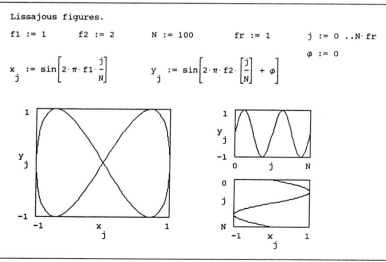

Figure 10.4   HM4, Lissajous figures: phase diagrams and phase differences.

There are three plot regions. The plot region y vs. x displays the Lissajous figures. The regions y vs. j and j vs. x show the individual oscillations of the two components. Note that the last plot is tipped on its side to correspond to the direction in which the x-aspect of the Lissajous motion takes place.

Start with $f_1 := 1$ and $f_2 := 2$. Look at the small plots. We see that x goes through one cycle while y goes through two cycles. Starting at the center of the larger plot, follow the motion. As x goes from zero to one (one-quarter of its cycle), y goes from zero to one and back to zero. As x returns from one to zero, y goes from zero to minus one and back to zero. Therefore, x has gone through one-half of a cycle, when y has gone through one complete cycle.

In a separate plot region, plot x_j, y_j vs. j for one cycle of the smaller frequency. Do this in a general way so that if, for example, f_1 is 98 and f_2 is 34, it still works.

Near the beginning of the document is the quantity fr, for fraction. When fr is 1, all N points are plotted. As fr is reduced, so is the upper limit. By plotting the figure with a reduced value for fr, you can determine where the Lissajous figure begins and in what direction it evolves. This is helpful, as the starting point and initial direction are not always clear in such plots, especially if $\phi \neq 0$.

Let $f_1 := 1$ and $f_2 := 1$ and process. In the small plots, we see the individual motions. In the y vs. x plot, where does the trace begin? In what direction does it move? Let $fr = 0.1$ and process. Next let $fr = 0.25$ and 0.5. Why are the 0.25 and 0.5 plots the same on the y vs. x graph?

Let $fr := 1$ and $\phi := 0.1$ and process. Watch both the y vs. j and j vs. x curves. Let ϕ take on the values $\pi/4$, $\pi/2$, and π. A Lissajous figure displaying a straight line, ellipse, or circle corresponds to equal frequencies for the x and y motions. Only the relative phase is different. What is the phase difference between the straight line and the circle? Does changing the sign of the phase difference change the appearance of the curve?

Let $\phi := 0$ and $f_2 := 1.1$ and process. Why doesn't the curve close?

Try the following values for (f_1, f_2, fr): (1, 2, 1), (1, 2, 0.2), (1, 2, 0.45), (2, 1, 0.45).

Change the y-function to cosine. Try (1, 2, 0.2), (1, 2, 0.5), (1, 2, 1).

With the functions for the x and y directions sine and cosine, try (1, 3, 1), (1, 3, 0.45), (1, 2, 0.45), (2, 1, 0.45).

Finally, with the functions for the x and y directions sine and sine, and for the case (2, 1, 1), let $\phi := 0$, 0.2, 0.6, 0.785. These curves are analogues to the circle, ellipse, and straight line when the frequency ratio was 1:1.

For some fun, try (20, 19, 1), (40, 39,1), (40, 47, 1), (48, 49, 1)($\phi = 0$ or $\phi = 0.785$).

10.2   Pendulums

The simple pendulum consists of a point mass suspended from a massless rod or string. A physical pendulum consists of a rigid body suspended from an axis. Pendulum motion is generally different for small and large amplitude oscillations. The motion can be damped or driven.

10.2.1   *Simple Pendulum*

When the pendulum bob is displaced from its equilibrium position, there is a restoring force equal to $m\,g\sin(\theta)$. The equation of motion is

$$-m\,g\sin(\theta) = m\,a = m\frac{d^2s}{dt^2},\qquad(10.12)$$

where s is the displacement, the arc length as measured from the equilibrium point. From the discussion of the spring-mass system, we know that a linear restoring force is necessary for simple harmonic motion. For the pendulum, there is a restoring force but it is not linear because the sine function is nonlinear. However, for small angles, $\sin(\theta) \approx \theta$. (Check the comparisons made in Chapter 2 for the range of accuracy of the small-angle approximation.) Using this approximation and substituting for s, the value $L\theta$, the equation becomes

$$-m\,g\,\theta = m\,L\,\frac{d^2\theta}{dt^2}.\qquad(10.13)$$

This equation is of the same form as that for the spring-mass system,

$$-k\,x = m\,\frac{d^2x}{dt^2},$$

which yielded

$$\omega = \sqrt{\frac{k}{m}}.$$

Similar analysis for the angular frequency of the pendulum yields

$$\omega = \sqrt{\frac{g}{L}} \qquad \text{or} \qquad T = \frac{2\pi}{\omega} = 2\pi\sqrt{\frac{L}{g}}. \qquad (10.14)$$

In a static situation, with the pendulum bob at the equilibrium point, the weight of the bob and the tension in the supporting string are equal and opposite. If a second string is attached to the bob and the bob is pulled slowly to the side (the pull being tangential to the circle in which the bob moves), the tension in the supporting string is reduced. The static tension in the string, T_s, is given by

$$T_s = m\,g\cos(\theta). \qquad (10.15)$$

When the bob swings freely along its circular path, there must be a force that constrains the bob to move in a circle. The dynamic tension, T_d, is given by

$$T_d = m\frac{v^2}{L} = m\,L\left(\frac{d\theta}{dt}\right)^2. \qquad (10.16)$$

The total tension, T_n, is the sum of these contributions.

• •   Load HM5, simple pendulum (see Fig. 10.5).

(Information from the Lissajous figure example will be used in this example. Examine that document first.)

To speed the calculations, the equations for the angular displacement, velocity, and acceleration are written explicitly rather than using derivatives. Maximum values of θ' and θ'' are θ'_m and θ''_m.

Note that ω refers to the frequency of the oscillations and depends on g and L. Do not confuse this ω with $d\theta/dt$, which represents the angular velocity of the pendulum bob. In this pendulum problem, ω is a constant while $d\theta/dt$ varies with angle.

The first plot region shows the curves $\theta(t)$, $\theta'(t)$, and $\theta''(t)$; the curves are scaled to have the same amplitude. Identify each curve.

Position the document on the screen so that the set of three phase diagrams (θ' vs. θ, θ'' vs. θ', and θ'' vs. θ) are visible. The diagrams are reminiscent of Lissajous figures. However, the motions are not independent but related by derivatives.

What is the phase relation between θ' and θ? Between θ'' and θ'? Between θ'' and θ?

Knowing the initial conditions, where does the θ' vs. θ curve begin? The θ'' and θ' curve? The θ'' and θ curve?

As time increases, predict the directions the paths take in each of the three cases. Let $fr = 0.1$ and process. (As before, fr is a control on the range of the calculations. Note assignment for t.) Were you right?

Now examine the tension statements and the last tier of three plots. Why does the total tension T_n go through two cycles in one period, T? The T_n vs. θ curve should be reminiscent of curves in the Lissajous figure study. What frequency ratio is associated with curves of this shape? What is the difference between the T_n vs. θ and T_n vs. θ' curves? Express your answer

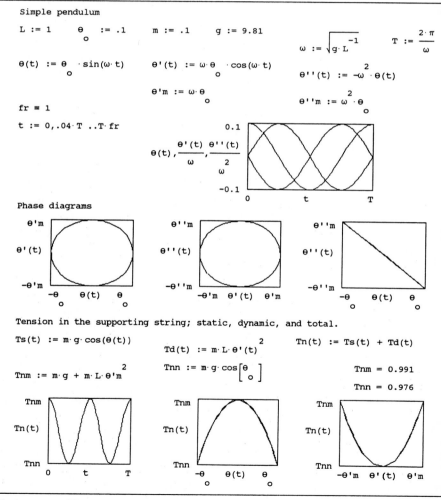

Figure 10.5 HM5, simple pendulum.

in terms of frequencies and phase relationships. Refer to the definitions of θ, θ', and θ''. In what direction do these T_n curves evolve? Let fr equal 0.1, 0.25, 0.5. What happened to the T_n vs. θ curve? Why? In the T_n vs. θ' curve, at what point is $\theta = 0$?

Plot T_s vs. t and T_s vs. θ. Plot T_d vs. t and T_d vs. θ. Notice the range of values, both maximum and minimum. Plot T_s vs. T_d. Plot T_d/T_s vs. t.

Damped Motion. If the amplitude of the oscillation decreases exponentially with time, the displacement is given by

$$\theta = \theta_o \sin(\omega t)\, e^{-t/\tau},$$

where τ is a time constant.

• •   Take the first and second derivatives of θ with respect to time. Express the results, as far as possible, in terms of θ and θ'. Note that you have more than one time-dependent term when you take the derivatives.

• •   Load HM6, simple pendulum with damping (see Fig. 10.6).

This document has the same general structure as the previous one; the difference is that exponential damping has been included. To save time, the derivatives are written explicitly. Check your values for the derivatives against θ' and θ''.

Identify θ, θ', and θ'' in the first plot. Are these curves precisely in phase as they were in the case with no damping? How do you decide? Are the peaks an appropriate measure?

Compare each of the three phase diagrams with those of the previous example. Follow the motion of the first, for example, thinking about velocity and displacement. How are these plots similar? How are they different? Why? What happens if $\tau = 10$?

Compare the tension plots with those of the previous example. In the T_n vs. t plot, the tension seems to be approaching some value. What value might that be?

In the T_n vs. θ plot, what point corresponds to the end of one cycle? Are the maxima in the T_n vs. θ curve all at $\theta = 0$?

Plot $T_s(t)$ vs. t. Plot $T_d(t)$ vs. t. Plot $T_s(t)$ vs. $T_d(t)$.

Examine different rates of damping. Let τ equal 4, 2, 1, 0.5. As the damping decreases, the plots should approach those of the previous example.

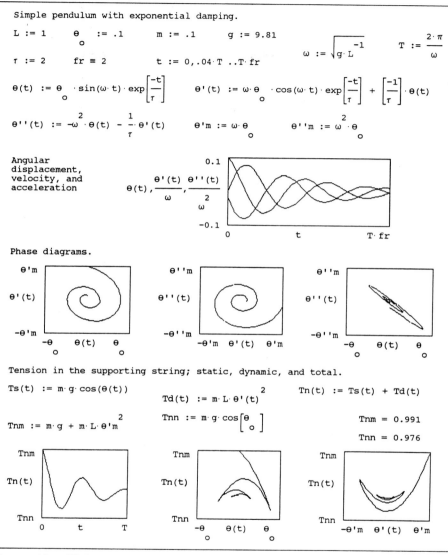

Simple pendulum with exponential damping.

$L := 1$ $\theta_o := .1$ $m := .1$ $g := 9.81$

$\omega := \sqrt{g \cdot L^{-1}}$ $T := \dfrac{2 \cdot \pi}{\omega}$

$\tau := 2$ $fr \equiv 2$ $t := 0, .04 \cdot T \, ..T \cdot fr$

$\theta(t) := \theta_o \cdot \sin(\omega \cdot t) \cdot \exp\left[\dfrac{-t}{\tau}\right]$ $\theta'(t) := \omega \cdot \theta_o \cdot \cos(\omega \cdot t) \cdot \exp\left[\dfrac{-t}{\tau}\right] + \left[\dfrac{-1}{\tau}\right] \cdot \theta(t)$

$\theta''(t) := -\omega^2 \cdot \theta(t) - \dfrac{1}{\tau} \cdot \theta'(t)$ $\theta'm := \omega \cdot \theta_o$ $\theta''m := \omega^2 \cdot \theta_o$

Angular displacement, velocity, and acceleration

$\theta(t), \dfrac{\theta'(t)}{\omega}, \dfrac{\theta''(t)}{\omega^2}$

Phase diagrams.

Tension in the supporting string; static, dynamic, and total.

$Ts(t) := m \cdot g \cdot \cos(\theta(t))$ $Td(t) := m \cdot L \cdot \theta'(t)^2$ $Tn(t) := Ts(t) + Td(t)$

$Tnm := m \cdot g + m \cdot L \cdot \theta'm^2$ $Tnn := m \cdot g \cdot \cos\left[\theta_o\right]$ $Tnm = 0.991$

$Tnn = 0.976$

Figure 10.6 HM6, simple pendulum with damping.

Large Amplitude Motion. As the amplitude of the pendulum's motion increases, the precision with which the values are determined decreases as the small-angle approximation becomes less suitable. In this example, we explore the motion using a numerical technique; the Euler algorithm is used in the simulation of the motion. The method applies for all angles from 0° to 180°. (For the large-amplitude case, consider the pendulum bob to be supported by a massless rod.)

The algorithm is essentially the same as that used in previous one-dimensional cases. The difference is that the acceleration, velocity, and displacement are expressed in angular, rather than linear, variables. Otherwise, the correspondence is complete.

The restoring force is $-m\,g\sin(\theta)$; the corresponding acceleration is $-g\sin(\theta)$. The angular acceleration $\alpha = a/r$. In this case, the angular acceleration is given by

$$\alpha = -\left(\frac{g}{L}\right)\sin(\theta). \tag{10.17}$$

• •   Load HM7, simple pendulum with large amplitude (see Fig. 10.7).

After the initial values and the range of iteration are specified, the equations to be iterated are written into an equation block. Verify that the algorithm is indeed the Euler algorithm. How would it be different if it were the Euler-Cromer algorithm?

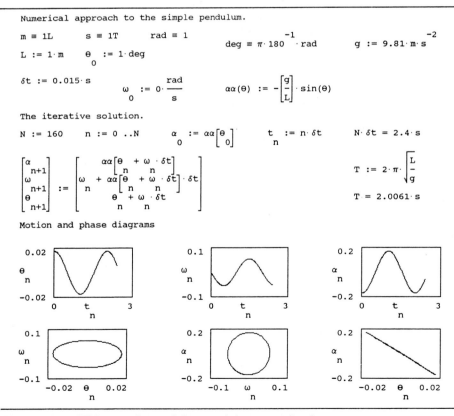

Figure 10.7 HM7, simple pendulum with large amplitude.

In this application, $\omega_n = d\theta_n / dt$.

We examine the results for small angles and compare with known results before considering cases for which the outcome is unknown (to us). Process the document. Examine the plot regions and compare with the undamped case.

Estimate the period. How does this value compare with the value for the simple pendulum, which, of course, has no dependence on θ.

Specify the tension and plot it vs. time, displacement, and angular velocity. Compare the results with the undamped case.

Next consider an initial angle of 90°. Before performing the calculation, anticipate the changes that will occur. When the pendulum is near 90°, is the magnitude of the acceleration large or small? Does the pendulum spend equal times for equal angular differences? Or does it spend more time in certain regions? Considering these questions will permit you to anticipate changes in the α vs. t or α vs. θ plots and in other associated plots.

Let $\theta = 90°$ and $N = 180$ and process. Estimate the period. Save this value.

The α vs. t curve shows regions that are nearly constant, as would be expected from the questions in the previous paragraph. These regions of nearly constant acceleration occur when $\theta \approx 90°$. That region of constant acceleration implies linear change in velocity, which is observed in the ω vs. t plot. Changes in the θ vs. t curve are subtle, and the curve does not look much different from that associated with the small-amplitude motion of a simple pendulum. The phase diagrams show a significant change as well.

Now anticipate the changes that will occur if the pendulum starts at 175°. This is difficult to do. Perhaps the easiest curve to predict is that of α vs. θ. At large angles, is the acceleration large or small? At the 90° positions, is the acceleration large or small? At the 0° positions, is the acceleration large or small? What phase diagram does this suggest?

Let $\theta = 175°$ and $N = 300$ and process. Estimate the period. Save this value.

Now the differences in each of the curves are quite striking. Did you guess the α vs. θ curve approximately? Spend a few minutes to see if you can, in your head, match the curves with the motion. To see where the phase diagrams begin and in what direction they evolve, reduce N to a fraction of that necessary for a complete cycle and process. Become familiar with these diagrams; they are a very useful way of presenting information.

• •   There are analytic solutions for large-amplitude oscillations. The period, for example, for oscillations with maximum amplitude θ_{max} is given by the series

$$T = 2\pi \sqrt{\frac{l}{g}} \left(1 + \frac{1}{2^2}\sin^2\left(\frac{\theta_{max}}{2}\right) + \frac{1}{2^2}\frac{3^2}{4^2}\sin^4\left(\frac{\theta_{max}}{2}\right) + \cdots \right). \quad (10.18)$$

How do your estimates of the period for the three cases above compare with the formula? The next term is given by

$$\frac{1}{2^2}\frac{3^2}{4^2}\frac{5^2}{6^2}\sin^6\left(\frac{\theta_{max}}{2}\right).$$

In integral form the period is given by

$$T = 4\sqrt{\frac{l}{2g}} \int_0^{\theta_{max}} \frac{d\theta}{\sqrt{\cos(\theta) - \cos(\theta_{max})}}. \quad (10.19)$$

Compare values with the series, with the integral, and with your estimated results.

With a numerical algorithm in place, it is relatively straightforward to introduce changes. However, changes may have unexpected consequences, and one should always explore to make sure that the behavior of the algorithm is appropriate to the situation being modelled.

For example, an oscillatory system with exponential damping was considered earlier. If damping is to be introduced in the numerical model, how might that be done? What would happen if, after each iteration, the magnitude of the acceleration term were reduced by some factor, and after many iterations the acceleration were reduced to zero? Would this result in damped oscillatory motion?

• •   Define the function

$$f(n) = \frac{N - n}{N}.$$

As n increases from zero to N, f decreases monotonically. Multiply the $\alpha\alpha$ term by $f(n)$. That is, on the right-hand side of the α, ω, θ equation block in HM7 change the top term to

$$\alpha\alpha(\theta_n + \omega_n \cdot \delta t) \cdot f(n).$$

Process this algorithm and look at the plot regions. Did the acceleration term reduce as we had anticipated? What about the θ and ω curves? Are they damped? Explain.

The function $g(n) = f(n)/f(n-1)$ decreases much more slowly than $f(n)$. Define the function $g(n)$. Remove the $f(n)$ term that was entered in the previous step from the top right-hand side of the expression. Multiply the $(\omega + \alpha\alpha)$ term, the center term on the right-hand side by $g(n)$ and process. Does this result in damped motion? Explain.

Remove $g(n)$ from the center term. Multiply the $(\theta + \omega)$ term, the lower term on the right-hand side, by $g(n)$. Does this result in damped motion?

The purpose of the previous examples was simply to show the effect of changing certain terms. The examples were not based on a physical model for damping. What if the resistance to the motion is proportional to the square of the velocity of the pendulum bob?

The angular acceleration

$$\alpha = a/r = -k\,\frac{v^2}{r} = -k\,r\,\omega^2.$$

Let $\mathrm{sgn}(\omega) = \omega/|\omega|$. Then replace both the $\alpha\alpha$ (one each in the α and ω equations) terms with

$$\alpha\alpha\Big(\theta_n + \omega_n \cdot \delta t\Big) - k \cdot L \cdot \omega_n^2 \cdot \mathrm{sgn}(\omega_n)$$

Don't forget the δt term in the ω equation. Let $k = 0.25 \cdot m^{-1}$.

Changing the sign of the $k \cdot L \cdot \omega^2$ terms would result in driven motion, though one would be hard pressed to imagine a driving force proportional to the square of the velocity. The motion would be driven at the natural frequency of the system.

A driving force can be added to the $\alpha\alpha$ terms. Leave the damping term in place and add a third term,

$$15 \cdot \sin(2 \cdot \pi \cdot t_n).$$

Note that the motion rather quickly responds to the driving force and the frequency of the motion changes within a few cycles. The rate at which this happens depends both on the strength of the driving force and on the damping term.

Physical Pendulum.   The physical pendulum, in contrast to the simple pendulum, does not have its mass concentrated at one point; the mass is distributed. The pendulum is suspended from an axis about which it is free to rotate. (For pendulum motion, why should the axis not pass through the center of mass?) In equilibrium, the center of mass is directly beneath the center of support, the axis. If the object is displaced from equilibrium through some angle θ, there is a restoring torque. If the distance from the center of mass of the object to the axis is d, the torque $(r \times F)$ is $d \cdot \sin(\theta) \cdot (m \cdot g)$. Applying $\sum \tau_{\text{ext}} = I\alpha$, the equation of motion is

$$-m\,g\,d\sin(\theta) = I\,\alpha = I\,\frac{d^2\theta}{dt^2}, \tag{10.20}$$

where I is the moment of inertia of the pendulum about the selected axis. The equation is similar to that of the simple pendulum. Limiting the amplitude to small angles permits us to use the small-angle approximation and the equation simplifies to

$$\frac{d^2\theta}{dt^2} = -\left(\frac{m\,g\,d}{I}\right)\theta \tag{10.21}$$

which yields

$$\omega = \sqrt{\frac{m\,g\,d}{I}}. \tag{10.22}$$

Again, in the expression for ω the numerator tells us of the restoring force, the denominator of the inertia.

• • Describe and plot the motion of a meter stick suspended 10 cm from one end.

The motion of a physical pendulum depends on the choice of axis. If the axis is selected far from the center of mass, the restoring torque is large, but so is the moment of inertia. Right at the center of mass, the moment of inertia is least but the restoring torque is zero. In the next document, we examine the effect of choosing different axes in the movement of a long, thin rod, in this case, a meter stick.

• • Load HM8, physical pendulum: changing the axis location (see Fig. 10.8).

We examine the properties of the meter stick as a physical pendulum in 1-cm steps from the center, at 50 points. We plot the restoring torque for some arbitrary angle and the moment of inertia (making use of the parallel axis theorem) as a function of distance from the center of mass. Even though neither curve has a maximum or minimum, their ratio does. We then plot the angular frequency, the period, and the frequency. We use the root function with the derivative of the period to find the location of the axis for which the period is a minimum.

Use the root function to find the maximum of the frequency curve.

Imagine that you can measure the period to an error of ±0.06 s. What is the largest range of location of the pivot point that could yield values within this error range?

The last two plots in the document are of two different lengths. One is that of a simple pendulum; the other is that of a physical pendulum.

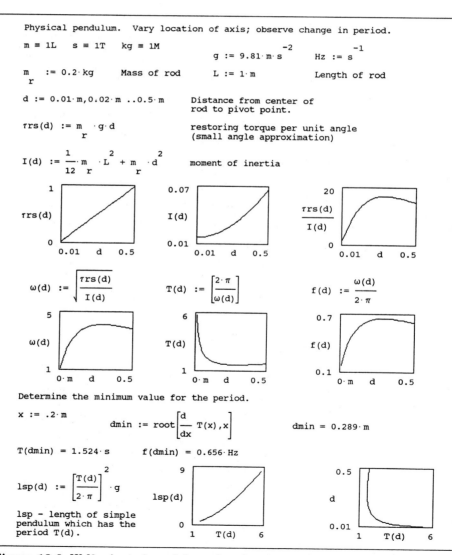

Figure 10.8 HM8, physical pendulum: changing the axis location.

The length of the physical pendulum is plotted vs. its period. The length of the simple pendulum is that length which has the same period as the physical pendulum.

• •   Perform a similar set of calculations for a thin cylinder pivoting about an axis parallel to the cylinder axis. Is there a minimum period? If yes, what is the ratio of the distance of the minimum axis from the axis of symmetry to the radius of the cylinder?

• •   Explore the large-amplitude motion of a meter stick. Compare the phase diagrams with that of a simple pendulum.

• •   A thin rod of length 15 cm and mass 10 g has a 25-g point mass attached to one end. The rod pivots about an axis 3 cm above the weighted end. A second point mass is attached above the pivot point and can be moved to any location on the rod above the pivot point. Find the period of the system as a function of the location of the upper mass. (Select magnitude of second point mass to suit.) This system is a kind of metronome.

You're trying to seduce me, right?

The Graduate

C H A P T E R

11

Waves

The oscillating systems that we have considered so far are of the form

$$x(t) = A\sin(\omega t),$$

where x describes displacement as a function of time. A wave is a disturbance that propagates through space. It requires the same sort of time description but also needs an analogous description for its movement through space. In our discussion of oscillatory systems, we used the variables period T, angular frequency ω, and frequency f. A spatial description requires similar quantities. The first two time-domain variables have common analogues; they are the wavelength λ and the wavenumber k. The wavelength is the distance between successive crests of a wave or the distance from any point in the wave to the corresponding point in the next wave with the same phase. The wave number k is a spatial frequency:

$$k = \frac{2\pi}{\lambda};$$

it is the analogue of

$$\omega = \frac{2\pi}{T}.$$

These descriptions are especially convenient for harmonic waves in which 2π corresponds to one cycle.

11.1 Wave Properties

Let the shape of a wave be represented by the function $y = f(x)$ at time $t = 0$. As the wave propagates, it maintains its original shape. We can follow any point on a wave that is travelling with velocity v, and after a time t, we will find that the point has moved a distance x equal to vt. In general, we can describe the displacement at any point x at time t in the form

$$y(x, t) = f(x - vt). \tag{11.1}$$

Given the displacement of the wave at any point x_o at time $t = 0$, at any time t at a distance $x = vt$ the displacement will be the same. Because the point is arbitrary, y describes the displacement of the wave in terms of position and time.

As a wave travels one wavelength, λ, in one period, T, the wave's velocity is given by

$$v = \frac{\lambda}{T} \qquad \text{or} \qquad v = \frac{\lambda}{2\pi}\frac{2\pi}{T} = \frac{\omega}{k}. \tag{11.2}$$

Consequently,

$$y(x, t) = f(x - \frac{\omega}{k} t). \tag{11.3}$$

If the waveform is sinusoidal, then $y(x, 0) = A \sin B(x - (\omega/k) t)$, where A and B are constants; A is the amplitude of the wave. As x goes from x_o to $x_o + \lambda$, the function must go through one cycle. Thus the constant B must be the wavenumber k and

$$y(x, 0) = A \sin(2\pi\frac{x}{\lambda}). \tag{11.4}$$

In general,

$$y(x, t) = A \sin 2\pi\left(\frac{x}{\lambda} - \frac{t}{T}\right). \tag{11.5}$$

The latter form reminds us that if x moves through one λ or if t moves through one T, y moves through one cycle.

Two different movements occur in wave propagation. For example, as waves move down a string, individual bits of the string oscillate back and forth but undergo no net movement. The combined motion of all the particles, the wave, propagates through the medium. We must distinguish between the displacement of particles from equilibrium and the distance the wave travels. We must distinguish between the velocity of the oscillating particles and the velocity of the wave as a whole.

• •   Load WAVE1, motion at a point vs. motion of the wave (see Fig. 11.1).

We define the parameters and give a description of the wave, $y(x, t) = \sin(kx - \omega t)$ and the derivative of y with respect to time, $y'(x, t)$. This velocity is the velocity of the individual particles along the string or within the medium through which the wave is propagating. Recall that the wave velocity, a constant, is given by ω/k or λf.

The plots are in the form of vertical bars rather than a continuous line. For the present example, this helps to emphasize that we are discussing the motion of individual points along the path. The plots permit us to see the displacements and velocities of the particles both as they are distributed in space and as they are spread out in time.

In the first group of three plots, the time t is zero. Imagine the wave frozen in time. At our leisure, we can walk alongside the wave and examine the displacement. The second plot shows the velocities of the particles at that instant. Compare these two curves carefully. At $x = \lambda/4$, at the peak of the curve, what is the velocity of those particles that have maximum displacement? At $x = \lambda/2$, where the displacement changes sign, what is the velocity of the particles? Pay special attention to the direction of the motion. How might the phase diagram contribute to your explanation? Over what portion of the wave is the particle velocity upward? Downward? Explain the overall propagation process in terms of the displacement and the velocities at particular points. If time is increased from zero, how will the y vs. x curve shift? Change the t value and verify.

In the next group of three plots, the position x is zero. Imagine standing at the $x = 0$ point and observing the displacement of the wave as time increases. The y vs. t plot shows the displacements that we would observe at $t = 0$, $t = 0.05$, $t = 0.1$, etc. At $x = 0$, $t = 0$, the displacement is zero. The descending portion of the wave is approaching. Distinguish carefully between the y vs. x and y vs. t curves. At $t = 0$, what is the velocity of the particle at $x = 0$? Why? Over what portion of the y vs. t curve is the particle velocity upward? Downward? If x is increased from zero, how will the y vs. t curve shift? Verify your answer.

The phase diagrams appear to be identical; yet the conditions $t = 0$, where x takes a range of values and $x = 0$ where t takes a range of values would appear to be different. Do the curves start in the same place? Do they evolve in the same direction?

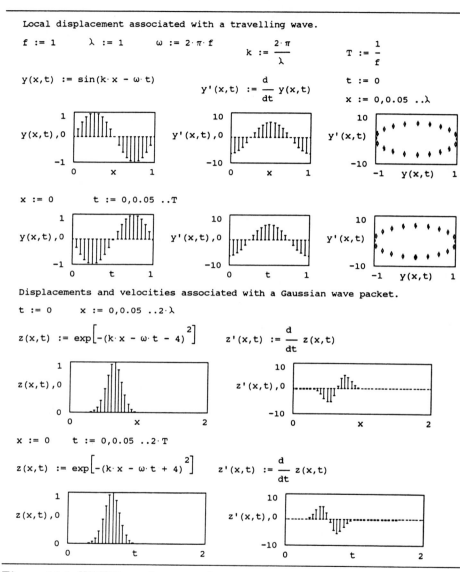

Local displacement associated with a travelling wave.

$f := 1$ $\lambda := 1$ $\omega := 2 \cdot \pi \cdot f$ $k := \dfrac{2 \cdot \pi}{\lambda}$ $T := \dfrac{1}{f}$

$y(x,t) := \sin(k \cdot x - \omega \cdot t)$ $y'(x,t) := \dfrac{d}{dt} y(x,t)$ $t := 0$

$x := 0, 0.05 \ ..\lambda$

$x := 0$ $t := 0, 0.05 \ ..T$

Displacements and velocities associated with a Gaussian wave packet.

$t := 0$ $x := 0, 0.05 \ ..2 \cdot \lambda$

$z(x,t) := \exp\left[-(k \cdot x - \omega \cdot t - 4)^2\right]$ $z'(x,t) := \dfrac{d}{dt} z(x,t)$

$x := 0$ $t := 0, 0.05 \ ..2 \cdot T$

$z(x,t) := \exp\left[-(k \cdot x - \omega \cdot t + 4)^2\right]$ $z'(x,t) := \dfrac{d}{dt} z(x,t)$

Figure 11.1 WAVE1, motion at a point vs. motion of the wave.

To see that the same concepts apply for nonharmonic waves, consider a travelling Gaussian waveform. Explain the z' vs. x and z' vs. t curves. What parameter should be changed to permit the z waveform to advance to larger x values? To larger t values? Verify your answer.

11.2   Superposition

Imagine two different waves passing through the same space at the same time. What happens when the waves overlap? Will each wave lose its individual identity? Will the collision change the properties (amplitude, frequency, phase) of the individual waves? We restrict our consideration to waves of small amplitude. Shock waves from an explosive event, such as a stroke of lightning or the beam from a high-intensity laser, are not of small amplitude and we exclude them. Given this caveat, the waves that we discuss obey linear wave equations. This means that when waves combine, the process is a linear one. In effect, each wave is independent of the other. Each wave contributes to the net amplitude of the resultant wave as if the other wave were not there. The principle of superposition tells us that the resultant wave is a linear combination of the contributing waves. At a given instant, the resultant wave is literally a sum of the components:

$$\Phi = \sum_i a_i \, \phi_i. \tag{11.6}$$

• •   Plot the sum of two waves. Let $v := 331$ and $f := 5 \cdot 10^2$. For the case $x = 0$, plot 2.5 cycles of the sum of $y_1 + y_2$ vs. time, where $y_1 := A_1 \cdot \sin(k\,x - \omega\,t)$ and $y_2 := A_2 \cdot \sin(k\,x - \omega\,t + \phi)$. Let $A_1 = 1$ and $A_2 = 0.8$. Let $\phi = 0$. Why do these curves look like $-\sin(\theta)$? What is the frequency of the sum? How will these curves change if $x = \lambda/4$? Is the frequency of the sum dependent on x? Dependent on ϕ? Predict the answer, then verify.

Let $t = 0$ and plot 2.5 cycles of the sum of $y_1 + y_2$ vs. position. Let ϕ equal 0°, 30°, 90°, and 180°. For $A_1 = 1$ and $A_2 = 1$, what phase angle results in a maximum value for the sum, $y_1 + y_2$, of one?

• •   Load WAVE2, a sum of nonharmonic waves travelling in opposite directions (see Fig. 11.2).

Two nonharmonic waves, $f(t,x)$ and $g(t,x)$ are defined. Notice that they both use the form $(x - v\,t)$ (although g describes a wave travelling in the negative x-direction and includes a plus sign). Note that f and g are Gaussian wave forms. Starting points are chosen for convenience.

The first plot region shows a sequence of wave forms depicting the wave as it progresses in the positive x-direction. The second region shows a similar sequence, starting from x_0 and propagating in the negative x-direction. The sum of those functions is $h(x)$; the factors a and b permit

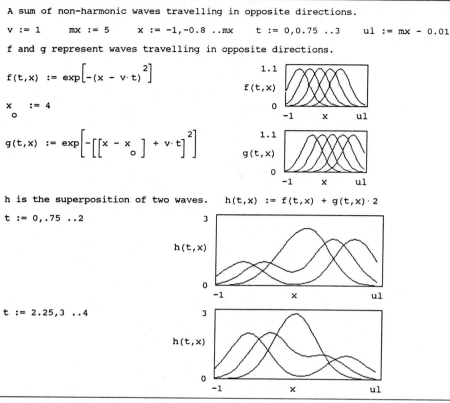

A sum of non-harmonic waves travelling in opposite directions.

v := 1   mx := 5   x := -1,-0.8 ..mx   t := 0,0.75 ..3   ul := mx - 0.01

f and g represent waves travelling in opposite directions.

$$f(t,x) := exp\left[-(x - v \cdot t)^2\right]$$

$$x_o := 4$$

$$g(t,x) := exp\left[-\left[\left[x - x_o\right] + v \cdot t\right]^2\right]$$

h is the superposition of two waves. $h(t,x) := f(t,x) + g(t,x) \cdot 2$

t := 0,.75 ..2

t := 2.25,3 ..4

Figure 11.2 WAVE2, a sum of nonharmonic waves travelling in opposite directions.

an adjustment of amplitude. The wave moving in from the right is given a larger amplitude to help distinguish the two curves. The first h-plot shows the sum at the times $t = 0$, 0.75, and 1.5. The second h-plot continues the sequence, showing the sums at the times $t = 2.25$, 3.0, and 3.75. As the sequence progresses, the waves, initially separate, gradually merge and pass on. Viewing the sum only at time $t = 2.1$, you might conclude that there is only one wave pulse.

To see only one or two curves or for a different spacing, change the t statements. Too many curves result in a cluttered diagram.

To check the details of the procedure, consider various values of (a, b). What would be expected for the cases $(1, 0)$ or $(0, 1)$? Try $(1, 1)$ and $(1, 0.2)$. Also try $(1, -1)$, $(1, -0.5)$, and $(1, -2)$.

• • Load WAVE3, sum of nonharmonic waves travelling in opposite directions, II (see Fig. 11.3).

This example is similar to the previous one, except that the two waves summed are a triangle and a trapezoidal wave. Examine the various sums. To observe any intermediate value, enter a value for *t* at the statement "The sum at time *t*." How does the spike occur? Adjust "The sum at time *t*" to examine. Change the values in the *t*-sequences to see other groupings.

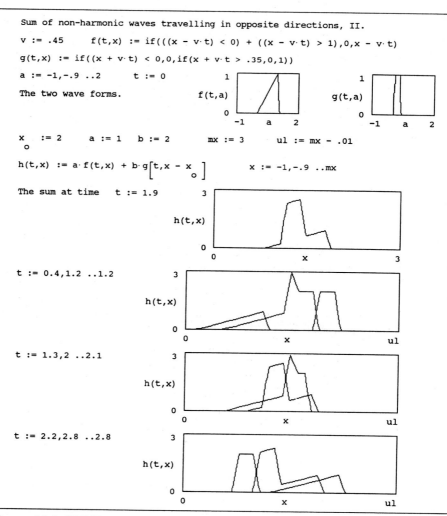

Figure 11.3 WAVE3, sum of nonharmonic waves travelling in opposite directions, II.

11.2.1 *Standing Waves*

The summing of two waves with equal amplitude, frequency, and wave-length, travelling in opposite directions results in a standing wave. The expression

$$y = A \sin(k x - \omega t) + A \sin(k x + \omega t) \tag{11.7}$$

is an example.

With the aid of the identity for the $\sin(\theta \pm \phi)$, this sum can be expressed as

$$y = 2A \sin(k x) \cos(\omega t). \tag{11.8}$$

The amplitude $2A$ is not surprising because the sum is of two waves with amplitude A. In the second expression for y, there is a separation of variables, $y = f(x) \cdot g(t)$; both the x and t portions of the curve can be described independently from the other. The $\cos(\omega t)$ term indicates that every element described has the same harmonic motion in time. The $\sin(k x)$ term indicates that the amplitude is dependent on position; in fact, there are some points where the amplitude is always zero. The zero points are determined according to the following condition, which makes the sine function zero:

$$k x = n \pi \quad n = 0, 1, 2\ldots \tag{11.9}$$

or

$$x = \frac{n \lambda}{2} \quad n = 0, 1, 2\ldots. \tag{11.10}$$

The points of zero amplitude are referred to as nodes, the points with maximum amplitude, antinodes.

• •   Load WAVE4, standing wave (see Fig. 11.4).

Two waves are defined: y_1 travels in the plus x-direction, and y_2 travels in the minus x-direction. For the present, ignore the factor B in the definition of y_2. There are two regions defining t. Only one should be enabled at a time.

Why are the functions written $f(t, x)$ and not $f(x, t)$?

Let fr take on the values 0, 0.3, 0.5, 0.8, and 1. Carefully explain the results when $fr = 0.5$ or $t = T/4$.

Disable the $t = fr \cdot T/2$ region; enable the t-range region. Process. Watch the sequence of cases. To repeat, press [Ctrl]r. Which points are nodes? Which are antinodes?

What happens if the amplitudes of the two waves are not equal? Try changing A in small steps and see how the sum changes.

Standing wave

$\lambda := .1$ $k := \dfrac{2 \cdot \pi}{\lambda}$ $f := 1$ $T := \dfrac{1}{f}$ $\omega := 2 \cdot \pi \cdot f$

One can look at either a single sum or a set of sums. First consider invidual sums, then disable the second t region and enable the first.

$x := 0, \dfrac{\lambda}{20} \; .. \lambda$ $t := 0, \dfrac{T}{16} \; .. \dfrac{T}{2}$ $fr := 1$ $t := fr \cdot \dfrac{T}{2}$ ▫

$A := 1$

$y1(t,x) := \sin(k \cdot x - \omega \cdot t)$ $y2(t,x) := A \cdot \sin(k \cdot x + B \cdot \omega \cdot t)$ $B \equiv 1$

$y(t,x) := \dfrac{y1(t,x) + y2(t,x)}{2}$

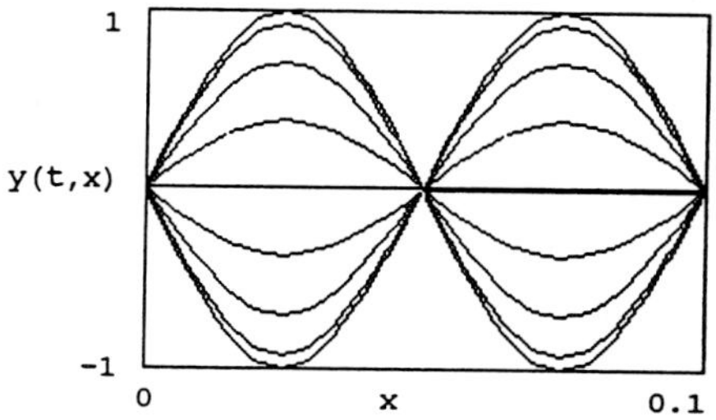

Figure 11.4 WAVE4, standing wave.

What happens if the frequencies of the two waves are not equal? Try changing B in small steps and see how the sum changes.

11.2.2 Shock Waves

Consider a sound source that emits short blasts of noise once per second. Sound waves propagate outward radially. After one second there is another blast, and another wave propagates outward. If the source is stationary, the spherical waves are concentric; if the source moves, they are not.

If the velocity of the source exceeds that of the outgoing wave, the successive spheres are spread out in such a manner that their edges form a cone-shaped wave front.

• • Load WAVE5, shock wave (see Fig. 11.5).

The velocity of the waves is c; the velocity of the source is v. Examine the equation for $r(t)$. How are the radii of successive curves determined?

Let $v = 0$, corresponding to a stationary source. Process. Let v take on the values 4, 8, 10, 12, 16, and 20.

The angle of the cone for $v > c$ is given by $\sin(\theta) = c/v$. Plot θ vs. v as v goes from $1.5\,c$ to $10\,c$.

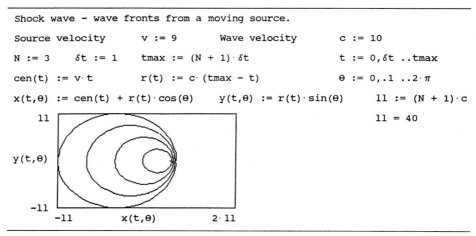

```
Shock wave - wave fronts from a moving source.

Source velocity        v := 9          Wave velocity        c := 10

N := 3      δt := 1     tmax := (N + 1)·δt                  t := 0,δt ..tmax

cen(t) := v·t           r(t) := c·(tmax - t)                θ := 0,.1 ..2·π

x(t,θ) := cen(t) + r(t)·cos(θ)      y(t,θ) := r(t)·sin(θ)      ll := (N + 1)·c

                                                              ll = 40
```

Figure 11.5 WAVE5, shock wave.

11.3 Fourier Series

Hook a microphone up to an oscilloscope and talk, sing, or play your favorite musical instrument. The microphone, a transducer, converts the pressure variations of the sound waves into voltage variations. This electrical signal, appropriately amplified, is used to drive the electron beam of the oscilloscope vertically, while at the same time an internally generated voltage drives the beam from left to right. That is, while the beam is moving from left to right with a uniform speed, the beam moves up and down according to the sound variations. The net effect is that the input signal (y-axis) is displayed as a function of time (x-axis).

If you display a single clear note — for example, from a flute or picolo — on the oscilloscope, it will look almost identical to a sinusoidal wave. However, if you sing the same note, the display will not be so smooth. The dominant oscillation will have the same overall motion, but the curve will not be smooth the way it was with a "clean" note. The difference is associated with the fact that the sounds that were sung are more complex; they contain more information than does the single pitched sound.

The clean signal is a sound wave that consists of essentially one frequency. The voice signal is more complex. It can be constructed from a combination of several different waves, each with its own frequency and amplitude. The oscilloscope display presents the information of the composite wave in the time domain, the time-amplitude composition.

The procedure known as harmonic analysis deals with the problem of finding the components of a signal such as that seen on the oscilloscope screen. Jean Baptiste Joseph Fourier, the French mathematician who accompanied Napoleon to Egypt, carried out the first extensive treatment of this process while developing the mathematical theory of the conduction of heat in solids. He was not the first to treat harmonic problems, but his name, his work, and his theorem have resulted in the generic name, Fourier series.

Fourier's idea is that some arbitrary function or signal can be expressed as an infinite series of certain prescribed functions. Here, those functions will be sines and cosines. Some examples of Fourier series will be presented below.

11.3.1 *Ancient Astronomy*

Long before Fourier, a less sophisticated form of harmonic analysis flourished. The ancients sought to describe the motion of the planets with various schemes. The most powerful idea, and one they exploited, was uniform circular motion.

Ptolemy's synthesis of planetary motion includes the system of epicycles, and this system of spheres is fundamentally the same as that used by Copernicus. (The present description will be in terms of circles rather than spheres.) A brief description of epicyclic motion follows.

A circle rotates uniformly about its center; refer to this circle as the deferent. At a fixed point on the circumference of the deferent, a second circle is attached; refer to this circle as an epicycle. The epicycle moves with the deferent as it rotates about its center; at the same time, the epicycle revolves about its own center (on the circumference of the deferent) with its own frequency. The combination of two circles moving with two frequencies can describe a variety of paths.

• • Load WAVE6, epicycles (see Figs. 11.6 and 11.7).

The deferent rotates uniformly with angular velocity ω_a. The x and y motions of a point on the circle are given by $x_i := A \cdot \cos(\omega_a t_i + \phi_a)$ and $y_i := A \cdot \sin(\omega_a t_i + \phi_a)$, respectively. The resulting motion is circular. If the motion of the epicycle is added in, the equations become

$$x_i := A \cdot \cos(\omega_a t_i + \phi_a) + B \cdot \cos(\omega_b t_i + \phi_b)$$
$$y_i := A \cdot \sin(\omega_a t_i + \phi_a) + B \cdot \sin(\omega_b t_i + \phi_b).$$

Deferent, epicycle, and equant.

Motion associated with a deferent is uniform circular motion.

$n := 36$ $i := 0 .. n$ $A := 1$ $fa := 1$ $\omega a := 2 \cdot \pi \cdot fa$ $\phi a := 0$

$t_i := \dfrac{i}{n}$ $\omega a \cdot t_n = 2 \cdot \pi$ $x_i := A \cdot \cos\left[\omega a \cdot t_i\right]$ $y_i := A \cdot \sin\left[\omega a \cdot t_i\right]$

Motion of deferent plus epicycle permits many possibilities. a refers to the deferent, b the epicycle. x and y represent the combined motion.

$A := 1$ $B := .5$ $fa := 1$ $fb := 0$ $\phi b := 0$

$\omega a := 2 \cdot \pi \cdot fa$ $\omega b := 2 \cdot \pi \cdot fb$

$xa_i := A \cdot \cos\left[\omega a \cdot t_i\right]$ $xb_i := B \cdot \cos\left[\omega b \cdot t_i + \phi b\right]$ $x_i := xa_i + xb_i$

$ya_i := A \cdot \sin\left[\omega a \cdot t_i\right]$ $yb_i := B \cdot \sin\left[\omega b \cdot t_i + \phi b\right]$ $y_i := ya_i + yb_i$

$mx := \max(x)$ $my := \max(y)$ $nx := |\min(x)|$ $ny := |\min(y)|$
$lm := if(mx > my, mx, my)$ $lm' := if(nx > ny, nx, ny)$ $lm := if(lm > lm', lm, lm')$

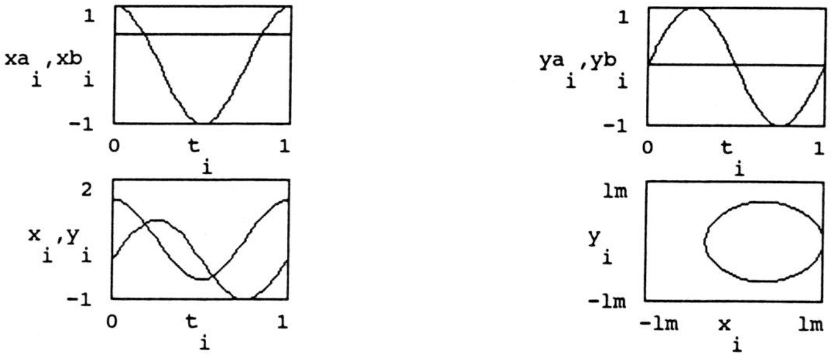

Figure 11.6 WAVE6, epicycles. (See the next figure for the rest of the document.)

The first two plots show the motion associated with x and y individually, and the associated circular motion. (At the beginning of the next section in the document, some of the quantities are redefined to keep them close to the plot regions of interest. These values can then be varied without having to move to the top of the document.) Note carefully what is plotted in each of the four plots — x-motion of the deferent and epicycle, y-motion of the deferent and epicycle, total x and y motions, all vs. t, and finally y vs. x. Explore the possible motions of the deferent-epicycle system. Observe all four plots regions as you proceed.

The equant. Motion takes place at constant distance from the center. The
rate at which the position changes is constant about an offset point.

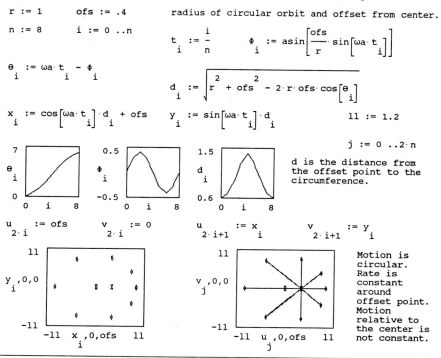

$r := 1$ $ofs := .4$ radius of circular orbit and offset from center.

$n := 8$ $i := 0 ..n$

$t_i := \dfrac{i}{n}$ $\phi_i := asin\left[\dfrac{ofs}{r} \cdot sin\left[\omega a \cdot t_i\right]\right]$

$\theta_i := \omega a \cdot t_i - \phi_i$

$d_i := \sqrt{r^2 + ofs^2 - 2 \cdot r \cdot ofs \cdot cos\left[\theta_i\right]}$

$x_i := cos\left[\omega a \cdot t_i\right] \cdot d_i + ofs$ $y_i := sin\left[\omega a \cdot t_i\right] \cdot d_i$ $ll := 1.2$

$j := 0 ..2 \cdot n$

$u_{2 \cdot i} := ofs$ $v_{2 \cdot i} := 0$ $u_{2 \cdot i+1} := x_i$ $v_{2 \cdot i+1} := y_i$

d is the distance from
the offset point to the
circumference.

Motion is
circular.
Rate is
constant
around
offset point.
Motion
relative to
the center is
not constant.

Figure 11.7 WAVE6 *continued.*

Let (A, B, f_a, f_b, ϕ_b) equal $(1, 0.5, 0, 1, 0)$. (Position the document so
that the line starting $A := 1$ is at the top of the screen.) Explain this and
each ensuing motion as it is displayed. Try $(1, 0.5, 1, 0, 0)$ and $(1, 0.5,
1, 1, 0)$. Be sure that you understand the difference between the previous
two cases. Try $(1, 0.5, 1, -1, 0)$. What affect will changing ϕ_b have on this
figure?

Next consider examples with different frequency ratios and different
phase angles. Try $(1, 0.5, 1, 2, 0)$, $(1, 0.5, 1, 2, \pi/4)$, and $(1, 0.5, 1, 2,
\pi/2)$. Try $(1, 0.5, 2, 1, 0)$ and $(1, 0.5, 2, 1, \pi/4)$.

Finally, increase the frequency of the epicycle. Try $(1, 0.5, 1, 3, 0)$ and
$(1, 0.5, 1, 4, 0)$.

Systems like these were used to fit the observational data of planetary motion. Other features included the minor epicycle, another circle,
attached to a fixed point on the epicycle and free to turn at its own frequency; the eccentric, in which motion was still uniform about the center,

but the earth was offset rather than at the center; and the equant, where uniform motion occurred relative to a point offset from the center but with the earth still located at the center. This last example is included as the last section of this document. You may wish to explore the other features on your own.

Motion associated with the equant has the effect of changing the velocity of the planetary motion relative to the center (see Fig. 11.7). The planet moves along a circle centered on the earth. The planet moves through equal angles in equal times about a point that is offset from the center. For which part of the orbit is the velocity the greatest relative to the central point? For which part is it the least? Make a crude plot of the velocity vs. time.

As elegant as the methods of Ptolemy and the ancients were, gradually the system failed for both philosophical and scientific reasons. Ultimately, it was Kepler who solved the problem of the planets. His three laws state that (1) planetary orbits are ellipses, and the sun is at one focus of the ellipse; (2) a line from the sun to the planet sweeps out equal areas in equal times; and (3) $T^2 \propto R^3$ where T is the period of planetary motion and R is the mean distance between planet and sun. (We examined the third law previously, in the section on dimensional analysis.) The second law is true because there is a central force. The first and third laws depend on the attractive force varying inversely with the square of the distance.

• • Load WAVE7, Kepler's second law (see Figs. 11.8 and 11.9).

We explore Kepler's second law by generating an orbit and noting the location of the orbiting body at uniform time intervals.

An equation for the ellipse is

$$r = \frac{a \cdot (1 - \epsilon^2)}{1 - \epsilon \cdot \cos(\theta)}. \tag{11.11}$$

Draw two radius vectors, from one of the foci to two different points of the orbital path that are near each other. Let the separation between the vectors be a small angle $\delta\theta$. The area contained between these radius vectors and the orbit is given approximately by

$$\delta A = \frac{1}{2} r^2 \delta\theta. \tag{11.12}$$

This can be determined by considering the area as that of a triangle with base r and height, the arc length, $r\,\delta\theta$.

The set of four plots shows the orbit (an ellipse with large eccentricity was selected to emphasize the changes), a subset of the individual radii (equal areas between each), and a plot of the radius and angle as a function of time. By increasing f, the number of vectors plotted is reduced, g changes the subsets for a given f; f and g are both integers; $g < f$.

In the final plot area, we show points spaced according to the equal area law. The values of k_1 and k_2 selected determine which triangles are to be outlined. The values should not exceed n. The equal area law has clear implications about the velocity at various points in the orbit. Compare this example with that of the equant above. Is the eccentric a better

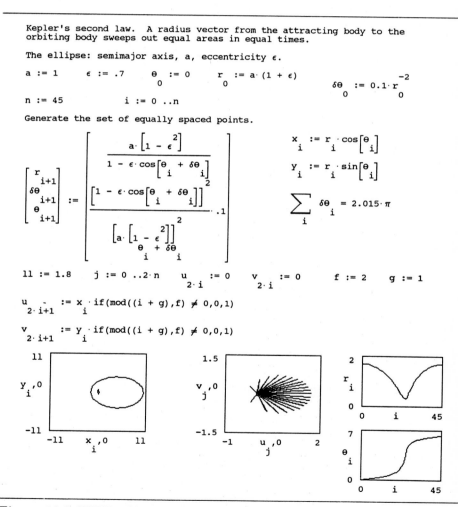

Figure 11.8 WAVE7, Kepler's second law. (See the next figure for the rest of the document.)

$k1 := 10$ $k2 := 25$ $n = 45$ $0 \le k1 \le n - 1$ □ $0 \le k2 \le n - 1$ □

$k := 0 \, .. \, 6$ $c_k := 0$ $d_k := 0$ $c_1 := x_{k1}$ $c_2 := x_{k1+1}$

$d_1 := y_{k1}$ $d_2 := y_{k1+1}$ $c_4 := x_{k2}$ $c_5 := x_{k2+1}$

$d_4 := y_{k2}$ $d_5 := y_{k2+1}$

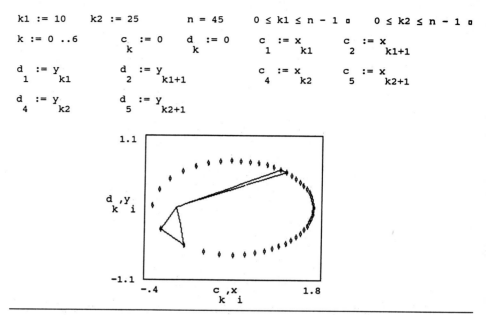

Figure 11.9 WAVE7 *continued.*

model to describe this phenomenon? Is the rotation approximately constant relative to the actual center of the ellipse? Plot the different motions in the same region for comparison.

The apparent epicyclic motion of a planet as seen from the earth is, of course, the result of viewing the motion of one orbiting body from another. The motion can be obtained from two elliptic orbits. First determine the elliptical motion; then determine the location of one body relative to the other.

• • Load WAVE8, elliptical orbits and retrograde motion (see Figs. 11.10 and 11.11).

The orbits for two different planets are calculated and plotted. The distance between the two planets is determined using the law of cosines. The angle as measured from the horizontal is determined using the law of sines and some basic geometry.

In the first plot region (see Fig. 11.11) are the two elliptical orbits of the planets about the central attracting body; we assume no interaction between the two planets. In the second plot region is the orbit of the outer

Determine two elliptical orbits. Then specify the location of the outer orbiting body relative to the inner orbiting body.

$a1 := 1$ $\quad\quad \epsilon1 := .1$ $\quad\quad a2 := 1.2$ $\quad\quad \epsilon2 := .15$

$n := 66$ $\quad\quad i := 0 ..n$ $\quad\quad\quad\quad\quad\quad\quad\quad\quad\quad\quad\quad aa := \left[\dfrac{a1}{a2}\right]^{1.5}$

$\theta1_0 := 0$ $\quad\quad r1_0 := a1 \cdot (1 + \epsilon1)$ $\quad\quad \delta\theta1_0 := 0.1 \cdot r1_0^{-2}$ $\quad\quad \delta\theta2_0 := aa \cdot \delta\theta1_0$

$\theta2_0 := 0$ $\quad\quad r2_0 := a2 \cdot (1 + \epsilon2)$

$$\begin{bmatrix} r1_{i+1} \\ \delta\theta1_{i+1} \\ \theta1_{i+1} \end{bmatrix} := \begin{bmatrix} \dfrac{a1 \cdot \left[1 - \epsilon1^2\right]}{1 - \epsilon1 \cdot \cos\left[\theta1_i + \delta\theta1_i\right]} \\[2em] \dfrac{\left[1 - \epsilon1 \cdot \cos\left[\theta1_i + \delta\theta1_i\right]\right]^2}{\left[a1 \cdot \left[1 - \epsilon1^2\right]\right]^2} \cdot .2 \\[2em] \theta1_i + \delta\theta1_i \end{bmatrix}$$

$x1_i := r1_i \cdot \cos\left[\theta1_i\right]$

$y1_i := r1_i \cdot \sin\left[\theta1_i\right]$

$\displaystyle\sum_i \delta\theta1_i = 4.212 \cdot \pi$

$$\begin{bmatrix} r2_{i+1} \\ \delta\theta2_{i+1} \\ \theta2_{i+1} \end{bmatrix} := \begin{bmatrix} \dfrac{a2 \cdot \left[1 - \epsilon2^2\right]}{1 - \epsilon2 \cdot \cos\left[\theta2_i + \delta\theta2_i\right]} \\[2em] \dfrac{\left[1 - \epsilon2 \cdot \cos\left[\theta2_i + \delta\theta2_i\right]\right]^2}{\left[a2 \cdot \left[1 - \epsilon2^2\right]\right]^2} \cdot .2 \cdot aa \\[2em] \theta2_i + \delta\theta2_i \end{bmatrix}$$

$x2_i := r2_i \cdot \cos\left[\theta2_i\right]$

$y2_i := r2_i \cdot \sin\left[\theta2_i\right]$

$\displaystyle\sum_i \delta\theta2_i = 2.207 \cdot \pi$

$rd_i := \sqrt{r1_i^2 + r2_i^2 - 2 \cdot r1_i \cdot r2_i \cdot \cos\left[\theta2_i - \theta1_i\right]}$

$\theta3_i := \text{asin}\left[\dfrac{r1_i}{rd_i} \cdot \sin\left[\theta2_i - \theta1_i\right]\right]$ $\quad\quad \theta e_i := \theta2_i - \theta1_i + \theta3_i$

$\theta_i := \theta1_i + \theta e_i$ $\quad\quad x_i := rd_i \cdot \cos\left[\theta_i\right]$ $\quad\quad y_i := rd_i \cdot \sin\left[\theta_i\right]$

Figure 11.10 WAVE8, elliptical orbits and retrograde motion. (See the next figure for the rest of the document.)

planet as seen by the inner planet. From an earth-centered frame, the system of epicycles invented by ancient astronomers was quite a reasonable way to account for planetary motion.

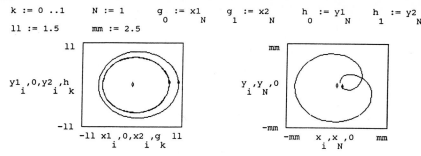

$$k := 0 \ldots 1 \qquad N := 1 \qquad g_0 := x1_N \qquad g_1 := x2_N \qquad h_0 := y1_N \qquad h_1 := y2_N$$

$$ll := 1.5 \qquad mm := 2.5$$

Every fifth point is plotted in the d vs c region and written to file in xcoor and ycoor.

$$j := 0 \ldots \frac{n}{5} \qquad c_j := x_{5 \cdot j} \qquad d_j := y_{5 \cdot j}$$

$$\text{WRITE}\left[xcoor\right] := c \qquad \text{WRITE}\left[ycoor\right] := d$$

Figure 11.11 WAVE8 *continued.*

The c[i and d[i data read in are the coordinate values from WAVE8 specifying the location of one orbiting body relative to another. See how well you can fit this data with a system consisting of a deferent and an epicycle.

$$n := \frac{66}{5} \qquad i := 0 \ldots n \qquad c_i := \text{READ}\left[xcoor\right] \qquad d_i := \text{READ}\left[ycoor\right]$$

$$mm := 2.5$$

Supply values for A, B, f, α, and ϕ. A "fair" match is possible with relatively simple values.   A is the radius of the deferent, B the epicycle, f is the frequency of the epicycle relative to that of the deferent, α and ϕ are phase angles.

$$A := 0 \qquad B := 0 \qquad f := 0 \qquad \alpha := 0 \qquad \phi := 0$$

$$\theta_i := 2 \cdot \pi \cdot \frac{i}{n} \qquad\qquad \Phi_i := 2 \cdot \pi \cdot \frac{i}{n} \cdot f$$

$$x_i := A \cdot \cos\left[\theta_i + \alpha\right] + B \cdot \cos\left[\Phi_i + \phi\right] \qquad y_i := A \cdot \sin\left[\theta_i + \alpha\right] + B \cdot \sin\left[\Phi_i + \phi\right]$$

Figure 11.12 WAVE9, fitting the data with an epicycle.

• •   Load WAVE9, fitting the data with an epicycle (see Fig. 11.12).

At the end of the last document, a small number of data points are written to disk. Those data points are read in at the beginning of this document. Supply values for A, B, f, α, and ϕ and see how well you can fit the data. The data can be fit with relatively simple values. The ancient astronomers were very clever. See how well you can fit this realistic data with a system composed of a deferent and a single epicycle. (Every once in a while, it is useful to stop and think of the kinds of computations that are being performed, computations of such magnitude that they would simply be prohibitive if you attemped them on your own.)

11.3.2   *Harmonic Series*

The complex motion of the planets can be described by various combinations of circular motion. In general, any periodic motion or function can be described by summing a series of sine and/or cosine functions, with different amplitudes and different frequencies:

$$f(t) = \frac{a_0}{2} + a_1 \cdot \sin(\omega\, t) + a_2 \cdot \sin(2\,\omega\, t) + \cdots$$
$$b_1 \cdot \cos(\omega\, t) + b_2 \cdot \cos(2\,\omega\, t) + \cdots \qquad (11.13)$$

To gain some insight into the process, examine the sum of a small number of sine functions of different frequencies.

• •   To perform a sum, two indices are necessary, one for the different frequency terms and the associated amplitudes, and one for the points at which the function is to be evaluated. For example, the frequencies might be f_j and the times t_i.

Try something simple. Create a sum with a maximum of four terms. Let $j = 1, \ldots, M$, where M can take on any integral value from one to four. (M could, in fact, be larger, but at this point four terms is enough.) Type $a_j :=$, and enter four simple values for amplitude. For example, let each successive amplitude be half the previous one. Type $f_j :=$, and enter four values for frequency — start for example, with the values one to four.

Observe the sum for two cycles of the lowest frequency. Let the number of points at which the sum is computed be N; start with $N = 60$. If processing is too slow, reduce N to 50 or 40. Let the time be specified as

$$t_i = \frac{i}{N} \cdot \frac{2}{f_1} \qquad \text{where} \qquad i = 0, \ldots, N.$$

Why does this statement correspond to two cycle of the lowest frequency?

Then define the y-values,

$$y_{i,j} = a_j \cdot \sin(2\,\pi\,f_j\,t_i).$$

To observe the individual sine curves, define $y'_{j,i} = y_{i,j}$. Plot $y'_{j,i}$ vs. t_i. M sine curves with different frequencies should be displayed.

Sum the individual curves. Define the sum

$$z_i := \sum_k y_{i,k} \qquad \text{where} \qquad k := 1, \ldots, 1.$$

By limiting the range of k, we limit the number of terms in the sum. Plot z_i vs. t_i. Increase the upper limit of k to four in steps of one. Observe how the shape develops.

If the series were a cosine series instead of a sine series, would the shape be the same? If sine and cosine differ by a fixed phase, won't the curve just be shifted? If not, why not? Define

$$yy_{i,j} := a_j \cdot \cos(2\,\pi\,f_j\,t_i) \qquad \text{and} \qquad zz_i := \sum_j yy_{i,j}.$$

Plot zz_i vs. t_i.

• •   Examine some sine and cosine series. Look at a limited region to minimize the computation time. Examine each sum with one, then two, and then three terms. Then, if you wish, increase the number of terms in the sum in larger steps.

For the region from $x = 0$ to $x = \pi$, explore in pairs the following sine and cosine series:

$$s_j := 2 \cdot \sum_i \frac{(-1)^{i+1}}{i} \sin(i \cdot x_j).$$

$$t_j := \frac{8}{\pi} \cdot \sum_i \frac{\cos((2 \cdot i - 1) \cdot x_j)}{(2 \cdot i - 1)^2},$$

and

$$s_j := \sin(x_j)$$

$$t_j := \frac{2}{\pi} - \frac{4}{\pi} \cdot \sum_i \frac{\cos(2 \cdot i \cdot x_j)}{4 \cdot i^2 - 1}.$$

For the range $x = 0$ to $x = \pi/2$, examine

$$s_j := \frac{2}{\pi} \cdot \sum_i \left(1 - \cos(\frac{i \cdot \pi}{2})\right) \cdot \frac{\sin(i \cdot x_j)}{i}$$

$$t_j := \frac{1}{2} - \frac{2}{\pi} \cdot \sum_i (-1)^i \cdot \frac{\cos((2 \cdot i - 1) \cdot x_j)}{2 \cdot i - 1}.$$

These series should approximate the functions x, $\sin(x)$, and 1.

• •   Load WAVE10, Lanczos smoothing (see Fig. 11.13).

After a finite number of terms are summed in a Fourier series, a certain amount of "ringing" remains. This is representative of the higher frequency elements that have been omitted. This ringing can be greatly

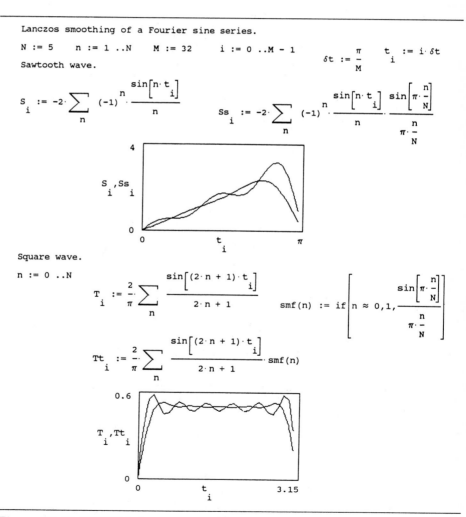

Figure 11.13 WAVE10, Lanczos smoothing.

reduced by including the Lanczos smoothing factor, or convergence factor. The factor is

$$\frac{\sin(n\pi/N)}{(n\pi/N)}.$$

As an example, the first sine series of the last problem is calculated and plotted. The same series is then plotted with the Lanczos convergence factor. The effect is to remove much of the high-frequency ringing that still remains after a finite number of terms are summed. A second example for a square wave series is shown. Change values of N in each case and observe the ringing and the quality of the smoothing.

The Fourier series is observed here in connection with the concept of superposition. Later, when we deal with optics, we will examine the fast Fourier transform, which provides a means of transforming the description of a signal between two different domains, for example, time and frequency.

But sir, that's Charlie's beach,

Charlie don't surf.

Apocalypse Now

C H A P T E R

12

Heat and
Thermodynamics

The concept of heat is approached in this chapter through a variety of problems: an asteroid striking the earth; Newton's law of cooling; the wind chill effect; and heat flow from the interior to the exterior of a house, where both convective and conductive effects are considered. The ideal gas law is compared with the van der Waals equation of state. The Carnot cycle is explored as we look first at the problem of isothermal and adiabatic transitions connecting two arbitrary points. We then explore the area enclosed by the cycle and ask questions about the conditions for maximum work and maximum efficiency.

12.1   Heat

Temperature is a subtle concept. For the present, consider temperature to be the quantity that a thermometer measures. The unit is the Kelvin or degree Celsius. Heat is the transfer of energy resulting from temperature differences. The energy unit, the Joule, is already familiar. The calorie, an energy unit used frequently in heat computations, is defined as the amount of energy necessary to raise the temperature of one gram of water from 14.5° C to 15.5° C. Before the concept of energy was clearly understood, it was a major revelation to realize that heat and work had similar measures. The relative sizes of the units are 1 cal = 4.186 J.

When heat is transferred to or from an object, the temperature or the phase of the object changes. The relation between the heat flow and the change in temperature is

$$\Delta Q = m\, c\, \Delta T, \tag{12.1}$$

where m is the mass of the object and c is the specific heat. The units of specific heat are energy per mass per temperature, for example, calories per gram per degree Celsius. Note that the specific heat depends on whether the substance is held at constant volume during the heat transfer process or, for example, the transfer takes place at constant pressure.

During a phase transition, a substance either absorbs or gives off heat without changing its temperature. The equation

$$\Delta Q = m\, L \tag{12.2}$$

expresses this relationship. L is the latent heat associated with the phase transition; ΔQ is the energy exchanged; and m is the mass. For water, the latent heat of fusion is 80 calories per gram. That is, 80 calories are required to change one gram of ice at 0°C to one gram of water at 0°C. Similarly, the latent heat of vaporization for water is 540 calories per gram.

• •   One postulated mechanism for the end of all life on earth is that a huge asteroid will collide with the earth. Let the asteroid land in the ocean, and make the assumption that half of its kinetic energy ultimately goes into evaporating water. (The actual energy transfer process is quite complex. See, for example, *Science*, 250, 1078 (1990).) When the evaporation has taken place, by how many meters will the combined oceans of the world have dropped?

Try several sizes of asteroid. An enormous asteroid could be 400 to 500 km in diameter. Assume it has a density similar to that of iron and an incoming velocity of 10^4 m/s. Plot the depth of ocean evaporated vs. the diameter of the asteroid.

12.1.1   *Newton's Law of Cooling*

An object warmer than its surroundings will cool; an object cooler than its surroundings will warm. Newton's law of cooling, an empirical statement, suggests that the rate of temperature change is proportional to the temperature difference between an object and its surroundings (s). That is,

$$\frac{dT}{dt} = -k\,(T - T_s),\tag{12.3}$$

where k is a positive constant. If $T > T_s$, dT/dt is negative and the temperature, T, decreases with time. If $T < T_s$, the reverse is true.

We will treat this problem both numerically and analytically. The analytic solution can be obtained by integration (the integration is not complicated; it involves the equivalent of integrating dx/x):

$$\int_{T_{\text{init}}}^{T} \frac{dT'}{T' - T_s} = -k \int_0^t dt'.$$

Integrating, we find

$$T = T_s + (T_{\text{init}} - T_s)\,e^{-kt}.\tag{12.4}$$

• • Take the derivative of T with respect to time and verify that the differential form of the equation is returned.

• • Verify that at $t = 0$, $T = T_{\text{init}}$. Evaluate T when t is very large.

• • Plot T_s and $(T_{\text{init}} - T_s)\exp(-kt)$ vs. t. Plot T vs. t. Verify that the expected behavior occurs whether $T_{\text{init}} > T_s$ or $T_{\text{init}} < T_s$. Remove the minus sign in the exponential. What happens to the solution?

• • Load HEAT1, Newton's law of cooling (see Fig. 12.1).

The analytic solution is presented and the temperature is plotted as a function of time. What is the effect of changing k?

Data associated with the cooling of an object are presented in tabular form. The data are taken at one-minute intervals. The temperature, TT_i, is in degrees Celsius.

Find the best value for the cooling constant, k, using the general curve fitting technique. First, plot TT_i and $T(k, T_i)$ with various values of k; when a reasonable fit is found, use this k value as the guess value in a fitting process. Minimize the sum of the squares of the differences between TT_i and $T(k, T_i)$.

Plot TT_i and $T(k, T_i)$ vs. t_i. Plot the difference, $TT_i - T(k, T_i)$ vs. t_i.

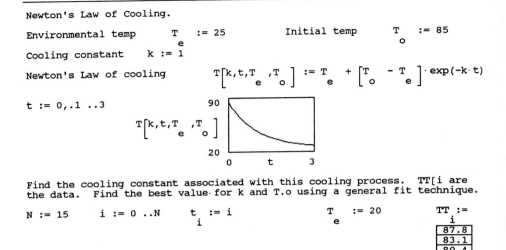

Newton's Law of Cooling.

Environmental temp T_e := 25   Initial temp T_o := 85

Cooling constant   k := 1

Newton's Law of cooling $T[k, t, T_e, T_o]$:= T_e + $[T_o - T_e] \cdot \exp(-k \cdot t)$

t := 0, .1 ..3

$T[k, t, T_e, T_o]$

Find the cooling constant associated with this cooling process.   TT[i are the data.   Find the best value for k and T.o using a general fit technique.

N := 15   i := 0 ..N t_i := i T_e := 20   TT :=

TT_i
87.8
83.1
80.4
76.7
76.1
74.3
72.5
71.0
69.2
67.8
66.4
65.3
64.1
62.8
61.8
60.6

Figure 12.1 HEAT1, Newton's law of cooling.

Try slightly larger and slightly smaller values for k and observe how the fit changes. From the appearance of the curves, if the data were available for 30 minutes instead of 15, would you guess that k would be the same, larger, or smaller? Why?

Now consider the problem using a numerical approach. Rewrite the differential equation for Newton's law of cooling in difference form. First express the equation in terms of finite steps:

$$\delta T = -k(T - T_s)\,\delta t \qquad (12.5)$$

and identify $\delta T = T_{j+1} - T_j$. The difference equation is (new temperature equals former temperature plus change)

$$T'_{j+1} = T'_j - k\,(T'_j - T_s)\,\delta t. \qquad (12.6)$$

To keep the various temperatures distinct, let the temperature, time and index for the analytic case be T, t, i and for the numeric case T', t', j.

What is the initial value T_0'? Let $N = 1$, let $j = 0 \ldots, N$ and let $\delta t = 15/N$. Let t_j' represent the elapsed time; define t_j'. Plot T_j' vs. t_j' and TT_i vs. t_i in the same plot region. Make the region of moderate size, say 10, 20, and process. In this example, for the particular value of k and for the limited period of time, the cooling, as determined analytically, does not deviate markedly from a straight line. Consequently, the error, on taking one 15-minute time step, is not as large as you might think. Let $N = 2$ and process. The kink between the 0 to 1 and 1 to 2 steps is noticeable. Try $N = 5$, 10, and 100.

How does the quality of the numerical fit compare with that of the analytical fit? How does the numerical result compare with the analytical result? Plot them together in the same plot region.

12.1.2 *Wind Chill*

As an object's temperature changes, there is a corresponding heat flow. As we noted earlier in our discussion of temperature change,

$$\Delta T = \frac{1}{m\,c} \Delta Q.$$

Writing this change per time and multiplying the right-hand side by A/A where A is the surface area, we get

$$\frac{\Delta T}{\Delta t} = \frac{A}{m\,c} \frac{\Delta Q}{A\,\Delta t} = \frac{A}{m\,c} H, \tag{12.7}$$

where H is the heat transfer per area per time. The wind chill temperature involves the quantity H.

Imagine that you are standing naked in the open on a windy winter day. How does the heat loss from your body depend on the air temperature, T, and wind velocity, v? Data (hot water bottle hung from a telephone pole) suggest that $H(v, T) = f(v) \cdot g(T)$.

• • Load HEAT2. Some data are presented on the velocity-dependent part of H, the function $f(v)$. Plot f_i' vs. v_i. From your knowledge of curve shapes (review your plots from the section on families of curves in Chapter 2), decide on an appropriate function with a maximum of three terms. Define a function $f(v)$ incorporating these terms; include in the argument list the parameters that are to be adjusted, for example, $f(a, v) = a v^2$. This particular velocity-dependent term, however, is not one that you should select. Guess the coefficients and plot the defined function together with the data. Adjust the values of the coefficients by hand until a decent fit is obtained. Change the terms in your function if necessary.

To improve on the values just obtained for the coefficients, use these values as guess values in a general fit method (see Chapter 2). This approach determines the coefficients using a given-minerr solve block. Recall that we want to minimize the sum of the squared errors, the errors being the differences between the data f_i' and the function that is to fit the data. (MathCAD is somewhat unpredictable here. Solutions may be slow, and the results depend somewhat on guess values. The results are not determined to the precision shown.) Plot the fitted curve and data in the same plot region.

There are a number of ways to fit the data in HEAT2. After you have obtained a fit, open HEAT3 for a brief examination of the data.

Whatever the specific form that f and g may take, the concept behind the wind chill temperature is that different sets of conditions (different temperatures and wind velocities) may result in the same heat flow. To determine the wind chill temperature, we equate the heat flows from two different cases: one case is based on the actual temperature and wind velocity, $H(T, v)$; the other, $H(T', v')$, is for a velocity $v' = 1.79$ m/s and T', the wind chill temperature. The question is what temperature T' will make

$$H(T', v') = H(T, v).$$

• •   Let $H(T, v) = f(v) \cdot (T_s - T)$. Express $H(T', v')$ similarly. Solve for T' in terms of $f(v)$, $f(v')$, T_s, and T. (Leave the $f(v)$'s in functional form; do not substitute an expression for $f(v)$.)

• •   Load HEAT4, wind chill (see Figs. 12.2 and 12.3).

We are now ready to explore the heat loss and the wind chill temperature as a function of the velocity and the temperature of the environment, T_s. The function $f(v)$ has the form described above in HEAT3; $g(T)$ is simply the temperature difference $(T_s - T)$. The wind chill temperature, in terms of the air temperature and velocity, $T'(T, v)$, is the form determined from the previous exercise.

For plotting purposes, the heat loss function H and the wind chill temperature function T' are defined twice with the order of the variables interchanged. For example, we write the heat loss function as $H(T, v)$ and $H'(v, T)$; they are equated to the same expression. This is necessary to plot the family of curves as a function of v (where we want the (T, v) form) or as a function of T (where we want the (v, T) form). To avoid a line connecting individual curves when we plot a family of curves, either the first or last point of each curve must lie outside the plot region. In

```
Wind chill - after H. R. Crane.

A range of wind velocities.          v := 2,4 ..20

A range of temperatures.             T := 10,0 ..-20

Parameters in the heat loss equation.      a := 10.45    b := 10    c := -1

T.s is the temperature of the exposed surface.          T  := 33
                                                         s
The empirical heat loss equation.
```

$$f(v) := \left[a + b\cdot\sqrt{v} + c\cdot v\right] \qquad H(T,v) := f(v)\cdot\left[T_s - T\right]$$

Equate two heat losses - one at actual wind speed and temperature, H(T,v), the other at the nominal speed v', 1.79 m/s and wind chill temperature T'. H(T,v) = H(T',v') Solve for T'.

```
v' := 1.79
```
$$T'(T,v) := T_s - \left[T_s - T\right]\cdot\frac{f(v)}{f(v')}$$

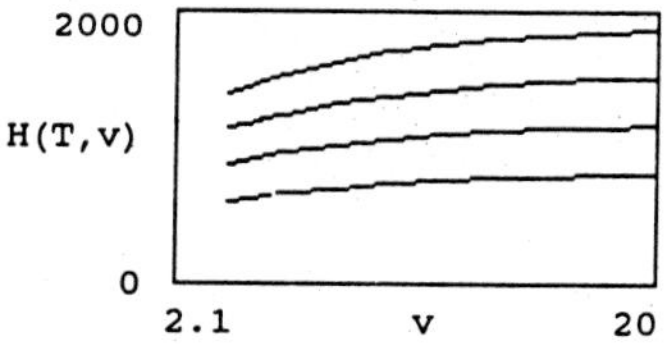

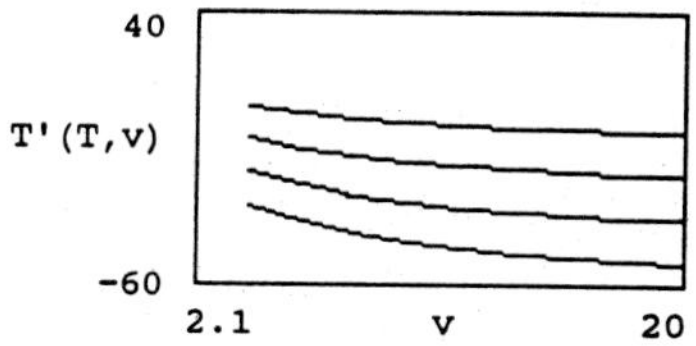

$$H'(v,T) := f(v)\cdot\left[T_s - T\right]$$
$$T1'(v,T) := T_s - \left[T_s - T\right]\cdot\frac{f(v)}{f(v')}$$

```
v := 2,6.5 ..20
```

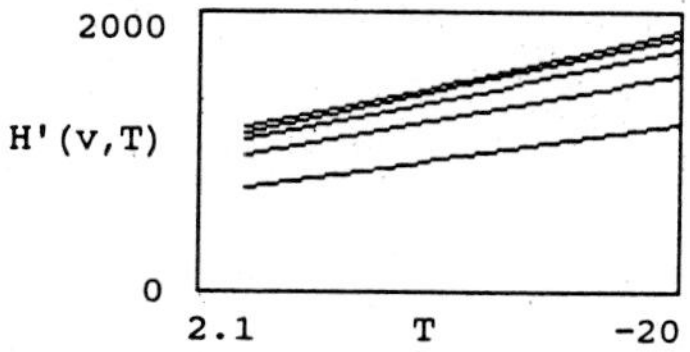

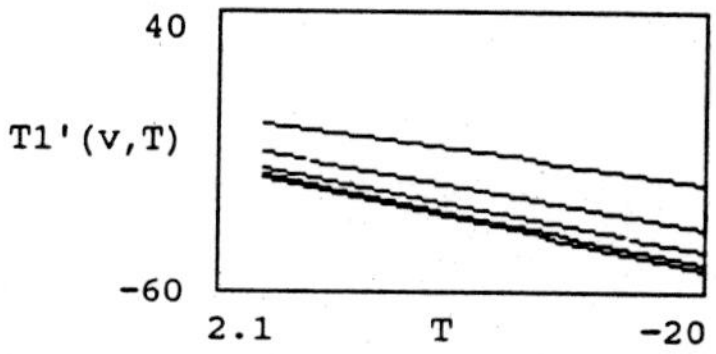

Figure 12.2 HEAT4, wind chill. (See the next figure for the rest of the document.)

this case, we set the lower ordinate limit to exclude either the smallest v or largest T values.

For each family of curves, identify the specific value of the parameter that goes with a particular curve.

In the function $f(v)$, the coefficients a, b, and c all have different units. In the last portion of the document, units are attached to the coefficients and all other necessary quantities. The procedure was to multiply in the complete set of desired units and divide out the units of the multiplying terms. G is equivalent to H. Including units in the expressions has the advantage that units can be specified in any system.

The coefficient a, b, and c all have different units. Units are included
in the expression below.

m := 1L   s := 1T   kg := 1M   C := 1Q

$$J := kg \cdot m^2 \cdot s^{-2}$$

cal := 4.186·J

h := 3600·s

kcal := 1000·cal

$$epat := kcal \cdot h^{-1} \cdot m^{-2}$$ epat - energy per area per time.

$$vel' := \frac{m}{s}$$

$$a' := a \cdot \frac{epat}{C} \qquad b' := b \cdot \frac{epat}{C} \cdot \frac{1}{\sqrt{vel'}} \qquad c' := c \cdot \frac{epat}{C \cdot vel'}$$

$$v' := 2 \cdot \frac{m}{s}, 4 \cdot \frac{m}{s} \; .. \; 20 \cdot \frac{m}{s} \qquad T' := 10 \cdot C, 0 \cdot C \; .. \; -20 \cdot C \qquad T'_s := 33 \cdot C$$

$$G(T', v') := \left[a' + b' \cdot \sqrt{v'} + c' \cdot v' \right] \cdot \left[T'_s - T' \right]$$

$$G\left[0 \cdot C, 5 \cdot \frac{m}{s} \right] = 917.752 \cdot epat \qquad H(0,5) = 917.752$$

2000·epat

G(T',v')

0

$$2.1 \cdot \frac{m}{s} \qquad v' \qquad 20$$

Figure 12.3 HEAT4 *continued.*

Define the Fahrenheit degree, *F*, miles, *mi*, and hours, *hr*. Plot the wind chill family of curves; show two sets of curves. Plot wind chill temperature vs. wind speed for several air temperatures and wind chill temperature vs. air temperature for several wind speeds. Put the limits of the abscissa in miles per hour and the limits of the ordinate in degrees Fahrenheit.

• •   One of the estimation problems near the beginning of the text was to determine the surface area of your body. Use this value in *H*. Instead of kcal per square meter per hour, use kcal per your body area per hour. If your entire body were exposed and if the body were able to maintain its surface area at a constant temperature (this is totally unreasonable), determine your weight loss as a function of time. (One pound is approximately 3500 kcal.) Plot your weight loss per hour for 0° C as a function of wind speed.

• •   Assume your body is able to produce heat at the rate of 150 kcal per hour. For a given external temperature and wind velocity, at what rate would the body temperature decrease? Plot body temperature vs. time for a person with a mass of 65 kg.

12.1.3   Heat Flow

If an insulator is placed between reservoirs at two different temperatures, the heat flow depends directly on the cross-sectional area of the insulator

A and on the temperature gradient across the insulator, that is, $\Delta T/\Delta x$. The constant of proportionality k, is the thermal conductivity of the material selected:

$$\frac{\Delta Q}{\Delta t} \simeq -kA\frac{\Delta T}{\Delta x}. \tag{12.8}$$

For an object of constant cross section A, under steady-state conditions (where temperatures throughout the insulator do not change with time), the flow of heat across any cross section must be the same. (If this were not true, the temperatures would change or something would melt or boil.) If $\Delta Q/\Delta t$ is constant, then for constant A $\Delta T/\Delta x$ must be constant. Just as constant dx/dt implies $x \propto t$, constant $\Delta T/\Delta x$ implies $T \propto x$. Therefore, the temperature change across the conductor is linear. The conduction heat flow equation becomes

$$\frac{\Delta Q}{\Delta t} = -kA\frac{T_2 - T_1}{L} \qquad \text{where} \qquad T_2 > T_1.$$

T_1 and T_2 are the temperatures of the reservoirs; L is the thickness of the insulator. This equation can be rewritten, where $H = \Delta Q/\Delta t$ (area is not included in this H, as it was in the wind chill example) as

$$(T_2 - T_1) = H \cdot \frac{L}{kA}.$$

The heat flow equation is analogous to Ohm's law for current flow in electrical circuits:

Quantity	Heat	Electrical
Flow	H	I
Condition that drives flow	$T_2 - T_1$	$V_2 - V_1$
Resistance to flow	$\Re = L/(kA)$	$R = L/(\sigma A)$
Ohm's law	$T_2 - T_1 = H\,\Re$	$V_2 - V_1 = I\,R$

(In engineering practice, the R-value of an insulator is just L/k; the A is not included.)

Heat flow through a wall, for example, might pass through drywall, then insulation, and finally the outer wall. Such a configuration is referred to as a compound slab when the cross section of each material is the same, but there is a sequence of materials with different resistances. The materials are in series and the resistances add:

$$T_2 - T_1 = H \cdot (\Re_1 + \Re_2 + \cdots).$$

Convective heat flow is complex and not easy to characterize quantitatively. For a vertical plate—for example, a wall—an empirical expression for the heat flow is

$$H_{\text{conv}} \propto (T_{\text{air}} - T_{\text{wall}})^{1.25}. \tag{12.9}$$

For horizontal plates—for example, the ceiling—the relation is similar. The constant varies depending on whether the heat is being exchanged with the air above or the air below and whether the plate is warmer or cooler than its surroundings.

Objects also lose or gain heat through radiation. All objects radiate electromagnetic energy continuously. How such energy is radiated depends on the temperature, the area radiating, and the properties of the surface. The relationship is

$$P = e\,\sigma\,A\,T^4, \tag{12.10}$$

where P is the power radiated in watts (Joules per second) (the same units as H); T is the temperature in Kelvin, unless otherwise stated; σ is the Stefan-Boltzmann constant $(5.67 \cdot 10^{-8}\,\text{J}/(\text{s}\,m^2\,\text{K}^4))$; and e, which varies from zero to one, is the emissivity of the surface. For a perfect absorber e is 1. Perfect absorbers are black when cool (the sun approximates an ideal black body radiator). For a perfect reflector e is 0. (A good reflector at one wavelength may be a good absorber at a different wavelength.)

Since the surroundings also radiate, the net energy exchange is

$$P = e\,\sigma\,A\,(T^4 - T_{\text{env}}^4), \tag{12.11}$$

where T_{env} is the temperature of the environment. The environment may not be uniform; in such a case you would have to take into account the various sources that are present.

12.1.4   Heat Flow from a House

Consider the heat flow from the interior to the exterior of a heated one-room house. Convective effects transfer energy from the warm interior to the inside walls. Heat is conducted through the walls to the exterior surface. Convective effects transfer energy from the exterior surfaces to the air beyond. Under steady-state conditions, all of these heat flows must be equal.

● ●   Load HEAT5, heat flow from a house (see Figs. 12.4 and 12.5).

The heat flow from the interior of a one-room house to the exterior is calculated. The model is based on the convective and conductive effects discussed above. Many details are not included, and so the model must be considered as a very basic one. (For example, no exchange of air is included in the model, and heat transfer through the floor is omitted.)

Heat loss from one room house through walls, ceiling, and windows.

$$m \equiv 1L \qquad s \equiv 1T \qquad kg \equiv 1M \qquad C \equiv 1Q \qquad hr \equiv 3600 \cdot s \qquad cm \equiv 0.01 \cdot m$$

$$J \equiv kg \cdot m^2 \cdot s^{-2} \qquad F \equiv \frac{5}{9} \cdot C \qquad \begin{array}{l} cal \equiv 4.186 \cdot J \\ in \equiv 2.54 \cdot cm \end{array} \qquad \begin{array}{l} BTU \equiv 252 \cdot cal \\ ft \equiv 12 \cdot in \end{array} \qquad W \equiv \frac{J}{s}$$

areas $\qquad Arcl := 750 \cdot ft^2 \qquad Arwin := 100 \cdot ft^2 \qquad Arwll := 945 \cdot ft^2$

thickness $\qquad \delta xwall := 4 \cdot in \qquad \delta xceil := 8 \cdot in \qquad \delta xwind := 0.125 \cdot in$

conductivity

$$kwall := 0.0002 \cdot \frac{cal}{s \cdot cm \cdot C} \qquad kceil := 0.0002 \cdot \frac{cal}{s \cdot cm \cdot C} \qquad kwind := .002 \cdot \frac{cal}{s \cdot cm \cdot C}$$

convection coef.

$$chvert := 0.4 \cdot 10^{-4} \cdot \frac{cal}{s \cdot cm^2 \cdot C^{1.25}}$$

$$chhoru := 0.6 \cdot 10^{-4} \cdot cal \cdot s^{-1} \cdot cm^{-2} \cdot C^{-1.25} \qquad chhord := 0.5 \cdot chhoru$$

Calculate the temperature of the interior and exterior wall surfaces.

$$Tins := 20 \cdot C \qquad Tsurfin := 10 \cdot C \qquad Tsurfout := 0 \cdot C \qquad Tout := -10 \cdot C$$

Given

$$chvert \cdot (Tins - Tsurfin)^{1.25} \approx kwall \cdot \frac{Tsurfin - Tsurfout}{\delta xwall}$$

$$2 \cdot chvert \cdot (Tsurfout - Tout)^{1.25} \approx kwall \cdot \frac{Tsurfin - Tsurfout}{\delta xwall}$$

$$\begin{bmatrix} Tsurfin \\ Tsurfout \end{bmatrix} := Find(Tsurfin, Tsurfout) \qquad \begin{array}{l} Tsurfin = 13.736 \cdot C \\ Tsurfout = -6.402 \cdot C \end{array}$$

$$\delta Tins := Tins - Tsurfin \qquad \delta Twall := Tsurfin - Tsurfout$$

$$\delta Tout := Tsurfout - Tout \qquad \delta Tins = 6.264 \cdot C \qquad \delta Tout = 3.598 \cdot C$$

$$\delta Twall = 20.138 \cdot C$$

$$Hwll := kwall \cdot \frac{\delta Twall}{\delta xwall} \qquad Hwll = 16.594 \cdot J \cdot [m^2 \cdot s]^{-1}$$

Calculate the temperature difference across the roof. $\qquad Tceilin := 10 \cdot C$

$$Troofout := 0 \cdot C$$

Figure 12.4 HEAT5, heat flow from a house. (See the next figure for the rest of the document.)

Because the document is long and should not exceed the two-page limit of the student version of MathCAD, the regions are close together; the document is still readable, however.

The house has one room with windows and a flat ceiling. A furnace maintains the interior at a constant temperature, T_{ins}. The surroundings are also at a constant temperature, T_{out}. The dimensions of the room are $25 \times 30 \times 9.5$ (feet). Each of the eight windows is 5×2.5 (feet).

```
Given
                              1.25                   Tceilin - Troofout
    chhord· (Tins - Tceilin)       ≈ kceil· ─────────────────────────
                                                        δxceil

                                1.25                 Tceilin - Troofout
    chhoru· (Troofout - Tout)        ≈ kceil· ─────────────────────────
                                                        δxceil

    ⎡ Tceilin⎤                               Tceilin = 15.091· C   Troofout = -7.181· C
    ⎢Troofout⎥ := Find(Tceilin,Troofout)
                                                 δTins' := Tins - Tceilin
    δTclrf := Tceilin - Troofout                 δTout' := Troofout - Tout

    δTins' = 4.909· C              δTout' = 2.819· C              δTclrf = 22.272· C

                      δTclrf                             J
    Hclrf := kceil· ─────────       Hclrf = 9.176· ─────────
                      δxceil                           2
                                                      m  · s
                                                                     Twindin := 10· C
Repeat temperature difference calculation for windows.
                                                                     Twindout := 0· C
Given
                              1.25                  Twindin - Twindout
    chvert· (Tins - Twindin)        ≈ kwind· ─────────────────────────
                                                        δxwind

                                   1.25              Twindin - Twindout
    2· chvert· (Twindout - Tout)        ≈ kwind· ─────────────────────────
                                                        δxwind

    ⎡ Twindin⎤                               Twindin = 1.103· C    Twindout = 0.853· C
    ⎢Twindout⎥ := Find(Twindin,Twindout)
                                                 δTwind := Twindin - Twindout

                      δTwind                          J         Twindout - Tout = 10.853· C
    Hwind := kwind· ─────────     Hwind = 65.969· ─────────     Twindin - Twindout = 0.25· C
                      δxwind                          2          Tins - Twindin = 18.897· C
                                                     m  · s

    Hwind := Hwind· Arwin        Hwll := Hwll· Arwll        Hcl := Hclrf· Arcl

    Hwind = 612.87· W                                       Hcl = 639.364· W
                                                   3
                                  Hwll = 1.457· 10  · W

    Htot := Hwind + Hwll + Hcl          Artot := Arwin + Arwll + Arcl

                Hwind                        Hwll                      Hcl
    FHwin := ─────────         FHwll := ─────────        FHcl := ─────────
                Htot                         Htot                     Htot

                      3
    Htot = 2.709· 10  · W     FHwll = 0.538        FHcl = 0.236       FHwin = 0.226
```

Figure 12.5 HEAT5 *continued.*

Check the values for the areas of the ceiling, Ar_{cl}, the windows, Ar_{win}, and the walls, Ar_{wll}.

The walls and ceiling are treated not as compound slabs but as uniform. We assign the same thermal conductivity to the walls and ceiling but permit them to have different thicknesses.

The convection coefficient for convective heat flow from a vertical plate is ch_{vert}, the coefficient for the interior vertical surface. Similarly, ch_{horu} is the convective heat flow coefficient for a horizontal plate facing up, the coefficient for the roof; ch_{hord} is the coefficient for the ceiling. Values for the exterior are double those of the interior as the air motion is generally greater on the outside.

The various heat flows are equated. For example, in the first solve block, the internal convective heat flow is equated with the conductive heat flow in the first equation. The second equation equates the convective heat flow outside and the conductive heat flow. The temperatures of the wall inside and out are determined. The temperature differences between the interior and the interior surface of the wall, between the interior and exterior surfaces of the wall, and between the exterior surface of the wall and the environment are determined.

Essentially the same calculation is repeated for the roof and for the windows. Note the difference between the temperature differences across the walls, the ceiling, and the windows. Explain the value for the temperature difference across a window.

Once the temperature differences are known, the heat flow can be computed. For example, H_{wll}, is the heat flow through the wall in energy per area per time. Determine the corresponding convective flow and verify that the conductive and convective heat flows are the same.

At the end of the document, the total heat flows are determined by including the specific areas. The total heat flow and the fraction of the heat through the walls, ceiling, and windows are determined.

If the walls had only two inches of insulation instead of four, by how much would the surface temperature of the walls change? By how much would the heat flow increase?

If the convective heat flow coefficient outside were not double the inside value but equal to it, by how much would the surface temperature of the ceiling and inside walls change? First, predict the sign of the change, then process.

If the net effect of adding storm windows were to reduce k_{wind} from 0.002 to 0.001, what would reduce heat flow more, adding two inches of insulation to the walls or installing storm windows? What results in a greater energy saving, adding two inches of insulation to the ceiling or adding storm windows?

How much heat transfer through radiation is there between the outside walls of the house and its surroundings? How does this compare with the net flow due to convection and conduction?

12.2 Ideal Gas

The experimentally observed interrelation among pressure, P, temperature, T, and volume, V, is remarkably similar in dilute gases of different composition. A summary of these observations is expressed in the equation of state for an ideal gas:

$$PV = nRT \tag{12.12}$$

where n is the number of moles of the gas and R is the universal gas constant, $R = 8.314\,\text{J}/(\text{mol K})$. The SI unit for pressure is the Pa (pascal), $Pa = N/m^2$.

• • Load HEAT6, ideal gas (see Fig. 12.6).

The properties of an ideal gas are explored graphically. Plots of P vs. V are shown for a series of temperatures. Each curve represents pressure and volume information for a given temperature; each of the curves is referred to as an isotherm. The two different regions show the curves in linear and in log-log plots.

Some manipulations were performed to set the limits to improve plot appearance, but this is not essential. However, to prevent the appearance of lines connecting the individual curves, one limit, in this case V_m, has been reduced.

Plot P vs. T curves for a series of volumes. Plot V vs. T curves for a series of pressures.

12.2.1 The Van der Waals Equation

As the number density of gas particles increases, the behavior of the gas deviates from the ideal. Many equations of state have been suggested. The van der Waals equation of state is one familiar variation. This equation attempts to account for two phenomena. As the number density of molecules increases, the volume available for each molecule decreases. In addition, molecules are subject to intermolecular forces; on average, these forces are attractive. This attraction tends to increase the pressure the particles exert. The van der Waals equation of state attempts to take into account these two considerations. The equation is

$$\left(P + \frac{a}{V^2}\right)(V - b) = nRT, \tag{12.13}$$

where the parameter b is a measure of the volume occupied by the gas molecules and a is a measure of the pressure increase.

• • Load HEAT7, van der Waals equation of state (see Fig. 12.7).

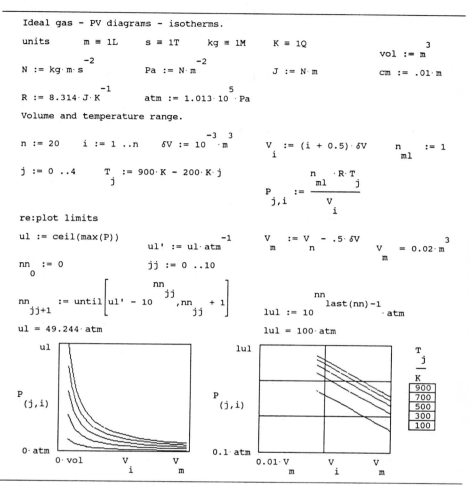

Figure 12.6 HEAT6, ideal gas.

A comparison is made between the van der Waals equation of state and the ideal gas equation. Substitute the following temperature values sequentially to see the deviations from the behavior described by the ideal gas law behavior associated with the van der Waals equation. Let T equal 500, 400, 360, 330, 300, 280, and 260. The a and b values are for CO_2.

Why does the volume start at $4 \cdot \delta v$? Plot $V_i - b$ vs. V_i.

In the following examples, you begin to get a sense of the role of each of the terms. Set the temperature at 500 K and process. If the a term were zero, how would the curve change? Enable the $a = 0$ region and check your

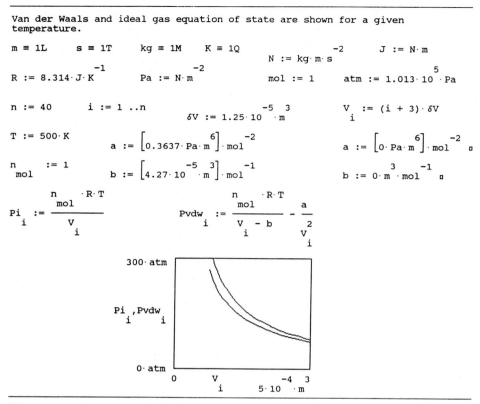

Van der Waals and ideal gas equation of state are shown for a given temperature.

$$m \equiv 1L \qquad s \equiv 1T \qquad kg \equiv 1M \qquad K \equiv 1Q$$

$$N := kg \cdot m \cdot s^{-2} \qquad J := N \cdot m$$

$$R := 8.314 \cdot J \cdot K^{-1} \qquad Pa := N \cdot m^{-2} \qquad mol := 1 \qquad atm := 1.013 \cdot 10^{5} \cdot Pa$$

$$n := 40 \qquad i := 1 .. n$$
$$\delta V := 1.25 \cdot 10^{-5} \cdot m^{3} \qquad V_i := (i + 3) \cdot \delta V$$

$$T := 500 \cdot K$$
$$a := \left[0.3637 \cdot Pa \cdot m^{6} \right] \cdot mol^{-2} \qquad a := \left[0 \cdot Pa \cdot m^{6} \right] \cdot mol^{-2} \quad _{□}$$

$$n_{mol} := 1 \qquad b := \left[4.27 \cdot 10^{-5} \cdot m^{3} \right] \cdot mol^{-1} \qquad b := 0 \cdot m^{3} \cdot mol^{-1} \quad _{□}$$

$$Pi_i := \frac{n_{mol} \cdot R \cdot T}{V_i} \qquad Pvdw_i := \frac{n_{mol} \cdot R \cdot T}{V_i - b} - \frac{a}{V_i^{2}}$$

Figure 12.7 HEAT7, van der Waals equation of state.

prediction. What if b were zero and a were not? Disable the $a = 0$ region and enable the $b = 0$ region and observe. Disable the $a = 0$ and $b = 0$ regions. Plot the following two terms in the same region: $n\,RT/(V - b)$ and $-a/V^2$ vs. V. Finally, define $V_i' = i \cdot \delta V$ and plot $P_{vdwi} + a/V_i^2$ vs. $V_i - b$ and Pi_i vs. V_i' in the same region.

12.2.2 *Isothermal and Adiabatic Changes*

When discussing the P vs. V curves at constant temperature, we made no mention of how the expansion might take place. Imagine the gas to be in a cylinder with a movable piston at one end. To ensure that the temperature remains constant during an expansion or compression, the cylinder is placed in contact with a heat reservoir while the change takes place.

If the cylinder is insulated and the gas expands or is compressed, the product PV is no longer a constant. The curve associated with such a process is an adiabat. For adiabatic processes, in which there is no transfer of heat between the gas and its surroundings, we have

$$PV^\gamma = \text{const} \quad \text{or} \quad P_i V_i^\gamma = P_f V_f^\gamma, \quad (12.14)$$

where γ is the ratio of specific heats at constant pressure and constant volume:

$$\gamma = \frac{c_p}{c_v}. \quad (12.15)$$

At constant volume, all the energy is associated with the change in temperature of the substance; all the energy is associated with the change of internal energy of the substance. At constant pressure, the same change in temperature occurs and in addition the volume of the substance changes. There is work associated with the change in volume that occurs. For monatomic gases $\gamma = 5/3$; for diatomic gases $\gamma = 7/5$; and for polyatomic gases $\gamma = 4/3$.

An adiabatic process can also be expressed in terms of T and V: or P and T:

$$T_i V_i^{\gamma-1} = T_f V_f^{\gamma-1}, \quad (12.16)$$

$$P_i^{1-\gamma} T_i^\gamma = P_f^{1-\gamma} T_f^\gamma. \quad (12.17)$$

• • Verify the T, V and P, T relations, given the PV^γ equation.

• • Select a value for P and for V. Plot an isotherm and an adiabat through that point (omit units).

• • Plot the analogous pairs of curves in T, V and P, T diagrams.

• • How different are the curves in the last two exercises as the gas changes from monatomic to diatomic? From diatomic to polyatomic?

In addition to just trying to appreciate the functional relationships expressed in these equations, we want to connect isothermal and adiabatic processes with the operation of a heat engine, a machine that converts heat energy into work. Such machines go through a cycle of absorbing energy from a hot reservoir and performing work and dumping energy to a cold reservoir and having work performed on them. Work is performed by the machine, as the gas expands; work is performed on the machine as the gas is compressed. If the machine is to be useful, the work performed during expansion must be greater than the work done on the machine during compression. The most efficient possible engine is one that follows isothermal and adiabatic expansions or compressions. Before we discuss the cycle of a heat engine, we investigate a few more questions about adiabats and isotherms.

Any two points on a PV diagram can be connected by an adiabat and an isotherm. Let (p_1, v_1) and (p_3, v_3) represent the two points that are selected. We draw an isotherm through the point (p_1, v_1) and an adiabat through (p_3, v_3) and find the point of intersection:

$$p_1 v_1 = p_2 v_2 \qquad \text{isotherm}$$

$$p_2 v_2^\gamma = p_3 v_3^\gamma \qquad \text{adiabat.}$$

Solving the first equation for v_2, substituting in the second, and solving for p_2 gives

$$p_2 = p_3^{1/1-\gamma} \left(\frac{v_3}{p_1 v_1} \right)^{\gamma/1-\gamma}$$

The volume $v_2 = p_1 v_1 / p_2$. Using MathCAD, it is just as easy to put the original equations in a solve block and let MathCAD solve for the particular values of p_2 and v_2.

• •   Load HEAT8, isotherms and adiabats (see Figs. 12.8 and 12.9).

When you enter the coordinates of the two points, (p_1, v_1) and (p_3, v_3), and a value for γ, the equations for the isotherm and adiabat are solved to determine the coordinates of the intersection point, (p_2, v_2).

Subscripts cannot be used in the argument of a find statement. Consequently, values for p_2 and v_2 are written without subscripts until the solutions are obtained. The values determined in a find statement can be assigned to subscripted variables. (An attempt to use subscripted results in a find statement results in the error message, "error in list.")

Just as each isotherm has associated with it a particular temperature, each adiabat has associated with it an analogous constant. K and L represent the constants associated with the points (p_1, v_1) and (p_3, v_3).

$P(V)$ and $P'(V)$ describe the isotherm and adiabat through (p_1, v_1). $Q(V)$ and $Q'(V)$ describe the isotherm and adiabat through (p_3, v_3). The other equations set the limits so that only the region of interest is plotted. Although this choice of limits presents the three points together with the corresponding isotherms and adiabats from case to case, it has the disadvantage of changing the scale and range. You may wish to add another plot region with fixed limits to see at the same time where the curves lie relative to the axes. Process. Which point corresponds to (p_1, v_1)? Which point corresponds to (p_3, v_3)? Which curves are isotherms? Which curves are adiabats? How do you know? Follow the path from (p_1, v_1) to (p_2, v_2) — the isotherm, and from (p_2, v_2) to (p_3, v_3) — the adiabat. (After processing, press [Ctrl]home to change values and [Ctrl]end and [F9] to see the results.)

Any two points in a pv diagram can be connected by an adiabat and an isotherm.

The coordinates of the two points and gamma.

$p_1 := 10$ $v_1 := 3$ $p_3 := 5.5$ $v_3 := 5$ $\tau := 1.33$

Find p2 and v2.   p2 := 5   v2 := 5   guess values

given $p_1 \cdot v_1 \approx p2 \cdot v2$

$p2 \cdot v2^{\tau} \approx p_3 \cdot v_3^{\tau}$ $\begin{bmatrix} p_2 \\ v_2 \end{bmatrix} := \text{find}(p2, v2)$

$p_2 = 7.81$ $v_2 = 3.841$

Characteristic values for the adiabats and isotherms.

$K := p_1 \cdot v_1^{\tau}$ $L := p_3 \cdot v_3^{\tau}$ $i := 1 .. 3$ $T_i := p_i \cdot v_i$

$K \cdot v_3^{-\tau} = 5.069$ $T_1 \cdot v_3^{-1} = 6$

$$\begin{array}{|c|}\hline T_i \\ \hline 30 \\ \hline 30 \\ \hline 27.5 \\ \hline \end{array}$$

$P(V) := \dfrac{T_1}{V}$ $P'(V) := \dfrac{K}{V^{\tau}}$ $Q(V) := \dfrac{T_3}{V}$ $Q'(V) := \dfrac{L}{V^{\tau}}$

Plot limit specifications.

$a := \text{if}\begin{bmatrix} v_3 > v_2 , v_3 , v_2 \end{bmatrix}$ $\text{hul} := \text{if}\begin{bmatrix} a > v_1 , a , v_1 \end{bmatrix} \cdot 1.1$ $\text{hul} = 5.5$

$b := \text{if}\begin{bmatrix} v_3 < v_2 , v_3 , v_2 \end{bmatrix}$ $\text{hll} := \text{if}\begin{bmatrix} b < v_1 , b , v_1 \end{bmatrix} \cdot 0.8$ $\text{hll} = 2.4$

$c := \text{if}\begin{bmatrix} p_3 > p_2 , p_3 , p_2 \end{bmatrix}$ $\text{vul} := \text{if}\begin{bmatrix} c > p_1 , c , p_1 \end{bmatrix} \cdot 1.1$ $\text{vul} = 11$

$d := \text{if}\begin{bmatrix} p_3 < p_2 , p_3 , p_2 \end{bmatrix}$ $\text{vll} := \text{if}\begin{bmatrix} d < p_1 , d , p_1 \end{bmatrix} \cdot 0.8$ $\text{vll} = 4.4$

$V := \text{hll}, \text{hll} + .2 .. \text{hul}$

Figure 12.8 HEAT8, isotherms and adiabats. (See the next figure for the rest of the document.)

Change v_3 to 4.5 and process. Why the switch? Explore. Determine the conditions on p_3 and v_3 so that $p_1 > p_2 > p_3$ and $v_1 < v_2 < v_3$.

Change the sequence so that (p_2, v_2) is connected to (p_1, v_1) by an adiabat and to (p_3, v_3) by an isotherm. Plot some examples.

12.3   The Carnot Cycle

A Carnot cycle includes four steps; each step connects two points; the last step connects the fourth point with the first. We start the cycle at point 1:

The path is an isotherm from 1 - 2
and an adiabat from 2 - 3.

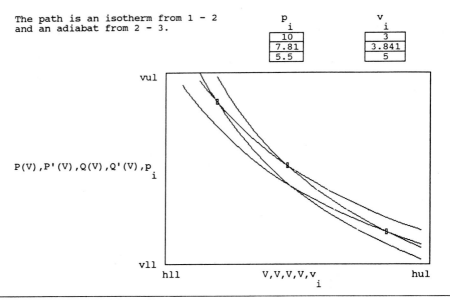

p
i
10
7.81
5.5

v
i
3
3.841
5

Figure 12.9 HEAT8 *continued.*

1. isothermal expansion   (1–2)
2. adiabatic expansion   (2–3)
3. isothermal compression (3–4)
4. adiabatic compression   (4–1).

In this sequence, $p_1 > p_2 > p_3$, and $v_1 < v_2 < v_3$. Trying to specify the p, v coordinates for the first three points leads to some restrictions. Recall the previous example in which you were asked to explore these restrictions. Any pair of points may be connected by an isotherm and an adiabat but the pressure and volume sequences may not be that desired for a Carnot cycle.

Given that $v_3 > v_1$, there are two additional conditions. The temperature at (p_3, v_3) must be less than that at (p_1, v_1). The temperature at (p_3, v_3) must be greater than the final temperature reached by an adiabat from (p_1, v_1) to v_3. These conditions can be expressed as

$$p_3 < \frac{p_1 \, v_1}{v_3} \qquad \text{and} \qquad p_3 > \frac{p_1 v_1^{\gamma}}{v_3^{\gamma}}.$$

In other words, the point (p_3, v_3) must have $v_3 > v_1$ and must lie between the isothermal and adiabatic curves through point (p_1, v_1). In the document, these two limiting quantities are expressed as $T_1 \cdot v_3^{-1}$ and $K \cdot v_3^{-\gamma}$. Given that $v_3 > v_1$, these are the limits of p_3.

Now consider the question of work done by the gas as it expands and is compressed and as the heat is absorbed and dumped during those same processes. Recall that the definition of work is

$$W = \int F\,dx.$$

In terms of pressure, this becomes ($P = F/A$)

$$W = \int P A\,dx = \int P\,dV. \tag{12.18}$$

During expansion, the work done by the gas is positive; during compression the work done by the gas is negative.

On a PV diagram, the area under the curve representing an expansion as it goes from initial to final value is equal to the work. If the expansion is along an isotherm, the work is given by

$$W = \int_{V_1}^{V_2} \frac{n\,R\,T}{V}\,dV = n\,R\,T \int_{V_1}^{V_2} \frac{dV}{V} = n\,R\,T \ln\left(\frac{V_2}{V_1}\right). \tag{12.19}$$

If the expansion is along an adiabat, the work is given by

$$W = \int_{V_1}^{V_2} \frac{P'\,V'^{\gamma}}{V^{\gamma}}\,dV = P'\,V'^{\gamma} \int_{V_1}^{V_2} \frac{dV}{V^{\gamma}}$$

$$= P'\,\frac{V'^{\gamma}}{1-\gamma}\left(V_2{}^{1-\gamma} - V_1{}^{1-\gamma}\right). \tag{12.20}$$

These results can be used directly, or we can let MathCAD perform the integrations for us.

We now examine the Carnot cycle, keeping track of work performed and heat exchanged. We describe the cycle starting from the point of minimum volume and maximum pressure:

1. Isothermal expansion from (p_1, v_1) to (p_2, v_2):

$$p_1 \cdot v_1 = p_2 \cdot v_2 \qquad\qquad v_2 > v_1;$$

work performed : $\displaystyle\int_{V_1}^{V_2} \frac{n\,R\,T_1}{V}\,dV.$

Heat absorbed equals work performed.

2. Adiabatic expansion from (p_2, v_2) to (p_3, v_3):

$$p_2 \cdot v_2^{\gamma} = p_3 \cdot v_3^{\gamma} \qquad\qquad v_3 > v_2:$$

$$\text{work performed}: \int_{V_2}^{V_3} \frac{p_2 v_2^{\gamma}}{V^{\gamma}}\, dV.$$

Heat exchanged is zero.

3. Isothermal compression from (p_3, v_3) to (p_4, v_4):

$$p_3 \cdot v_3 = p_4 \cdot v_4 \qquad\qquad v_4 < v_3;$$

$$\text{work performed}: \int_{V_3}^{V_4} \frac{n\,R\,T_3}{V}\, dV.$$

Work is done on the gas; heat is given up.

4. Adiabatic compression from (p_4, v_4) to (p_1, v_1):

$$p_2 \cdot v_2^{\gamma} = p_4 \cdot v_4^{\gamma} \qquad\qquad v_1 < v_4$$

$$\text{work performed}: \int_{V_4}^{V_1} \frac{p_4 v_4^{\gamma}}{V^{\gamma}}\, dV.$$

Heat exchanged is zero.

• •   Adapt the previous document to plot a complete Carnot cycle.

• •   Load HEAT9, Carnot cycle (see Figs. 12.10 and 12.11).

For a given set of parameters, a rough plot of the Carnot cycle is shown. The work associated with each of the four steps is calculated using the explicit expressions that were shown above and using a direct integration process. The total work performed is calculated, and the efficiency is determined.

In the plot region, straight lines connect points 1, 2, and 3. (Because the document is long, we skip a functional expression here.) The line does not continue around the entire cycle as in this representation; the line from 4 to 1 may intersect either the $1 - 2$ or the $2 - 3$ line.

If T_1, V_1, and V_3 are fixed, by how much can T_3 vary and still have a Carnot cycle? Observe the position of (p_2, v_2) and (p_4, v_4) as T_1 is changed.

Starting with (T_1, T_3, v_1, v_3) as $(300, 100, 1, 6)$, let v_3 increase slowly and observe the changes.

Carnot cycle $\qquad\qquad$ N := 4 $\qquad$ i := 1 ..N

Specify, parameters, temperatures of hot and cold reservoirs, and minimum and maximum volumes.   (Values are subject to restrictions.)

n := 1 $\qquad$ R := 8.31 $\qquad$ τ := 1.67 $\qquad$ β := τ - 1

T_1 := 300 $\qquad$ T_3 := 150 $\qquad$ V_1 := 1 $\qquad$ V_3 := 5

Determine remaining values of p, V, and T.

$T_2 := T_1$ $\qquad$ $T_4 := T_3$ $\qquad\qquad$ $p_1 := \dfrac{n\cdot R\cdot T_1}{V_1}$ $\qquad$ $p_3 := \dfrac{n\cdot R\cdot T_3}{V_3}$

$p_2 := p_3\cdot\left[\dfrac{T_3}{T_2}\right]^{\frac{\tau}{1-\tau}}$ $\qquad$ $p_4 := p_1\cdot\left[\dfrac{T_1}{T_4}\right]^{\frac{\tau}{1-\tau}}$ $\qquad$ $V_2 := \dfrac{p_1\cdot V_1}{p_2}$ $\qquad$ $V_4 := \dfrac{p_3\cdot V_3}{p_4}$

pu := p_1·1.1 $\qquad$ pl := p_3·0.8 $\qquad$ vl := V_1·0.8 $\qquad$ vu := V_3·1.1 $\qquad$ j := 1 ..3

p_i
2.493·10³
1.403·10³
249.3
442.99

V_i
1
1.777
5
2.814

T_i
300
300
150
150

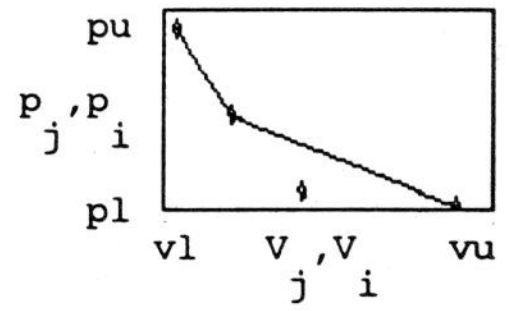

Determine the work performed and heat exchanged by the gas in each segment.

$W_{12} := n\cdot R\cdot T_1\cdot\ln\left[\dfrac{V_2}{V_1}\right]$ $\qquad$ $W_{23} := \dfrac{p_2\cdot V_2^{\tau}}{-\beta}\cdot\left[V_3^{-\beta} - V_2^{-\beta}\right]$ $\qquad$ $W_{12} = 1.433\cdot10^3$

$\qquad\qquad\qquad\qquad\qquad\qquad\qquad\qquad\qquad\qquad\qquad\qquad\qquad\qquad$ $W_{23} = 1.86\cdot10^3$

$W_{34} := n\cdot R\cdot T_3\cdot\ln\left[\dfrac{V_4}{V_3}\right]$ $\qquad$ $W_{41} := \dfrac{p_1\cdot V_1^{\tau}}{-\beta}\cdot\left[V_1^{-\beta} - V_4^{-\beta}\right]$ $\qquad$ $W_{34} = -716.6$

$\qquad\qquad\qquad\qquad\qquad\qquad\qquad\qquad\qquad\qquad\qquad\qquad\qquad\qquad$ $W_{41} = -1.86\cdot10^3$

$\delta Q_{12} := W_{12}$ $\qquad$ $\delta Q_{23} := 0$ $\qquad$ $\delta Q_{34} := W_{34}$ $\qquad$ $\delta Q_{41} := 0$

Figure 12.10 HEAT9, Carnot cycle. (See the next figure for the rest of the document.)

By noting the shape of the Carnot cycle, you can estimate when the greatest amount of work will be performed per cycle, that is, when the area enclosed by the paths that outline the cycle is the greatest. Maximum efficiency occurs when the temperature difference between the two reservoirs is the greatest.

Does the maximum value for work per cycle occur at the same point as that of maximum efficiency? Make a rough plot of the work per cycle

Compare with values from direct integration.

$$WW_{12} := \int_{V_1}^{V_2} \frac{n \cdot R \cdot T_1}{V}\, dV \qquad WW_{23} := \int_{V_2}^{V_3} \frac{p_2 \cdot V_2^{\tau}}{V'^{\tau}}\, dV'$$

$$WW_{12} = 1.433 \cdot 10^3$$

$$WW_{23} = 1.86 \cdot 10^3$$

$$WW_{34} := \int_{V_3}^{V_4} \frac{n \cdot R \cdot T_3}{V}\, dV \qquad WW_{41} := \int_{V_4}^{V_1} \frac{p_1 \cdot V_1^{\tau}}{V'^{\tau}}\, dV'$$

$$WW_{34} = -716.6$$

$$WW_{41} = -1.86 \cdot 10^3$$

The total work performed.

$$W_{tot} := W_{12} + W_{23} + W_{34} + W_{41} \qquad W_{tot} = 716.6$$

$$WW_{tot} := WW_{12} + WW_{23} + WW_{34} + WW_{41} \qquad WW_{tot} = 716.6$$

$$W_{12} + W_{34} = 716.6 \qquad WW_{12} + WW_{34} = 716.6$$

Efficiency can be expressed in several equivalent ways. Work performed over heat extracted from the hot reservoir is one.

$$Eff := 1 - \frac{T_3}{T_1} \qquad Eff = 0.5 \qquad \frac{W_{tot}}{\delta Q_{12}} = 0.5$$

Figure 12.11 HEAT9 *continued.*

over the allowed range of temperatures for T_3. (For various values of T_3, observe W_{tot}.) How much work is performed when $T_3 = T_1$? How much work is performed per cycle when T_3 is at its minimum?

How does the quantity of work performed in the adiabatic expansion and compression compare? Is this a general conclusion? Can you prove this?

Do you expect me to talk?

No, Mr. Bond, I expect you to die.

Goldfinger

CHAPTER
13

Kinetic Theory

When discussing the properties of a gas, we considered such macroscopic quantities as pressure and temperature. Kinetic theory takes a different approach and provides a description of the properties of a gas from a microscopic point of view. Here we consider questions about the velocity distribution of molecules in a gas. The velocity distribution is considered as a packet of gas spreads out in time and is observed at a detector. Finally, a simple simulation of thermal equilibration is presented. A hot object is placed in a cool environment and the energy migrates according to a two-dimensional random walk.

13.1   Velocity Distribution

A molecular model for an ideal gas is that of a large number of independent, identical molecules moving randomly. Collisions are elastic, and if no energy is exchanged between the gas and its surroundings, the speed distribution remains the same and is given by

$$N(v) = 4\pi N\left(\frac{m}{2\pi kT}\right)^{3/2} v^2 e^{-mv^2/2kT}. \tag{13.1}$$

$N(v)dv$ is the number of molecules in the gas with speeds between v and $v + dv$, k is Boltzmann's constant (the gas constant per molecule; R is the gas constant per mole), and T is the absolute temperature. N is the total number of molecules in the sample.

• • Load KT1, Maxwell-Boltzmann distribution (see Fig. 13.1).

The distribution function is examined by creating plots of the distribution showing its dependence on temperature and mass.

New quantities in the parameter list include N_2 and O_2; these are the masses of one mole of molecular nitrogen and one mole of molecular oxygen; mN_2 and mO_2 are the corresponding molecular masses, and Av is Avogadro's number.

The sum of all particles in each velocity range should equal the total number of particles. Verify that

$$\int N(v,T)\,dv = Nm. \tag{13.2}$$

We use Nm for the number of molecules so that there is no confusion with the distribution function itself.

Maxwell-Boltzmann velocity distribution.

Parameters

$k := 1.38 \cdot 10^{-23}$ $N2 := 0.028$ $Av := 6.022 \cdot 10^{23}$ $mN2 := \dfrac{N2}{Av}$

$O2 := 0.032$

$Nm := 10^6$ $T := 300$

The distribution equation.

$$N(v,T) := 4\cdot\pi\cdot Nm\cdot\left[\frac{mN2}{2\cdot\pi\cdot k\cdot T}\right]^{1.5}\cdot v^2\cdot\exp\left[\frac{-mN2\cdot v^2}{2\cdot k\cdot T}\right]$$

$v := 0, 50 \,.. 1500$

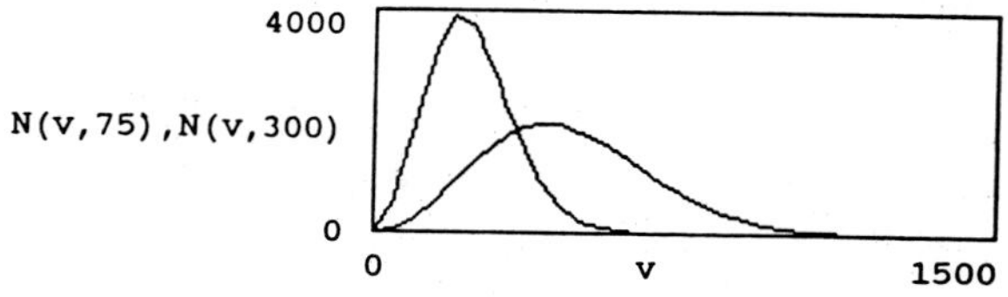

$N(v,75), N(v,300)$

Figure 13.1 KT1, Maxwell-Boltzmann distribution.

For $T = 300$, is an upper limit for v of 1500 adequate? For $T = 1200$, what fraction of the molecules have speed ranges between 0 and 1500?

The average translational kinetic energy per molecule is related to the temperature by

$$\frac{1}{2} m \overline{v^2} = \frac{3}{2} k T, \tag{13.3}$$

where $\overline{v^2}$ is the average value of the square of the velocity. The root mean-squared velocity v_{rms} (the square root of the mean of the square of the velocity) is

$$v_{rms} = \sqrt{\overline{v^2}} = \sqrt{\frac{3 k T}{m}}. \tag{13.4}$$

Other means of the velocity (for example, average velocity and most probable velocity) have the same dependence on temperature and mass.

The most probable speed is that associated with the peak of the velocity distribution. The root/derivative method is useful in determining this value. Keep the guess value close to the actual value to avoid spurious results; the guess values can be estimated from the plots.

Explore the relation between temperature and most probable velocity; make several comparisons. You need not plot the distributions to determine the velocities. Verify the expected dependence.

Explore the relation between mass and most probable velocity. Make several comparisons and verify the expected dependence.

At what velocity do the distribution curves for N_2 and O_2 intersect? How precisely would velocity distribution measurements have to be in order to distinguish between molecular nitrogen and molecular oxygen?

The average velocity is obtained from

$$v_{av} = \frac{\int v \cdot N(v,T)dv}{\int N(v,T)dv}. \tag{13.5}$$

The denominator should be familiar.

The rms velocity is given by

$$v_{rms}^2 = \frac{\int v^2 \cdot N(v,T)\,dv}{\int N(v,T)dv}. \tag{13.6}$$

For $T = 300$, determine the most probable velocity, v_{mp}, the average velocity, v_{av}, and the root-mean-squared velocity, v_{rms}. Verify that $v_{rms} > v_{av} > v_{mp}$. Superimpose plots of these individual points (plot type v, for example) on the corresponding velocity distribution.

13.2   Mean Free Path

Three quantities describing a dilute gas are the pressure, the molecular number density, and the mean free path. Pressure is a result of momentum transfer due to collisions. If the number density n_ρ — the number of particles per volume — is reduced, the pressure is reduced proportionately: $P \propto n_\rho$. Within the gas, the mean free path — the distance a molecule travels, on average, between collisions — increases as the number density decreases. Each of these quantities can be expressed in terms of either of the others.

The mean free path depends on the effective cross section (cross-sectional area) of a molecule. If the cross section is very small, the particle will undergo few collisions, and therefore it will have a large mean free path. If the molecules are approximated by spheres of the same size, a collision will occur if the center-to-center distance of adjacent molecules is less than the diameter, d. An approximation to the cross section for spherical molecules is πd^2.

A very simple way to visualize and approximate the mean free path in terms of number density follows. The number density is the number of particles per volume. The inverse of the number density is the volume per particle. If we consider this volume to be a right circular cylinder with a cross section equal to the cross section for a molecule, then the length of the cylinder is an approximate value for the mean free path. When the velocity distribution is included in the analysis, the cross section is expressed as $\sqrt{2}\,\pi d^2$. This reasoning results in a mean free path of

$$\lambda = \frac{1}{n_\rho}\frac{1}{\sqrt{2}\,\pi d^2} \tag{13.7}$$

• • Load KT2, number density, pressure, and mean free path (see Fig. 13.2).

Examine the connections between pressure, number density, and mean free path. For the calculation, one consistent set of values is necessary for the three quantities that we wish to discuss. The cross-sectional area is defined, and six functions are written. Each quantity is expressed in two separate functions, each function is expressed in terms of one of the other two variables. Paralleling this set of functions is a set of single-valued computations showing how to obtain, for example, pressure from number density or from mean free path. The units are mixed, but they can be changed to any corresponding unit that is defined. All arguments require units. Pressure readings associated with vacuum gauges are often expressed in torr, a pressure corresponding to one millimeter of mercury or 1/760 of an atmosphere. Readings in the range of 10^{-6} to 10^{-7} torr are readily achieved and are common in many experimental settings. To reach pressures of 10^{-10} torr or less, more precautions are required.

Define $n_{\rho_i} = 10^i \cdot cm^{-3}$, where $i = 1, \ldots, 20$. Plot (all log-log scales) $P_1(n_{\rho_i})$ vs. n_{ρ_i}, $\lambda_1(n_{\rho_i})$ vs. n_{ρ_i} and $\lambda_1(n_{\rho_i})$ vs. $P_1(n_{\rho_i})$.

The distance from the earth to the sun, approximately 1.5×10^8 km, is referred to as an astronomical unit. If the number density of hydrogen

---

Relations between number density, pressure, and mean free path

m := 1L   s := 1T   kg := 1M   gm := .001·kg   cm := .01·m

$N := kg \cdot m \cdot s^{-2}$ $Pa := N \cdot m^{-2}$ $atm := 1.103 \cdot 10^5 \cdot Pa$ $torr := \dfrac{1}{760} \cdot atm$

torr = 145.132·Pa $760 \cdot torr = 1.103 \cdot 10^5 \cdot Pa$ torr = 0.132·%·atm

Molecular hydrogen is considered.

$Av := 6.022 \cdot 10^{23}$ $M_{H2} := 2 \cdot gm$ $\rho_{H2} := 8.99 \cdot 10^{-2} \cdot kg \cdot m^{-3}$

ρ is the number density at standard temperature and pressure.

$\rho := \rho_{H2} \cdot \dfrac{Av}{M_{H2}}$ $\rho = 2.707 \cdot 10^{19} \cdot \dfrac{1}{cm^3}$ Ps := atm

$d := 2 \cdot 10^{-10} \cdot m$ molecular diameter $A := \sqrt{2} \cdot \pi \cdot d^2$ collision cross section

We express pressure P, mean free path λ, and number density n, in functional form. Each quantity can be expressed in terms of either of the others.

$P1(n) := \dfrac{Ps}{\rho} \cdot n$ $P1\left[10^{12} \cdot cm^{-3}\right] = 3.694 \cdot 10^{-8} \cdot atm$

$P2(\lambda) := \dfrac{Ps}{\rho \cdot \lambda \cdot A}$ $P2(5.627 \cdot m) = 3.694 \cdot 10^{-8} \cdot atm$

$\lambda1(n) := \dfrac{1}{A} \cdot \dfrac{1}{n}$ $\lambda1\left[10^{12} \cdot cm^{-3}\right] = 5.627 \cdot m$

$\lambda2(P) := \dfrac{Ps}{\rho \cdot P \cdot A}$ $\lambda2\left[3.694 \cdot 10^{-8} \cdot atm\right] = 5.627 \cdot m$

$n1(P) := \dfrac{\rho}{Ps} \cdot P$ $n1\left[3.6943 \cdot 10^{-8} \cdot atm\right] = 1 \cdot 10^{12} \cdot cm^{-3}$

$n2(\lambda) := \dfrac{1}{A} \cdot \dfrac{1}{\lambda}$ $n2(5.627 \cdot m) = 1 \cdot 10^{12} \cdot cm^{-3}$

Figure 13.2 KT2, number density, pressure, and mean free path.

molecules in interstellar space is 10 per cubic centimeter, what is the mean free path in astronomical units?

The wavelength of green light is roughly 5.5×10^{-7} m. What is the mean free path when the number density is 10^{20} molecules per cubic centimeter? Express the result in wavelengths of green light. For the same number density, what is the pressure in atmospheres? What pressure corresponds to a mean free path of one wavelength of green light?

In the previous plots of the Maxwell-Boltzmann speed distribution function, we considered the distribution at one moment. Imagine a source of gas connected to a vacuum chamber through an electronically controlled valve. (Or, we could rotate a wheel in front of the gas beam, with a tiny slot cut in it. For every rotation of the wheel, gas would briefly pass through the slot.) Gas enters the chamber in the plus x-direction.

The gas packet initially has a very tiny spread in the x-direction. The molecules have a distribution of speeds in the x-direction, but at $t = 0$ the packet has not yet spread out. As time passes, those molecules with larger x-velocities travel farther than the slower ones and the packet spreads.

• • Load KT3, time of flight (see Figs. 13.3 and 13.4).

Observe the spread of the packet of molecules. Determine at what rate the molecules arrive at a detector some distance away.

For simplicity, treat the speed distribution as if all velocities are in the x-direction. The distribution number vs. velocity is plotted as was done earlier. Now, however, we plot the distribution vs. distance rather than velocity. In the second plot region, the packet of molecules is shown at two different times, t_1 and t_2. The plots are type s; this permits a comparison of the relative widths of steps between one distribution and the other, giving a clear sense of the spreading of the packet. To observe the packet at earlier times, let $\delta t = 10^{-5.3}$ s. To observe them at a later time, let $\delta t = 10^{-4.1}$ s. (The times are arbitrary but suit the conditions.)

Now consider the detector located at the vertical line near the right-hand side of the plot, a distance, d_{sep}, from the source. Clearly, the detector sees the fastest molecules first. At $\delta t = 10^{-5}$ s (check these as we go), particles in the highest-velocity segment (of the d_2 curve) are beginning to arrive at the detector. As δt increases from $10^{-4.5}$ s to $10^{-4.2}$ s, we can watch the progression.

Now consider events at the detector itself. The time of arrival of particles at the detector is inversely related to the velocity. The time-of-flight data constitute a nonlinear mapping of the velocity data.

In the last group of three plots, we show again the velocity distribution, followed by two examples of the number distribution in time. The upper limit of the abscissa shows the relative scales. The last plot is a close-up look at the first 0.5 ms of the distribution.

Particles with velocities greater than the most probable velocity are compressed into the leading edge of the n vs. t plot. Those with slower velocities — that is, those before the peak in the n vs. v curve — have their arrivals more spread out in time. In the last plot, we look only at the high-velocity, small-time portion of the curve.

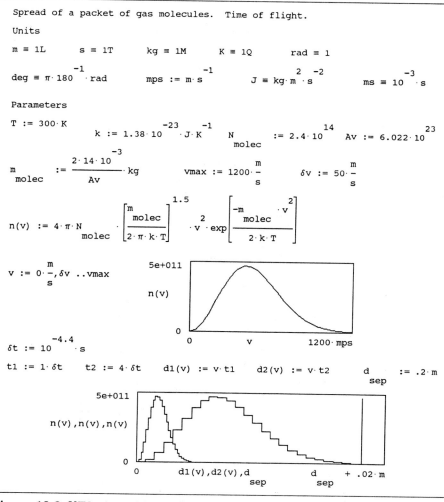

Figure 13.3 KT3, time of flight. (See the next figure for the rest of the document.)

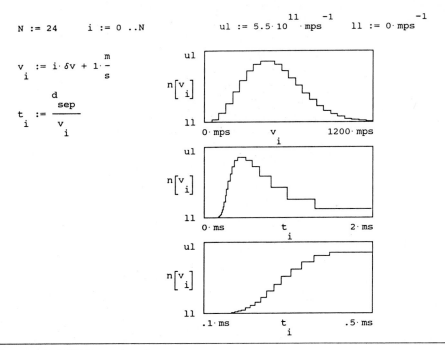

$$N := 24 \qquad i := 0 \; .. \; N$$

$$v_i := i \cdot \delta v + 1 \cdot \frac{m}{s}$$

$$t_i := \frac{d_{sep}}{v_i}$$

$$ul := 5.5 \cdot 10^{11} \cdot mps^{-1} \qquad ll := 0 \cdot mps^{-1}$$

Figure 13.4 KT3 *continued.*

Convince yourself that you understand how these plots correspond by restricting the range of i. For example, let $i = 5, \dots, 15$ or $14, \dots, 24$ or $0, \dots, 10$.

To distinguish between the faster velocities, we need good time discrimination. How much time separates the arrival at the detector of the molecules traveling at 1200 m/s from those traveling at 1150 m/s?

Make a semi-log plot of the time intervals between successive velocity groups. (The molecules are not really in discrete groups, but for this example we will imagine that they are.)

How would the time resolution requirements change if the distance d_{sep} was reduced to 0.1 m?

How would the number of counts per time be different if the species were N_2 and O_2? (Look at KT1.) What requirements would there be to differentiate between N_2 and O_2 if we consider only velocities less than the most probable?

13.3 Random Walk

Random walks can be used to simulate many different types of events. They are used here to simulate the transfer of energy units from a hot body to a cold body. In a thermal equilibration process, the hot body cools and the cool body warms. Before that problem is considered, we explore the random walk briefly, first in one dimension and then in two.

In a simple one-dimensional random walk, an object moves along a line — for example, the x-axis — in steps of equal size. The direction of the step is determined by a random process. The net displacement from the starting point is on the order of the step size times the square root of the number of steps.

• • Plot a one-dimensional random walk. Let the number of steps be 100 and let the step size be equal to one. A very simple difference equation is all that is needed; each new value, x_{i+1}, is the previous value, x_i, plus or minus one step. To create a random sequence of ± 1 values for the walk, we raise -1 to the power ceil(rnd(2)). The rnd(2) statement generates a number between 0 and 2. The ceil (rnd(2)) operation converts the number generated by the rnd process to the smallest integer larger than the number, which in this case is 1 or 2; and, of course $-1^1 = -1$; and $-1^2 = +1$. Thus repeated calls to this function generate a random sequence of ± 1 values.

To be sure the concepts are familiar, let $j = 1, \ldots, 10$ and let $y_j = $ rnd(2). Display y_j and ceil(y_j) in two columns side by side. Delete after you have considered the results.

Calculate the x_i as described and plot i vs. x_i.

A histogram provides a useful way to display the location of a particle for an entire random walk process. Create a histogram showing how many times the walk has led to each x-position. Let the number of intervals be the quantity $(x_{max} - x_{min})$ (use MathCAD's max and min functions). Define two indices; let j run from zero to the number of intervals, and let k run from zero to the number of intervals minus one. Define the intervals with j and plot the histogram with k. Change the probability from 50:50 to 60:40 or some other value, and observe a net drift. What rate of drift would you expect? Test your hypothesis.

With probability 50:50, let the step size depend on direction. For example, let a step in the plus x-direction be 20% greater than a step in the negative x-direction. What kind of behavior would you expect? Test your hypothesis.

• •   Load KT4, two-dimensional random walk (see Figs. 13.5 and 13.6).

One to four different two-dimensional random walks can be viewed and examined. Each walk consists of n steps (j index). The index i specifies the number of independent walks. The initial positions are arranged so that the paths of the separate walks cannot lie directly on top of each other. Within one walk, however, it is possible and likely that some paths are repeated.

The set of $+1$ and -1 values for all the steps of each of the walks is represented by $f_{i,j}$. In a completely separate process, values for g_j and h_j are determined; these values specify the direction the steps will take. The

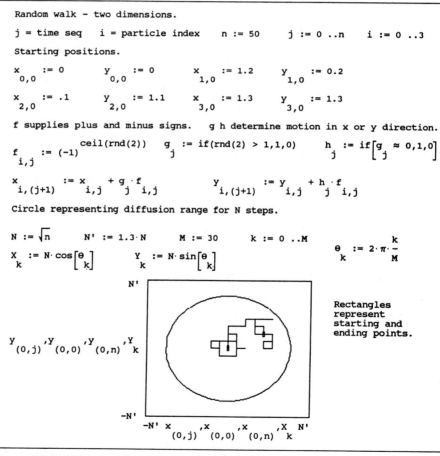

```
Random walk - two dimensions.

j = time seq   i = particle index   n := 50   j := 0 ..n   i := 0 ..3

Starting positions.

x      := 0        y      := 0        x      := 1.2      y      := 0.2
 0,0                0,0                1,0                1,0

x      := .1       y      := 1.1      x      := 1.3      y      := 1.3
 2,0                2,0                3,0                3,0

f supplies plus and minus signs.   g h determine motion in x or y direction.

           ceil(rnd(2))    g  := if(rnd(2) > 1,1,0)    h  := if[g  ≈ 0,1,0]
f    := (-1)             j                           j       j
 i,j

x       := x     + g · f          y       := y     + h · f
 i,(j+1)    i,j    j   i,j          i,(j+1)    i,j    j   i,j

Circle representing diffusion range for N steps.

N := √n        N' := 1.3·N        M := 30        k := 0 ..M
                                                              k
X  := N·cos[θ ]        Y  := N·sin[θ ]            θ  := 2·π·-
 k           k          k           k              k         M
```

Rectangles represent starting and ending points.

Figure 13.5 KT4, two-dimensional random walk. (See the next figure for the rest of the document.)

Four walks displayed simultaneously.   N' := N'·1.2

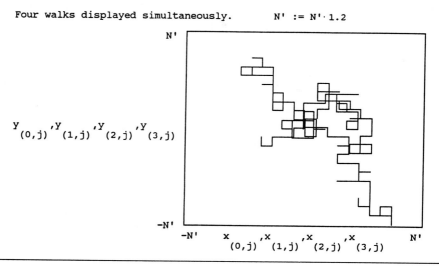

Figure 13.6 KT4 *continued.*

statement for g is a rnd statement that determines whether or not to step in the x-direction. The statement for h directs a motion in the y-direction if there is no motion in the x-direction.

A circle with radius $\sqrt{n}$ is shown together with the walk. The starting and ending points of the walk are shown as open rectangles.

To observe different random sequences, move the cursor to the $f_{i,j}$ region and press [F9]. Each time [F9] is pressed, a new set of random values are calculated. Observe a number of cases.

The second plot region is disabled. To see four different random walks simultaneously, let $i = 0, \ldots, 3$ and enable the second plot region. Four different walks are shown in the second plot region. The different walks are readily distinguished only on a color monitor. Reduce the upper limit of i to reduce the number of walks.

The g and h statements randomly select steps in the x- and y-directions. Change the g and h statements so that the probability for taking a step in the x-direction is twice that of taking a step in the y-direction. Observe a number of examples. Change the x and y step sizes and observe the net change in the pattern.

13.3.1   *Simulation of Thermal Equilibration*

A warm body placed in cold surroundings will lose heat to the exterior. As this process takes place, the warm body cools and the cool surroundings warm. After a long enough time period, the body and its surroundings come to thermal equilibrium — their temperatures become the same. We simulate such a process using a two-dimensional random walk. (A three-dimensional walk would be more realistic, but, for this software, would require too much memory and too much processing time.)

The environment is represented by a large rectangle; the object is represented by a smaller rectangle contained within the larger one. Energy units are represented as tiny open rectangles (plot type o). The number of energy units per area is a measure of the temperature. Initially, all the energy units are within the object; none are in the exterior region.

The energy units migrate according to a two-dimensional random walk. Energy is conserved: no energy units can be lost; nor can any be added during the process. An energy unit can migrate from the object to the surroundings or from the surroundings to the object without restriction. However, if an energy unit passes through the outer boundary of the environment, it reappears on the opposite side. This process is a type of periodic boundary condition. The temperature is proportional to the number of energy units per area. The temperature changes as the energy units migrate.

• •   KT5, simulation of thermal equilibration (see Figs. 13.7 and 13.8).

The document KT5 uses much memory and is computation intensive. It is advisable to exit MathCAD and reload, but do not load KT5 yet.

The statements $x_{i,0}$ and $y_{i,0}$ provide the initial positions of the $m + 1$ energy units. If $m + 1 = int^2$, where $int = 2, 3, 4$, then the units are arranged in a square array. Any value of m is, in principle, allowed. However, for $m = 3$, there are only four energy units and the results are not very interesting. Values greater than 15 require increased computation time and more memory than may be available.

Enter by hand the statements from the beginning of the document for $m, i, n, j, s, x_{i,0}$, and $y_{i,0}$. For $m = 3, 8$, and 15, explore the x and y statements which make use of the mod and floor functions. These statements make possible an efficient way to specify the initial conditions. Print out tables of values and plot $y_{i,0}$ vs. $x_{i,0}$. What happens with intermediate values of m? When you are finished with this exploration, reload MathCAD.

Load KT5. The first plot region displays the energy units, the boundary of the object, and the boundary of the surroundings.

The f, g, and h statements have precisely the same function as in the two-dimensional walk document. The x and y statements are complicated because of the boundary conditions. Nested if statements take care of two boundary conditions at once; for example, if x is larger than the plus limit go just inside the minus limit; and if x is less than the minus limit go just inside the plus limit; otherwise, let x go to its new value.

```
Random walk - equilibration.

j = time seq   i = particle index

m := 15    i := 0 ..m        n := 50      j := 0 ..n

Postion m+1 particles in a rectangular array.
```

$$s := \sqrt{m+1} \qquad x_{i,0} := \mod(i,s) \qquad y_{i,0} := \text{floor}\left[\frac{i}{s}\right]$$

```
Set limits to the outer region.  Show boundary of object. Location of energy.

lim := 9       mlim := -lim + 1      plim := lim - 1      limp := lim + 1

k := 0 ..4     ss := s - 0.5      r  := ss     r  := -ss      r  := r
                                   k            2             3    2
t  := -ss      t  := ss      t  := t
 k              1              2    1              limp
```

$$y_{(i,0)}, t_k$$

```
stpsz := 1
                                              -limp
The functions for the two-dimensional         -limp x    ,r  limp
walk.                                               (i,0)  k
```

$$f_{i,j} := (-1)^{\text{ceil}(rnd(2))} \qquad g_{i,j} := \text{if}(rnd(2) > 1,1,0) \qquad h_{i,j} := \text{if}\left[g_{i,j} \approx 0,1,0\right]$$

$$c_{i,j} := \left[\overrightarrow{\left[g_{i,j} \cdot f_{i,j}\right]}\right] \cdot stpsz \qquad d_{i,j} := \left[\overrightarrow{\left[h_{i,j} \cdot f_{i,j}\right]}\right] \cdot stpsz$$

```
The energy units are not to be lost.  If they wander off to the left, they
reappear at the right, etc.  These are known as periodic boundary conditions.
```

$$\begin{bmatrix} x_{i,j+1} \\ y_{i,j+1} \end{bmatrix} := \left[\text{if}\begin{bmatrix} x_{i,j} \ldots > lim, mlim, \text{if}\begin{bmatrix} x_{i,j} \ldots < -lim, plim, \ x_{i,j} \ldots \\ + c_{i,j} & + c_{i,j} & + c_{i,j} \end{bmatrix} \end{bmatrix} \\ \text{if}\begin{bmatrix} y_{i,j} \ldots > lim, mlim, \text{if}\begin{bmatrix} y_{i,j} \ldots < -lim, plim, \ y_{i,j} \ldots \\ + d_{i,j} & + d_{i,j} & + d_{i,j} \end{bmatrix} \end{bmatrix} \right]$$

Figure 13.7 KT5, simulation of thermal equilibrium. (See the next figure for the rest of the document.)

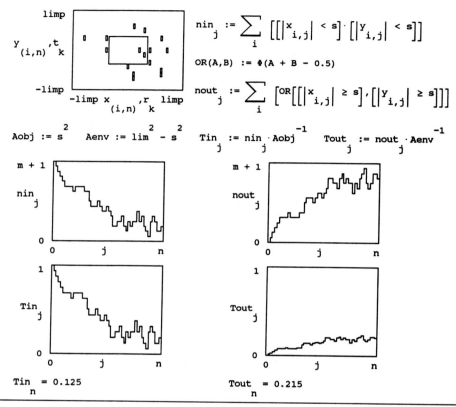

$$nin_j := \sum_i \left[\left[\left|x_{i,j}\right| < s\right] \cdot \left[\left|y_{i,j}\right| < s\right]\right]$$

$$OR(A,B) := \Phi(A + B - 0.5)$$

$$nout_j := \sum_i \left[OR\left[\left[\left|x_{i,j}\right| \geq s\right] \cdot \left[\left|y_{i,j}\right| \geq s\right]\right]\right]$$

$$Aobj := s^2 \qquad Aenv := lim^2 - s^2 \qquad Tin_j := nin_j \cdot Aobj^{-1} \qquad Tout_j := nout_j \cdot Aenv^{-1}$$

$$Tin_n = 0.125 \qquad\qquad Tout_n = 0.215$$

Figure 13.8 KT5 *continued.*

If the magnitude of either x or y is greater than s, then the energy unit is outside the object. A logical OR function is used to determine the status. The logical OR $(A+B)$ returns a 1 if either A or B is 1. (A and B are restricted to the values 0 and 1.) A MathCAD statement expressing logical OR is $OR(A, B) := \Phi(A+B-0.5)$. If the argument of Φ is greater than or equal to 0, the function returns a 1; otherwise, it returns a 0. The conditions for x and y are the A and B statements.

For the count of the number of energy units inside the object, the n_{in} statement, the multiplication is equivalent to a logical AND. Both conditions must be true for the product to be 1; otherwise, it is 0.

In the final group of plot regions, the first is the arrangement of energy units after the nth step. The next two plot regions show the number of energy units inside the object and outside the object (inside the environment) as a function of the number of steps. The last two plot regions show the "temperatures," the number of energy units divided by the area. Because the number of energy units is small ($m + 1$), significant fluctuations are expected.

Place the cursor in the f-region and press [F9] for a new set of values; or just press [Esc], type pro for process, and press return.

Change the step size; use small integral values. This will permit the energy units to migrate farther without increasing the number of steps.

Reduce lim from 9 to 6 (lim must be geater than s). This change reduces the size of the environment. How should the final temperature in this case compare with that in the previous case? Explore.

Simplify the document to a one-dimensional form. Use a periodic boundary condition. Define temperature as the number of energy units per length.

> Sam, let a friend tell you, your life is going wrong.
> Records is a dead-end department,
> no Security Level worth a damn,
> it's impossible to get noticed.
> Yes, I know, fantastic, marvellous, wonderful.
> Remember me to Alison and the twins.
> Triplets.
> Triplets? God, how time flies!
>
> *Brazil*

CHAPTER
14

Electric and Magnetic Fields

In most beginning texts, examples of the electric field include a few cases with discrete charges, considering specifically both the point charge and a very small collection of point charges. The development, quite logically, then moves on to continuous distributions such as a line charge or a charged ring. We examine here what might be considered transitions between discrete and continuous charge distributions.

For example, we consider the case of discrete charges uniformly spaced along a straight line, and we ask when the assemblage looks like a line charge, when like a point charge, and when like neither.

Similarly, for magnetic fields, the fields associated with a circular current loop and for a very large number of loops joined in a solenoid are considered. We explore the transition between the cases first by considering the field due to a pair of current-carrying loops and then by considering a finite solenoid constructed from a series of current loops.

Finally, in Section 14.2.2 we approach a number of very important equations from the point of view of dimensional analysis. You should not skip this section.

14.1   Electric Field

The magnitude of the electric field associated with a point charge is given by

$$E = \frac{1}{4\,\pi\,\epsilon_o}\frac{q}{r^2},\qquad(14.1)$$

where E is the field, q is the charge, r is the distance from the point charge to the location where the field is evaluated, and ϵ_o is the permittivity of free space, a constant analogous to G in Newton's law of gravitation. The direction of the field is radially outward (inward) for a positive (negative) charge.

• •   Load EM1, electric field due to a small number of point charges (see Fig. 14.1). (This problem was suggested in part by John Davis.)

Given two or more charges, determine the field (magnitude and direction) at any point; and if a charge is at that point, determine the force on that charge.

Enter the total number of points, N; this includes points where there are charges and other points where the field is to be determined. Then enter the locations (x_i, y_i) and the charges q_i at those locations. Enter 0 for charge, when the field is desired at a charge-free location. Separate values with commas; the values appear in tabular form. The plot shows the locations of the points as open rectangles. The origin is represented with a diamond.

At each point (x_i, y_i), the x- and y-components of the field due to all the other charges are determined (Ex_j, Ey_j). The total field is determined from the components. The force is determined from the fundamental relation $F = q\,E$. The field, force, and direction are presented in tabular form.

Just above the final plot regions, $m\ (\le N)$ specifies the index of the point at which the field is to be plotted. In the last plot, we see the location of the point specified and the field vector. Given the other charges, consider the magnitudes and directions of the individual fields and argue for the final direction. Considering examples with the machine builds confidence in problem solving intuition.

Try some simple cases with two charges before trying more complex examples. For example, consider the field of a dipole at various points. Then consider cases with three and four charges.

If charges are distributed uniformly over a long, straight wire, the associated electric field alongside the wire no longer falls off as $1/r^2$, the

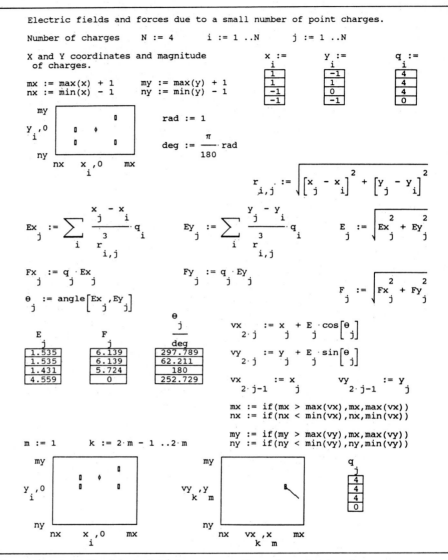

Figure 14.1 EM1, electric field due to a small number of point charges.

point charge dependence, but as $1/r$. The relation is

$$E = \frac{1}{4\pi\epsilon_o}\frac{2\lambda}{r},$$

(14.2)

where λ is the linear charge density, the charge per length along the wire. This result can be obtained by integrating the contributions to the field from all the charge elements, or it can be obtained using Gauss's law.

It is a large change to go from a few point charges to a continuous charge distribution such as that of a line charge. We consider the transition between these two cases by evaluating the field for a small number of charges uniformly distributed along a straight line.

Place two positive charges q on a vertical line. Draw the perpendicular bisector to the line containing the two charges. Each charge is a distance d from the intersection of the two lines. We wish to calculate the field at a point p on the bisecting line a distance r from the line containing the charges.

The field due to each charge at the point r is (ignoring constants) $E = q/r^2$. The components parallel and perpendicular to the bisecting line are $E\cos(\theta)$ and $E\sin(\theta)$. Because the two charges are symmetrically placed relative to the bisecting line, these perpendicular components are equal and opposite; they sum to zero. The components parallel to the bisecting line add. Each parallel component is

$$E_{\text{parallel}} = E\cos(\theta) = \frac{q}{r^2 + d^2}\cos(\theta).$$

If we let $q = 1$ and note that $\tan(\theta) = d/r$, the total parallel field is given by

$$E_{\text{parallel}} = \frac{2}{r^2 + d^2}\cos\left(\text{atan}\ \frac{d}{r}\right). \tag{14.3}$$

If there are n pairs of charges, each pair symmetrically placed as was the pair just described, the total field is similarly described for each pair. In the document, $E_{ni,k}$ expresses the total field at a point due to each charge pair; sE_i is the total field at one point due to all the charges.

For purposes of comparison, we calculate several different fields: (1) the field due to n charge pairs distributed uniformly along a line, sE_i; (2) the field due to a point charge, with total charge $2n$, located at the midpoint of the line of charges, E_p; (3) the field due to a continuous infinite line charge with the same charge per length as that associated with the charge line, E_l; and (4) the field due to a continuous finite line charge with the same length and same charge per length as the charge line. The line charge density is

$$\lambda = \frac{charge}{length} = \frac{1}{2 \cdot hs},$$

where hs is half the charge separation distance between the charges spread along the line.

• •   Load EM2, electric field due to a series of point charges (see Figs. 14.2 and 14.3).

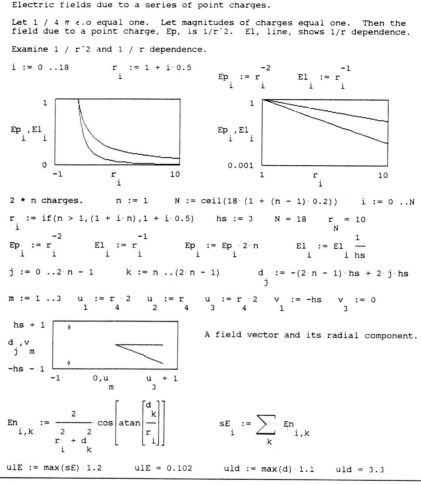

Electric fields due to a series of point charges.

Let 1 / 4 π ϵ.o equal one. Let magnitudes of charges equal one. Then the field due to a point charge, Ep, is 1/r^2. El, line, shows 1/r dependence.

Examine 1 / r^2 and 1 / r dependence.

$i := 0 ..18$ $r_i := 1 + i \cdot 0.5$ $Ep_i := r_i^{-2}$ $El_i := r_i^{-1}$

2 * n charges. $n := 1$ $N := ceil(18 \cdot (1 + (n - 1) \cdot 0.2))$ $i := 0 ..N$

$r_i := if(n > 1, (1 + i \cdot n), 1 + i \cdot 0.5)$ $hs := 3$ $N = 18$ $r_N = 10$

$Ep_i := r_i^{-2}$ $El_i := r_i^{-1}$ $Ep_i := Ep_i \cdot 2 \cdot n$ $El_i := El_i \frac{1}{i \ hs}$

$j := 0 ..2 \cdot n - 1$ $k := n ..(2 \cdot n - 1)$ $d_j := -(2 \cdot n - 1) \cdot hs + 2 \cdot j \cdot hs$

$m := 1 ..3$ $u_1 := r \cdot 2$ $u_2 := r$ $u_3 := r \cdot 2$ $v_1 := -hs$ $v_3 := 0$

A field vector and its radial component.

$$En_{i,k} := \frac{2}{r_i^2 + d_k^2} \cdot cos\left[atan\left[\frac{d_k}{r_i}\right]\right] \qquad sE_i := \sum_k En_{i,k}$$

$ulE := max(sE) \cdot 1.2$ $ulE = 0.102$ $uld := max(d) \cdot 1.1$ $uld = 3.3$

Figure 14.2 EM2, electric field due to a series of point charges. (See the next figure for the rest of the document.)

In the first two plots, a comparison is made of the field due to a point charge and due to a line charge. The plots are linear and log-log. We set all the constants equal to 1. We examine only the dependence on position. Be sure that you know which curve is which and why. It is necessary to see these dependences clearly, so we can compare our calculations with these two extreme cases.

N and r are display controls. For larger n, the number of charge pairs, the region of interest moves to larger r, so the range of r is dependent

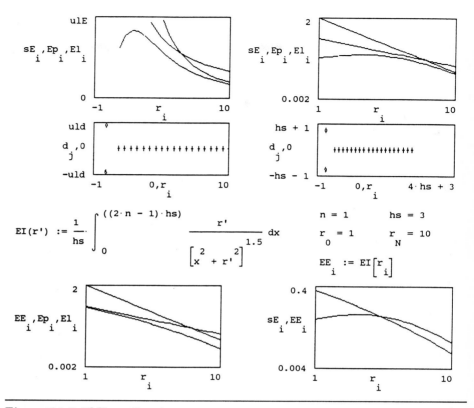

Figure 14.3 EM2 *continued.*

on *n*. For the curve to be reasonably smooth, the number of points is increased slightly as the range increases (the increase is not great because the computation time increases proportionately).

In the next plots, we show the fields due to the discrete distribution, the point charge, and the infinite line charge. The fields are plotted in linear and log-log plots. The location of the charges and the location of the points at which the field is calculated are also shown. There are two plots that show these points. In the first plot the abscissa corresponds to the field plot just above it. The ordinate is chosen to show all the charges. In the similar plot to the right, the *x*- and *y*-axes have the same scale so the relative spacing between charges and points at which the field is calculated is the same. This plot is not directly correlated with the log-log plot above it. Finally, we plot the field associated with a short rod, EE_i, together with that from the discrete charge distribution.

Go back to the plots of sE, E_p, and E_l and of d_j. Concentrate for now on this set of four plots. As you consider various cases, compare the total length of the charge distribution $(n-1) \cdot 2 \cdot hs$ with r_i and consider in which regions the curves sE and E_p and the curves sE and E_l have the same dependence on r.

Identify which curve is which. Why does the sE curve have a maximum at small r? Just beyond the maximum, which curve, point charge, or line charge better approximates sE? At large r, which curve better represents sE? Why?

Predict the changes that will occur if the half charge separation, hs, is reduced from 3 to 1. Test your prediction.

Let $hs = 3$ again and process the document to remind yourself of the shapes. Let $n = 2$ and process. Note how the sE field representation shifts in relation to the line charge representation.

Let $n = 4$ and process. Remember that the first of the spacing plots shows the total number of points and charges; the second shows the relative spacings. How would you characterize the sE field in comparison with E_p and E_l?

Let $n = 4$ and $hs = 1$. Look at the second spacing plot to get a sense of the spacing and range for point charges needed to give the impression of a line charge. How would you characterize the sE field in comparison with E_p and E_l?

The integral shown at the end of the document is obtained by integrating the contributions to the electric field due to individual charge elements along a uniformly charged rod. (MathCAD will do the actual integration; however, it is useful to know what it is calculating.) The field due to a charge element is given by

$$dE = \frac{1}{4\pi\epsilon_o} \frac{dq}{R^2}. \tag{14.4}$$

The radial component of the field is given by $dE_r = dE \cdot \cos(\theta)$. Express dq in terms of the line charge; $dq = \lambda dx$. R is the total distance from a charge element dq to the point where the field is to be calculated; $R = \sqrt{r^2 + x^2}$ where r is the radial distance and x is the distance along the charged rod from its center. The angle is specified by $\cos(\theta) = r/R$.

Because the rod is symmetric, integrate from the center to one end and double the result. Set $1/4\pi\epsilon_o = 1$:

$$dE = \frac{\lambda dx}{r^2 + x^2}\cos(\theta); \tag{14.5}$$

$$E = 2 \int_0^{\text{end}} \frac{\lambda dx}{r^2 + x^2} \frac{r}{\sqrt{r^2 + x^2}} = \frac{1}{hs} \int_0^{\text{end}} \frac{r}{(r^2 + x^2)^{3/2}} \, dx. \qquad (14.6)$$

Disable the regions for E_n, sE, and the four plot regions following them. Observe the final two plot regions for $hs = 3$ and $n = 1$, 2, 4. Both plots are log-log. Notice the degree of similarity between the discrete calculation, sE, and the continuous calculation, EE, as n goes from 1 to 4. Also compare the cases of the infinitely long line charge and the point charge. Compare the length of the charged rod with the distance to the "transition" region.

• •   A third interesting case for the electric field is that due to an infinite surface. There is no dependence on r; the field is constant. (For a point charge, $E \propto r^{-2}$; for an infinite line charge, $E \propto r^{-1}$; for an infinite surface charge $E \propto r^{-0}$.) A surface could be approximated as a set of parallel line charges. Examine the field due to such an array.

Now, instead of examining the field along a line perpendicular to the line of charge (a line containing a small number of uniformly distributed discrete charges), consider the field along a line parallel to this same line of charge. A comparison is made between the discrete charge case and that of a single point charge with the same net charge.

• •   Load EM3, electric field due to a series of point charges: parallel path (see Figs. 14.4 and 14.5).

First the field due to a point charge is calculated at points along a line, where the minimum distance between the line and the charge is r. The y_i' determine the position along the line where the field is calculated.

The next plot shows the arrangement of charges (diamonds) and the points at which the field is calculated (pluses). The separation between these two lines is r. The number of charge pairs is n, and the location of the charges is given by d_j. The field is calculated at the points specified by y_i. $Er_{i,j}$ is a measure of the individual contributions to the field perpendicular to the line at the y_i due to the charges at d_j; $Ep_{i,j}$ is the corresponding parallel component. Es is a measure of the total field.

Examine the parallel and perpendicular components of the field. Sketch the anticipated shape before performing the plot.

We would expect that at distances that are large compared to the length of the charge distribution, the field would be approximately that of a point charge. At very small distances, we would expect to see the local structure. At intermediate distances, we would expect to see a transition between these two cases.

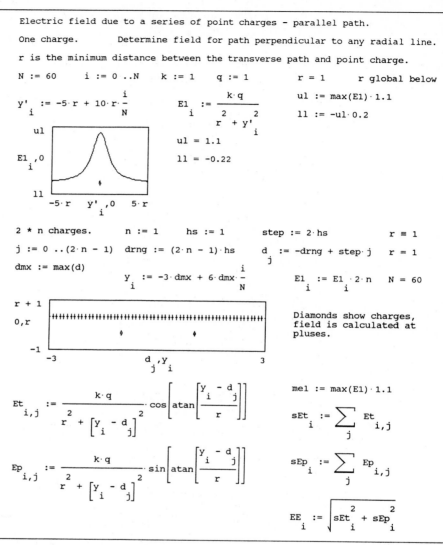

Electric field due to a series of point charges - parallel path.

One charge.   Determine field for path perpendicular to any radial line.

r is the minimum distance between the transverse path and point charge.

$N := 60$ $i := 0 .. N$ $k := 1$ $q := 1$ $r = 1$ r global below

$$y'_i := -5 \cdot r + 10 \cdot r \cdot \frac{i}{N} \qquad E1_i := \frac{k \cdot q}{r^2 + y'^2_i} \qquad ul := \max(E1) \cdot 1.1$$

$$ll := -ul \cdot 0.2$$

$$ul = 1.1$$

$$ll = -0.22$$

$2 * n$ charges. $n := 1$ $hs := 1$ $step := 2 \cdot hs$ $r \equiv 1$

$j := 0 .. (2 \cdot n - 1)$ $drng := (2 \cdot n - 1) \cdot hs$ $d_j := -drng + step \cdot j$ $r = 1$

$dmx := \max(d)$

$$y_i := -3 \cdot dmx + 6 \cdot dmx \cdot \frac{i}{N} \qquad E1_i := E1_i \cdot 2 \cdot n \quad N = 60$$

Diamonds show charges,
field is calculated at
pluses.

$$Et_{i,j} := \frac{k \cdot q}{r^2 + \left[y_i - d_j\right]^2} \cdot \cos\left[\operatorname{atan}\left[\frac{y_i - d_j}{r}\right]\right] \qquad mel := \max(E1) \cdot 1.1$$

$$sEt_i := \sum_j Et_{i,j}$$

$$Ep_{i,j} := \frac{k \cdot q}{r^2 + \left[y_i - d_j\right]^2} \cdot \sin\left[\operatorname{atan}\left[\frac{y_i - d_j}{r}\right]\right] \qquad sEp_i := \sum_j Ep_{i,j}$$

$$EE_i := \sqrt{sEt_i^2 + sEp_i^2}$$

Figure 14.4 EM3, electric field due to a series of point charges: parallel path. (See the next figure for the rest of the document.)

The plot shows the magnitude of the actual field and compares it with the field that would result if all the charge were concentrated at one point at the center of the distribution. With $n = 1$, $r = 10$, and $N = 40$, is there much difference between the two field determinations? Let $r = 2$ and process. Let $r = 1$ and process. (For $r < 2$, plots are more precise if N is increased from 40 to 60.)

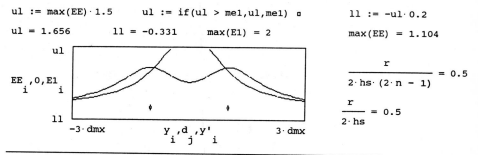

Figure 14.5 EM3 *continued.*

Let (n, N) equal $(2, 60)$. At what distance r, compared to the charge separation distance, does the individual structure show? Is the length of the charge distribution relevant to the previous question? In terms of these lengths, at what radial distance is there a sense of an extended charge? At what distance does the group look like a point charge?

Explore the field for a variety of values of n and r.

14.1.1 *Electric Flux*

Gauss's law, one of the four basic laws of electricity and magnetism, relates the charge within a closed surface to the net electric flux through the surface.

$$\Phi_E = \frac{q}{\epsilon_o} \qquad \text{where} \qquad \Phi_E = \iint_{\text{closed surface}} \mathbf{E} \cdot d\mathbf{A}, \qquad (14.7)$$

where $\mathbf{E} \cdot d\mathbf{A}$ is a vector dot product. A measure of surface area, $d\mathbf{A}$ is represented by a vector normal to the surface. In documents EM4 and EM5, we consider some elementary aspects of flux through a surface.

• • Load EM4, electric flux through a surface (see Fig. 14.6).

The surface and the normal to the surface are represented in the plot region of the document. The purpose of the bulk of the code is simply to determine the coordinates of the surface and a vector normal to the surface representing $d\mathbf{A}$. To find the slope of the normal vector, recall that the slopes of perpendicular lines are related by $m_1 \cdot m_2 = -1$. The solve block is used to determine the coordinates of the endpoint of the normal vector.

The series of vertical lines (created using the subdivision parameter for plot regions) represents the electric field. If θ were zero, the angle between $d\mathbf{A}$ and $\mathbf{E}$ would be zero; the cosine of the angle (dot product) would be one, and the flux would be at its maximum. As θ increases, the flux

Flux through a surface in a uniform electric field.

The vertical subdivision lines represent the field. The surface, at angle
θ to the horizontal, is represented by a normal vector perpendicular to it.
θ is a measure of the angle between the surface (normal) and the electric
field.

$$\text{rad} \equiv 1$$

$$\deg \equiv \pi \cdot 180^{-1} \cdot \text{rad}$$

θ ≡ 30·deg   Let θ take on any value   Do not use zero degrees as
              between 1 and 90 degrees. this gives infinite slope to
                                         the normal. Approximate zero
cos(θ) = 0.866   with 1*deg.

given $y' - y_a \approx m2 \cdot \left[x' - x_a\right]$ $\left[x' - x_a\right]^2 + \left[y' - y_a\right]^2 \approx 0.2$

$\begin{bmatrix} x_2 \\ y_2 \end{bmatrix} := \text{find}(x',y')$

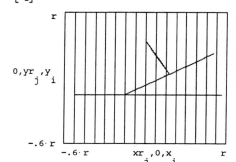

Flux is E * dA or E dA cos(θ);
the direction of dA is the normal
to the surface.

As you vary the angle note how
many field lines pass through the
actual surface.

Note relation between number of
field lines intersected by surface
and the cos(θ).

Let field have strength 10; area is a square, with side r.

E := 10 $A := r^2$ $\Phi := E \cdot A \cdot \cos(\theta)$ Φ = 8.66

Plot information.   r ≡ 1   i ≡ 0 ..4 $x_0 \equiv 0$ $y_0 \equiv 0$ j ≡ 0 ..1

$x_1 \equiv r \cdot \dfrac{\cos(\theta)}{2}$ $y_1 \equiv r \cdot \dfrac{\sin(\theta)}{2}$ $x_3 \equiv x_1$ $y_3 \equiv y_1$ $x_4 \equiv 2 \cdot x_1$ $y_4 \equiv 2 \cdot y_1$

$m1 \equiv \dfrac{y_1}{x_1}$ $m2 \equiv \dfrac{-1}{m1}$ $x_a \equiv x_1$ $y_a \equiv y_1$ $x' \equiv x_a - 1$ $y' \equiv y_a + 1$

$xr_0 \equiv -0.5$ $yr_0 \equiv 0$ $xr_1 \equiv 0.95$ $yr_1 \equiv 0.95$

Figure 14.6 EM4, electric flux through a surface.

decreases. We can visualize this flux through the surface by "counting"
the number of lines that pass through the surface.

Let θ take on different values between 1° and 90°. Relate the number
of field lines through the surface with magnitude of the cosine of θ and
with the value yielded by the flux calculation at the end of the document.

• •   Load EM5, flux through a surface from a point charge (see Fig. 14.7).

Field lines radiate from a point source. The flux through two surfaces, one closed and one plane, is determined. The initial code specifies how to draw the field lines and the two surfaces.

Parameters to control are located just above the plot region. The radius of the closed surface is r; the coordinates of the center of the closed surface are (x_c, y_c); the coordinates of the center of the plane surface are (c', d'); and the length and orientation of the plane surface are L and ϕ, respectively.

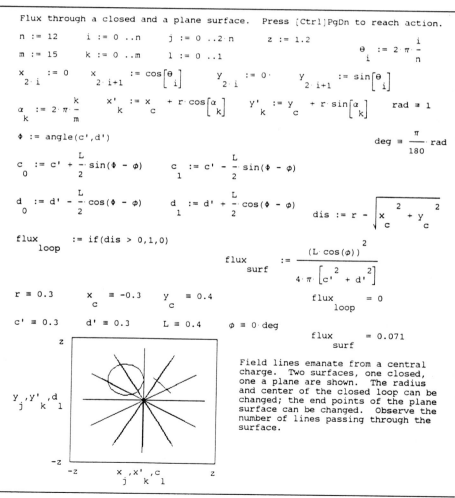

Flux through a closed and a plane surface.   Press [Ctrl]PgDn to reach action.

$n := 12$ $i := 0 \ ..n$ $j := 0 \ ..2 \cdot n$ $z := 1.2$

$m := 15$ $k := 0 \ ..m$ $l := 0 \ ..1$ $\theta_i := 2 \cdot \pi \cdot \dfrac{i}{n}$

$x_{2 \cdot i} := 0$ $x_{2 \cdot i+1} := \cos\left[\theta_i\right]$ $y_{2 \cdot i} := 0 \cdot$ $y_{2 \cdot i+1} := \sin\left[\theta_i\right]$

$\alpha_k := 2 \cdot \pi \cdot \dfrac{k}{m}$ $x'_k := x_c + r \cdot \cos\left[\alpha_k\right]$ $y'_k := y_c + r \cdot \sin\left[\alpha_k\right]$ $rad \equiv 1$

$\Phi := angle(c',d')$ $deg \equiv \dfrac{\pi}{180} \cdot rad$

$c_0 := c' + \dfrac{L}{2} \cdot \sin(\Phi - \phi)$ $c_1 := c' - \dfrac{L}{2} \cdot \sin(\Phi - \phi)$

$d_0 := d' - \dfrac{L}{2} \cdot \cos(\Phi - \phi)$ $d_1 := d' + \dfrac{L}{2} \cdot \cos(\Phi - \phi)$ $dis := r - \sqrt{x_c^2 + y_c^2}$

$flux_{loop} := if(dis > 0,1,0)$

$flux_{surf} := \dfrac{(L \cdot \cos(\phi))^2}{4 \cdot \pi \cdot \left[c'^2 + d'^2\right]}$

$r \equiv 0.3$ $x_c \equiv -0.3$ $y_c \equiv 0.4$ $flux_{loop} = 0$

$c' \equiv 0.3$ $d' \equiv 0.3$ $L \equiv 0.4$ $\phi \equiv 0 \cdot deg$

$flux_{surf} = 0.071$

Field lines emanate from a central charge. Two surfaces, one closed, one a plane are shown. The radius and center of the closed loop can be changed; the end points of the plane surface can be changed. Observe the number of lines passing through the surface.

Figure 14.7 EM5, flux through a surface from a point charge.

The net flux through the loop and surface is shown. The flux through the surface is only approximate; the procedure fails when the surface is close to the central charge.

To get a sense of scale when specifying coordinates, note that the field lines are of length one; the plot limit, z, is 1.2. Keep the surfaces in this range.

Examine the loop first. Let (x_c, y_c, r) equal $(-0.4, 0.4, 0.4)$. Every field line that enters the surface also exits the surface, and the next flux through the loop is zero. Let $r = 0.7$. Now the central charge is enclosed, and every line passes through the surface once. There is a net flux through the surface. Try several values of x, y, and r. Observe the intersections of the field lines with the loop.

Let L equal $0.1, 0.5$, and 0.9. Note the value for $flux_{surf}$. With $L = 0.5$, let ϕ equal $0°$, $30°$, $60°$, and $90°$ and observe the change in the surface orientation and the attendant change in flux. Let $d' = 0$, $c' = 1$, $L = 0.5$, and $\phi = 0$. Note the values for $flux_{surf}$ as c' decreases. Let c' equal 1, 0.8, 0.6, 0.4, 0.2, and 0.1. The flux through the surface is now greater than the flux through the loop when it contains the central charge. As $c \to 0$, the flux should go to 0.5. How is $flux_{surf}$ calculated (a ratio of what to what)? Why is this expression valid only for values of L rather less than the magnitude of the distance of the surface from the charge? Can you write an expression that will determine the flux for the plane surface whether the surface is close to or far from the central charge? Explore with various parameter values.

14.2   Magnetic Field

The magnetic field due to a long straight current carrying wire is given by

$$B = \frac{\mu_o}{4\pi}\frac{2I}{r}. \tag{14.8}$$

The magnitude of the magnetic field decreases as r^{-1} as the distance from the wire increases (just like the electric field dependence associated with a long, straight, charged wire). If the wire lies along the y-axis, then in the x-y plane, the field is in the $-z$ direction for positive x and in the $+z$ direction for negative x.

● ●   Plot the magnitude of the magnetic field due to a current-carrying wire as a function of distance from the wire. Let the wire lie along the

y-axis. Let x take on plus and minus values. Let $z = 0$. Avoid evaluating the field right at the wire, where $x = 0$. The sign of the calculated field should correspond to the orientation of the B-field along the z-axis.

• • Plot the magnitude of the magnetic field due to a pair of parallel current-carrying wires. Consider the cases in which currents are in the same direction and in opposite directions. Let the wires be parallel to the y-axis and placed symmetrically to either side of it in the x-y plane. Let $z = 0$. Consider values of x both between and outside the pair of wires. Avoid calculating the field at the wires. Examine the field when the currents are not equal.

The magnetic field along the axis of a current-carrying loop is given by

$$B_x = \frac{\mu_o\,I}{2}\,\frac{R^2}{(x^2 + R^2)^{3/2}}. \tag{14.9}$$

The center of the loop is at the origin; the loop lies in the y-z plane; the field is along the x-axis; and R is the radius of the loop.

• • Define a function $B(R, x)$, and plot the B-field due to a circular current loop as x goes from $-3R$ to $+3R$. Where is the B-field a maximum? Plot $B(R, x)/B_{\max}$ vs. x/R. When the field is one-half the maximum, what is the value x/R? When the field is one-quarter the maximum? One-tenth?

• • Load EM6, field due to a pair of current loops: Helmholtz coils (see Fig. 14.8).

Before examining the field due to a pair of current loops, we review the field due to one loop. The field is shown in the first plot region; the maximum is at the center of the loop. The normalized field is plotted in the next region. The given-find solve block permits us to determine the distance at which the field has fallen to any fraction, fr, of the maximum. Use of the place marker is convenient here.

Next we consider two coils of radius r oriented parallel to the y-z plane, centered on the x-axis, and situated at $x = \pm hsep$. Let currents flow in the same sense in the coils so the axial fields have the same direction and add.

The field due to each of the coils is specified, and their sum, B_t, is defined. The initial separation between the coils is $4\,r$ ($hsep = 2\,r$). The total field is plotted; vertical lines indicate the location of the coils. The individual fields are plotted just below. Compare the individual fields and the sum.

Magnetic field due to a pair of coaxial, circular, current loops.

First the field due to one loop.

$$\mu_o := 4 \cdot \pi \cdot 10^{-7} \qquad I := 1 \qquad\qquad B(r,x) := \frac{\mu_o}{2} \cdot I \cdot \frac{r^2}{\left[x^2 + r^2\right]^{1.5}}$$

Plot the field for a fixed radius r as a function of the axial distance z.

$$r \equiv 0.1 \qquad xl := 3 \cdot r \qquad x := -xl, -xl + .01 .. xl$$

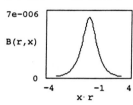
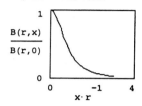

$$x' := 0.2 \cdot r \qquad fr := 0.5$$

given $\quad \dfrac{B(r,x')}{B(r,0)} \approx fr \qquad f(fr) := find(x') \qquad f(0.5) = 0.766 \cdot r$

$\qquad\qquad\qquad\qquad\qquad\quad d := 2 \cdot r \qquad\qquad f(0.5) = 0.383 \cdot d$

A pair of loops are located along the x-axis at + hsep and - hsep, hsep being half the separation distance.

$$B1(r,x) := \frac{\mu_o \cdot I}{2} \cdot \frac{r^2}{\left[(x + hsep)^2 + r^2\right]^{1.5}} \qquad B2(r,x) := \frac{\mu_o \cdot I}{2} \cdot \frac{r^2}{\left[(x - hsep)^2 + r^2\right]^{1.5}}$$

$$Bt(r,x) := B1(r,x) + B2(r,x)$$

$$hsep \equiv 2 \cdot r \qquad 2 \cdot hsep = 4 \cdot r \qquad Bt(r,hsep) = 6.373 \cdot 10^{-6}$$

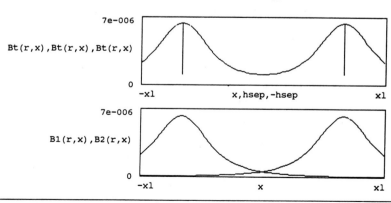

Figure 14.8 EM6, field due to a pair of current loops: Helmholtz coils.

Let $hsep \equiv 1\,r$ and process. (Disable the B_1, B_2 plot region for faster performance.) The overlap between the fields is greater, but the field "sags" in the center. Let $hsep \equiv 0.25\,r$. Now the separation is small enough that the total field approximates that of a single coil.

Let $hsep = 0.5\,r$. Eliminate from the plot the lines showing the coil's location from the plot (that is, let the plot region be $Bt(r, x)$ vs. x). Change the abscissa limits to $-hsep$ and $hsep$. Change the lower ordinate limit to $Bt(r, hsep)$ and the upper ordinate limit to $B(r, 0) \cdot 1.01$. Observe the shape of the field between the coils. Let $hsep = 0.51\,r$. Is the region as uniform right at the center? Does the region in which the field is almost constant change in size? If you let $hsep = 0.52\,r$, is the beginning of a "sag" in the center of the field apparent? How does the field at the center change if $hsep = 0.48\,r$? What is the "best" separation value?

Helmholtz coils, where the coil separation is nominally equal to the radius, are used as a relatively easy method for producing a region of uniform field. Sometimes the coils are used to cancel another field to create a region with a near-zero field.

14.2.1 Solenoid

We approach the solenoid in a similar fashion. We consider the total B-field from a set of current-carrying coils. The coils have the same radius as before and are arranged along the z-axis. The intensity of the field can be determined along the axis of the solenoid by summing the contributions due to the individual coils. In this way, the field can be determined at any point along the axis both inside and outside the solenoid. The field falls off quite abruptly near the ends of the solenoid. The field for a very long "ideal" solenoid, $B = \mu_o n I$, is a constant; the expression gives no information about the variations in the field associated with a solenoid of finite length.

• • Load EM7, approximating a solenoid with a small number of current-carrying coils (see Fig. 14.9).

The field is created by a set of $2\,m$ uniformly spaced current-carrying coils with centers located at points d_j along the z-axis. The field is calculated at a set of locations z_i. $B_{i,j}$ is the field at z_i due to the coil at d_j; B_i' is the field at z_i due to all the coils; Bs is the field of an ideal solenoid; and sl is just a display control that can be selected to be any fraction of the maximum value for the field.

The field due to the coils, B', and the ideal solenoid field are shown in the first plot region. The locations of the coils are also displayed at the chosen height, sl.

Solenoid - on-axis magnetic field.

$\mu_o := 1$ $I := 2$ $r := 1$ $hsep := .5$ $step := 2 \cdot hsep$

$n := (2 \cdot hsep)^{-1}$ $m := 1$ m - # of pairs of coils.

n - # of coils per length

$d[j]$ - location of coils; $z[i]$ - locations where field calculated.

$j := 0 \ ..2 \cdot m - 1$ $drng := (2 \cdot m - 1) \cdot hsep$ $d_j := -drng + step \cdot j$

$N := 41$ $i := 0 \ ..N$

$$z_i := -1.5 \cdot drng + 3 \cdot drng \cdot \frac{i}{N}$$

$B[i,j]$ - field at $z[i]$ due to coil at $d[j]$; $B'[i]$ - field at $z[i]$ due to all coils
Bs - field of ideal solenoid.

$$B_{i,j} := \frac{\mu_o}{2} \cdot I \cdot \frac{r^2}{\left[r^2 + \left[z_i - d_j\right]^2\right]^{1.5}}$$

$$B'_i := \sum_j B_{i,j}$$ $mB' := max(B')$

$$sl := mB' \cdot 0.8$$

$$Bs := \mu_o \cdot n \cdot I$$

$$ul := if(Bs > mB', Bs, mB') \cdot 1.05$$

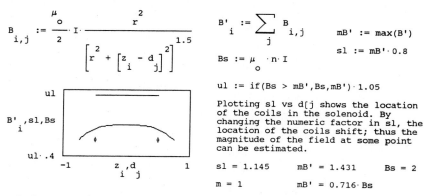

B'_i, sl, Bs

$ul \cdot .4$

-1 z_i, d_j 1

Plotting sl vs $d[j]$ shows the location of the coils in the solenoid. By changing the numeric factor in sl, the location of the coils shift; thus the magnitude of the field at some point can be estimated.

$sl = 1.145$ $mB' = 1.431$ $Bs = 2$

$m = 1$ $mB' = 0.716 \cdot Bs$

Calculate the field at the end of the solenoid and compare with the maximum.

$$B_e := \sum_j \left[\frac{\mu_o}{2} \cdot I \cdot \frac{r^2}{\left[r^2 + \left[drng - d_j\right]^2\right]^{1.5}}\right]$$

$mB' = 1.431$ $B_e = 1.354$

$$\frac{B_e}{mB'} = 0.946$$ $$\frac{B_e}{Bs} = 0.677$$

Figure 14.9 EM7, approximating a solenoid with a small number of current-carrying coils.

Finally, the magnitude of the field is determined at the end of the set of coils, and its value is compared with the maximum field and the ideal solenoid field.

Let $m = 2, 3, 4, 5,$ and 8. For $m = 8$, reduce N to 20. The "dip" is not real; the apparent dip is due to a fortuitous choice of values of z. Let $N = 21$ and observe the change. (Choose parameters carefully to avoid being mislead.)

Let $m = 1$ and set up the Helmholtz coil case.

If r is reduced or increased, how will the field change? Try $N = 40$, $m = 4$, and $r = 0.5$ (or 2). How does changing $hsep$ alter the field? What is the effect of changing the magnitude of I? Summarize your observations.

14.2.2 Dimensional Analysis

Several important relationships involving electric and magnetic fields, energy, volume, and power can be obtained using dimensional analysis. The last example generates the Larmor formula, a relationship that is not easily derived but is readily delineated using dimensional analysis.

• • Determine the expressions for energy density in electric and magnetic fields. For each case there are five quantities to be considered: energy En, volume V (we are considering energy density), the constants ϵ_o and μ_o, and the fields themselves, either E or B. Four fundamental units — mass, length, time, and charge — are necessary for the analysis. Therefore, each field can be determined with one group. The two groups include the variables, $(En, V, \epsilon_o, \mu_o, E)$ and $(En, V, \epsilon_o, \mu_o, B)$.

• • Load EM8. This file contains the starting point for this problem and can be used for the rest of the problems in this section (although not every quantity is included). You must set up the solve block and determine the exponents.

Do any of these quantities have a zero exponent and drop out? In each of the two examples, solve for En/V in terms of the other variables. Check your results by determining the units of the group equal to En/V.

• • Electromagnetic radiation, including light, carries both energy and momentum. Energy flux is the energy passing through some area per unit of time; call it S. Find the dimensionless group associated with S, ϵ_o, μ_o, E, and B. Solve for S.

• • Form the dimensionless groups to determine momentum density and momentum flux.

• • Form a dimensionless group from the quantities ϵ_o, μ_o, and c, the speed of light. In this very important case, the constant is unity.

When a charge is accelerated, radiation is emitted. The Larmor equation relates the power radiated to charge and acceleration. Determine the fundamental nature of the Larmor relation through dimensional analysis.

• • Form a dimensionless group from the quantities q (charge), a (acceleration), P (power), ϵ_o, and μ_o. Use the relation from the previous example to eliminate μ_o. Form the group; then solve for P. You will discover that

$$P \propto \frac{q^2 \, a^2}{\epsilon_o \, c^3}.$$

The constant which you cannot obtain has the value $(1/4\pi) \cdot (2/3)$. Determining, from dimensional analysis, how the power radiated varies with charge and acceleration is a treat. Remember this if you should take a more advanced course in electricity and magnetism.

I can feel it, Dave; my mind is going.

2001

CHAPTER
15

Applications of the Lorentz Force

The forces on a charged particle due to electric and magnetic fields may result in a variety of motions. The possible controls over such particles have been exploited in a large variety of instruments and machines, where particles can be deflected, confined, accelerated, focused, and so on. The net force, known as the Lorentz force, is given by

$$\mathbf{F} = q\mathbf{E} + q(\mathbf{v} \times \mathbf{B}). \qquad (15.1)$$

The velocity of a charged particle under the influence of an electric field changes both in magnitude and, unless the motion is collinear with a uniform field, direction. Under the influence of a magnetic field, only the direction may be changed. In all the cases considered here, these forces are much larger than the gravitational force, and gravity is ignored. Consider first the motion of a charged particle in a constant, uniform electric field. The motion corresponds competely to that of a massive particle in a uniform gravitational field with no air resistance. For example, in two-dimensional motion, if the electric field is oriented in the y-direction, there is no acceleration in the x-direction and the x-component of the velocity is constant. If the field is directed downward, positively charged particles will follow familiar parabolic trajectories, and we use the familiar equations for trajectory and range.

15.1   Parallel-Plate Electrostatic Analyzer

The fact that charged particles move in parabolic trajectories in a constant, uniform electric field can be exploited to construct an electrostatic analyzer, a device that separates particles according to their energy. We consider first a device consisting of a pair of parallel plates separated by a distance d; a voltage V is applied across the plates. The electric field between the plates is uniform in the y-direction; the field is zero in the x-direction. The acceleration experienced by a charged particle in the region between the plates is

$$a_y = \frac{q}{m} E \qquad \text{where} \qquad E = \frac{V}{d}. \qquad (15.2)$$

If the quantities q, m, and E, are constant, a_y is constant. Given the constant acceleration in one direction, the particles follow parabolic trajectories.

Particles enter the field region through a slit in the lower plate (at $y = 0$) making an angle $\theta = 45°$ with respect to the horizontal. They follow a parabolic trajectory and are detected in the $y = 0$ plane. The angle at which the particles enter the region cannot realistically be so constricted that all particles enter only at angle θ. The acceptance angle α is a measure of the deviation ($\pm$) from the central angle θ. If the particles deviate from ideal entry in the z-direction as well and enter at angle β, the initial values of the x- and y-components of the velocity are reduced. When both these possibilities are taken into consideration, the initial values for v_{ox} and v_{oy} are

$$v_{ox} = v_o \cos(\theta + \alpha) \cdot \cos(\beta) \qquad v_{oy} = v_o \sin(\theta + \alpha) \cdot \cos(\beta). \qquad (15.3)$$

• •   Verify the relations for v_{ox} and v_{oy}. By what fraction are v_{ox} and v_{oy} reduced if β is 5°?

• •   Load EML1, the parallel-plate electrostatic analyzer (see Fig. 15.1).

For reasons that will become clear momentarily, choose $\theta = 45°$. Initially, let conditions be ideal: $\alpha = 0$, $\beta = 0$. The separation between the plates is d; the applied voltage is V.

For the modest field of 15 V, across 10 cm, what is the acceleration of an electron in g's? (A description of acceleration in g's may be useful for describing accelerations of massive objects on earth, but not necessarily for charged particles.)

The initial velocity in the x-y plane is $v_{oxy}(En)$; the velocity is specified in terms of the initial energy, En. $R(En)$ is the range of the particle

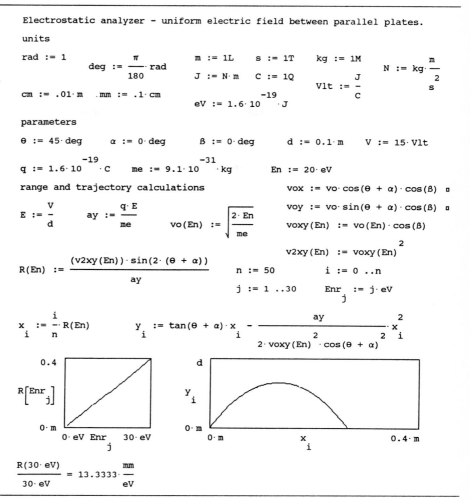

Electrostatic analyzer - uniform electric field between parallel plates.

units

$rad := 1$

$deg := \dfrac{\pi}{180} \cdot rad$

$m := 1L$ $s := 1T$ $kg := 1M$

$J := N \cdot m$ $C := 1Q$ $N := kg \cdot \dfrac{m}{s^2}$

$Vlt := \dfrac{J}{C}$

$cm := .01 \cdot m$ $mm := .1 \cdot cm$

$eV := 1.6 \cdot 10^{-19} \cdot J$

parameters

$\theta := 45 \cdot deg$ $\alpha := 0 \cdot deg$ $\beta := 0 \cdot deg$ $d := 0.1 \cdot m$ $V := 15 \cdot Vlt$

$q := 1.6 \cdot 10^{-19} \cdot C$ $me := 9.1 \cdot 10^{-31} \cdot kg$ $En := 20 \cdot eV$

range and trajectory calculations

$vox := vo \cdot cos(\theta + \alpha) \cdot cos(\beta)$ ▫

$voy := vo \cdot sin(\theta + \alpha) \cdot cos(\beta)$ ▫

$E := \dfrac{V}{d}$ $ay := \dfrac{q \cdot E}{me}$ $vo(En) := \sqrt{\dfrac{2 \cdot En}{me}}$ $voxy(En) := vo(En) \cdot cos(\beta)$

$v2xy(En) := voxy(En)^2$

$R(En) := \dfrac{(v2xy(En)) \cdot sin(2 \cdot (\theta + \alpha))}{ay}$ $n := 50$ $i := 0 .. n$

$j := 1 .. 30$ $Enr_j := j \cdot eV$

$x_i := \dfrac{i}{n} \cdot R(En)$ $y_i := tan(\theta + \alpha) \cdot x_i - \dfrac{ay}{2 \cdot voxy(En)^2 \cdot cos(\theta + \alpha)^2} \cdot x_i^2$

$\dfrac{R(30 \cdot eV)}{30 \cdot eV} = 13.3333 \cdot \dfrac{mm}{eV}$

Figure 15.1 EML1, the parallel-plate electrostatic analyzer.

(check the kinematic equations). The trajectory equation expresses y_i in terms of x_i.

The range is plotted as a function of energy. From this we can determine a very important property of the analyzer, the dispersion. Dispersion, in this case, is a measure of the spatial separation of the particles per energy difference. In this particular case, the range vs. energy curve is linear and the slope gives the dispersion. It is expressed here in mm/eV. Dispersion can be expressed in many forms. In optics, the dispersion can be expressed as angular separation per difference in wavelength.

Dispersion is a separation divided by a difference in the property being measured.

Resolution is often discussed along with dispersion. This property is a measure of the ability to distinguish the difference between adjacent groups of a similar character. For example, in this device if the acceptance angle is not zero, all the particles of a given energy will not focus at one point. They will be distributed; there will be a characteristic line shape associated with the detection of many particles. Resolution, a dimensionless number, is a measure of the total energy, for example, divided by the energy width of the line. The narrower the width of the line for a given energy, the higher is the resolution. The higher the resolution, the smaller the real differences in energy that can be distinguished from each other. When we consider the magnetic spectrometer, we will determine a line shape by means of a simulation.

Change the range function to $R(En, \alpha)$. Let α_k range from $-5°$ to $5°$ in steps of $1°$. Plot $R(En, \alpha_k)$, $R(En, 0)$ vs. α_k. How much does the range vary? What energy does this correspond to? (This can be handled easily in a solve block or by using the dispersion information.)

If this energy difference is a measure of the line width, what is the resolution?

If the initial angle were $30°$, what would the dispersion and resolution be? At $60°$? What is the difference in range between the extreme trajectories for a central angle of $30°$ and deviation angles of $\pm 5°$ and the case where the central angle is $45°$? Plot the trajectories.

While it was already known that the maximum range occurs at $45°$ and that larger or smaller angles result in a smaller range, we see now that for trajectories starting with a range of angles this phenomena results in what we refer to as first-order focusing (there is no focusing at $30°$). The folding over of the ranges for initial angles symmetrically spaced about $45°$ reduces the spread of the ranges and increases resolution.

θ and α specify the angles in the x-y plane. β is a measure of the initial velocity in the z-direction. Let $\alpha = 0$. Change v_{oxy} to be a function of β. Change the range to be a function of α and β. Plot $R(0, \beta)$ vs. β as β goes from $-5°$ to $5°$. (Just change enough to get the plot; don't worry about unessential regions.) Finally, plot $R(5°, \beta_k)$, $R(0, \beta_k)$, $R(0, 0)$ vs. β_k. If the limits of α and β are $5°$, over what distance range might the electrons appear? To what range of energies does this spread correspond?

Since all deviations from the ideal entry angle of $\theta = 45°$, $\alpha = 0$, and $\beta = 0$, result in a reduced range, the greatest range is the truest measure of the particle's energy.

Would this system work for protons? Test your ideas. Plot the electric field strength necessary to focus protons at a distance of 0.5 m as a function of energy of the proton. Are these realistic field strengths?

15.2   Magnetic Focusing Spectrometer

A 180° magnetic focusing spectrometer has focusing properties somewhat similar to those of the electrostatic analyzer described in the previous section. The spectrometer has a uniform B-field in the z-direction. Particles enter the field at the origin, in the x-y plane. The initial velocity is in the y-direction. Particles are detected along the x-axis after having completed approximately one-half of a circular orbit.

Unlike the electrostatic analyzer, the orbits of the particles in a magnetic focusing spectrometer are circular. Because B is vertical and velocity is in the x-y plane, $v \times B = v B$. Thus the force due to magnetic field $F = q(v \times B) = q v B$, which is constant in the x-y plane and perpendicular to v. These are the necessary conditions for uniform circular motion, a constant force perpendicular to the velocity.

Applying Newton's second law, we can determine the radius of the orbit:

$$q v B = m \frac{v^2}{r} \qquad \text{or} \qquad r = \frac{m v}{q B}. \qquad (15.4)$$

A magnet is sometimes referred to as a momentum selector because the radius r is proportional to the momentum, mv. The angular frequency of a charged particle moving in a circular orbit is

$$\omega = \frac{v}{r} = \frac{q B}{m}. \qquad (15.5)$$

• •   For B-fields of $0.1\,T$ and $1\,T$, create log-log plots of radius vs. energy for both electrons and protons. Let the kinetic energy take on values of 10^neV where $n = 1, \ldots, 5$ for the electrons and $n = 3, \ldots, 7$ for the protons. This calculation ignores relativistic effects, which arise as particle velocities approach the speed of light.

• •   Protons are to follow an orbit with $r = 0.5\,m$. Plot B-field strength vs. proton kinetic energy.

• •   In the electrostatic analyzer that we considered in the previous section, we found that the range was proportional to the energy. Is the same true for the magnetic analyzer that we have just described? Plot range (diameter of circular orbit) as a function of energy. What B-field would result in the same range for 20 eV electrons as we found for the electrostatic analyzer of the previous section?

• •   If $B = 1.31 \cdot 10^{-4}\,T$, plot the diameter of the electron orbits vs. E as the energy ranges from 1 eV to 20 eV. Which analyzer, electrostatic or magnetic, has the better dispersion at 20 eV? (How does the strength of this B-field compare with that of the earth's magnetic field?)

Line shape.   If a particle originates at the origin and remains in the x-y plane but its initial angle deviates from the y-axis by the angle α, the range is reduced. The effect is similar to the reduction in range associated with α in the electrostatic analyzer. There is first-order focusing.

The focusing can be visualized by imagining a circular orbit with one point of the circumference fixed at the origin and the diameter on the x-axis. This corresponds to an orbit with entry along the y-axis. Now rotate the circle about the fixed point, the origin, $\pm\alpha$. Convince yourself that these circular orbits intersect the x-axis at $2\,r\cos(\alpha)$ for both $\pm\alpha$. So just as in the case of the trajectories in the electrostatic analyzer, trajectories of the same energy but deviating by $\pm\alpha$ from the ideal entry angle focus at the same point, a little short of the ideal entry case.

Given a magnetic focusing spectrometer with an acceptance range of $\pm\alpha$, if electrons are emitted from a source with equal probability into any angle, what will the line shape look like? We know that the case $\alpha = 0$ has the greatest range. We know there is first-order focusing. This gives us an inkling of the shape; we can, however, get a much better sense of the shape by running a simulation.

To determine the line shape for a source of finite width $\pm s$ and a spectrometer with an acceptance angle $\pm\alpha$, define the function

$$x(x_o, \theta) := 2 \cdot r \cdot \cos(\theta) + x_o, \tag{15.6}$$

where x_o is the initial x-value (which is limited by the width of the source) and θ is the angle at which the particle is emitted. We can calculate the value of the function many times since the initial values for x_o and θ can take on random values within the allowed range ($\pm s$, $\pm\alpha$). After a sufficient number of range values have been determined, the data are plotted in a histogram; the result is a simulation of a line shape displaying the number of trajectories within a given range as a function of range.

• •   Load EML2, line shape (see Fig. 15.2).

Note that s is half the source width, and α is the magnitude of the maximum deviation angle. The values for the various ranges are z_i. The operation

$$\text{rnd}(2 \cdot C) - C \tag{15.7}$$

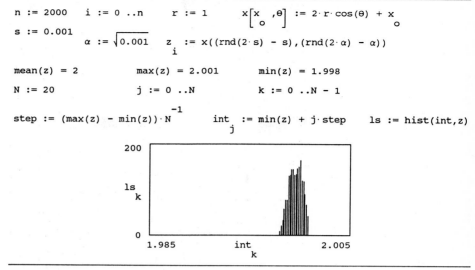

```
n := 2000    i := 0 ..n    r := 1      x[x ,θ] := 2·r·cos(θ) + x
                                         [ o ]                   o
s := 0.001
            α := √0.001    z  := x((rnd(2·s) - s),(rnd(2·α) - α))
                            i

mean(z) = 2           max(z) = 2.001      min(z) = 1.998

N := 20               j := 0 ..N         k := 0 ..N - 1

                              -1
step := (max(z) - min(z))·N        int  := min(z) + j·step    ls := hist(int,z)
                                      j
```

Figure 15.2 EML2, line shape.

generates random numbers in the range $\pm C$. The number of electron orbits, for which the range is calculated, is n. (Start with a smaller n if you have a slow machine.) The shape that you see plotted in EML2 is characteristic of the best compromise between source width and acceptance angle ($\alpha = \sqrt{s}$). The line shape can be examined in more detail by changing the plot limits. Process a few times to obtain some sense of the statistical fluctuations. (Repeat by moving the cursor to the first rnd region and processing [F9].) In each case make an estimate of the resolution.

Examine cases where one source of error is zero. Let $s := 0$ and $\alpha := 0.1$. Let $s := 0.001$ and $\alpha = 0$. Observe a number of cases.

Let $s := 0.003$ and $\alpha = \sqrt{0.001}$. The result is a line with a central region of nearly uniform height. Observe a number of cases.

Let $s := 0.001$ and $\alpha = 0.1$; this gives a longer trail-off at lower energies. Observe a number of cases.

15.3 Cylindrical Electrostatic Analyzer

Our final analyzer example is that of a cylindrical focusing electrostatic analyzer. The analyzer consists of two plates that lie along circles concentric with the z-axis. Both plates start at the x-axis and extend through an angle of approximately 130° into the second quadrant. Particles enter the space between the plates from the positive x-axis in the plus y-direction. A detector is placed at that location where first-order focusing occurs.

When a potential is applied across the plates, the electric field between them varies as $1/r$, the field associated with a long charged wire or cylinder. The field strength is selected to permit particles of a given energy to pass along a circular arc. Substituting in the equation of motion the quantity qE for the force, we have

$$q\,|E| = \frac{m\,v^2}{r} \qquad \text{so} \qquad |E| = \frac{m\,v^2}{q\,r}.$$ (15.8)

The field is directed radially inward for positively charged particles. θ is the angle through which the particle has passed in its transit from the entry point to the detector. The x- and y-components of the acceleration can be expressed as

$$ax = \frac{q\,E}{m}\cos(\theta) \qquad \text{and} \qquad ay = \frac{q\,E}{m}\sin(\theta).$$ (15.9)

• •   Load EML3, cylindrical electrostatic analyzer (see Figs. 15.3 and 15.4).

Calculations are performed for three trajectories. Values for the energies and angles of deviation must be specified for each. The field is adjusted to pass the zeroth ray along a circular trajectory between the plates.

This calculation requires lots of memory. If a number of calculations have been performed since you last loaded MathCAD, you should quit MathCAD and reload. Units are not included so as not to use additional memory.

The velocity form of the Verlet algorithm is used to compute the particle trajectories. (The Euler-Cromer algorithm is fine for more rapid exploration but in this case is slightly less precise; it also requires less memory. If you experience memory difficulties, simplify the algorithm to the Euler-Cromer form. All the features examined are essentially the same. The angle at which the trajectories focus is less precisely located but is very close, and the specific value of the angle is not the central issue.)

The parameters and initial conditions are specified. The energy, entered in eV, is converted to Joules by multiplying by the charge of the proton, q. The range of the time scale in which successive steps of the iterative process are considered is in nanoseconds.

Electrostatic cylindrical analyzer.

parameters

$$q := 1.6 \cdot 10^{-19} \qquad m := 9.1 \cdot 10^{-31} \qquad rad := 1 \qquad deg := \frac{\pi}{180} \cdot rad$$

three trajectories $j := 0 \,..2$ $En_j :=$

15
13
17

$\alpha_j :=$

0·deg
0·deg
0·deg

$En_j := En_j \cdot q$

$$v_j := \sqrt{2 \cdot En_j \cdot m^{-1}}$$

Iterated solution. Initial conditions, parameters user defined functions to implement the velocity form of the Verlet algorithm.

$$n := 80 \qquad i := 0\,..n \qquad x_{0,j} := 1 \qquad y_{0,j} := 0 \qquad \theta_{0,j} := 0$$

$$vx_{0,j} := v_j \cdot \sin\left[\alpha_j\right] \qquad vy_{0,j} := v_j \cdot \cos\left[\alpha_j\right]$$

$$r(x,y) := \sqrt{x^2 + y^2}$$

$$ax_{0,j} := -v_0^2 \cdot r\left[x_{0,j}, y_{0,j}\right]^{-1} \cdot \cos\left[\theta_{0,j}\right] \qquad ay_{0,j} := -v_0^2 \cdot r\left[x_{0,j}, y_{0,j}\right]^{-1} \cdot \sin\left[\theta_{0,j}\right]$$

$$a(x,y) := -v_0^2 \cdot r(x,y)^{-1} \qquad ns := 10^{-9} \qquad \delta t := 14 \cdot ns$$

$$D(x,vx,ax) := x + vx \cdot \delta t + 0.5 \cdot ax \cdot \delta t^2$$

$$c(x,vx,ax,y,vy,ay) := \cos(\text{angle}(D(x,vx,ax),D(y,vy,ay)))$$

$$s(x,vx,ax,y,vy,ay) := \sin(\text{angle}(D(x,vx,ax),D(y,vy,ay)))$$

$$VX(x,vx,ax,y,vy,ay) := vx + 0.5 \cdot (ax + a(x,y) \cdot c(x,vx,ax,y,vy,ay)) \cdot \delta t$$

$$VY(x,vx,ax,y,vy,ay) := vy + 0.5 \cdot (ay + a(x,y) \cdot s(x,vx,ax,y,vy,ay)) \cdot \delta t$$

$$\begin{bmatrix} ax_{(i+1),j} \\ ay_{(i+1),j} \\ vx_{(i+1),j} \\ vy_{(i+1),j} \\ x_{(i+1),j} \\ y_{(i+1),j} \end{bmatrix} := \begin{bmatrix} a\left[x_{i,j}, y_{i,j}\right] \cdot c\left[x_{i,j}, vx_{i,j}, ax_{i,j}, y_{i,j}, vy_{i,j}, ay_{i,j}\right] \\ a\left[x_{i,j}, y_{i,j}\right] \cdot s\left[x_{i,j}, vx_{i,j}, ax_{i,j}, y_{i,j}, vy_{i,j}, ay_{i,j}\right] \\ VX\left[x_{i,j}, vx_{i,j}, ax_{i,j}, y_{i,j}, vy_{i,j}, ay_{i,j}\right] \\ VY\left[x_{i,j}, vx_{i,j}, ax_{i,j}, y_{i,j}, vy_{i,j}, ay_{i,j}\right] \\ x_{i,j} + vx_{i,j} \cdot \delta t + \frac{1}{2} \cdot ax_{i,j} \cdot \delta t^2 \\ y_{i,j} + vy_{i,j} \cdot \delta t + \frac{1}{2} \cdot ay_{i,j} \cdot \delta t^2 \end{bmatrix}$$

Figure 15.3 EML3, cylindrical electrostatic analyzer. (See the next figure for the rest of the document.)

Several functional forms are defined to simplify the equation block; these include the position, acceleration, cosine, and sine. Note that VX and VY are expressions of the velocity form of the Verlet algorithm.

In the equation block, acceleration, velocity, and position are iterated for each component. Finally, the trajectories are plotted both in

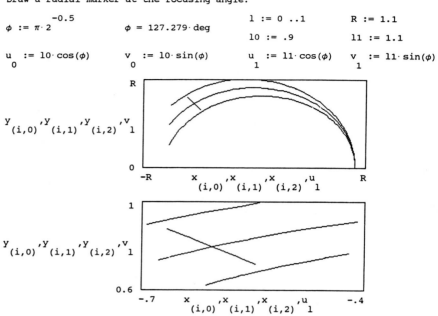

Draw a radial marker at the focusing angle.

$\phi := \pi \cdot 2^{-0.5}$ $\phi = 127.279 \cdot \text{deg}$ $i := 0 .. 1$ $R := 1.1$

$l0 := .9$ $l1 := 1.1$

$u_0 := l0 \cdot \cos(\phi)$ $v_0 := l0 \cdot \sin(\phi)$ $u_1 := l1 \cdot \cos(\phi)$ $v_1 := l1 \cdot \sin(\phi)$

Figure 15.4 EML3 *continued.*

entirety and in close up at the focus region. A marker, a short radial line, is drawn at the angle $\phi = \pi/\sqrt{2}$, which is the theoretical focus angle.

First determine a rough measure of the dispersion. The initial conditions are for energies of 15, 13, and 17 eV with a 0° deviation angle. The quantities l_0 and l_1, just above the plot regions, specify the distance from the origin of the starting and ending points of the radial marker. Change these values until the radial line just touches the outer and inner trajectories. This provides a measure of the spread which occurs in this case for different values of energy. Express the dispersion in mm/eV. Is the dispersion a constant? Is there an asymmetry? If yes, on which side is the dispersion greater?

Now examine the focusing. Let all the energies be 15. Let the α's be 0°, 5°, −5°. Does the focusing occur where predicted? Adjust the values for l_0 and l_1 to get a sense of the line width. Estimate the resolution.

Find the kinetic energy, E', for a particle with deviation angle $\alpha = 0°$, whose trajectory intersects the 15 eV, $\alpha = -5°$ trajectory at the focusing angle. Use your value for the dispersion to select an energy. Then show the two trajectories.

Find the kinetic energy, E', for a particle with deviation angle $\alpha = -5°$, whose trajectory intersects the 15 eV, $\alpha = 0°$ trajectory at the focusing angle.

If, instead of having the expected $1/r$ field dependence, the field was radial but the magnitude was independent of the radial position (that is, constant in magnitude), what would the new focusing angle be?

15.4   Trajectories in Crossed E- and B-Fields

A problem commonly found in elementary texts is that of a particle passing through a region of crossed electric and magnetic fields (for example, E_y, B_z, and velocity in the x-direction). The magnitudes of the fields are adjusted so that particles of a particular energy pass through this velocity filter undeflected :

$$F_{Ey} + F_{By} = 0 \quad \text{or} \quad q\,E_y = q\,v\,B_z \quad \text{and} \quad v = \frac{E_y}{B_z}. \quad (15.10)$$

Leaving the problem at this stage may leave some false impressions.

• •   Load EML4, Wien filter (see Fig. 15.5).

Let K be the electron energy for which there should be no deflection. The initial parameters are specified and the field strengths are adjusted to pass an electron with energy K. Let K' be the kinetic energy of the particle sent through the filter. The deviation angle from the x-axis is θ.

Let $K' = 10\,\text{eV}$ and process. Then let $K' = 9.9\,\text{eV}$ and $10.1\,\text{eV}$. Determine the dispersion? Do trajectories diverge from the central path as expected?

Looks can be deceiving. Change the upper limit of the abscissa from $4\,\text{cm}$ to d (15 cm) and process with $K' = 10\,\text{eV}$. Then, let $K' = 2\,\text{eV}$ and $K' = 12\,\text{eV}$. The motion is probably more complex than might be surmised from the case of zero deflection.

The problem of crossed E- and B-fields is a rich one. We explore this problem further. The configuration remains the same: the electric field is in the y-direction, and the magnetic field is in the z-direction.

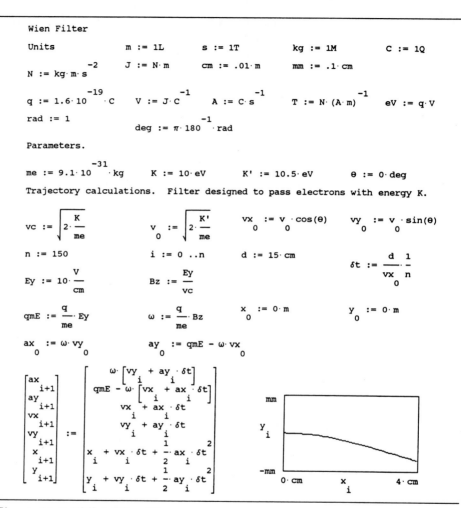

Wien Filter

Units

$$m := 1L \qquad s := 1T \qquad kg := 1M \qquad C := 1Q$$

$$N := kg \cdot m \cdot s^{-2} \qquad J := N \cdot m \qquad cm := .01 \cdot m \qquad mm := .1 \cdot cm$$

$$q := 1.6 \cdot 10^{-19} \cdot C \qquad V := J \cdot C^{-1} \qquad A := C \cdot s^{-1} \qquad T := N \cdot (A \cdot m)^{-1} \qquad eV := q \cdot V$$

$$rad := 1$$
$$deg := \pi \cdot 180^{-1} \cdot rad$$

Parameters.

$$me := 9.1 \cdot 10^{-31} \cdot kg \qquad K := 10 \cdot eV \qquad K' := 10.5 \cdot eV \qquad \theta := 0 \cdot deg$$

Trajectory calculations. Filter designed to pass electrons with energy K.

$$vc := \sqrt{2 \cdot \frac{K}{me}} \qquad v_0 := \sqrt{2 \cdot \frac{K'}{me}} \qquad vx_0 := v_0 \cdot \cos(\theta) \qquad vy_0 := v_0 \cdot \sin(\theta)$$

$$n := 150 \qquad i := 0 \, .. \, n \qquad d := 15 \cdot cm \qquad \delta t := \frac{d}{vx_0} \cdot \frac{1}{n}$$

$$Ey := 10 \cdot \frac{V}{cm} \qquad Bz := \frac{Ey}{vc}$$

$$qmE := \frac{q}{me} \cdot Ey \qquad \omega := \frac{q}{me} \cdot Bz \qquad x_0 := 0 \cdot m \qquad y_0 := 0 \cdot m$$

$$ax_0 := \omega \cdot vy_0 \qquad ay_0 := qmE - \omega \cdot vx_0$$

$$\begin{bmatrix} ax_{i+1} \\ ay_{i+1} \\ vx_{i+1} \\ vy_{i+1} \\ x_{i+1} \\ y_{i+1} \end{bmatrix} := \begin{bmatrix} \omega \cdot [vy_i + ay_i \cdot \delta t] \\ qmE - \omega \cdot [vx_i + ax_i \cdot \delta t] \\ vx_i + ax_i \cdot \delta t \\ vy_i + ay_i \cdot \delta t \\ x_i + vx_i \cdot \delta t + \frac{1}{2} \cdot ax_i \cdot \delta t^2 \\ y_i + vy_i \cdot \delta t + \frac{1}{2} \cdot ay_i \cdot \delta t^2 \end{bmatrix}$$

Figure 15.5 EML4, Wien filter.

We consider a particle starting from rest. The particle experiences an accelerating force $F = q\,E$. There is no magnetic force initially, because the velocity is zero. Under the acceleration of the E-field, the particle gains velocity and begins to interact with the B-field. As the velocity increases, the magnetic force increases, and the particle is deflected more and more until its direction is opposite that of its initial motion. The particle is now moving against the electric field, so it slows and stops, and then the cycle repeats. As a result of this motion, there is a net drift of a positively charged particle in the $E \times B$ direction.

• • Load EML5, motion of a charged particle in crossed E- and B-fields (see Fig. 15.6).

This program requires lots of memory. It may be prudent to exit MathCAD and reload.

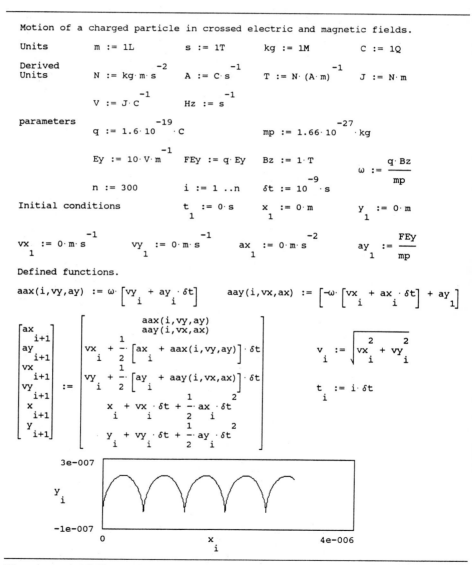

Motion of a charged particle in crossed electric and magnetic fields.

Units   m := 1L   s := 1T   kg := 1M   C := 1Q

Derived
Units $N := kg \cdot m \cdot s^{-2}$ $A := C \cdot s^{-1}$ $T := N \cdot (A \cdot m)^{-1}$ $J := N \cdot m$

             $V := J \cdot C^{-1}$ $Hz := s^{-1}$

parameters $q := 1.6 \cdot 10^{-19} \cdot C$ $mp := 1.66 \cdot 10^{-27} \cdot kg$

             $Ey := 10 \cdot V \cdot m^{-1}$ $FEy := q \cdot Ey$ $Bz := 1 \cdot T$ $\omega := \dfrac{q \cdot Bz}{mp}$

             $n := 300$ $i := 1 .. n$ $\delta t := 10^{-9} \cdot s$

Initial conditions $t_1 := 0 \cdot s$ $x_1 := 0 \cdot m$ $y_1 := 0 \cdot m$

$vx_1 := 0 \cdot m \cdot s^{-1}$ $vy_1 := 0 \cdot m \cdot s^{-1}$ $ax_1 := 0 \cdot m \cdot s^{-2}$ $ay_1 := \dfrac{FEy}{mp}$

Defined functions.

$aax(i,vy,ay) := \omega \cdot \left[vy_i + ay_i \cdot \delta t \right]$ $aay(i,vx,ax) := \left[-\omega \cdot \left[vx_i + ax_i \cdot \delta t \right] + ay_1 \right]$

$$\begin{bmatrix} ax_{i+1} \\ ay_{i+1} \\ vx_{i+1} \\ vy_{i+1} \\ x_{i+1} \\ y_{i+1} \end{bmatrix} := \begin{bmatrix} aax(i,vy,ay) \\ aay(i,vx,ax) \\ vx_i + \frac{1}{2} \cdot \left[ax_i + aax(i,vy,ay) \right] \cdot \delta t \\ vy_i + \frac{1}{2} \cdot \left[ay_i + aay(i,vx,ax) \right] \cdot \delta t \\ x_i + vx_i \cdot \delta t + \frac{1}{2} \cdot ax_i \cdot \delta t^2 \\ y_i + vy_i \cdot \delta t + \frac{1}{2} \cdot ay_i \cdot \delta t^2 \end{bmatrix}$$

$v_i := \sqrt{vx_i^2 + vy_i^2}$

$t_i := i \cdot \delta t$

Figure 15.6 EML5, motion of a charged particle in crossed E- and B-fields.

The initial conditions have the particle start at the origin with zero velocity. The Verlet algorithm is used.

Position the y vs. x plot near the bottom of the screen and process. Observe the motion that was described. Go through the argument again so that it becomes clear to you.

What is an approximate value for the drift velocity?

Based on your knowledge of the motion and your reading of the y vs. x graph, make rough plots by hand of eight situations (the cases are given below). Try to determine the general shape; don't worry about numerical values. Draw two and let MathCAD plot the same two, and so on. These are tough, but give them your best shot. For each one whose general shape you predict, count one. A score of two is not bad; three is very good; four is excellent; and eight is amazing. Take your time; think carefully about each one before having MathCAD spill the beans. Try to ask questions that will nail down a few points.

The eight cases are (1) vx_i vs. x_i, (2) vy_i vs. x_i, (3) ax_i vs. x_i, (4) ay_i vs. x_i, (5) vx_i vs. y_i, (6) vy_i vs. y_i, (7) ax_i vs. y_i, and (8) ay_i vs. y_i. There is a great deal of information here worth pondering.

Try some other initial conditions; let (vx_1, vy_1) equal $(-1, 0)$ and $(-2, -5)$.

Delete the plot regions that were just created. Now add a weak, constant electric field in the x-direction. Let $E_x = 1\,\text{V}/\text{m}$. Define FEx and adjust ax_1 and aax appropriately. Predict the effect on the motion of this added field and verify.

If you're not going to kill me, I have things to do.

Darkman

CHAPTER
16

Circuits

We approach dc circuits through two common examples, the voltage divider and the Wheatstone bridge. In these, examples we find application of Kirchhoff's laws and a general approach to dc circuit problems. We then consider briefly the charging and discharging of capacitors, and the use of diodes. Combining a resistor, a capacitor, and a diode in one unit, we construct a simple power supply. Finally, we consider how to construct a simple amplifier using a tunnel diode in a voltage divider circuit.

16.1 DC Circuits

Voltage and current are quantities that are basic to all circuits. The voltage, V, (in volts) between two points in a circuit indicates the work done on a charge as it moves from one point to the other in a circuit. A battery is a voltage source; there is a potential difference between its terminals. Voltage must be measured between two points. Frequently voltage measurements are indicated at one point with an implicit reference to a ground point at V = 0. (Take a piece of copper pipe and drive it well into the ground; the voltage of the pipe is ground potential.) If the voltage is specified at a point, the implication is that the number actually specifies the potential difference between that point and ground.

Current is a measure of charge per time flowing through a cross section of a wire or other circuit element. The current unit is the ampere. The direction of current is from more positive potential to less positive potential. Current flows through a circuit element.

Two laws useful in dc circuit analysis are (1) Kirchhoff's current law and (2) Kirchhoff's voltage law. These two laws can be stated briefly as: (1) at any point in a circuit, the sum of all currents flowing *in* equals the sum of all currents flowing *out*, and (2) the algebraic sum of the voltage changes across all the elements around any closed loop of a circuit is zero.

We consider the circuit elements: the resistor, the capacitor, and the diode. The voltage-current relationship in each of these devices is different. The resistor is a device in which the current through the element is proportional to the voltage across it. This statement is known as Ohm's law:

$$i = \frac{v_2 - v_1}{R}, \tag{16.1}$$

where v_2 and v_1 are the voltages at either end of the resistor. The unit of resistance is the ohm (Ω). The voltage change across a resistor, moving in the direction of current flow, is $-iR$; this is called a voltage drop. Going across the resistor against the current results in a voltage increase of iR.

In the circuits considered here, the connecting wire between elements is assumed to have zero resistance. Consequently, there is no voltage drop across these wires. All points on a length of wire are at the same voltage.

Since resistors in series have the same current passing through them, the net resistance for resistors in series (see Fig. 16.1) is the sum of the individual resistances:

$$R_{\text{tot}} = R_1 + R_2 + \cdots = \sum_i R_i. \tag{16.2}$$

Since resistors in parallel have the same voltage across them, resistors in parallel (see Fig. 16.2) add in terms of their reciprocals:

Figure 16.1 Two resistors in series.

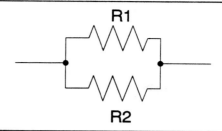

Figure 16.2 Two resistors in parallel.

$$\frac{1}{R_{\text{tot}}} = \frac{1}{R_1} + \frac{1}{R_2} + \cdots = \sum_i \frac{1}{R_i} = \sum_i R_i^{-1}$$

$$R_{\text{tot}} = \left(\sum_i R_i^{-1}\right)^{-1}. \tag{16.3}$$

16.1.1   The Voltage Divider

The voltage divider is a very common circuit element. The divider consists, in this case, of two resistors in series (see Fig. 16.3). A dc voltage source is included, so there is a voltage to divide. We want to know the voltage at the point (node) between the two resistors R_1 and R_2; we refer to this voltage as v_{out}. (The common point between the negative terminal of the battery and resistor R_2 is at ground.)

Current flows from the voltage source through R_1, through R_2, and back through the battery. Because R_1 and R_2 are in series, the current

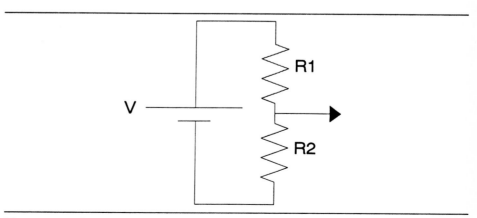

Figure 16.3 Voltage divider circuit.

through them is the same. Apply Kirchhoff's voltage law, starting at the minus terminal of the battery. The path takes us across the battery from the minus terminal to the plus terminal (so the voltage change is $+v$), across R_1 in the direction of the current $(-i\,R_1)$, across R_2 in the direction of the current $(-i\,R_2)$, and back to the starting point, so the sum is zero:

$$v - i\,R_1 - i\,R_2 = 0 \qquad \text{or} \qquad i = \frac{v}{R_1 + R_2}.$$

Starting from ground, we can get to the v_{out} node by going across R_2 against the current. The output voltage from the divider is then

$$v_{\text{out}} = +i\,R_2 = \frac{R_2}{R_1 + R_2}\,v. \qquad (16.4)$$

• •   Verify that the same expression for v_{out} is obtained by the path that includes the battery and R_1.

• •   Load CIRC1, voltage divider circuit (see Fig. 16.4).

A voltage divider consisting of a voltage source and two resistors in series is analyzed for the case that the sum of the two resistors is a constant. Although the results are easily obtained, they should be well understood; the voltage divider will be revisited in several following applications.

A solve block, with the find statement in functional form, returns the values for the current and R_1 when R_2 is specified. One equation in the solve block is an expression of Kirchhoff's voltage law for the circuit. The other assures that the total resistance remains a constant. Try several values for R_2 and observe the results.

A sequence of values is obtained by defining R_{2i} and substituting it in calls on f, the find statement of the solve block. In the first plot region, the magnitudes of both the resistances and the total current are plotted against the R_1 values. In the second plot region, the voltages across R_1 and R_2 and their sum are plotted against the R_1 values. Be careful to determine which curve is associated with which resistor. Which curve corresponds to v_{out}? The abscissa for these plots is R_{1i}. How would the curves appear if plotted against R_{2i}?

Let $R_1 = 100\ \Omega$. Let R_2 go from 20 to 980 Ω (the sum $R_1 + R_2$ is no longer a constant). Plot v_{out} vs. R_2. What is the voltage range for v_{out}? How is this case different from the previous one?

Summarize the properties of a voltage divider.

• •   Load CIRC2, voltage divider with load (see Fig. 16.5).

The voltage divider circuit.

The common potentiometer used in the laboratory is a resistor with three connection points, three terminals. Two of the connections are at either end of the resistor and do not change. The third contact can slide along the length of the resistor. At any given contact point the total resistance is divided into two resistances R1 and R2. The sum is, of course, constant.

$$V := 5 \qquad R1 := 1 \qquad R2 := 4$$

$$R := R1 + R2 \qquad\qquad I := 1$$

$$\text{given} \qquad V - I \cdot R1 - I \cdot R2 \approx 0 \qquad R1 + R2 \approx R$$

$$f(R2) := find(I, R1)$$

$$R2 := 3$$

$$f(R2) = \begin{bmatrix} 1 \\ 2 \end{bmatrix} \qquad \text{I is the upper value, R1 the lower.}$$

The values for I and R1 can be written using subscripts on the function f.

$$I := f(R2)_0 \qquad R1 := f(R2)_1 \qquad I = 1 \qquad R1 = 2$$

We can look at an entire sequence by letting R2 take on a sequence of values.

$$n := 5 \qquad i := 0 \text{ ..} n$$

$$R2_i := \begin{bmatrix} i \\ - \\ n \end{bmatrix} \cdot R \qquad I_i := f \begin{bmatrix} R2_i \end{bmatrix}_0 \qquad R1_i := f \begin{bmatrix} R2_i \end{bmatrix}_1$$

$$V1_i := I_i \cdot R1_i \qquad V2_i := I_i \cdot R2_i \qquad VV_i := V1_i + V2_i$$

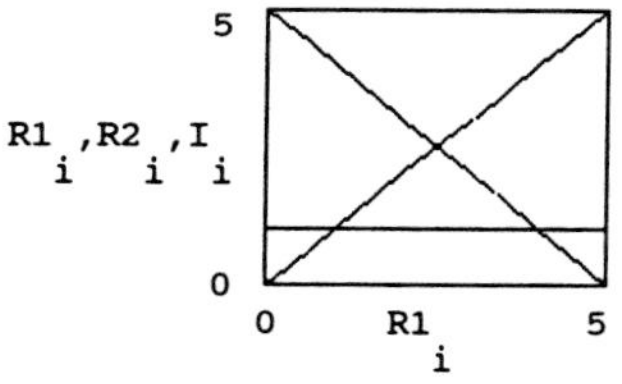

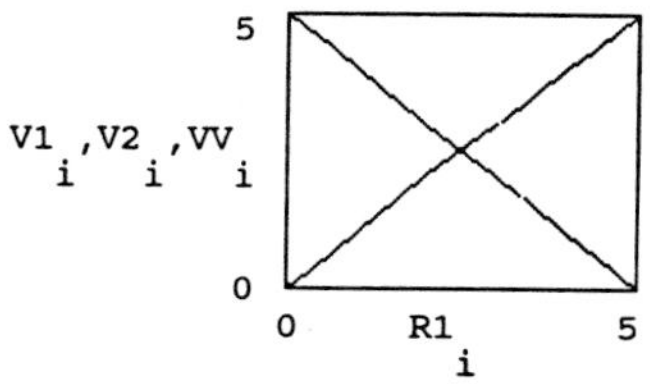

Figure 16.4 CIRC1, voltage divider circuit.

The behavior of a loaded voltage divider deviates somewhat from the behavior we studied in the previous example. This circuit is sufficiently common that you should be very familiar with it. A load resistor R_3 is added to the voltage divider we discussed in the previous example. The resistor is in parallel with R_2. A solve block is again set up in functional form. In the solve block are three equations: a statement of the voltages for each of the two loops in this circuit and a current statement at the branching node. (There are three simple loops that could be drawn for this circuit; only two are independent; any two will do.) For any value of R_3, f returns the currents I_1, I_2, and I_3; v_{out} is calculated using the value of I_3.

Let R_3 take on values much larger than, equal to, and much smaller than R_2. Predict the values of the output voltages before calculating $f(R_3)$.

The voltage divider circuit.

Connect a third resistor from the central tap point to the lower edge of the potentiometer and examine the new circuit.

I2 is the current through R2; I3 is the current through R3. Their sum is the current through R1.

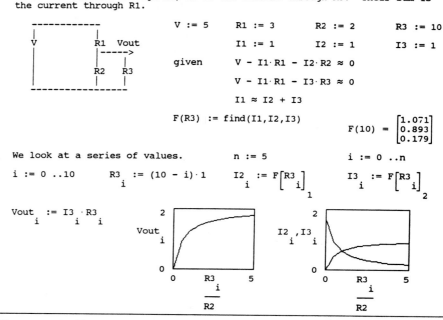

Figure 16.5 CIRC2, voltage divider with load.

If $R_2 = R_1$ and $R_3 = \infty$, what is v_{out}?

If $R_2 = R_1$ and $R_3 = 0$, what is v_{out}?

In the second part of the document, the values of I_2, I_3, and v_{out} are determined as a function of R_3. Is the total current constant? Plot the total current supplied by the voltage source as a function of R_3 and explain the curve, including the value at the intercept.

If $R_1 = 1\Omega$, how do the curves change in terms of qualitative shape and overall magnitude?

Note that v_{out} is defined as $I_3 \cdot R_3$. Why not $I_2 \cdot R_2$?

What effect will there be on the curves if the multiplier of $(10 - i)$ in R_3 is changed to 2 or 5?

Make a summary statement of the effect of R_3 on the divider circuit.

16.1.2   *Wheatstone Bridge*

The Wheatstone bridge has many applications. Here we want to find the value of an unknown resistance by a comparison/balancing process with known resistances. The unknown is placed in a circuit with known resistances. The known values are adjusted until a null — a zero for a particular current — is achieved; then the unknown matches the known value.

The circuit is two two-resistor voltage dividers connected to the same voltage source (see Fig. 16.6). The outputs of the two dividers are connected to each other through a low-resistance galvanometer, a device able to indicate the presence of small currents. Moving-coil galvanometers typically have resistances in the range of 25 to 500 Ω and sensitivities (a kind of inverse dispersion specification) range from 0.2 to 0.0001 μA/ mm.

• •   Load CIRC3, Wheatstone bridge (see Fig. 16.7).

The four resistors in the voltage dividers of the bridge circuit, R_1 through R_4, have as their base value R. The galvanometer resistance is represented by R_5. For the time being, it is irrelevant which resistor is the unknown. What we want to gain is some sense of the current in R_5 as the bridge is unbalanced, and also, given a particular galvanometer sensitivity, how accurately an unknown can be determined.

A solve block is set up with six equations and six unknowns: three voltage loop equations and three current node equations. The find statement is in functional form. A specification of the resistance, R_3, returns the currents in each of the resistors and the total current. The specific R in the $f(R)$ expression can be changed to any one of the five resistors.

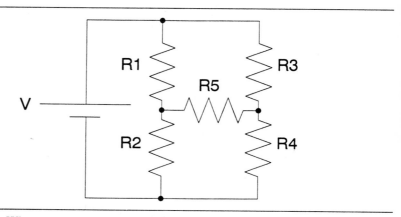

Figure 16.6 Wheatstone bridge circuit.

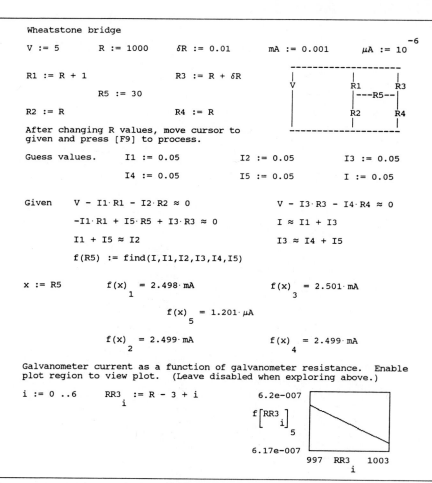

```
Wheatstone bridge
                                                                                    -6
V := 5        R := 1000      δR := 0.01        mA := 0.001      μA := 10

R1 := R + 1                  R3 := R + δR
            R5 := 30
R2 := R                      R4 := R
After changing R values, move cursor to
given and press [F9] to process.

Guess values.      I1 := 0.05         I2 := 0.05         I3 := 0.05
                   I4 := 0.05         I5 := 0.05         I := 0.05

   Given    V - I1·R1 - I2·R2 ≈ 0            V - I3·R3 - I4·R4 ≈ 0
            -I1·R1 + I5·R5 + I3·R3 ≈ 0       I ≈ I1 + I3
            I1 + I5 ≈ I2                     I3 ≈ I4 + I5
            f(R5) := find(I,I1,I2,I3,I4,I5)

x := R5         f(x)  = 2.498·mA             f(x)  = 2.501·mA
                    1                            3
                        f(x)  = 1.201·μA
                            5
                f(x)  = 2.499·mA             f(x)  = 2.499·mA
                    2                            4
```

Galvanometer current as a function of galvanometer resistance. Enable
plot region to view plot. (Leave disabled when exploring above.)

```
i := 0 ..6      RR3  := R - 3 + i            6.2e-007
                   i
                                          f⎡RR3 ⎤
                                           ⎣    i⎦
                                                  5
                                         6.17e-007
                                                   997  RR3  1003
                                                          i
```

Figure 16.7 CIRC3, Wheatstone bridge.

RRx_i represents a series of values to be substituted in f. Leave the plot region disabled when you are using the first section of the document.

In the plot region, R_3 goes from $R - 3$ to $R + 3$ in steps of one. The plot is of I_5 vs. R_3. What is the slope, the ratio of galvanometer current per change in R_3, in $\mu A/\Omega$?

How much does the galvanometer's resistance affect the ability to balance the circuit? Change the find statement to $f(R_5)$. Let RR take on the values from 20 to 420 in steps of 40. Plot the current in the galvanometer vs. the RR resistance values. For small changes in R_3, is the response symmetric around the balance value?

Let $R_3 = R - \delta R$ and repeat. What happens to the current values?

Let $R_5 = 0\,\Omega$. Keep the ratio $R/\delta R = 10^5$. How does the current I_5, $f(0)_5$, change as R takes on the values 10^n where $n = 0, 1, \ldots, 4$? (Remember, keep the ratio constant.) Repeat with $R_5 = 100\,\Omega$.

A standard way of balancing the bridge is with $R_1 = R_3$ and $R_2 = R_4$, but it is not necessary that $R_1 = R_2$. How does the sensitivity change if $R_2 = 5 \cdot R_1$ and $R_3 = R + \delta R$?

How does the sensitivity change if $R_1 : R_2 = R_3 : R_4$ and $R_3 = 10\,R_1$? Examine for the case where R_1 varies from its balance value and for the case where R_3 varies from its equilibrium value. Let the deviations cover the same percent change.

16.2   Capacitors

A capacitor is a device capable of storing separated charge. The relation

$$Q = CV \tag{16.5}$$

indicates that the stored charge, $\pm Q$, stored is proportional to the applied voltage; the capacitance, C, is the constant of proportionality. The unit of capacitance is the farad, F.

The net capacitance of capacitors in parallel is the sum of the individual capacitances:

$$C_P = \sum C_i. \tag{16.6}$$

The net capacitance of capacitors in series is the reciprocal of the sum of reciprocals (as for resistors in parallel):

$$C_S = \left(\sum C_i^{-1}\right)^{-1}. \tag{16.7}$$

• •   Write functions for the combinations: $C_P(C_1, C_2)$ and $C_S(C_1, C_2)$. Test them.

When voltage is applied to a dc circuit containing a capacitor, current flows, charging the capacitor. After some time, the voltage across the capacitor approaches the applied voltage and no further current flows. Capacitors block constant current; transients such as charging currents are not considered to be dc, even though they may come from a dc source.

In circuits with resistors and capacitors, we frequently need to know the time that it takes for a capacitor to charge or discharge. Consider the following circuit. An uncharged capacitor is in series with a voltage source, a resistor, and an open switch. When the switch is closed, the circuit is complete and current begins to flow. The current is given by

$$i = \frac{V}{R} e^{-t/RC}. \tag{16.8}$$

As the capacitor charges, the current decreases exponentially. The charge on the capacitor, initially zero, builds in time:

$$q = CV(1 - e^{-t/RC}). \tag{16.9}$$

When $t = 0$, $i = V/R = i_o$; when $t = RC$, $i = i_o \cdot 1/e$. The product RC is known as the time constant. Verify that the units of RC are time.

After one time constant, the current is reduced to $1/e$ of its maximum value at $t = 0$.

When $t = 0$, the charge $q = 0$. After one time constant,

$$q = CV\left(1 - \frac{1}{e}\right) = 0.632\, CV.$$

• •   Let $V = 10$, $R = 5 \cdot 10^5$, and $C = 10 \cdot 10^{-6}$. At $t = 0$ a switch is closed, completing the circuit composed of a battery, capacitor, and resistor in series. The capacitor is initially uncharged. Plot the current as a function of time, $i(t)$. Define $i'(t) = d/dt\, i(t)$. How does $i'(0) \cdot RC$ compare with v/R? Interpret this. (Remember, RC has units of time.)

Plot the charge on the capacitor as a function of time. Define $q'(t) = d/dt\, q(t)$. How does $q'(0)$ compare with $i(0)$? How does $q'\, RC$ compare with CV? Interpret.

When a capacitor discharges, both the charge and current decrease:

$$q(t) = CV e^{-t/RC} \qquad i(t) = \frac{V}{R} e^{-t/RC}. \tag{16.10}$$

• •   Plot these curves on a semilog plot. How many time constants elapse as q falls from its maximum value at $t = 0$ to $1/2$, $1/4$, $1/10$ of the maximum?

16.3   Diodes

When a diode is on, its dynamic resistance, $\Delta V/\Delta I$, is, roughly, constant and relatively small. When a diode is off, its resistance is comparatively very large. The diode is a nonlinear device, in contrast to the resistor. The solid-state diodes, to which we refer, have two terminals, which are called the cathode and anode, for historical reasons. The diode is on if the anode is approximately 0.7 V more positive than the cathode. We consider our ideal diode to be either on or off. Because of the change in resistance with the change in direction of the applied voltage, the diode is frequently used as a rectifier, permitting current to flow in one direction but not the other.

Consider a circuit comprised of voltage source, diode, and resistor in series (see Fig. 16.8). The anode of the diode is connected to the positive terminal of the voltage source. If the source voltage, v_{in}, is greater than 0.7 V, the diode is on and current flows. If v_{in} is less than 0.7 V, the diode is off and no current flows. When there is no current, $iR = 0$ and $v_{out} = 0$. When $v_{in} > 0.7$ V, the voltage across the resistor is $v_{in} - 0.7$. So we can write

$$v_{outi} = \text{if}(v_{ini} > 0.7, v_{ini} - 0.7, 0).$$

The voltage across the diode itself, $v_{dioi} = v_{ini} - v_{outi}$. If $v_{out} = 0$, $v_{dio} = v_{in}$; that is, the entire voltage appears across the diode.

• •   For $v_{ini} = 3\sin(\omega t)$, sketch two cycles of the input and output voltages. Sketch two cycles of v_{outi} and v_{dioi} together.

• •   Load CIRC4, simple diode circuit: half-wave rectifier (see Fig. 16.9).

An input signal is specified. An if statement defines the output, the voltage across the resistor, of this diode circuit. The voltage across the diode is specified in terms of the input voltage and the voltage across the resistor.

In the first plot region, the input and output voltages are shown together. Why is the amplitude of the v_{out} curve always less than that of v_{in}?

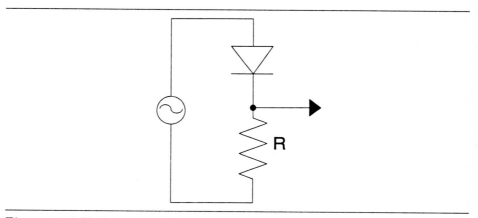

Figure 16.8 Half-wave rectifier circuit.

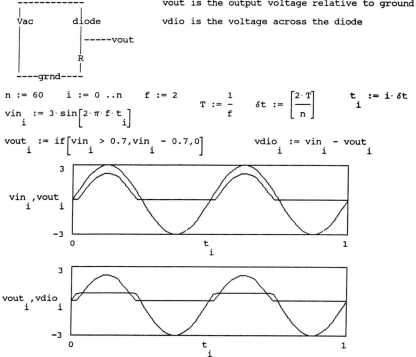

```
Circuit consists of ac source, diode, and resistor in series.   The cathode
of the diode is connected to the resistor.

    ------------                  vout is the output voltage relative to ground.
    |           |
    Vac         diode             vdio is the voltage across the diode
    |           |
    |           |-----vout
    |           |
    |           R
    |           |
    ----grnd----
```

$$n := 60 \qquad i := 0\ ..n \qquad f := 2 \qquad T := \frac{1}{f} \qquad \delta t := \left[\frac{2 \cdot T}{n}\right] \qquad t_i := i \cdot \delta t$$

$$vin_i := 3 \cdot sin\left[2 \cdot \pi \cdot f \cdot t_i\right]$$

$$vout_i := if\left[vin_i > 0.7, vin_i - 0.7, 0\right] \qquad vdio_i := vin_i - vout_i$$

Figure 16.9 CIRC4, simple diode circuit: half-wave rectifier.

Why is the v_{out} curve positive or zero, but never negative?

Explain the shape of the curve showing the voltage across the diode. Is there a portion of the curve for which v_{dio} and v_{out} are identical? Explain.

Examine the shapes of the v_{outi} and v_{dioi} curves. What will the sum of $v_{outi} + v_{dioi}$ look like? Verify your answer.

Predict how the plot will change if $v_{ini} = 1 \cdot sin(2\,\pi\,f\,t_i)$. Change the amplitude and verify your answer. What if the amplitude is 15?

This circuit is known as a half-wave rectifier; the output follows the input during half of the voltage cycle.

• •   A full-wave rectifier can be constructed with four diodes (see Fig. 16.10). When $v_{in} > 1.4$ V, both diodes D_1 and D_2 will turn on and current

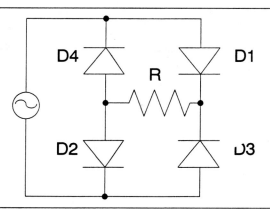

Figure 16.10 Full-wave rectifier: diode bridge.

will flow through R. When $v_{\text{in}} < -1.4\,\text{V}$, both diodes D_3 and D_4 will turn on and current will flow through R in the *same* direction as it did when $v_{\text{in}} > 1.4\,\text{V}$.

Change the v_{out} statement in CIRC4 so that it describes a full-wave rectifier. Two conditions are to be specified; therefore, two if statements (or a nested pair of if statements) are needed. The statement

$$v_{\text{out}\,i} = \text{if}(v_{\text{in}\,i} > 1.4, v_{\text{in}\,i} - 1.4, 0)$$

specifies one condition. Fill in the missing values for the second if statement:

$$v_{\text{out}\,i} = \text{if}(v_{\text{in}\,i} \quad , \quad , v_{\text{out}\,i}).$$

The second condition overrules part, but not all, of the specification of the first statement. Combine these two if statements into a single nested pair of if statements. Write these conditions with one if statement using the magnitude of v_{in}, $|v_{\text{in}\,i}|$.

For small signals, the loss in signal amplitude resulting from the voltage drop across the diode(s) may be unacceptable. In this case, the use of additional circuitry is required. An operational amplifier may be included to create a precision rectifier. This circuit compensates for the diode drop. Rectification by the diode still occurs, but the apparent voltage drop due to the diode becomes approximately zero instead of the 0.7 V that we see here.

If we add a capacitor to the original one-diode half-wave rectifier circuit, we can radically change the output of the circuit. Let the capacitor be in parallel with the resistor (see Fig. 16.11).

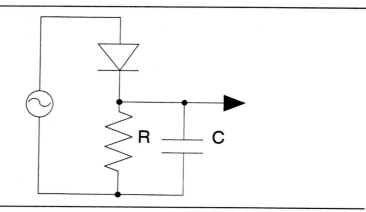

Figure 16.11 Half-wave rectifier with capacitor.

When the diode is on, the capacitor voltage rapidly follows the voltage across the resistor/capacitor pair, $(v_{\mathrm{in}i} - v_{\mathrm{dio}i})$. The capacitor voltage changes promptly because the resistance through which it must charge is small. However, when the diode is off, the capacitor can discharge through R. (It cannot discharge through the diode, because when the diode is off its resistance is very large.)

For an input voltage source that varies sinusoidally with time, an ac source, the capacitor charges during one half (approximately) the cycle and discharges in the other half. If the time constant RC is short compared to the period of oscillation of the voltage source, the capacitor discharges almost completely in each cycle. However, if the time constant is on the order of or several times greater than the period of oscillation of the input voltage source, then the capacitor discharges only a small fraction of its total charge before it is charged again.

The if statement for such a condition is slightly more complex than the previous case. The voltages at the two terminals of the diode are $v_{\mathrm{in}j}$ and $v_{\mathrm{c}j}$ (v_c and v_{out} are identical). If $v_{\mathrm{in}j} - v_{\mathrm{c}j} > 0.7\,\mathrm{V}$, the diode is on, and the voltage across the capacitor is the voltage applied. Otherwise, the capacitor discharges through the resistor R and the voltage decreases as

$$V = V_o\, e^{-t/RC}. \qquad (16.11)$$

However, because we are iterating this procedure in small steps it is convenient to approximate the exponential with

$$e^{-t/RC} \approx 1 - \frac{\delta t}{RC}. \qquad (16.12)$$

• •   Load CIRC5, half-wave rectifier plus capacitor; a simple dc power supply (see Fig. 16.12).

The first if statement reflects the discussion above. Either the diode is on and the voltage across the capacitor, which is the output voltage, follows the applied voltage or the diode is off and the capacitor discharges through the resistor.

Circuit consists of ac source, diode, and a parallel resistor and capacitor in series with the diode.

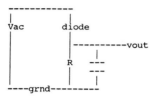

The voltage across the capacitor, vc, and the output voltage, vout, are identical.

$$n := 100 \quad i := 0 \,..\, n \quad f := 60 \quad T := \frac{1}{f} \quad \delta t := \frac{2 \cdot T}{n} \quad t_i := i \cdot \delta t$$

$$vin_i := 3 \cdot \sin\left[2 \cdot \pi \cdot f \cdot t_i\right] \qquad j := 0 \,..\, n - 1 \qquad vc_0 := 0$$

$$R := 2 \cdot 10^3 \qquad C := 10^{-5} \qquad R \cdot C = 0.02 \qquad T = 0.017 \qquad R \cdot C = 1.2 \cdot T$$

$$vc_{j+1} := if\left[vin_j - .7 > vc_j , vin_j - .7 , vc_j \cdot \left[1 - \frac{\delta t}{R \cdot C}\right]\right]$$

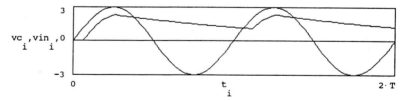

The output of a four diode bridge circuit with a capacitor in parallel with the resistor. Charging occurs twice as frequently.

$$vc_{j+1} := if\left[\left|vin_j\right| - 1.4 > vc_j , \left|vin_j\right| - 1.4 , vc_j \cdot \left[1 - \frac{\delta t}{R \cdot C}\right]\right]$$

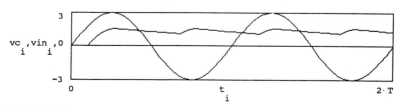

Figure 16.12 CIRC5, half-wave rectifier plus capacitor; a simple dc power supply.

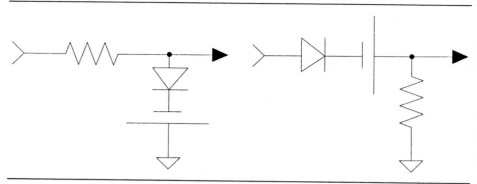

Figure 16.13 Diode clamps.

The initial values for R ($2\,\mathrm{k\Omega}$) and C ($10\,\mu\mathrm{F}$) result in a time constant slightly longer than the period of oscillation associated with the input signal. (The place marker is useful in expressing RC in terms of T.)

If R is increased from $2\,\mathrm{k\Omega}$ to $8\,\mathrm{k\Omega}$, how will the output curve change? Observe the output curve for a variety of R and C values and input voltages.

If $RC \approx$ several T, the output voltage is nearly constant. What is the approximate value of the dc output voltage when $R = 2\,\mathrm{k\Omega}$? When $R = 8\,\mathrm{k\Omega}$? How much current is drawn through the $8\,\mathrm{k\Omega}$ load resistor?

The second if statement specifies the output voltage for a four-diode full-wave bridge rectifier. In this case, charging occurs twice as frequently and the decay period is cut in half; thus the output is somewhat smoother.

For the case of the load resistor, R, having the value $2\,\mathrm{k\Omega}$, compare the "ripple" — that is, the difference between the maximum and minimum output voltages — for the two circuits?

• • Write appropriate if statements and show outputs for the diode circuits in Fig. 16.13. For each of these circuits, there are four permutations — two orientations for the diodes and two orientations for the battery.

16.4   Tunnel Diode Amplifier

The tunnel diode has the unusual property of local negative resistance over part of its operating range. Making use of this feature, an amplifier circuit can be created by assembling a voltage divider made up of a tunnel diode and a resistor (see Fig. 16.14).

Negative resistance means that for some range of voltages for an increase in voltage there is a corresponding decrease in current. This condition occurs for the tunnel diode over a small part of its operating range. To achieve amplification, the diode must be biased, made to operate, at least in part, in the negative resistance range of the tunnel diode (the bias sets the voltage point at which the diode operates when the signal voltage is zero).

• •   Load CIRC6, tunnel diode amplifier (see Figs. 16.15 and 16.16).

First recall the behavior of a normal resistor $(R = V/I = \delta V/\delta I)$. In a plot of current vs. voltage, the slope of the curve $(\delta I/\delta V)$ is the inverse of the resistance. If we were to specify $I(V)$, then the derivative of that function would be the inverse of the resistance, $dI/dV = \mathrm{inv}\,R(V)$, and $R(V) = \mathrm{inv}\,R(V)^{-1}$.

These operations are performed in the first section of the document. The current, the inverse of the resistance, and the resistance are plotted as a function of voltage. When the resistance of a resistor is evaluated in this way, it is a constant, identical to the originally specified value even though it is obtained here through the differentiation process.

If the slope of the curve increases, does this indicate an increase or decrease in resistance?

The same procedure is then followed for the tunnel diode. A prototypical characteristic curve, $i(v)$, a cubic expression, is shown. The derivative

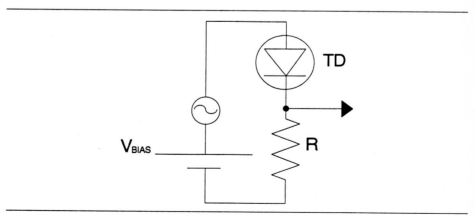

Figure 16.14 Tunnel diode amplifier.

Tunnel Diode   - characteristics.

Typical ohmic resistor - current voltage characteristics. Resistance determined from the inverse of the slope.

R := 2   I := 1   V := 0,0.2 ..5

$I(V) := \dfrac{V}{R}$ $invR(V) := \dfrac{d}{dV} I(V)$

$R(V) := invR(V)^{-1}$

invR(1) = 0.5   R(1) = 2

I(V),invR(V),R(V)

v := 0,0.1 ..3

Tunnel diode - current voltage characteristics and effective resistance

$i(v) := v^3 - 4 \cdot v^2 + 4.2 \cdot v$ $invr(v) := \dfrac{d}{dv} i(v)$ $r(v) := invr(v)^{-1}$

V := 1   a := root(invr(V),V)   a = 0.719

V := 2   b := root(invr(V),V)   b = 1.948

V := 1.5 $c := root\left[\dfrac{d}{dV} invr(V),V\right]$ c = 1.333

i(v),invr(v),0,invr(v),invr(v)

v,v,v,a,b

i(v),r(v),0

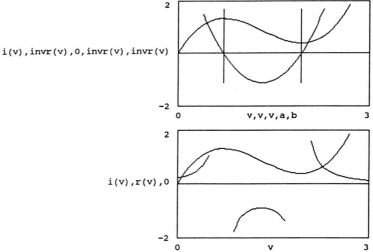

Figure 16.15 CIRC6, tunnel diode amplifier. (See the next figure for the rest of the document.)

yields the inverse of the dynamic resistance, invr(v); the dynamic resistance is determined by taking the inverse.

To determine the range over which the resistance is negative, we determine those voltage values where the slope of the characteristic curve, i(v),

Tunnel diode amplifier

Input signal - dc component $v_{dc} := 1$

ac component $\omega := 5000$ $T := 2 \cdot \pi \cdot \omega^{-1}$ $\delta t := T \cdot .05$ $t := 0, \delta t \,..\, 2 \cdot T$

$v_{sig}(t) := 0.1 \cdot \sin(\omega \cdot t)$

Input signal. $vin(t) := v_{dc} + v_{sig}(t)$ $R := 0.8$

Output signal.   Form is the same as that of a two resistance voltage divider.

$$vout(t) := \frac{R}{R + r(vin(t))} \cdot vin(t)$$

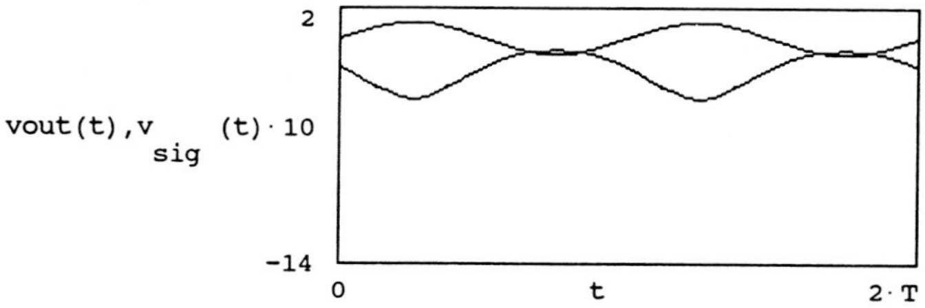

$vout(t), v_{sig}(t) \cdot 10$

Figure 16.16 CIRC6 *continued*

is zero. These points mark the transition between positive and negative resistance. We also calculate the voltage at which the negative resistance is a maximum. Keep these three values — a, b, and c — in mind when changing the bias voltage. How does the resistance vary as the voltage increases from a and b? From b and c?

We plot the characteristic curve, and the derivative, $invr(v)$. The edges of the negative resistance region are marked. Examine the slope of the characteristic curve and compare it with the plot of the derivative. Note where the $invr(v)$ curve is positive and where it is negative; these also indicate the same areas of positive and negative resistance (taking an inverse does not change the sign).

In the second plot region, the $i(v)$ curve is plotted again, together with $r(v)$. Examine the resistance curve in detail. Explain the shape of the curve, qualitatively.

So far, this is all characteristics (just the properties of the tunnel diode), no amplifier circuit. Now construct a voltage divider circuit with the tunnel diode in place of one of the resistors. Include as the voltage source both an adjustable dc voltage supply (the bias voltage) and an ac signal source.

According to our study of voltage dividers, the output from this voltage divider circuit is, as we have seen,

$$v_{\text{out}} = \frac{R}{R + r_{td}} \cdot v_{\text{in}}, \qquad (16.13)$$

where the tunnel diode resistance has been substituted for one of the resistances. The input signal is the sum of the dc bias voltage and the ac signal voltage. If

$$v_{\text{dc}} + |v_{\text{sig}}| < a \qquad \text{or if} \qquad v_{\text{dc}} - |v_{\text{sig}}| > b,$$

then the negative resistance region is avoided and there is no amplification. However, if

$$v_{\text{dc}} + |v_{\text{sig}}| < b \qquad \text{and} \qquad v_{\text{dc}} - |v_{\text{sig}}| > a,$$

then the circuit is operating entirely within the negative resistance region and amplification will occur. The operating range need only be partly within the negative resistance range for some amplification to occur. As the resistance is dependent on voltage, so is the amplification. Consequently, signals at different voltages will be amplified to different degrees and distortion will occur.

Let the signal voltage be relatively small, with an amplitude of 0.1 V, for example. Let the bias voltage take on a sequence of values. The voltage applied to the diode ranges between the values $v_{\text{dc}} \pm |v_{\text{sig}}|$. Observe the change in character of the output voltage as seen in the sequence of plots as v_{dc} starts at 0.5 V and increases in steps of 0.1 V. Keep in mind the values a, b, and c and the tunnel diode resistance as these changes occur. Cover the voltage range from a to c. Adjust the multiplier of v_{sig}, in the plot region, so that the plotted amplitudes of the input and output signals are roughly the same.

At what point is the gain of the amplifier (ratio of output and input signals) the greatest? When the voltage b is within the extremes of the input signal, why does the output appear as it does? Compare output signals when the maximum of the input is just less than b, and when the minimum of the input is just greater than b. Explain the difference.

Unfortunately, tunnel diodes are difficult to use and consequently are not common circuit elements. However, the concepts of characteristic curve, bias voltage, amplification, and distortion are general.

Back off man, I'm a scientist.

Ghostbusters

CHAPTER
17

Optics

In this chapter, we take a close look at Snell's law of refraction, consider refraction from the point of view of Fermat's principle of least time, and consider the case where the index of refraction varies continuously within a medium. Because the law of refraction informs us of angles but does not give us any information about the relative intensities of the refracted and reflected beams, we take a quick look at the Fresnel equations.

We describe refraction in terms of light rays that travel in straight lines within a uniform medium. This description is legitimate if the smallest dimension of an object presented to the incident radiation is very much greater than the wavelength of that radiation. If this condition is fulfilled, diffraction effects can be ignored.

We then examine the interference of electromagnetic radiation in Young's two-slit experiment. The summing of phasors is considered, as is the problem of interference from a series of slits. The problem of single-slit diffraction is treated, and finally the ability to resolve source is considered. The Rayleigh criterion is explored. Radiation patterns from several sources close together are presented in exercises dealing with subtracting lines from a composite.

17.1   Refraction

In section 2.4, on curve fitting, we examined some data associated with incident and refracted light passing from air to water. Comparing the data with Snell's law, we obtained a best fit value for the index of refraction. Snell's law can be stated as

$$n_1 \sin(\theta_1) = n_2 \sin(\theta_2), \tag{17.1}$$

where the angles θ_1 and θ_2 are measured from the normal to the interface between the two media characterized by their indices of refraction, n_1 and n_2. Expressed in terms of velocities, the index of refraction is

$$n = \frac{c}{v}, \tag{17.2}$$

where c is the speed of light in a vacuum and v is the velocity of light in the medium with index n. The law is sometimes specified with one index, for example, n_{21}, which is the index of refraction of medium 2 relative to medium 1.

$$n_{21} = \frac{n_2}{n_1} = \frac{v_1}{v_2}. \tag{17.3}$$

Typical values of n range from 1 to 1.7.

• •   Plot the velocity of light in a medium vs. n, as n ranges over the values suggested. By what percent does the velocity change for the values of n considered?

• •   Load OPT1, Snell's law of refraction (see Figs. 17.1 and 17.2).

Snell's law is straightforward, yet important enough that it should be explored. In the document, the x-axis is the interface between two different optical media. The index of refraction is n_1 when $y > 0$ and n_2 when $y < 0$. The angle of incidence is θ_1 and the angle of refraction is θ_2. Both angles are measured from the normal.

Enter values for n_1 and n_2 . Observe the value for θ_{1MAX}. Enter a value for θ_1 where $|\theta_1| < |\theta_{1MAX}|$. This restriction depends on the critical angle, which we will discuss later.

Of all the code after the assignment of n_1, n_2, and θ_1, the calculation of θ_2 is pertinent; θ_2 is the refracted angle. The purpose of the rest of the code is to set up the details of the figure — the incident and refracted rays and the arcs indicating the incident and refracted angles. Some scaling is set up so that the rays will have appropriate relative lengths. Limits for the plot region are also specified so that the ratio of height to width remains constant.

Snell's law.

Enter values for n1, n2, and θ1, the angle of incidence.
The magnitude of θ1 cannot be greater than the magnitude of θ1_MAX.

$n1 \equiv 1$ $\qquad$ $n2 \equiv 1.6$ $\qquad\qquad$ $\theta1\_MAX \equiv if\left[n1 > n2, asin\left[\dfrac{n2}{n1}\right], \dfrac{\pi}{2}\right]$ $\qquad$ $rad \equiv 1$

$\theta1\_MAX \equiv 90 \cdot deg$ $\qquad\qquad\qquad\qquad\qquad\qquad\qquad\qquad\qquad\qquad\qquad deg \equiv \dfrac{\pi}{180} \cdot rad$

$\theta1 \equiv 45 \cdot deg$ $\quad$ $|\theta1| < |\theta1\_MAX|$ $\quad$ $x_1 \equiv tan(\theta1)$ $\quad$ $y_1 \equiv 1$ $\quad$ $y_3 \equiv -y_1$

$\theta2 \equiv asin\left[\dfrac{n1}{n2} \cdot sin(\theta1)\right]$

$\qquad\qquad\qquad\qquad x_3 \equiv |y_3| \cdot tan(|\theta2|) \cdot \dfrac{-x_1}{|x_1|}$ $\qquad$ $f \equiv 1$

$\theta2 = 26.228 \cdot deg$ $\qquad\qquad\qquad\qquad\qquad\qquad\qquad\qquad\qquad\quad i \equiv 1 \mathbin{..} 3$

given

$$\left[x_3^2 + y_3^2\right]^{0.5} \cdot f \approx \left[x_1^2 + y_1^2\right]^{0.5} \qquad f := find(f) \qquad f = 1.269$$

$$x_3 := f \cdot x_3 \qquad y_3 := f \cdot y_3$$

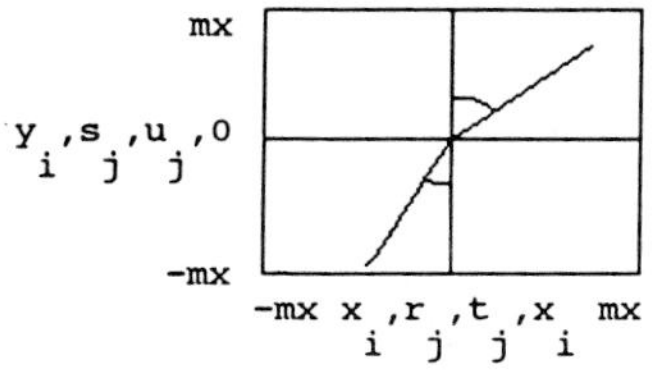

More information needed to draw the figure.

$mxx \equiv if\left[\left[|x_1| > |x_3|\right], |x_1|, |x_3|\right]$ $\qquad\qquad$ $mx \equiv if\left[mxx > y_1, mxx, y_1\right] \cdot 1.35$

$m \equiv 5$ $\qquad\qquad\qquad$ $step1 \equiv \dfrac{\theta1}{m}$ $\qquad step2 \equiv \dfrac{\theta2}{m}$ $\quad j \equiv 0 \mathbin{..} m$

$\qquad\qquad\qquad\qquad\qquad\qquad\qquad\qquad\qquad\qquad step2 = 0.092$

$\phi_j \equiv \left[angle\left[x_1, y_1\right] + step1 \cdot j\right]$ $\qquad\qquad \tau_j \equiv \dfrac{3 \cdot \pi}{2} - step2 \cdot j$ $\qquad R \equiv \dfrac{mx}{3}$

$r_j \equiv R \cdot cos\left[\phi_j\right]$ $\quad$ $s_j \equiv R \cdot sin\left[\phi_j\right]$ $\quad$ $t_j \equiv R \cdot cos\left[\tau_j\right]$ $\quad$ $u_j \equiv R \cdot sin\left[\tau_j\right]$

Figure 17.1 OPT1, Snell's law of refraction. (See the next figure for the rest of the document.)

Sometimes, it is possible to bring only the most pertinent regions to the beginning of a document and place all the computation at the end. To do this, you must make use of the global equality. However, you cannot make a solve block global.

It may be convenient to move the θ_1 region near the plot region; the global equality permits this. It may also be desirable to move the n_1 and n_2 regions. Change the assignment to global if this is done.

Try a series of angles, large and small; consider different refraction indices, including the cases of $n_1 > n_2$ and $n_2 > n_1$.

The refracted angle in terms of the incident angle. The derivative points
out how rapidly the refracted angle changes compared to the incident angle.

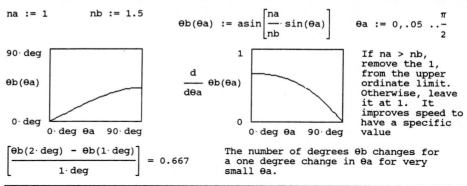

$na := 1$ $nb := 1.5$

$\theta b(\theta a) := asin\left[\dfrac{na}{nb} \cdot sin(\theta a)\right]$ $\theta a := 0, .05 \,.. \dfrac{\pi}{2}$

If na > nb,
remove the 1,
from the upper
ordinate limit.
Otherwise, leave
it at 1. It
improves speed to
have a specific
value

$\left[\dfrac{\theta b(2 \cdot deg) - \theta b(1 \cdot deg)}{1 \cdot deg}\right] = 0.667$

The number of degrees θb changes for
a one degree change in θa for very
small θa.

Figure 17.2 OPT1 *continued.*

If medium 2 is glass with $n_2 = 1.5$ and if medium 1 is air with $n_1 = 1$, observe the case of $\theta_1 = 45°$. Now pour water, $n = 1.33$, on top of the glass so that the air is replaced with water. With θ_1 the same, how does θ_2 change?

With $n_1 = 1.48$ and $n_2 = 1.5$, examine the case for $\theta_1 = 10°, 40°, 70°$, and $89°$. (We will want to recall this result later in the chapter.)

A change in θ_1, $\delta\theta_1$, results in a change in θ_2 of $\delta\theta_2$. $\delta\theta_2/\delta\theta_1$ depends on the value of θ_1. For the case $n_1 < n_2$, does $\delta\theta_2/\delta\theta_1$ increase or decrease as θ_1 increases from smaller to larger angles?

Now move to the remainder of the document. We refer to media 1 and 2 as *a* and *b* just to keep the names distinct. (This is not strictly necessary unless, after this portion of the document, you wished to refer to the quantities in the first part of the document.)

Snell's law is written in functional form. Indices and a range of incident angles are specified. The refracted angle is plotted as a function of the incident angle. The derivative of this function, the change in the refracted angle relative to the incident angle, is also plotted vs. the incident angle.

As θ_a goes from 0° to 90°, we see at once the range of angles spanned by θ_b. It is also interesting that the slope of this curve is greatest for small angles.

Let $n_a = 1.49$ and $n_b = 1.5$. Examine the same curves.

For a ray originating in the medium of larger index of refraction, the angle of refraction is larger than the angle of incidence. If the angle of refraction is 90°, then the incident angle is the critical angle.

Define the critical angle $\theta_c(n_a, n_b)$. Let $n_a = 1$ and let n_b take on a range of values from 1.1 to 1.9 in steps of 0.1. Plot the critical angle as a function of the index of refraction n_b. Let $n_a = 1.33$ and $n_b = 1.4, \ldots, 1.9$. Plot $\theta_c(n_a, n_b)$ vs. n_b.

17.1.1   *Fermat's Principle of Least Time*

Fermat's principle of least time states that the path taken by a beam of light between any pair of points is that path which takes the least time.

• •   Load OPT2, Fermat: least time (see Fig. 17.3).

To test this conjecture, two points, (x_1, y_1) and (x_2, y_2), are selected on either side of an interface. A series of x-values intermediate between the values of x_1 and x_2 are selected along the interface, and the time is determined from point 1 to the particular point on the interface, $t_1(x)$, and from that point to point 2, $t_2(x)$. The two times are summed, $t(x)$. Plots of these times vs. x are shown. The position for which the minimum time occurs is determined using the root/derivative procedure. Finally, the time corresponding to that x-location for the minimum is determined.

To verify that the location is in correspondence with Snell's law, we determine the angles of incidence and refraction, θ_1 and θ_2, in terms of the x- and y-values of the three points involved. Values of $n_1 \cdot \sin(\theta_1)$ and $n_2 \cdot \sin(\theta_2)$ are then compared. (Given the number of different numerical processes, the agreement is quite good.)

Explain how the angles θ_1 and θ_2 are determined.

Finally, we plot the path for the minimum time.

Try a series of values for x_1 and x_2 ($x_1 \neq x_2$), and for n_1 and n_2. (As the problem is set up, $y_1 > 0$ and $y_2 < 0$.)

If n_1 is fixed and n_2 is increased, how will the point on the interface move? Explain why in terms of velocities.

• •   Perform a similar calculation to show that the reflection process is also one of least time. Show that the least time is consistent with the law of reflection, where the angle of incidence equals the angle of reflection. Within one medium, is minimum distance an equally good rule?

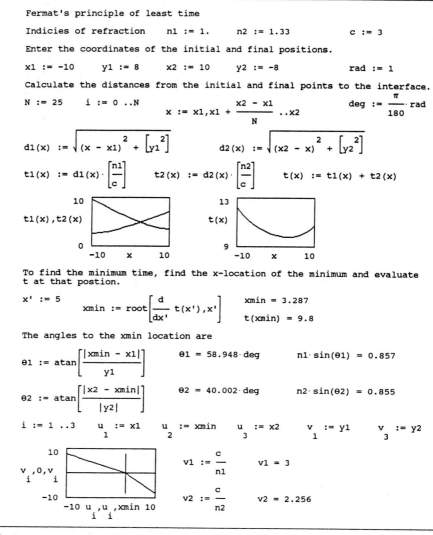

Fermat's principle of least time

Indicies of refraction   n1 := 1.   n2 := 1.33   c := 3

Enter the coordinates of the initial and final positions.

x1 := -10   y1 := 8   x2 := 10   y2 := -8   rad := 1

Calculate the distances from the initial and final points to the interface.

N := 25   i := 0 ..N $x := x1, x1 + \dfrac{x2 - x1}{N} ..x2$ $deg := \dfrac{\pi}{180} \cdot rad$

$d1(x) := \sqrt{(x - x1)^2 + \left[y1^2\right]}$ $d2(x) := \sqrt{(x2 - x)^2 + \left[y2^2\right]}$

$t1(x) := d1(x) \cdot \left[\dfrac{n1}{c}\right]$ $t2(x) := d2(x) \cdot \left[\dfrac{n2}{c}\right]$ $t(x) := t1(x) + t2(x)$

To find the minimum time, find the x-location of the minimum and evaluate t at that postion.

x' := 5 $xmin := root\left[\dfrac{d}{dx'} t(x'), x'\right]$ xmin = 3.287

                                              t(xmin) = 9.8

The angles to the xmin location are

$\theta 1 := atan\left[\dfrac{|xmin - x1|}{y1}\right]$ $\theta 1 = 58.948 \cdot deg$ $n1 \cdot sin(\theta 1) = 0.857$

$\theta 2 := atan\left[\dfrac{|x2 - xmin|}{|y2|}\right]$ $\theta 2 = 40.002 \cdot deg$ $n2 \cdot sin(\theta 2) = 0.855$

$i := 1 ..3$ $u_1 := x1$ $u_2 := xmin$ $u_3 := x2$ $v_1 := y1$ $v_3 := y2$

$v1 := \dfrac{c}{n1}$ v1 = 3

$v2 := \dfrac{c}{n2}$ v2 = 2.256

Figure 17.3 OPT2, Fermat: least time.

As stated, Fermat's principle is not strictly correct. The path is not necessarily a minimum. It is an extremum and has a stationary value. It could be a maximum, a minimum, or even a point of inflection where the tangent is horizontal.

For example, locate at the foci of an elliptical mirror the two points between which the rays travel; all paths are equal in distance and time. Adjacent points contribute similarly to the reflection. It is also possible to construct a mirror with such curvature that the point of reflection is a maximum time.

Fermat's principle is similar to the concept of least action in mechanics. Fermat's principle can be written

$$\delta \int \frac{ds}{v}. \tag{17.4}$$

This is an extremum. The extremum of the integral of kinetic energy minus potential energy can be reduced to

$$\delta \int v\, ds. \tag{17.5}$$

This, too, is an extremum.

17.1.2   *Refraction in an Inhomogeneous Medium*

In inhomogeneous media, the index of refraction of a substance may change gradually with position. Optical examples where such a change can be observed include the "wet road" effect and rays from the sun at sunset. Earthquake waves are subject to similar behavior.

• •   Load OPT3, refraction in an inhomogeneous medium (see Fig. 17.4).

Consider a medium in which the index of refraction decreases with depth. We approximate this medium with a series of slabs: The index of refraction is constant within one slab; the index varies from one slab to the next. The index, in this case, is described by

$$n(y) = n_0 + \delta n \cdot \frac{y}{d}, \tag{17.6}$$

where y is incremented in steps of d, the thickness of the slabs of constant index.

A ray is directed downward into the medium; the incident angle is θ_1. Snell's law is applied at the interface between successive slabs. Recall from the OPT1 study of Snell's law that when the indices are close (for example, 1.48 and 1.5), the bending at most angles is slight. As the index decreases with depth, the refraction angle increases. The refracted angle at one interface is the incident angle at the next. Thus, as the ray descends, the incident angle continue to increase.

This computation process stops at the critical angle. Snell's law states that $\sin(\theta_2) = (n_1 / n_2) \cdot \sin(\theta_1)$. When $(n_1 / n_2) \cdot \sin(\theta_1) \geq 1$, or, for the until statement, when $1 - n_1 / n_2 \sin(\theta_1)$ goes negative, the critical angle has been reached and the process stops.

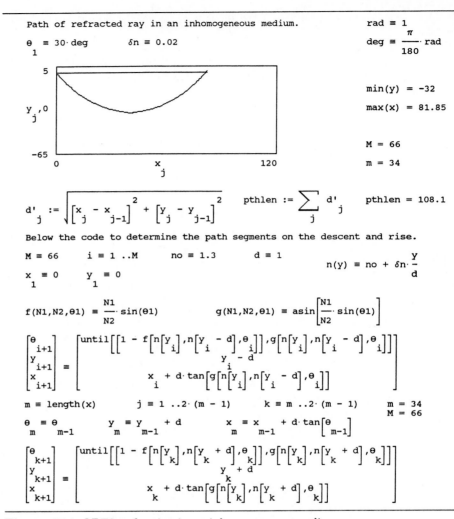

Figure 17.4 OPT3, refraction in an inhomogeneous medium.

At this point the ray is reflected, the angle ($\theta_m = \theta_{m-1}$) and then the process reverses, and the ray returns to the surface. At each step x is incremented by

$$\delta x = d \cdot \tan(refraction\ angle).$$

The incident angle, θ_1, can take on values between $1°$ and $75°$. The iteration range M should be greater than or equal to the number of steps m to reach the critical angle, otherwise reflection will occur before the critical angle is reached.

Process the document.

Plot $n(y_i)$ vs. y_i. Use plot type s. Is the radius of curvature of the path smaller in regions of larger n or smaller n?

At what angle does the ray penetrate the deepest?

At what angle does the ray traverse the largest distance in the x-direction? Explore this region carefully (use steps of 1°); there is a surprise here.

At what angle is the path length the ray follows the greatest?

17.2   Fresnel Equations: Intensity of Reflected and Refracted Rays

A ray incident on an interface will be partly reflected and partly transmitted. The angle of the transmitted ray is given by Snell's law. The amplitudes of the reflected and transmitted rays are given by the Fresnel equations. The intensities are related to the squares of the amplitudes. These equations can be derived from Maxwell's equations. The equations themselves are not difficult, but they are sufficiently complicated that their form is not immediately obvious.

The equations for the reflection and transmission coefficient are

$$R_p = \left(\frac{(n_1 \cos(\theta_1) - n_2 \cos(\theta_2))}{(n_1 \cos(\theta_1) + n_2 \cos(\theta_2))} \right)^2 \tag{17.7}$$

$$T_p = \frac{n_2 \cos(\theta_2)}{n_1 \cos(\theta_1)} \left(\frac{2 \, n_1 \cos(\theta_1)}{(n_1 \cos(\theta_1) + n_2 \cos(\theta_2))} \right)^2 \tag{17.8}$$

$$R_l = \left(\frac{(n_2 \cos(\theta_1) - n_1 \cos(\theta_2))}{(n_1 \cos(\theta_2) + n_2 \cos(\theta_2))} \right)^2 \tag{17.9}$$

$$T_l = \frac{n_2 \cos(\theta_2)}{n_1 \cos(\theta_1)} \left(\frac{2 \, n_1 \cos(\theta_1)}{(n_1 \cos(\theta_2) + n_2 \cos(\theta_2))} \right)^2 , \tag{17.10}$$

where p and l refer to the perpendicular and parallel polarizations, respectively, of the electric field vector; vectors that represent the incident, reflected, and transmitted rays lie in a plane — parallel polarization, for example, means that the electric field vector is parallel to this plane.

• •   Load OPT4, Fresnel equations (see Fig. 17.5).

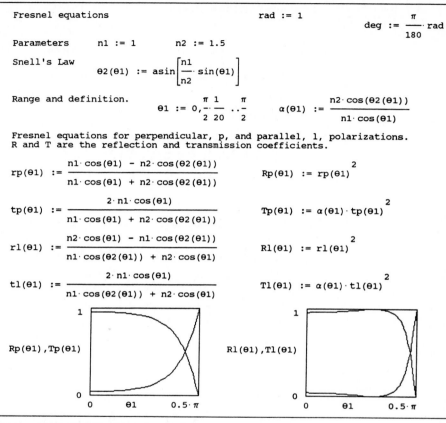

Figure 17.5 OPT4, Fresnel equations.

Here, θ_2 is the refracted angle as determined by Snell's law, in terms of the incident angle. The reflection, R, and transmission, T, coefficients indicate the fraction of the incident energy that is either reflected or transmitted.

Snell's law permits the expression of θ_2 in terms of θ_1. The equations are written as functions of θ_1. The perpendicular and parallel cases are plotted separately. Examine the curves for various values of n.

In the case of R_l, the reflection coefficient is zero at one point. This angle is Brewster's angle. Determine Brewster's angle using the root/derivative method.

When θ_1 equals Brewster's angle, what is θ_2? At this angle, what is the sum of θ_1 and θ_2? (Polarized sunglasses are especially useful near this angle, because they are designed to absorb the perpendicular polarization.)

Find the angle at which the reflected and transmitted rays carry the same energy. Do this for both the parallel and perpendicular polarizations. Examine the dependence on n.

For unpolarized incident radiation, the total reflection coefficient, R, and the total transmission coefficient, T, are the averages of the perpendicular and parallel coefficients. Define and plot these coefficients R and T.

How do the R and T curves change as n_2 takes on smaller and larger values (for example, $n = 1.2$ or $n = 1.9$)?

Plot the amplitudes r_p, t_p vs. θ_1 and r_l, t_l vs. θ_1.

For an air-glass ($n = 1.5$) interface and unpolarized incident radiation, for what range of incident angles in air does the refracted ray have 80% or more of the incident energy? 70%? 50%?

17.3   Interference

Radiation from a coherent source (for example, laser light) is incident upon a pair of rectangular slits. The radiation is diffracted as it passes through each slit. In effect, each slit acts as a source of coherent radiation. Radiation from the slits that arrives at a particular point interferes. The electric field vectors of the two waves superpose. That is, the net electric field at some point, P, is the sum of the individual electric fields, which in general have a nonzero phase difference between them. At point P, the electric fields from the two slits can be written

$$E_1 = E_0 \sin(\omega t + \phi_1) \qquad \text{and} \qquad E_2 = E_0 \sin(\omega t + \phi_2).$$

The phase difference between the two waves depends on the path difference between the slits and the point P. Let the distance between slit 1 and point P be S_{1P} and the distance between slit 2 and point P be S_{2P}. The path difference, $\delta p = S_{1P} - S_{2P}$, is related to the phase difference $\delta \phi$ between the two waves as

$$\frac{\delta \phi}{2\pi} = \frac{\delta p}{\lambda}. \tag{17.11}$$

If $\delta p / \lambda$ has an integral value, then there is constructive interference. If $\delta p / \lambda$ has an odd half integral value, then there is destructive interference.

The standard arrangement for Young's two-slit experiment are: (1) The planes containing the slits and the viewing screen are parallel; (2) The slit separation is d; the distance between the planes containing the slits and the screen is D; $D \gg d \gg \lambda$; (3) In the viewing plane, distances are measured along a line perpendicular to the orientation of the slits; (4) The observation distance is y; the observation angle θ is equal to $\tan^{-1}(y/D)$.

Given these conditions, the path difference, δp, can be written

$$\delta p = d \sin(\theta),$$

and the interference conditions for constructive interference can be written

$$\frac{\delta p}{\lambda} = \frac{d \sin(\theta)}{\lambda} = m \qquad (17.12)$$

where $m = 0, 1, 2, \ldots$. For destructive interference we have

$$\frac{\delta p}{\lambda} = \frac{d \sin(\theta)}{\lambda} = m + \frac{1}{2} \qquad (17.13)$$

where $m = 0, 1, 2, \ldots$.

• •   In a carefully laid out Young's two-slit experiment, a peak can be located to the nearest 0.3 mm. In this case, $\lambda = 5 \cdot 10^{-7}$ m, $d = 10^{-4}$ m, and $D = 4$ m. (If you wish to use units for this example, define the meter to be mt; m is the traditional symbol for the order of interference, and n is tied up as the index of refraction.)

Define $y(m)$ to be the y-location on the screen of the maxima, associated with constructive interference, of order m. Take into account both the sine and tangent functions as needed; do not use the small-angle approximation. Define a second function $y'(m)$ locating the maxima as a function of m, only in this case use the small-angle approximation.

Plot $y(m)$ vs. m and plot $y(m) - y'(m)$ vs. m as $m = 1, \ldots, 30$. At what value of m is the difference between $y(m)$ and $y'(m)$ equal to 0.3 mm? What is the spacing between successive orders for small m? How does this spacing depend on d? If d were reduced to $5 \cdot 10^{-5}$ m (in MathCAD use mt), would the difference between $y(m)$ and $y'(m)$ be apparent at lower, higher, or unchanged values of m?

• •   Using the equations for E_1 and E_2 at the beginning of this section, define the terms and plot a few cycles of $E_1 + E_2$. Let $\phi_1 = 0$. Let ϕ_2 successively take on the values 0, π, 2π. Which phase angles correspond to constructive and destructive interference?

Knowing that

$$\sin(\alpha) + \sin(\beta) = 2 \sin\left(\frac{\alpha + \beta}{2}\right) \cos\left(\frac{\alpha - \beta}{2}\right), \qquad (17.14)$$

show that $E_1 + E_2$ can be written

$$2\, E_0 \cos\left(\frac{\phi_1 - \phi_2}{2}\right) \sin\left(\omega t + \frac{\phi_1 + \phi_2}{2}\right). \qquad (17.15)$$

What are the amplitude and phase angle of this sum? Plot this function and verify that this form and the form plotted by adding E_1 and E_2 directly are equivalent.

With a larger number of similar vectors, it is still possible to write the sum as the product of a phase-related term and a time-dependent term.

To calculate the intensities, it is necessary to know whether the radiation is coherent or incoherent. For coherent radiation, the vector sum of the individual amplitudes is determined and this resultant amplitude is squared. This value is proportional to the intensity. Because of phase differences, the intensity at a particular point can be less than that produced by any of the individual sources.

For incoherent radiation, the individual amplitudes are squared. These squared amplitudes are then added; this sum is proportional to the intensity. In this case, the intensity at a point cannot be less than that produced by any individual source.

• •   Plot the intensity associated with E_1, with E_2, and with the sum $E_1 + E_2$. For the case $\phi_1 = 0$ and $\phi_2 = \pi$, how does the intensity of E_1 or E_2 compare with the intensity of the sum? Where is the energy?

When we observe the interference pattern from the two-slit experiment, for example, we observe the intensity not as a function of time but as a function of position. Our eyes, and most other light-sensitive devices, are incapable of observing the time variation of rapidly fluctuating signals — they detect an average.

• •   Verify that the average of $\sin^2(\theta)$ over one cycle is $1/2$. Let MathCAD perform the integration for you.

The intensity is proportional to the square of the amplitude, so we have

$$I \propto (2\, E_0)^2 \cos^2\left(\frac{\phi_1 - \phi_2}{2}\right) \sin^2\left(\omega\, t + \frac{\phi_1 + \phi_2}{2}\right)$$

$$I_{\text{av}} = I_0 \cos^2\left(\frac{\phi_1 - \phi_2}{2}\right) \qquad \text{and} \qquad I_0 \propto (2\, E_0)^2.$$

The phase difference is related to the path difference by

$$\delta\phi = \frac{2\pi}{\lambda}\, d\sin(\theta),\qquad(17.16)$$

so we can rewrite

$$I_{av} = I_0 \cos^2\left(\frac{\pi\, d\sin(\theta)}{\lambda}\right).\qquad(17.17)$$

It is frequently convenient to define an angle α:

$$\alpha = \frac{\pi\, d\sin(\theta)}{\lambda} = \frac{k\, d}{2}\sin(\theta)$$

and express the average intensity as

$$I_{av} = I_0 \cos^2(\alpha).\qquad(17.18)$$

•• Plot I_{av} vs. $d\sin(\theta)$ as $d\sin(\theta)$ goes from $-2.5\,\lambda$ to $2.5\,\lambda$. (Remember this example when we approach this problem in the next chapter using the fast Fourier transform.)

17.3.1 Phasors

Visualize E_1 in terms of a rotating vector. A vector of magnitude E_0 rotates counterclockwise about the origin. The angle between the positive x-axis and the vector is $\theta_p = \omega t + \phi$. The projection of this phasor, this rotating vector, on the y-axis (the vector's y-component) represents E_1. This is consistent with our description $E_1 = E_0 \sin(\omega t + \phi_1)$. We can represent E_2 similarly. The phase difference between the two vectors, $\phi_2 - \phi_1$, is independent of time. Consequently, as the two vectors rotate, they are always separated by the same angle, their phase difference. If we form the vector sum of E_1 and E_2 at $t = 0$ and allow the resultant to rotate, the y-projection is the same as the sum of the projections of the two individual vectors.

Associated with the two-slit experiment would be two phasors. For a series of n slits, there would be n phasors. If the slits are uniformly spaced, the phase difference between successive phasors would be the same. We consider the case of uniformly spaced slits (constant phase difference).

•• Load OPT5, phasor sums (see Fig. 17.6).

The number of phasors, N, is, for example, equal to the number of rectangular slits illuminated by the source. We assume that the phasors are all of the same magnitude. The phase difference between successive phasors is ϕ.

Calculate the amplitude for a given number of phasors at a specified phase angle.

(N and θ are entered near the plot.)

The number of phasors to be summed. $n := 1 ..N$

Enter the phase angle. $rad \equiv 1$

$$deg \equiv \frac{\pi}{180} \cdot rad$$

$$X_0 := 0 \qquad Y_0 := 0$$

Calculate the components. $r := 1$

$$x_n := r \cdot \cos((n-1) \cdot \phi) \qquad y_n := r \cdot \sin((n-1) \cdot \phi)$$

Calculate the location of the ends of each successive phasor.

$$X_n := X_{n-1} + x_n \qquad Y_n := Y_{n-1} + y_n \qquad m := 0 ..N$$

To draw the resultant, draw from the beginning to the end.

$$k := 0 ..1 \qquad RX_1 := X_N \qquad RY_1 := Y_N$$

$$RM := \left[RX_1^2 + RY_1^2 \right]^{0.5} \qquad mx := if(max(X) > max(Y), max(X), max(Y)) \cdot 1.1$$

Make the plot square.

$N \equiv 3 \qquad \phi \equiv 40 \cdot deg \qquad RM = 2.532$

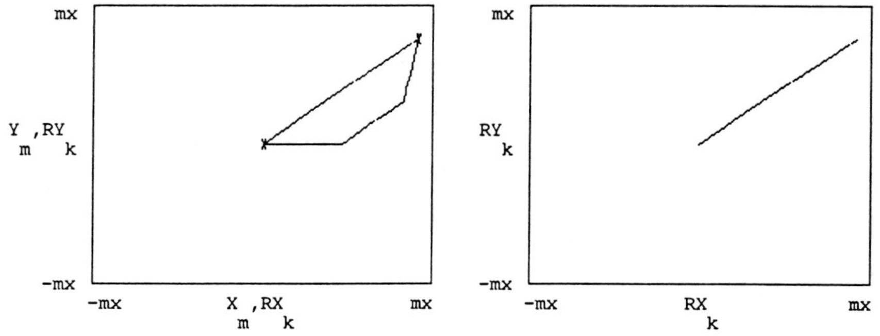

Figure 17.6 OPT5, phasor sums.

Let $N = 2$. Let ϕ take on the values 0°, 45°, 90°, 135°, 180°. Notice that the magnitude of the resultant RM changes as the phase angle changes. Where is RM a maximum? A minimum? Let ϕ equal 225° and 360°. Make a rough plot, by hand, of the amplitude RM vs. ϕ (save this for comparison when looking at OPT6). The intensity is proportional to the square of the resultant.

Let $N = 3$. What is the maximum amplitude? At what phase angle does the first minimum occur? Demonstrate. At what phase angle will the next maximum occur? What is the amplitude of this maximum as compared to the maximum at $\phi = 0$? Record this value.

Find the next minimum and next maximum. What are the phase angles?

Let $N = 10$. Let $\phi = 5°$. What is the maximum possible amplitude with $N = 10$? At what phase angle will the first minimum occur? Demonstrate. Where will the next maximum occur? What is its amplitude? Record the value. Verify that you have the correct angle by increasing and decreasing the phase angle in steps of 1°; watch RM for the value of the magnitude. Is the maximum exactly where you thought it would be? Now find the last maximum before $\phi = 360°$. Record the magnitude. Let $\phi = 180°$. Compare the magnitudes of the maxima.

• •   Load OPT6, amplitude vs. angle for an N-phasor system (see Fig. 17.7).

In OPT6, phasors are summed at a series of angles. The phasors are not shown, only the sums. This document is computation intensive, so be patient with large values of N.

Let $N = 2$ (near plot region with global equality). Observe the plot structure and compare it with the hand plot you made for $N = 2$ in OPT5. The peaks are of equal amplitude and of magnitude N.

Let $N = 3$. At what angles do the maxima occur? What is the magnitude of the maximum occurring at $\phi = 180°$? Refer to your notes from OPT5 for comparison.

Where do the minima occur? Express the phase difference for destructive interference between adjacent slits in terms of π and N, the total number of slits.

Let $N = 4$. How many subsidiary maxima are there? How many minima are there between successive principal maxima?

Let $N = 10$. (This takes a minute but it's worth it.) Notice how the subsidiary maxima lean to the "outside." (Recall that in the previous exercise you were asked if the maxima were exactly where you thought they would be.) The maxima are not precisely centered between the minima. Also note that the maxima are not of the same magnitude. Compare with your values from the previous exercise. Examine the plot with the ordinate as a log scale. Why does the plot appear in separate segments?

We note that as N increases, the peaks with phase angle $2\pi n$ dominate. The maximum amplitude of the peaks increases (proportional to N), and the peaks become narrower.

Calculate the amplitude for multi-slit interference.

The number of phasors to be summed. Insert any value between 2 and 20. (Too large values will run subscripts out of bounds.)

$M := 6 \cdot N$ The number of angles at which the sum is to be evaluated. (If the calculation is too slow, reduce the numerical factor to 5 or 4.)

$i := 1 .. N$ $j := 0 .. M$ $\theta_j := \dfrac{j}{M} \cdot 2 \cdot \pi$

Calculate the x and y components of each phasor. $r := 1$

$$x_{i,j} := r \cdot \cos\left[(i - 1) \cdot \theta_j\right] \qquad y_{i,j} := r \cdot \sin\left[(i - 1) \cdot \theta_j\right]$$

$$X_{0,0} := 0 \qquad Y_{0,0} := 0 \qquad$$ For the plot, choose a reference point; here, start at the origin.

Determine the x and y components of the sums.

$$X_{i,j} := X_{(i-1),j} + x_{i,j} \qquad Y_{i,j} := Y_{(i-1),j} + y_{i,j}$$

Calculate the amplitude at each angle.

$$R_j := \left[\left[X_{i,j} - X_{0,0}\right]^2 + \left[Y_{i,j} - Y_{0,0}\right]^2\right]^{0.5}$$

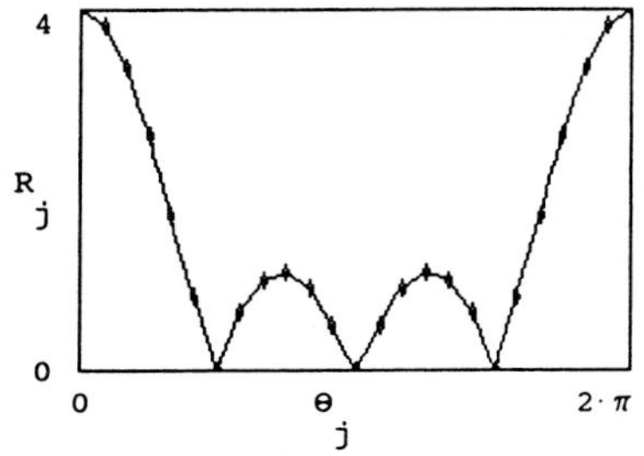

$N \equiv 4$

Figure 17.7 OPT6, amplitude vs. angle for an N-phasor system.

For each of the cases just considered, for $N = 2$, 3, 4, and 10, at what observation angle does the principal maximum where $\phi = 2\pi$ occur? For the same cases, what is the angular width of each of these maxima?

● ● Go back to OPT5. What if the intensities from the sources are not equal? Make the necessary changes in the document to assign different amplitudes (r) to the different phasors.

For $N = 2$, try the ratio 2:1. How are the maxima and minima affected?

Try a number of examples.

What physical conditions might be associated with unequal intensities?

• •   Make similar adjustments to OPT6. Let $N = 2$. Consider the ratio 2:1. Compare with the previous example using phasors.

Order does make a difference. Let $N = 3$. Let the intensities take on the values (0.6, 1.2, 1.4), (0.6, 1.4, 1.2), and (1.2, 0.6, 1.4).

Let $N = 4$ and consider the four cases (0.6, 1.2, 1.4, 0.6), (1.2, 0.6, 0.6, 1.4), (1.2, 0.6, 1.4, 0.6), and (1.2, 1.4, 0.6, 0.6).

17.4   Diffraction

In considering the process of diffraction from a single rectangular slit, imagine that the slit is subdivided into a series of even narrower rectangles. Let each rectangle, each section of the slit opening, act as a source of waves (Huygens wavelets). For this configuration of sources, minima occur when

$$a \sin(\theta) = m\,\lambda \qquad m = 1, 2, 3 \ldots, \tag{17.19}$$

where a is the slit width.

We can approach this relation as a limiting case of interference. For multislit interference, $\delta p = d\sin(\theta)$, where δp is the path difference between adjacent slits and $\delta\phi$ is the corresponding phase difference. If we consider this set of slits to be points within our diffraction slit, then we have

$$d = \frac{a}{N} \qquad \text{and} \qquad \delta p = \frac{a}{N}\sin(\theta)$$

where a is the slit width, d is the separation between adjacent source points within the slit, and N is the number of source points.

For destructive interference, the phase difference is π radians for every $N/(2\,m)$ source points. Between adjacent source points the phase difference is

$$\delta\phi = \frac{\pi}{N/(2\,m)}. \tag{17.20}$$

Substituting in our relation for path difference and phase difference, we find

$$\frac{a}{N}\sin(\theta)\frac{1}{\lambda} = \frac{\pi}{(N/2\,m)}\frac{1}{2\pi}$$

so that the condition for single-slit diffraction minima is given by

$$a \sin(\theta) = m\,\lambda \qquad m = 1, 2, 3 \ldots.$$

In terms of wavelength, the phase difference between adjacent "points" within a single slit can be written as

$$\delta\phi = \frac{2\pi}{\lambda}\,\delta p = k\,d\sin(\theta).$$

In expressing the intensity, one-half the total phase difference from one end of the slit to the other, β, is a useful quantity:

$$\beta = \frac{N\,\delta\phi}{2} = \frac{N\,k\,d\sin(\theta)}{2} = \frac{k\,a}{2}\sin(\theta). \tag{17.21}$$

It can be shown that the total electric field, E, is proportional to $\sin(\beta)/\beta$. The intensity as a function of the angle θ is given by

$$I(\theta) = I_0\left(\frac{\sin(\beta)}{\beta}\right)^2 \qquad \text{where} \qquad \beta = \beta(\theta). \tag{17.22}$$

• • Plot $I(\theta)/I_0$ vs. β as β goes from -3π to 3π. (Remember this when we approach the same problem in the next chapter using the fast Fourier transform.)

The minima occur when $\sin(\beta) = 0$ or

$$\beta = m\,\pi \qquad \text{where} \qquad m = 1, 2, 3,\ \ldots.$$

These minima are the same as those expressed by equation 17.19. The maxima occur where

$$\frac{dI}{d\beta} = 0.$$

• • Show that

$$\frac{dI}{d\beta} = I_0\,\frac{2\sin(\beta)\,(\beta\cos(\beta) - \sin(\beta))}{\beta^3}.$$

If $dI/d\beta = 0$, then $(\beta\cos(\beta) - \sin(\beta)) = 0$ or $\tan(\beta) = \beta$. Values of β that solve this equation give the locations of the maxima.

Determine the location of the maxima of the E-field. Is the relationship for these maxima the same as the location of maxima as determined from intensity expressions?

• • Plot $\tan(\beta), \beta$ vs. β as β goes from 0 to $5\pi/2$. In plotting $\tan(\beta)$, select β values judiciously so as to avoid calculations at $\beta = (\pi/2)\cdot(2\,m+1)$. Also, it may be useful to limit the ordinate range. The intersection points of the curves $\tan(\beta)$ and β are the solutions. Use a given-find procedure to find the first two nontrivial solutions to the equation $\tan(\beta) = \beta$. Find the corresponding θ.

In Young's two-slit experiment, the intensity at any point depends on both diffraction and interference effects:

$$I_{\text{diff}} \propto \frac{\sin^2(\beta)}{\beta^2} \qquad I_{\text{int}} \propto \cos^2(\alpha).$$

Thus

$$I \propto \frac{\sin^2(\beta)}{\beta^2} \cdot \cos^2(\alpha),$$

where

$$\alpha = \frac{k\,d}{2}\sin(\theta) \qquad \text{and} \qquad \beta = \frac{k\,a}{2}\sin(\theta).$$

• •   Plot I vs. θ as θ goes from $\sin^{-1}(-3\lambda/a)$ to $\sin^{-1}(3\lambda/a)$. Let the constant of proportionality be one. (See Chapter 18.)

• •   Examine the intensity pattern for the four-slit case. Include both interference and diffraction effects. Plot the total intensity as a function of angle.

• •   For a circular aperture of radius r (as opposed to a rectangular slit or aperture) the intensity is given by

$$I \propto \left(\frac{J_1(k\,r\sin(\theta))}{k\,r\sin(\theta)}\right)^2.$$

Plot I vs. $k\,r\sin(\theta)$ as $k\,r\sin(\theta)$ takes on values from -10 to 10. Verify that

$$\theta_{\min} = \tan^{-1}\left(1.22\,\lambda/2\,r\right) \simeq 1.22\frac{\lambda}{2\,r}. \qquad (17.23)$$

The Bessel functions are standard functions inMathCAD, just as are sine and cosine.

If sources are close together, the diffraction patterns resulting from the passage of light through an aperture may overlap. A recording device — for example, the eye — sees the sum of the intensities. (There is no coherence between the radiation from the separate sources; thus we sum the intensities.) In observing a light pattern, it may not be clear how many sources are involved and what their relative strengths may be. One criterion for being able to distinguish between two images, two central maxima, is known as Rayleigh's criterion. The concept is that two sources of equal intensity are resolved if the central maximum of one pattern falls at the first minimum of the other. Another way to express this criterion is to give the intensity amplitude at the dip between the two central maxima.

The first minimum of a slit diffraction pattern occurs at the angle

$$\theta = \frac{\lambda}{a} \qquad \text{(in the small-angle approximation).}$$

The diffraction patterns from the two sources separated as specified by the Rayleigh criterion have equal intensities at half this angle. Substituting in the equation for β this angle for θ we obtain

$$\beta = \frac{ka}{2}\sin(\theta) = \frac{2\pi a}{\lambda}\frac{\lambda}{2\,2a} = \frac{\pi}{2}.$$

The intensity of each pattern at $\theta = \lambda/2a$ is

$$I \propto \frac{\sin^2(\beta)}{\beta^2} = \frac{1}{(\pi/2)^2} = \frac{4}{\pi^2}.$$

The total intensity is double this value because there are equal contributions from the two sources,

$$\frac{I}{I_0} = \frac{8}{\pi^2}. \qquad (17.24)$$

Thus the Rayleigh criterion indicates a dip between maxima of approximately 20% to say that the peaks are resolved. Clearly this choice is somewhat arbitrary. Other criteria can be defined.

• • Suggest a different set of criteria for the resolution of two diffraction patterns of equal intensity. Test your suggestion.

• • Load OPT7, single-slit diffraction (see Figs. 17.8 and 17.9).

In OPT7, we examine the sums of diffraction patterns and consider how well they are resolved. The amplitude is plotted instead of intensity in some cases because the magnitudes of the subsidiary intensity maxima are too small in linear plots. Recall that the maxima and minima are in the same location in both amplitude and intensity plots. We plot I vs. θ three times: linear, linear with the ordinate range reduced, and semi-log. We also show y vs. I.

The intensity patterns from two single-slit sources of width a, separated by a distance d, are $I_1(y)$ and $I_2(y)$. (The sources are at $\pm d/2$. Note that y, not θ, is the argument.) There is no coherence between the radiation from the two sources.)

When d is of the order of the slit separation in the two-slit interference experiment (10^{-4}) the central maxima are not resolved. We could not easily distinguish between the case where there are two sources of amplitude one very close together and the case where there is one source of amplitude two. Test this. Try several different values of slit separation.

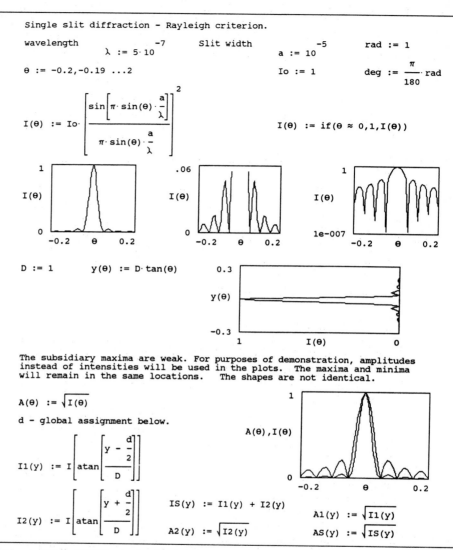

Single slit diffraction - Rayleigh criterion.

wavelength $\lambda := 5 \cdot 10^{-7}$ Slit width $a := 10^{-5}$ rad := 1

$\theta := -0.2, -0.19 \ldots 2$ Io := 1 $deg := \dfrac{\pi}{180} \cdot rad$

$$I(\theta) := Io \cdot \left[\dfrac{\sin\left[\pi \cdot \sin(\theta) \cdot \dfrac{a}{\lambda}\right]}{\pi \cdot \sin(\theta) \cdot \dfrac{a}{\lambda}} \right]^2$$ $I(\theta) := if(\theta \approx 0, 1, I(\theta))$

$D := 1$ $y(\theta) := D \cdot \tan(\theta)$

The subsidiary maxima are weak. For purposes of demonstration, amplitudes instead of intensities will be used in the plots. The maxima and minima will remain in the same locations. The shapes are not identical.

$A(\theta) := \sqrt{I(\theta)}$

d - global assignment below.

$$I1(y) := I\left[atan\left[\dfrac{y - \dfrac{d}{2}}{D}\right]\right]$$

$$I2(y) := I\left[atan\left[\dfrac{y + \dfrac{d}{2}}{D}\right]\right]$$ $IS(y) := I1(y) + I2(y)$ $A1(y) := \sqrt{I1(y)}$

      $A2(y) := \sqrt{I2(y)}$ $AS(y) := \sqrt{IS(y)}$

Figure 17.8 OPT7, single-slit diffraction. (See the next figure for the rest of the document.)

In the final set of three plots, we see the individual amplitudes, the total intensity, and the intensity of one source in both linear and semi-log plots.

Process with $d \equiv 10^{-2} \cdot (1, 3, 4, 5, 6,$ and perhaps $10)$. Observe the location of the first minimum in relation to the central maximum and the size, if any, of the dip between the maxima.

When d is of the order of the slit separation in the two-slit interference
experiment (10^-4), the peaks are not distinguishable. From the graph, one
could not distinguish, for example, between two sources of amplitude one very
close to each other and one source of amplitude two. Change the d value.

$y := -0.15, -0.145 \ ..0.15$

$d \equiv 10^{-2} \cdot 1$

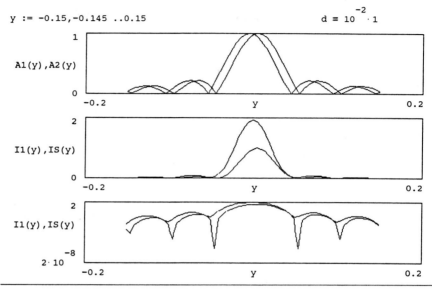

Figure 17.9 OPT7 *continued.*

As you go through the sequence observe how I_1 fits into the sum in
both the linear and log-log plots. At what point does it seem reasonable
to think that there is more than one source? At what point are the two
sources resolved according to the Rayleigh criterion?

With $d = 4 \cdot 10^{-2}$, observe the sum when $I_2 = I_2 \cdot 1.2$ and $I_2 = I_2 \cdot 5$.
The specification of resolution becomes more problematic as the difference
in intensities is taken into account.

• •   Three intensity functions UI_1, UI_2, and UI_3 are given in OPT8.
Your task is to determine the intensity and location of the sources that
make up the composite line. Two of the composites contain two lines; one
contains three. Slit widths are equal; intensities need not be. I_0 and c are
the parameters to determine.

It is suggested that you define a function with specific values of I_0
and c, for example, $I_a(y) = I$(your value for amplitude, your value for
shift $- c$, y). Plot the unknown and your fitted line in the same region.
Guided by the experience you gained from OPT7, adjust your I_0 and c
values to correspond to one component of a composite line. When satisfied
with the adjustment of the parameters, plot $UI(y) - I_a(y)$ vs. y. If the

unknown is composed of two lines and if $UI - I_a$ looks like a single line shape then the parameters of the first line were well chosen. Next define $I_b(y) = UI(y) - I_a(y)$ and then find the parameters associated with I_b by fitting another line shape to it. If there are three lines, the procedure will have to be repeated. Amplitudes, in this example, can range between 0 and 2; c can be plus or minus; I_0 and c values are all even tenths.

I've seen things that you people wouldn't believe.
Attack ships on fire off the shoulder of Orion.
I've watched c-beams glitter in the dark near the Tannhäuser gate.
All those moments will be lost in time ... like tears in rain.

Blade Runner

Fast Fourier Transform

When a signal, such as the representation of a portion of a song on an oscilloscope screen, is expressed in terms of a Fourier series, the components are still expressed in the time domain. A general expression of a Fourier series is

$$f(t) \sim \frac{1}{2}a_0 + \sum_n (a_n \cos(nt) + b_n \sin(nt)). \qquad (18.1)$$

The coefficients give us information about the amplitudes of the various components. The description is one of time and amplitude.

However, it is also possible to display information about the signal in the frequency domain, where the information displayed would show the frequency-amplitude composition. The time and frequency representations of a signal are different, but equivalent, representations of the same function. The fast Fourier transform (FFT) is a means of converting the signal from the time domain to the frequency domain. The inverse transform will convert from the frequency domain to the time domain.

18.1   Sampling Rate

The FFT is a discrete transform. It operates not on a continuous function but on a set of values of the function taken at uniform time intervals. Recall how a function is plotted in MathCAD, for example, a sine curve:

$$n := 10 \qquad i := 0 \dots n \qquad f := 1 \qquad \omega := 2 \cdot \pi \cdot f$$

$$t_i := 2 \cdot \pi \cdot \frac{i}{N} \qquad y_i := \sin(\omega \cdot t_i). \qquad (18.2)$$

It is helpful to think of these plots as being constructed from a sampled set of values. The t_i are uniformly spaced in time. A line may be drawn through the points to provide a continuous curve, but the basis for the plot is a finite number of uniformly spaced points.

From previous plotting examples using MathCAD, a loose rule of thumb was developed as to the number of points needed per cycle to represent a function adequately. That number, however, was determined more from a sense of aesthetics than of necessity. From an information standpoint, what is the necessity? How frequently do we need to sample a signal in order to represent it adequately? Before we answer that directly, think back to the last movie that you saw with a clear shot of the wheels of a vehicle accelerating from rest. First the wheels rotate as would be expected, then the direction of rotation reverses. (A film of an airplane propeller would behave similarly.) Why?

Movie cameras take 24 still photographs each second. The film is held in register in the film plane, and the shutter is opened briefly, permitting the film to be exposed; while the shutter is closed, the hold on the film is relaxed and the film is advanced one frame, and the process is repeated. Projectors operate similarly. The film is held in register, and a shutter (albeit of a different type from that in the camera) permits light to pass through the film and illuminate the screen; while the shutter blocks the light, the film is advanced one frame, and the process is repeated.

The motion of the wheel (or propeller) is thus sampled 24 times per second. Imagine the camera moving in the frame of the wheel so that translational motion is removed. Assume that there is one point on the wheel, not at the center, that we can easily observe.

At a slow rate of rotation, each successive frame (sample) shows the observation point advanced from the previous frame. We perceive a simple rotation. As the rotation rate increases, the angle rotated between successive views increases. When the angle reaches 180°, or two samples per rotation, the perceived rotation rate is at its maximum. Further increases in the rotation rate make the wheel appear to be rotating in the opposite

$$\delta := 170 \qquad \delta' := 190 \qquad n := 10 \qquad i := 0 \,..\, n$$

$$a_i := i \cdot \delta \qquad a_i := \text{mod}\left[a_i, 360\right] \qquad a'_i := i \cdot \delta' \qquad a'_i := \text{mod}\left[a'_i, 360\right]$$

$$a''_i := 360 - a'_i \qquad a''_i := \text{mod}\left[a''_i, 360\right]$$

a_i	a'_i	a''_i
0	0	0
170	190	170
340	20	340
150	210	150
320	40	320
130	230	130
300	60	300
110	250	110
280	80	280
90	270	90
260	100	260

Figure 18.1 Comparison of 170° and 190° rotation steps: a represents motion in the clockwise direction for the 170° case; a' represents motion in the clockwise direction for the 190° case; and a'' represents the 190° motion as measured in the counterclockwise direction. The counterclockwise motion described by a'' is equivalent to 170° motion in the clockwise direction.

direction. As the rotation rate continues to increase, the apparent angular velocity will decrease until it reaches zero (see Fig. 18.1).

For example, consider two motions. In one, a uniform wheel with one viewing spot turns through the angle $\delta = 170°$ between successive views of the wheel; the rotation angle is represented as $a_i = i \cdot \delta$. Because we cannot distinguish different revolutions but only the location of the spot, we write $a_i = \text{mod}(a_i, 360)$. This provides only the locations and not the net angle through which the wheel has turned. If the turning angle between successive views were $\delta' = 190°$, then the location would be given by a'_i in Fig. 18.1.

If we imagined that the wheel were turning in the opposite direction, then the a'_i data would be that as shown as a''_i. These data are the same as those for a_i. That is, motion through successive angles of 190° appears the same as motion through successive angles of 170° in the opposite direction. We see the smaller angle and the backward motion.

When the rotation rate and the sampling rate are equal (one sample per cycle), the wheel appears to be stationary. (This effect is similar to that used in a common laboratory technique for measuring rotation rates using a strobe light.) Further increases in the angular velocity result in a repetition of the previous observations: increasing angular velocity up to a maximum, reversal of apparent direction, and decreasing angular velocity. Consequently, several different rotation rates yield the same apparent motion, and if the film sequence is our only data, we can no longer distinguish the different rates. This folding process, the representation of high frequencies masquerading as low frequencies, is known as *aliasing*. We will come back to this later in the chapter.

The only way to be sure of seeing the correct rotation rate is to put on the wheel a governor, which will limit the maximum rotation frequency to half the sampling frequency. Stated slightly differently, no less than two samples per cycle of the highest frequency are required.

This maximum frequency, known as the Nyquist critical frequency, is given by

$$f_{Nc} = \frac{1}{2} \cdot f_{\text{sampl}} \qquad (18.3)$$

or

$$\frac{1}{\delta t_{Nc}} = \frac{1}{2 \cdot \delta t_{\text{sampl}}} \qquad (18.4)$$

and

$$\delta t_{\text{sampl}} = \frac{\delta t_{Nc}}{2} = \frac{1}{2 f_{Nc}}, \qquad (18.5)$$

where δt_{sampl} is the maximum allowable time interval between samples. (Note: The name δt_{sampl} will be written without the subscript, δt, in all future use.) Given a sampling rate, f_{Nc} is the maximum frequency that can be legitimately be observed. (Some information, possibly all, is lost at the limit.) Or given a frequency, f_{Nc}, that must be observed, f_{sampl} is the minimum sampling frequency. Similarly, δt_{sampl} in the above expression is the maximum allowable time interval between samples if f_{Nc} is to be observed. (A smaller sampling time would mean a greater frequency and would be suitable.)

The role of the governor above is essentially that of a mechanical lowpass filter; a lowpass filter passes frequencies below a level determined by the filter and blocks higher frequencies. Electrical signals are similarly prepared by being passed first through a lowpass filter. When this is done, we know the maximum possible frequency that can be passed and can then select a sampling rate that assures that no information is lost and that aliasing will not occur.

This description is not just an analogy. It describes the problem of sampling signals in general. Earlier, we noted the relation between uniform circular motion and simple harmonic motion. From the Fourier series examples, we know that any signal may be constructed from a summation of individual sinusoidal waves. The sampling problem for a rotating wheel is the same as that for a signal, where one rotation rate of the wheel corresponds to one Fourier component of our signal.

A practical rule about MathCAD's FFT is that the number of samples should be an integral power of two (and the power should not be less than three). If the data do not include that number, pad the data with zeros so that the vector in which the data are stored has the requisite number of elements.

In the time domain, the data are representations of the value of some signal or function, taken at uniform time intervals, δt. In the frequency domain, the data are representations of the value of amplitude and phase of the Fourier components of the original function. The data are presented at uniform frequency intervals, δf.

When data are plotted in the time and frequency domains, the traditional procedure is to represent the data in the time domain with a continuous curve, while the frequency domain is often represented as amplitudes at specific frequencies. That is, the frequency information is presented at discrete frequencies. Instead of a continuous curve, the graph is of uniformly spaced free-standing vertical lines.

18.2   Nuts and Bolts of MathCAD's FFT

A single frequency wave, a sinusoidal wave, is not an inappropriate place to start. The waveform is familiar, and other examples are all variations on the basic theme. In particular, take the FFT of $y(t) = \sin(\omega t)$.

However, before we treat a specific example in detail, an outline of a general approach for implementing a transform is presented. A detailed MathCAD solution is then presented.

- Specify the maximum frequency value of the various discrete frequencies of the function being sampled. Determine the time interval δt between samples (see eq. 18.5). (This is the largest allowed time interval. Smaller time intervals are fine; they would result in more samples.)

- Specify the number of samples and the time interval between samples. These choices may be constrained. A specific time period may need to be spanned. The number of samples conveniently handled is limited; the FFT requires that the number of samples be a power of two. Or it might be desirable to have the spacing of elements in the frequency domain take on a particular value. The values δt, δf, and N are interrelated.

- Create a vector — for example, y_i — that contains the sampled values of the desired function. The procedure is very much the same as preparing data to be plotted.

- The FFT is executed with one command — for example, $q = \text{fft}(y)$ — subscripts are not included in the statement. A plot of the results is the most immediate way to assess the transform. It is convenient to use the error bar plot type (e). If both the magnitude of the transform and zero are plotted along the ordinate, the transform is presented in the conventional form of amplitudes at specific frequencies. The actual calculation performed by MathCAD's operator fft is

$$q_j = \frac{1}{\sqrt{N}} \sum_{k=1}^{N} v_k e^{2\pi i (j/N)k}. \tag{18.6}$$

- The inverse transform is also accomplished with one statement — for example, $iq = \text{ifft}(q)$. In some cases, it is useful to start in the frequency domain and construct a particular wave using the inverse FFT. The actual calculation performed is similar to that for the FFT except for the minus in the exponential:

$$iq_j = \frac{1}{\sqrt{N}} \sum_{k=1}^{N} w_k e^{-2\pi i (j/N)k}. \tag{18.7}$$

It is often useful to determine several other quantities that can aid in keeping track of the data in the transform process. The quantities are specified in terms of a particular frequency, f, the period ($T = 1/f$), the sampling time interval δt, and the number of samples, N (the number of intervals is $(N-1)$).

The total time sampled: $t_{\text{tot}} = (N-1) \cdot \delta t$.

The number of cycles in this time: $n_c = t_{\text{tot}}/T = t_{\text{tot}} \cdot f$.

The number of samples per cycle: $s_c = (N-1)/n_c = T/\delta t$.

The spacing between elements in the frequency domain:

$$\delta f = f \cdot \frac{s_c}{N} = \frac{1}{\delta t \cdot N}. \tag{18.8}$$

Specific steps for implementing MathCAD's FFT of a single sine wave are:

1. Specify the frequency, f. Define T and ω. Determine the maximum possible δt_{max}.

2. Specify the δt to be used.

3. Specify the number of data samples, N. The number should be some power of two, $N = 2^m$, where m is some integer greater than two. Values for N could be 8, 16, 32, 64, ... In selecting this value, it may be useful also to define and evaluate the number of samples per cycle, s_c.

4. Calculate the interval δf in the frequency domain.

5. Specify an index i to range from 0 to $N - 1$. (It takes on N values.)

6. Calculate the times associated with the given sampling rate, $t_i := i \cdot \delta t$.

7. Calculate the values for the function at those times, $y_i := \sin(\omega \cdot t_i)$.

8. Take the FFT, $q := \text{fft}(y)$. Just use the vector name; no subscripts are needed.

9. The variable q has fewer elements than y; one more than half as many. Because the first element is in the 0-position, the index of the last element of q is $N / 2$; call it M. Set up an index j, for q, that runs from 0 to M. Evaluate q_j. Ignore values with magnitudes like 10^{-13}; that is, consider them to be zero. (It may be convenient to change the format statement so that these values are represented as zero.)

10. Plot the magnitude of q and the zero line (ordinate) vs. the index (abscissa), that is $|q_j|$, 0 vs. j. Change the plot type to e. Let the abscissa range from -1 to $M + 1$ so that all the elements can be seen within the plot region. Let the lower limit of the ordinate be a small negative number, -0.1 or -1 (adjust to please the eye) so that the bar lines do not start from the lower edge of the graph. Because it is the magnitude of q that is plotted, q's complex nature is obscured.

11. Take the inverse transform of q, $iq := \text{ifft}(q)$, and plot iq_i vs. i. Compare it with the plot y_i vs. i.

• •   Load FFT1, FFT of a sine wave (see Fig. 18.2).

Be aware that starting with a wave of a single frequency does not necessarily mean that the transform will have only one nonzero element. A transform will result in a single nonzero element only if the frequency of the signal is an integral multiple of the frequency interval δf.

For example, if the frequencies, as represented in the frequency domain, range from 0 to 8 in integral steps, and if the frequency of the input signal is some nonintegral value such as 2.4, then to represent this signal all the frequencies will be required. On the other hand, if the frequency has an integral value, only the corresponding component of the transform will be nonzero. (Integers are represented by a single line in this case because they are multiples of δf, not because they are integers.)

• •   The file FFT1 contains the listings for the above example. Load and run it and gain some feeling for the role of the quantities δf, f, N, s_c, and n_c in the FFT process. Take the transform of a sinusoidal wave, change

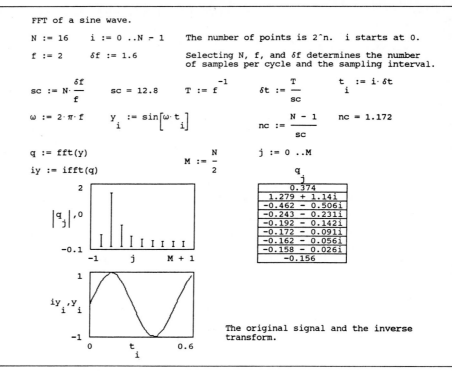

Figure 18.2 FFT1, FFT of a sine wave.

the value of δf, take the transform again, and observe the change in the transform. Follow the steps outlined below first, then try some variations of your own, and learn to control the process.

How many samples per cycle are there in this case?

Is there more than one nonzero element in the transform? Is f an integral multiple of δf?

Note that the plot of the transform contains nine elements. What are the frequencies that are associated with these lines? Write an expression for f_j and evaluate it.

Leaving f and N unchanged, find the value of δf that will yield the number of samples per cycle to be two. (Try different values of δf.)

What has happened to the transform in this case? Look at the numerical values as well as the plot. Is the problem because $s_c = 2$, or is there some other reason?

Leaving everything else the same, change the expression $y_i = \sin(\omega t_i)$ to $y_i = \sin(\omega t_i + \pi / 4)$ and process the document. What happened to the transform in the previous step?

How many nonzero elements are there in the transform? What frequencies do the elements in the transform now represent?

Changing only δf, let the transform have only one nonzero element, and let it be the sixth element instead of the eighth.

Changing δf again, let the transform's only nonzero element be the first (not the zeroth). How do f and δf compare? How many cycles of data are represented?

When δf is one, what frequency range is represented?

In the graph showing y_i and iy_i, there is only one curve. Why?

Take the FFT of the signal: $y_i := y_{1i} + y_{2i}$ where $y_{1i} := \sin(\omega t_i)$ and $y_{2i} := \sin(\omega t_i + \pi / 4)$. Let f be an integral multiple of δf. Take the inverse transform. Plot y_{1i}, y_{2i}, and the inverse transform all in the same plot region. Try a few different phase angles.

How is the transform different if $y_i := 3y_{1i} + y_{2i}$? Try a few different amplitudes.

Repeat with $y_i := y_{1i} + y_{2i}$ and $y_{1i} := \sin(\omega t_i)$ and $y_{2i} := \sin(2\omega t_i)$. Try various combinations of frequency multiples.

18.3   Interpreting the Numbers in the Transform

After the FFT of some function has been performed, the transform values are stored in a vector, q for example. The values q_j contained in this vector, generally complex, provide as much information about the original signal as did the sampled values, the y_i, that were used to generate the transform.

Each element of the transform vector q provides information about one frequency component of the original signal. Note that although the original signal might consist of only one frequency, when transformed into the frequency domain, it may be represented by a series of elements, each with a different frequency and none exactly equal to the original. Reversing the process, from each element of the transform vector q, one component of the original signal can be reconstructed. The original signal could be reproduced by reconstructing all the components and summing them. The inverse transform does recreate the original sampled signal directly and simply. However, it is useful to be able to interpret the information contained in the individual elements of the FFT rather than just to treat the process as a black box.

Each element in the vector q gives information about the amplitude, phase, and frequency of one of the component waves that make up the original signal. If the number of sampled values is N, where $N = 2^m$, the number of elements in the vector q is $N/2 + 1$. The relationship for the amplitudes and phases of the components waves is

$$A_j = \frac{2}{\sqrt{N}}|q_j| \tag{18.9}$$

and

$$\phi_j = -angle(\text{Re}(q_j), \text{Im}(q_j)). \tag{18.10}$$

Expressing the relationship for the phase angle using MathCAD's angle function is essential here; the arctangent is inadequate because of the restricted range of the returned angle.

The equation that relates the information of the jth element in the frequency domain to its corresponding expression in the time domain is

$$comp_{j,i} = A_j \cos(2\pi f_j t_i + \phi_j), \tag{18.11}$$

where $f_j = j \cdot \delta f$. Note that j refers to a particular element of the transform (frequency domain), and i refers back to the sequence of times in the time domain, where the signal is being reconstructed. The complete signal is generated by a simple sum of the components — with the notable exception of the elements that begin and end the list. The amplitudes of the zeroth and last (Mth) components must be divided by two before summing or being used in other analysis.

Just as A_j and ϕ_j can be expressed in terms of real and imaginary parts of q_j, a single component of the signal in the frequency domain, the real and imaginary parts of q_j can be expressed in terms of A_j and ϕ_j. The transform, of course, does this; but if the frequency is a multiple of δf and maps to a single line in the frequency domain, the real and imaginary parts (a, b) of the nonzero element in q are given by

$$a = A \cdot \cos(\phi) \cdot \frac{\sqrt{N}}{2} \tag{18.12}$$

and

$$b = A \cdot \sin(\phi) \cdot \frac{\sqrt{N}}{2}. \tag{18.13}$$

• •   In the previous document, let f be a multiple of δf. Take the transform and evaluate the one nonzero element. Evaluate a and b and compare.

Remember that for a single frequency signal, only if f is an integral multiple of δf will there be only one nonzero element of the FFT. Conversely, any single-frequency signals with frequencies other than integral multiples of δf will have multiple nonzero elements in the transform.

• •   The following exercises involve using and interpreting the values in the transform q.

Reload file FFT1 and run it with the original values. Note that most of the values for q are complex.

Let δf take on the values 2, 1, and 0.5. For each case record the nonzero values. (The single nonzero value is the same in each case.)

Define rad $\equiv 1$ and deg $\equiv (\pi / 180) \cdot$ rad.

Let the subscript k represent an element of the transform under consideration. In this case let $k := 4$.

Define the phase angle ϕ_k in terms of the angle expression as given above. Evaluate ϕ_k twice; in the place marker of the first, enter π, and in the second, enter deg. Process the document.

The equation for *comp* above is expressed in terms of the cosine function and the phase angle. If the cosine were to be shifted by the angle ϕ_k (from the previous step), what function would result? What function did we begin with?

Plot $comp_{k,i}$ vs. i (or t_i) and compare it with y_i. What procedure(s) would show that two signals were the same? Compare $comp_{k,i}$ with iq_i, the inverse FFT of q. Note that the original signal can be reconstructed from the q information component by component or all at once using the inverse FFT.

Near the top of the document define $\Phi := \pi / 4$ and alter the expression for y_i to read $y_i := \sin(\omega \cdot t_i + \Phi)$. Process the document. How many nonzero elements are there? Repeat for $\Phi = \pi / 2$ and $\pi / 3$. Does changing the phase angle change which elements are nonzero?

• •   Load FFT2, intepreting the elements in the transform (see Fig. 18.3).

Start in the frequency domain. Assign values to a vector, q, to create the signal $y_i := 3\sin(9\pi t_i + \pi/3)$. Take the inverse transform to verify.

Start in the frequency domain. Assign values to a vector, q, to create the signal $y_i := 5\cos(1000\pi t_i + \pi/6)$. Let $N := 64$. Take the inverse transform to verify.

Starting in the frequency domain, construct the time domain signal without using the inverse transform. Examine the real and complex parts of the elements of the transform.

$M := 16$ $j := 0 ..M$ $fa := 2$ $fb := 4$ $N := 2 \cdot M$ $ii := 0 ..N - 1$

a, b, c, and d are the real and imaginary parts of the two nonzero frequency components, fa and fb. $q.fa = a + bi$; $q.fb = c + di$.

Select values for a, b, c, d, so that the sum of the squares of real and imaginary parts equals half the square root of N.

$nrm := \sqrt{N} \cdot 0.5$ $nrm = 2.828$

$a := .6$ $c := 0.1$

$$b := \sqrt{nrm^2 - a}$$ $$d := \sqrt{nrm^2 - c}$$

$q_j := 0$ $q_{fa} := a + b \cdot i$ $q_{fb} := c + d \cdot i$

$a = 0.6$ $c = 0.1$

$x := ifft(q)$ $b = 1.571$ $d = 1.679$

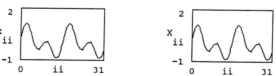

$$b := if\left[\frac{b \cdot b}{(|b|)^2} \approx -1, 0, b\right]$$ $$d := if\left[\frac{d \cdot d}{(|d|)^2} \approx -1, 0, d\right]$$ Avoid letting b or d be imaginary.

Construct the time domain signal from the frequency components.

$pha := -angle(a,b)$ $phb := -angle(c,d)$

$$A1 := \sqrt{a^2 + b^2} \cdot nrm^{-1}$$ $$A2 := \sqrt{c^2 + d^2} \cdot nrm^{-1}$$ $$\theta_{ii} := 2 \cdot \pi \cdot \frac{ii}{N}$$

$$X_{ii} := A1 \cdot cos\left[fa \cdot \theta_{ii} + pha\right] + A2 \cdot cos\left[fb \cdot \theta_{ii} + phb\right]$$

Compare the signal created using the inverse FFT with the constructed signal.

Figure 18.3 FFT2, intepreting the elements in the transform.

18.4   Digital Filtering

Once the time amplitude signal has been converted to the frequency domain, various manipulations of the data are possible. We show a simple filtering scheme.

The fundamental idea is that the noise is uniformly distributed over the entire spectrum, whereas the signal is concentrated at certain frequencies. By removing those elements in the transform whose magnitude is less than some arbitrary value, some of the noise can be removed. Of course, some signal information will be lost as well. Taking the inverse transform of the filtered frequency information, we can observe the results of the filtering process in the time domain.

• •   Load FFT3, digital filtering (see Figs. 18.4 and 18.5).

The signal y is the sum of two sinusoidal signals of different frequency. Noise is generated and added to the signal. We then observe the transform of the original signal, t_y, the noise, t_n, and the signal plus noise, t_z.

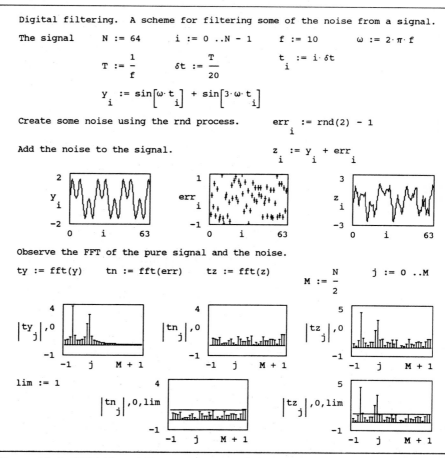

Digital filtering.   A scheme for filtering some of the noise from a signal.

The signal $N := 64$ $i := 0 .. N - 1$ $f := 10$ $\omega := 2 \cdot \pi \cdot f$

$$T := \frac{1}{f} \qquad \delta t := \frac{T}{20} \qquad t_i := i \cdot \delta t$$

$$y_i := \sin\left[\omega \cdot t_i\right] + \sin\left[3 \cdot \omega \cdot t_i\right]$$

Create some noise using the rnd process. $err_i := rnd(2) - 1$

Add the noise to the signal. $z_i := y_i + err_i$

Observe the FFT of the pure signal and the noise.

ty := fft(y)   tn := fft(err)   tz := fft(z) $M := \frac{N}{2}$ $j := 0 .. M$

lim := 1

Figure 18.4 FFT3, digital filtering. (See the next figure for the rest of the document.)

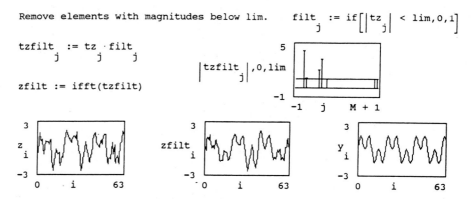

Figure 18.5 FFT3 *continued*.

The transform of the noise and the data plus noise are shown together with a horizontal line at the level *lim*. By arbitrarily adjusting the value of *lim*, we can see the number of frequency components that would be eliminated. t_{zfilt} shows what remains.

A final set of plots show the corrupted signal, the filtered signal, and the ideal data. The result is not perfection, but it is a significant improvement. The high-frequency noise has been removed; some low-frequency noise and some of the signal have been removed as well.

Try this with different levels of noise, different frequency values, and different values of *lim*.

Can you think of other filtering schemes that you could implement? Try them.

18.5   Aliasing

Earlier, the notion was introduced that the number of samples per cycle (of the highest frequency component of the signal) must be at least two. To see why this must be so, violate the rule and see what happens. If the signal is of one frequency, the result is easier to observe.

The following provides one means of examining the problem.

• •   Set up a document for performing a FFT with 17 elements in the frequency domain. (Define N, i, M, j, δf, f, ω, s_c, T, δt, and t_i — or load FFT2, which has these quantities at the beginning.) Let δf equal one. Given this set of parameters, what would be the maximum allowed value of f that the FFT can correctly process? (The frequency value when the number of samples per cycle is two.)

Take the FFT of the function $y_i = \cos(\omega t_i)$. Plot the FFT in the standard way. Let f take on the values 14, 15, $\ldots$, 18. What happens to the frequency (as interpreted in the frequency domain) when it exceeds the maximum allowed value? Continue taking transforms with $f = 30$, 31,$\ldots$, 34.

These procedures clearly demonstrate that high-frequency signals — that is, signals of sufficiently high frequencies that less than two samples per cycle occur — fold back into the legitimate frequency domain. They do so in a way that renders them indistinguishable from the lower frequency signals that they masquerade.

• •   Write an expression for f' (a frequency outside the proper range) in terms of f, N, and some arbitrary constants that will give the same transform as some f within the range. Try not to look at the answer that follows. Base your expression on the empirical observations that you just made when looking at the different frequencies and observing the foldover.

Test your result with several different sets of values. Let y represent the properly sampled signal; let z represent the high-frequency signal that appears to have the same frequency as y. Test them by calculating the expression $z_i := \cos(\omega' t_i)$, where $\omega' := 2\pi f'$, and taking the transform $q' := \mathrm{fft}(z)$. Plot y_i, z_i vs. t_i and plot the magnitude of the transforms q and q'. If your expression is correct for f', the plot of z_i should lie exactly over the curve for y_i. The transforms should be identical as well. Does your expression work for nonintegral values? (The answer is $f' = k N \pm f$ where $k = 1, 2, \ldots$.)

It is especially interesting to plot the two functions, $y(f)$ and $z(f')$, which appear the same when using the δt above, with a new value $\delta t'$ that is much smaller. When this is done, both signals are adequately defined and can be seen as distinct. By observing where the curves intersect, it becomes intuitively clear as to how these two signals that are so different could be interpreted as the same.

• •   Load file FFT4 (see Fig. 18.6). This file demonstrates all the points outlined above in the exercises. Define $q' = \mathrm{fft}(z)$ and plot q' in the same way as q is plotted. How do q and q' compare? What are the associated frequencies? How do the plots of y_i and z_i compare? Why? Try some other frequency combinations that result in similar transforms and y, z curves.

Aliasing.   Two different frequency signals appear the same in both the time and frequency domains.

$$N \equiv 16 \qquad i := 0\,..N - 1 \qquad \delta f := 1$$

$$f \equiv 2.5 \qquad \omega := 2\cdot\pi\cdot f \qquad\qquad sc := N\cdot\delta f\cdot f^{-1}, \qquad sc = 6.4$$

$$f' \equiv 18.5 \qquad \omega' := 2\cdot\pi\cdot f' \qquad sc' := N\cdot\delta f\cdot f'^{-1} \qquad sc' = 0.865$$

$$T := f^{-1} \qquad \delta t := T\cdot sc^{-1} \qquad t_i := i\cdot\delta t$$

$$y_i := \cos\left[\omega\cdot t_i\right] \qquad z_i := \cos\left[\omega'\cdot t_i\right] \qquad q := fft(y) \qquad q' := fft(z)$$

Plots of the two signals, showing the points at which the signal was sampled.

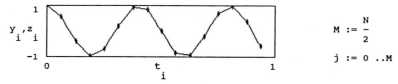

$$M := \frac{N}{2}$$

$$j := 0\,..M$$

The transforms of the two signals are also identical.

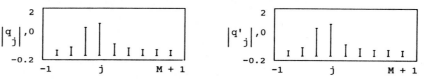

Let the period between samples be reduced by a factor of 16.   Plot one fourth of the time range shown above.

$$k := 0\,..4\cdot N - 1 \qquad \delta t' := \frac{\delta t}{16} \qquad tt_k := k\cdot\delta t'$$

$$yy_k := \cos\left[\omega\cdot tt_k\right] \qquad zz_k := \cos\left[\omega'\cdot tt_k\right]$$

The separation between points, as sampled initially.

$$\frac{f'}{f} = 7.4 \qquad angsep := \frac{2\cdot\pi}{sc} \qquad angsep' := \frac{2\cdot\pi}{sc'} \qquad \begin{array}{l} angsep = 56.25\cdot deg \\ angsep' = 416.25\cdot deg \end{array}$$

$$rad \equiv 1 \qquad deg \equiv \pi\cdot 180^{-1}\cdot rad$$

Figure 18.6 FFT4, an example of aliasing. These frequencies are indistinguishable given the sampling limitations.

At the end of the document is a graph displaying the original function, y_i, sampled at δt (the points are shown as open rectangles), and the functions y and z, called yy and zz, sampled at 16 times the previous rate. Explore this a bit, for example; change f and f' and observe the results.

The equation for f' above indicates which frequencies will have common intersection points as shown in the graph. Because the FFT process assumes that frequencies above the maximum ($s_c < 2$) are not present, the lower frequency is the only choice consistent with the data.

In audio recording, if any frequencies above 20 kHz are first removed from the signal by a filtering process, and if the signal is then sampled at a frequency greater than 40 kHz, then precise information about all frequencies below 20 kHz is theoretically possible. Other practical factors, like noise, may get in the way of a perfect recording, but they are not directly associated with the value of the sampling rate.

18.6   Spatial Frequency and Period

The FFT provides a mechanism for passing back and forth between the frequency and time domains. Similarly, the FFT provides a mechanism for treating a different pair of domains, spatial frequency and spatial period. Whereas the first example was that of frequency f (or ω) and period T, the second is that of wavenumber k and wavelength λ. For example, the amplitude and phase of a diffraction pattern is related to the amplitude and phase of the spatial measure of the diffracting object.

We explore this relationship by considering the rectangular slits of, for example, the Young's two-slit interference experiment, as having a certain amplitude x where the slit openings are located, and zero amplitude elsewhere.

• •   Load FFT5, two-slit pattern (see Fig. 18.7).

The slit openings are defined by setting x-values over the entire range to be zero. Then a few specific values representing the slits are set equal to one. See the k and l indices. In the document, we consider the cases of single-slit and double-slit simultaneously; y represents the single-slit and is defined in the same manner as x.

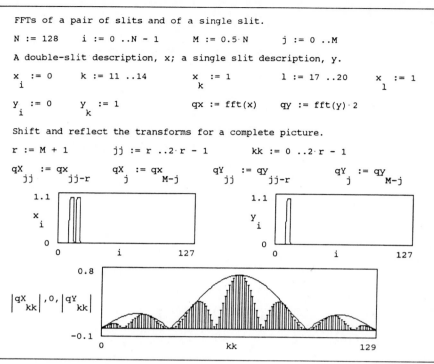

Figure 18.7 FFT5, two-slit pattern

A plot of the FFTs, qx and qy, would show only one half of the pattern. To see the pattern in more typical form, we do two things. First take the transform and then shift the entire set of elements to the right. If M is the number of elements in the transform, each element is shifted over M steps. Then we reverse the order of the elements in the transform and put these reversed elements in place of the original, in the first M spaces. The entire pattern is shown by qX. Since qX represents two slits, and qY only one, the intensity of qY is doubled for purposes of comparison.

We see the combined interference and diffraction effects that one would expect in a double-slit combination. The single-slit pattern is plotted in the same space, showing the modulating envelope expected from the diffraction effects.

Let $k := 14 \ldots 14$ and $l := 18 \ldots 18$. Observe now the interference and diffraction effects. Explain the results and the differences from the previous example in terms of interference and diffraction.

Observe the following cases:

$$k := 13\dots14; \quad l := 17\dots18;$$
$$k := 6\dots14; \quad l := 17\dots25;$$
$$k := 13\dots14; \quad l := 27\dots28;$$
$$k := 11\dots14; \quad l := 27\dots30.$$

Explore the behavior in a general way. Make the slits narrower or wider. Change the separation between the slits. In each case provide a qualitative explanation for each observed change.

What happens if the two slits are not assigned the same x-magnitude? Compare your results with those of the previous chapter.

Increase the number of slits to three and compare your results with those of the previous chapter. Try four slits.

• •   Examine single-slit diffraction; remove all double-slit related regions from the previous document. First let there be one slit one unit in width. Observe the width of the transform pattern. At what point does the first zero occur in the pattern? Now let the slit width be two units. At what point does the first zero in the pattern now occur? Let the width be four, and again find the zero.

In each case, what is the product of slit width and distance to the first zero in the pattern?

These observations are related to the uncertainty principle. The slit width is a measure of the uncertainty in position as a photon (or an electron in an analogous experiment) passes through the slit. Call this value Δx. After the photon (electron) passes through the slit, the spread of the diffraction pattern is a measure of the momentum of the photon in the x-direction.

When the slit is narrow, the diffraction pattern is wide. As the slit width increases, the pattern width decreases. The quantum mechanical relation for the uncertainty principle in terms of position and momentum is

$$\Delta x \cdot \Delta p \geq \hbar. \tag{18.14}$$

The products you observe of slit width and distance to the first zero should be approximately constant.

• •   Another method for gaining experience with this general concept is to add a set of waves with different frequencies and make some observations about the envelope associated with the sum.

Plot two cosine waves as a function of x, $\cos(kx)$. Let one wave number be 10 and the other 14. Let the plot range include about eight cycles of the slower frequency. Plot the individual waves in one region and plot the sum separately. Observe the modulation resulting from the sum of two similar frequency waves. If the k-values are described as spanning a range from $k + \Delta k$ to $k - \Delta k$, what is k? What is Δk? If the width Δx is defined as the distance from the maximum to the half maximum, what is Δx? What is the product $\Delta k \cdot \Delta x$?

Next plot the sum of four waves with wavenumbers 10, 11.33, 12.67, and 14. What are the values for Δk, Δx, and the product $\Delta k \cdot \Delta x$?

Repeat for eight waves with wavenumbers uniformly spaced between 10 and 14.

The product $\Delta x \cdot \Delta p$ and the product $\Delta x \cdot \Delta k$ can be related through the deBroglie relation

$$\lambda = \frac{h}{p}. \tag{18.15}$$

$$\Delta x \cdot \Delta k = \Delta x 2\pi \frac{1}{\Delta \lambda} = \Delta x 2\pi \frac{\Delta p}{h} \approx 1. \tag{18.16}$$

An alternate form of the uncertainty principle is

$$\Delta E \cdot \Delta t \geq \hbar, \tag{18.17}$$

where ΔE refers to the uncertainty in energy and Δt the uncertainty in time.

• • Create a vector, y_i, to describe a sine wave with eight cycles. Display the FFT of this single-frequency sine wave. Let f be an integral multiple of δf. The transform should have only one nonzero element.

In a region after the definition of the vector y, let $y_i = 0$ for the first two and last two cycles of the display. (Define two indices j, k; let j have the same values as i for the first two cycles and let k have the values for i for the last two cycles; let y_j and y_k equal zero.) In the plot, there should be four cycles left in the center. Take the FFT of y and observe the width of the transform.

Repeat this process, reducing the number of nonzero cycles first to two and then to one. Each time, observe the shape of the transform and estimate the width.

As the observation time of the signal decreases, we observe an increase in the number of harmonics needed to describe the signal. This spread in frequencies is directly related to energy: $E = hf$ and $\Delta E \propto \Delta f$. Again,

FFT of a Gaussian waveform.

$N := 32$ $i := 0 \ ..N - 1$ $\delta t := 0.5$ $a := 0.8$

$$t_i := i \cdot \delta t - \frac{N \cdot \delta t}{2} \qquad\qquad y_i := \exp\left[-a \cdot t_i^2\right]$$

$q := \text{fft}(y)$ $M := \text{last}(q)$ $j := 0 \ ..M$

Shift and reflect the transform for a complete picture.

$k := 0 \ ..2 \cdot M$ $q'_{j+M} := q_j$ $q'_j := q_{M-j}$

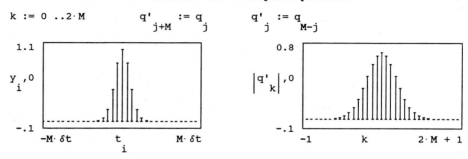

Figure 18.8 FFT6, FFT of a Gaussian waveform.

the product of time expressed in cycles and the width of the transform should be approximately constant.

• •   Load FFT6, FFT of a Gaussian waveform (see Fig. 18.8).

A related phenomenon is that of the transform of a Gaussian wave-shape. Observe the width of the original shape and that of its transform. Alter the width of the original shape by changing the constant in the exponential of y. What can you conclude about the product of the widths in each case?

> That test of yours. The Voight-Kampff test …
> did you ever take it yourself?
>
> *Blade Runner*

CHAPTER
19

Special Topics

In this final chapter, several unrelated topics are discussed. The first is an introduction to the concept of chaos using the logistic equation. The second is an introduction to a classic problem in quantum mechanics, the problem of a finite square well, sometimes referred to as a particle in a box. We also examine several details of nuclear decay series and finally look at the problem of extracting a signal buried in noise.

19.1   Chaos: The Logistic Equation

The logistic equation has a deceptively simple appearance. The difference form of the equation is

$$x_{i+1} = 4\,r\,x_i\,(1 - x_i), \tag{19.1}$$

where

$$0 < x < 1, \qquad \text{and} \qquad 0 < r \leq 1.$$

To start enter a value for x_0 and return the value for x_1. This value is substituted back into the equation to generate the next value, x_2, and so on. We have examined difference equations earlier, but the values changed gradually. That is not always the case here. An examination of this non-linear equation provides a quick introduction to some features of chaotic phenomena. (For a more detailed study of these concepts see, for example, H. Gould and J. Tobochnik, *An Introduction to Computer Simulation Methods.*)

• •   Before we ask the computer to perform the substitutions, it is a good idea to generate one sequence of values by hand (given that we are dealing with an unfamiliar nonlinear equation).

Write the equation as $f(x) = 4\,r\,x\,(1-x)$. Let $r = 0.5$. Let the initial value, $x_0 = 0.3$. Generate the first six values for this sequence. Start by taking $f(0.3)$ and then substituting that result in f, for example, $f(0.462)$. Continue.

Given this specific value for r, the x-values converge to a stable value very quickly.

• •   Load ST1, logistic equation (see Fig. 19.1).

The logistic equation and a value for r are defined and a series of values for x are computed. Next $f(x)$ is plotted vs. x. A particular value, x_a, is marked on the $f(x)$ curve and on the x vs. x curve.

Change the x_a value until $f(x_a) = x_a$.

Simplify the plot region to $f(x)$, x vs. x. Change r values. Note the change in amplitude of the f-curve and the shift in the intersection point between the two curves.

Next, the values are shown that you should have obtained in the exercise above that you did by hand. A plot of these values is shown, computed using the function f and a subscripted variable.

Pay careful attention to the recursive nature of the function; note the values of the functional forms $f(f(x))$, $f(f(f(x)))$, and so on.

When observing the overall behavior in the following examples, distinguish between the initial transient behavior and the behavior after many iterations. Also after many iterations, note whether the x-values converge to a single value (a stable fixed point), to a pair of values (attractors of period two), or to something more complex.

• •   Examine values of x_i vs. i for different values of r. Let $N = 15$,

Logistic equation.

r := 0.75   x := 0,0.05 ..1   f(x) := 4·r·x·(1 - x)   xa := 0.3

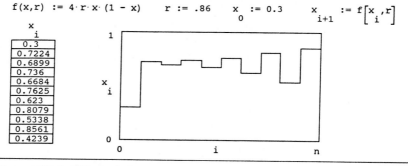

A sequence of values is generated. The function is written a second time in order that the new r value be used.

r := 0.5   n := 10   i := 0 ..n   f(x) := 4·r·x·(1 - x)

Note the recursive nature of the function.

f(0.3) = 0.42

f(0.42) = 0.4872   f(f(.3)) = 0.4872

f(0.4872) = 0.4997   f(f(.42)) = 0.4997   f(f(f(.3))) = 0.4997

f(0.4997) = 0.5   f(f(f(f(.3)))) = 0.5

f(0.5) = 0.5

Plot a sequence of values. For a general statement of x, it is useful to include r in the argument list. Above, it would have made for more clutter.

f(x,r) := 4·r·x·(1 - x)   r := .86 x_0 := 0.3 x_{i+1} := $f\left[x_i , r\right]$

x_i

0.3
0.7224
0.6899
0.736
0.6684
0.7625
0.623
0.8079
0.5338
0.8561
0.4239

Figure 19.1 ST1, logistic equation.

$i = 0,\ldots,N$, $x_0 = 0.4$, and $r = 0.1$. Enter the difference equation in subscripted form. Plot x_i vs. i; set ordinate limits at 0 and 1.

To get a rough sense of the behavior of equation 19.1, let r take on values from 0.1 to 0.9 in steps of 0.1.

Repeat the sequence of r values for $x_0 = 0.8$. How does the final behavior depend on the initial value of x_0? On the value of r?

For what range of r-values do the values of x converge to zero? Let $N = 100$ and change the ordinate plot limits to 0 and 0.1. (For these *r*-values $x = 0$ is a stable fixed point.) When $r > 0.2$ consider increments as small as 0.02 (for example, let $r = 0.20, 0.22, \ldots$).

Increase r to 0.7. There is a transitory behavior that dies out. Let $N = 200$ and increase r in steps of 0.01. (Two hundred iterations is not really adequate to decide whether the oscillations will die out or persist, but we will not be too fussy.) What is the approximate upper limit of r for which the iterated values of x converge to a single value?

Let r increase still further, in steps of 0.02. Note that the quantity x oscillates between two values (after the transients at the outset). How large can r be before this stable period two behavior changes?

Let $k := N - 10 \ldots N$, and display x_k in tabular form and in a plot vs. k.

For $r = 0.8$, what are the x-values of the attractors? Repeat for $r = 0.82$.

Repeat for $r = 0.87$. How many attractors are there now?

Repeat for $r = 0.89$. How many attractors are there now?

• • Load ST2, logistic map (see Fig. 19.2).

In the previous study we examined x for various r. In this document, we plot a summary of all the information obtained in the previous example. (This document requires lots of memory. Exit MathCAD and reload.) This document takes a minute to process, so study the code while Math-CAD is doing the work.

In studying the behavior of the logistic equation, we are interested in values of x as a function of r. Usually, the transient behavior is not of interest. The equation is iterated $(N + P)$ times. Only the last P values are plotted (k index). If the last P values of x are the same, as they are for small r, then only one point appears. The values of L and M and the index j are used to specify the values of r. (The map is pale because of MathCAD's limitations, including, for example, the need to store everything. To pursue these calculations in more detail, it is necessary to use a standard programming language.)

Correlate the x vs. r plot with the results from the previous example. Recall, for example, the values for x as r increased above 0.7, and recall those values of r where the number of attractors increased.

• • Load ST3, graphical display of the iteration process (see Fig. 19.3).

```
f(x,r) := 4·r·x·(1 - x)        the function to be iterated

N := 25           the number of "transient" calculations

P := 30           the number of x-values plotted

i := 0 ..N + P      the total number of iterations

L := 40      M := 95        j := L ..M

      j                    the r-values
r  := -
 j    M

X     := .1              initial x-value
 0,j

X      := f⎡X    ,r ⎤      calculate the values
 i+1,j     ⎣ i,j  j⎦

k := N ..N + P             select the plot range
```

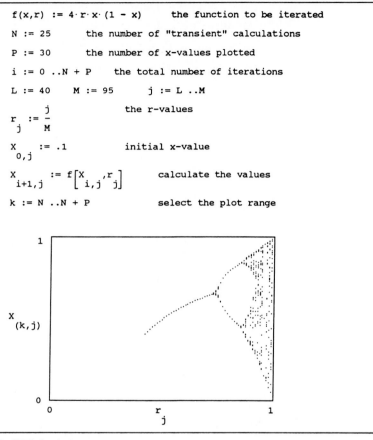

Figure 19.2 ST2, logistic map.

The iteration process starts with a particular x-value. The corresponding $f(x)$ is determined. This f-value is the next x-value, and so on. A line on the graph following this process gives a visually appealing view that should aid your intuition.

Start with a point on the x vs. x line. Draw a vertical line to the f-curve. Draw a horizontal line to the x vs. x line. Draw another vertical line to the f-curve and continue in this way. The process may lead to a stable point, to a pair of attractors, or to something more complex.

In the first plot, we show x_i vs. i, something that should now be familiar. In the second plot, we show $f(x)$ vs. x, x vs. x, and the line we described following the iterative path. Each x-value leads to an f-value that is the next x-value. The vectors XX and YY contain the coordinates

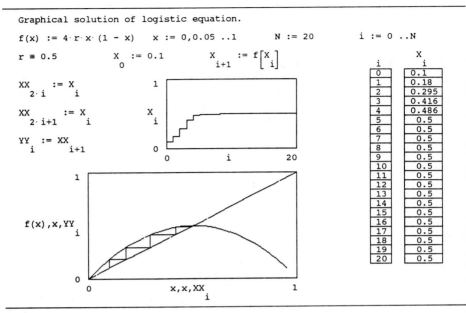

Figure 19.3 ST3, graphical display of the iteration process.

of these points. XX_0 and XX_1 contain the same x-value, x_0; XX_2 and XX_3 contain the x_1 value. The XX-values continue in this sequence. The YY values are offset by one. YY_0 has the x_0 value; YY_1 and YY_2 have the x_1 value. Thus we get the sequence of horizontal and vertical shifts.

Let $r = 0.6$. Change the limits of the second plot region to 0.45 and 0.7 for both axes. This is an easily visualized example of the iteration process "homing in" on a stable attractor.

Change the plot limits back to 0 and 1 and let $r = 0.2$ and process. Let $r = 0.7$ and process. Here, we see the oscillations diminishing in size.

Let $r = 0.75$. Now we see a stable attractor of period two.

Let $r = 0.82$. What do we have here?

Let $r = 0.84$. The values are not yet stabilized.

Let $r = 0.88$. The graph seems to be closing on itself. Examine this case carefully. What is happening?

• •   Let $r = 0.88$ and $x_0 = 0.512$. Define $g(x) = f(f(x))$. Change the iterative equation to $x_{i+1} = g(x_i)$. Change the plot region label to $g(x)$ and process. Explain the results. Where are the other two values that were present when we used $f(x)$? Find them.

• •   Another function that can be explored is:

$$f(x) = r \cdot \sin(\pi x). \qquad (19.2)$$

Look at graphical solutions for values 0.82, 0.84, 0.8637, 0.8651, and 0.9 to see examples of period 2, 4, 8, 16, and chaotic behavior. (Professor Philip Pennance suggested these values.) Another function is

$$f(x) = x \cdot e^{r\,(1-x)}. \qquad (19.3)$$

Examine r-values around and between 2 and 2.8.

19.2   Finite Square Well

A classic problem of quantum mechanics is that of a particle in a one-dimensional box. The particle's behavior is described, not by Newton's second law, but by the time-dependent form of Schrödinger's equation. We solve the time-independent equation form of the equation to determine the wave function and energy states of the system. This equation is

$$-\frac{\hbar^2}{2\,m}\frac{d^2\Psi}{dx^2} + V\,\Psi = E\,\Psi, \qquad (19.4)$$

where $\hbar$ is Planck's constant divided by $2\,\pi$; m is the mass of the particle; x is position; V is the potential energy; E is the total energy; and Ψ is the wave function. This equation is quite different from Newton's second law, where x describes the position of the particle. Here, $|\Psi|^2$ is the probability of locating the particle within a given region. (See, for example, A. P. French and Edwin F. Taylor, *Introduction to Quantum Physics*, for a clear and lucid introduction to this equation.)

Imagine a particle contained within a one-dimensional box, free to move in the interior, colliding with the walls and rebounding, or possibly escaping. In a classical picture, one might visualize a marble rolling on a track that is flat in the interior and inclined at the edges. As the particle moves into the edge regions, the potential energy increases, and if the marble's energy is not too great, it will stop and return along the track. An analogous example with an electrically charged particle can be described. The particle is placed in a field-free region surrounded by a region with an electric field. The particle moves freely in the interior but is restrained from leaving the area by the forces associated with the field at the edges.

In quantum mechanics, we treat a similar problem but cannot describe the precise location of the particle within the box. It is fundamentally impossible to specify both the position and velocity of the particle simultaneously, as we noted in our examination of the FFT. The wave function provides information about the probability that the particle is located within a certain region. A series of measurements on similar systems would indicate the particle's location in correspondence with the square of the magnitude of the wave function.

One feature of these quantum systems is that not all energies are possible. Only certain values can be consistent with a given potential; the possible energy values of an electron in the field of a proton, the hydrogen atom, is an example. The problem of a particle in a one-dimensional box is much simpler than that of an atom but it does exhibit certain fundamental properties of quantum mechanical systems.

Our goal is to find the possible energies of a particle in a box, a potential well. If the energy is properly selected, the wave function trails off to zero as the distance from the well increases, indicating that the probability of locating the particle far from the well must go to zero. In fact, the wave function must go to zero as the distance from the well approaches inifinity. If an energy is selected which is not the correct one for the system, the value of ψ quickly diverges as the distance from the box increases.

The goal is to achieve some qualitative understanding, not to determine specific numerical values for a particular system. Consequently, we simplify the equation by letting the constants equal unity (but we do not lose the minus sign). The scaled equation is

$$\frac{d^2\Psi}{dx^2} = (V - E)\,\Psi. \tag{19.5}$$

This equation can be converted to a difference equation, in the same manner as the differential equation expressing Newton's second law was converted. The Euler algorithm is sufficient to provide the necessary qualitative behavior:

$$\frac{d^2\Psi}{dx^2} = (V - E)\,\Psi \qquad \frac{d^2x}{dt^2} = -\frac{k}{m}\,x \tag{19.6}$$

$$\delta^2\Psi_{i+1} = (V - E)\,\Psi_i \qquad a_{i+1} = -\frac{k}{m}\,x_i \tag{19.7}$$

$$\delta\Psi_{i+1} = \delta\Psi_i + \delta^2\Psi_i\,\delta x \qquad v_{i+1} = v_i + a_i\,\delta t \tag{19.8}$$

$$\Psi_{i+1} = \Psi_i + \delta\Psi_i\,\delta x \qquad x_{i+1} = x_i + v_i\,\delta t. \tag{19.9}$$

• •   Load ST4, particle in a box: finite square well (see Fig. 19.4).

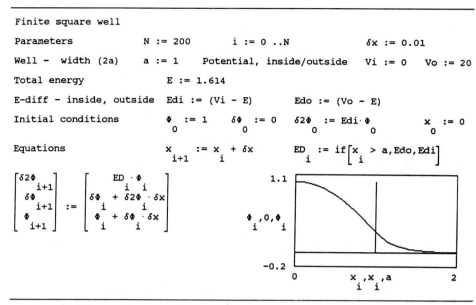

Figure 19.4 ST4, particle in a box: finite square well.

(If the response is too slow, let $N = 160$ and $\delta x = 0.0125$.)

The width and depth of the well are specified. Inside the well the particle is free; at the edges of the well the potential energy increases by V. The energies, E, that we consider are less than V. Consequently, the wave function should show that the probability of finding the particle inside the well is significantly greater than that of finding it outside the well. On the other hand, the wave function must make a smooth transition as it passes from within the well to outside the well. Consequently, there is some possibility of finding the particle outside the well even though this is energetically not allowed in classical terms.

The initial values of E and V_0 are 1.39 and 10. Process. As noted above, if a possible energy is selected, the wave function must go to zero as the distance from the well increases. Note that within the well, the curvature of the wave function is toward the axis (abscissa), and outside the well, the curvature is away from the axis. This sense of curvature (and its energy dependence) is a powerful tool for qualitative descriptions of wave functions for various wells.

Increase E to 1.45 and observe the shape of the wave function.

Decrease E to 1.3 and observe the shape of the wave function.

For the previous two examples, describe where there was too much curvature and where there was not enough. Devise a rule so that by looking at a wave function for this problem you can tell if the energy is too high or too low.

Let $V = 20$ and $E = 1.39$. Process. Is the energy 1.39 too large or too small? Clearly, the energy levels depend on the potential, V_0. Find the appropriate E-value for the lowest energy state.

With V_0 still 20, let $E = 13.75$. How is this shape different? Be specific. What can you say about the difference in curvature between this case and the previous one, the lowest energy state?

Let $V_0 = 20$, $\Phi_0 = 0$, $\delta\Phi_0 = 1$, and $E = 6.4$. How is this state different from the other examples? How many energy levels are there for this $V_0 = 20$, $a = 1$ well?

If the well width is increased, does the number of possible states change? Keep $V_0 = 20$.

For the original width, what happens if V is increased to 100? Find the lowest energy level and compare this wave function with the $V = 20$ case. What is happening to the wave function near the edges of the well? Let $V = 1000$ and compare again.

19.3   Radioactive Decay Series

Nuclei that are radioactive transform by emitting alpha particles (^{4}He nuclei) or beta particles (electrons or positrons). The probability that any particular nucleus will decay per unit time is given by the probability constant, λ. This constant is known as the radioactive decay constant. The decay rate, the number of decays per unit time, is proportional to the number of nuclei in the sample:

$$\frac{dN}{dt} \propto - N.$$

If N is doubled, then there are twice as many decays per unit time. The minus sign indicates that as the nuclei decay, fewer nuclei remain (in the original state). The decay rate, dN/dt, is the number of radioactive nuclei present multiplied by the probability that a nucleus will decay per unit time. This product, $N\lambda$, is referred to as the activity of the sample. The equation

$$\frac{dN}{dt} = - \lambda N \qquad (19.10)$$

is easily integrated and yields

$$N = N_0 \, e^{-\lambda t}, \tag{19.11}$$

where N_0 is the number of nuclei present at $t = 0$. The units of λ are time^{-1}.

The half-life of a sample is that time period during which one-half of the radioactive nuclei have decayed. We obtain the half-life by substituting for N the value $N_0/2$ in equation 19.11 and rearranging. The half-life is specified by

$$t_{1/2} = \frac{\ln(2)}{\lambda}. \tag{19.12}$$

● ●   Find the times at which one-tenth and nine-tenths of the nuclei have decayed. Specify your answers in terms of the half-life.

● ●   For $N_0 = 10^6$ and $\lambda = 1$, plot N vs. t for three half-lives. Plot the activity for three half-lives. What does the area under the activity curve represent? Integrate the activity as time goes from zero to infinity (of course, if you are using MathCAD to perform the integration, simply let the upper limit be a large value compared to the half-life, $10\times$, for example).

Not infrequently, a radioactive nuclide decays into a nuclide that is also radioactive. Some decays may involve a sequence of ten or more decays. It is not difficult to keep track of such decays.

● ●   Load ST5, alpha decay series (see Fig. 19.5).

In radioactive decays or in low-energy nuclear reactions, the particles emitted or exchanged include β^-, β^+, α, γ, p, and n, where p and n represent the proton and the neutron. If any one of these particles is emitted, the change in the number of neutrons and protons in the nucleus is listed in the matrix, X. Given the number of neutrons and protons and the particle emitted, the function A' returns the number of neutrons and protons remaining. This is a rather minor bookkeeping matter. However, it is more useful when a series of decays occur, such as in the α decay series.

For example, in d_i are listed one sequence of decays associated with the decay of ^{232}Th. The amusing feature is that the decays are listed in terms of the names, for example, α, and not in a direct numeric form. In the matrix B is listed a summary of the decay sequence in terms of the total number of nuclides, A, the atomic number, Z, and the neutron

An examination of some elementary features of nuclear decay or reaction.

In the matrix X, are the changes in value of proton and neutron number associated with a particular decay.
ß – m or p for negatron or positron decay. τ is gamma decay. ec is electron capture.   The numerical values refer to columns in the X matrix.

$$X := \begin{bmatrix} 1 & -1 & -2 & 0 & -1 & 0 \\ -1 & 1 & -2 & 0 & 0 & -1 \end{bmatrix} \qquad \beta_m := 0 \qquad \beta_p := 1 \qquad \alpha := 2 \qquad \tau := 3$$

$$p := 4 \qquad n := 5 \qquad ec := 1$$

A single decay is obtained with the function A'. Give initial P,N values and specify decay mode.

For example, carbon 14 beta minus decay would be

$$A'(P,N,d) := \begin{bmatrix} P \\ N \end{bmatrix} + X^{<d>}$$

$$A'\begin{bmatrix} 6,8,\beta_m \end{bmatrix} = \begin{bmatrix} 7 \\ 7 \end{bmatrix}$$

A sequence is similarly obtained. m is the number of decays in the sequence. P[0 and N[0 are the initial values for the proton and neutron number. d[i lists the decay sequence. B lists the sequence for A, Z, and N.

$$m := 10 \qquad i := 0 \; .. \; m - 1 \qquad j := 0 \; .. \; m \qquad P_0 := 90 \qquad N_0 := 142 \qquad d :=$$

$$P_{i+1} := P_i + X_0^{<d_i>} \qquad N_{i+1} := N_i + X_1^{<d_i>} \qquad Z := P$$

$$A_j := N_j + P_j \qquad B^{<0>} := A \qquad B^{<1>} := P \qquad B^{<2>} := N \qquad z := 82 \; .. \; 90$$

$$El :=$$

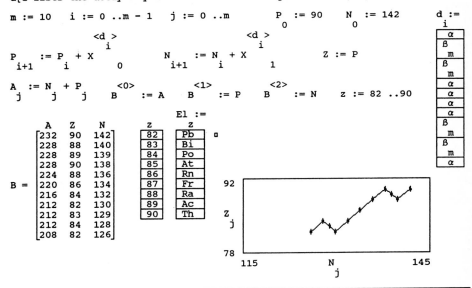

	A	Z	N		z	z	
	232	90	142		82	Pb	□
	228	88	140		83	Bi	
	228	89	139		84	Po	
	228	90	138		85	At	
	224	88	136		86	Rn	
B =	220	86	134		87	Fr	
	216	84	132		88	Ra	
	212	82	130		89	Ac	
	212	83	129		90	Th	
	212	84	128				
	208	82	126				

d list (right column): α, β_m, β_m, α, α, α, α, β_m, β_m, α

Figure 19.5 ST5, alpha decay series.

number, N. Once the decay is specified, it can be plotted and examined easily.

The plot shown is in the Z vs. N form. Plot the corresponding data as A vs. N.

Plot two of the decay sequences associated with ^{235}U. All these β are β minus:

$$\alpha, \; \beta, \; \alpha, \; \alpha, \; \alpha, \; \alpha, \; \beta, \; \alpha, \; \beta, \; \alpha \qquad (19.13)$$

and

$$\alpha, \ \beta, \ \alpha, \ \beta, \ \alpha, \ \alpha, \ \alpha, \ \alpha, \ \beta, \ \beta, \ \alpha. \tag{19.14}$$

Plot separately and together in the same region. Look at both Z vs. N and A vs. N forms.

Such sequences provide information about the path but not about numbers of a specific nuclide as a function of time. Consider a decay such as that of

$$^{131}\text{Te} \rightarrow \ ^{131}\text{I} \rightarrow \ ^{131}\text{Xe}. \tag{19.15}$$

If at $t = 0$ there are N_0 Te nuclei, what are the numbers of Te, I, and Xe nuclei as a function of time?

In general, for a decay $A \rightarrow \ B \ \rightarrow \ C$, the activities of A and B are $A\lambda_A$ and $B\lambda_B$. The rate of change of the number of B nuclides is supply minus loss, that is

$$\frac{dB}{dt} = A\lambda_A - B\lambda_B. \tag{19.16}$$

If $A = A_0 e^{-\lambda_A t}$, then B can be expressed as

$$B = A_0 \left(\frac{\lambda_A}{\lambda_B - \lambda_A} \right) \left(e^{-\lambda_A t} - e^{-\lambda_B t} \right). \tag{19.17}$$

The activities of A and B are given by

$$A\lambda_A = A_0 \lambda_A e^{-\lambda_A t}$$

$$B\lambda_B = A_0 \left(\frac{\lambda_A \lambda_B}{\lambda_B - \lambda_A} \right) \left(e^{-\lambda_A t} - e^{-\lambda_B t} \right) \tag{19.18}$$

$$= A \left(\frac{\lambda_A \lambda_B}{\lambda_B - \lambda_A} \right) \left(1 - e^{-(\lambda_A - \lambda_B)t} \right).$$

• •   Load ST6, nuclear decay series (see Fig. 19.6).

Enter values for the half-lives of A and B. Display in linear and semilog form the values of A and B as a function of time. Examine the shapes of the two curves as T_A ranges from $10 \, T_B$ to $0.1 \, T_B$. For what relative values of half-life does B reach its maximum at the largest time? Do the A and B curves always intersect? If the answer is no, find the ratio of T_A/T_B, which corresponds to the limiting case. Viewing the curves on a semilog graph is useful here. Let $\delta t := T \cdot 0.5$, and let t go to $15 \cdot T$. Change the lower limit of the semilog plot to 10^1. Increase the vertical size if you like.

The accumulation of stable end products can be obtained by equating the sum of all nuclide decays at time t plus the active nuclei remaining to the initial value. For example, if B is stable, $A + B = A_0$, where A is

---

```
Nuclear Decay Series

Enter values for the half-lives  and initial numbers of A nuclides.  Do not
give the two half-lives identical numerical values.
```

$$TA_{hlf} := .5 \qquad TB_{hlf} := 1 \qquad\qquad Ao := 10^6$$

```
Decay constants    λA := ln(2)·TA    -1              λB := ln(2)·TB    -1
                                hlf                               hlf
```

$$A(t) := Ao \cdot \exp(-\lambda A \cdot t) \qquad B(t) := Ao \cdot \left[\frac{\lambda A}{\lambda B - \lambda A}\right] \cdot (\exp(-\lambda A \cdot t) - \exp(-\lambda B \cdot t))$$

$$T := \text{if}\left[TA_{hlf} > TB_{hlf}, TA_{hlf}, TB_{hlf}\right] \qquad \delta t := T \cdot 0.1 \qquad t := 0.1 \cdot \delta t, \delta t \ .. 3 \cdot T$$

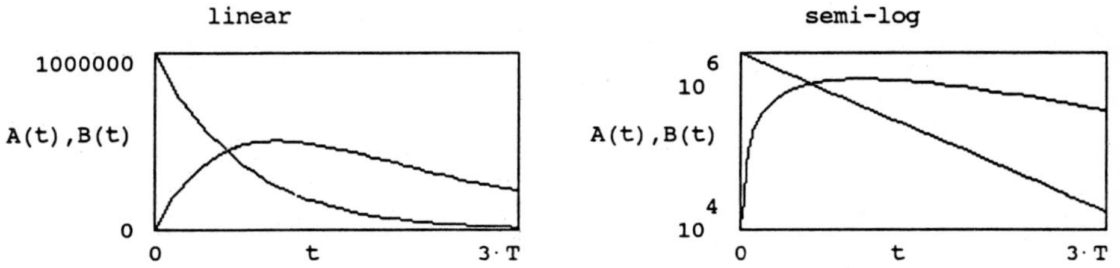

Figure 19.6 ST6, nuclear decay series.

---

a function of time:

$$A_0\, e^{-\lambda_A t} + B = A_0 \qquad \text{or} \qquad B = A_0\,(1 - e^{-\lambda_A t}). \qquad (19.19)$$

To express in terms of A, we note that $A = A_0 e^{-\lambda_a t}$ or $A_0 = A e^{\lambda_a t}$:

$$A + B = A\, e^{\lambda_a t} \qquad \text{or} \qquad B = A\,(e^{\lambda_A t} - 1). \qquad (19.20)$$

Similarly, in the decay $A \rightarrow B \rightarrow C$, $C = A_0 - A - B$. The time dependence of C can be expressed as

$$C = A_0 \left(1 - e^{-\lambda_A t} - \frac{\lambda_A}{\lambda_B - \lambda_A}\left(e^{-\lambda_A t} - e^{-\lambda_B t}\right)\right). \qquad (19.21)$$

• • For the case $A \rightarrow B$, plot A, B vs. t.

• • For the case $A \rightarrow B \rightarrow C$, plot A, B, C vs. t.

19.4   Signal Averaging

Noise is the bane of all experimental scientists. Many experimental techniques have been developed to improve the signal to noise ratio. Here we provide a glimpse at one process, signal averaging.

If a signal's amplitude is small compared to the noise surrounding it, observing a clean signal may be impossible. However, if the signal repeats or is periodic, then we have a handle by which we can greatly improve our ability to distinguish the signal from the noise which masks it. If there is a means to latch onto the periodicity or repeatability of the signal, we can sample the data starting at the same point in the data sequence over and over again. If we can do this, the signal will tend to make essentially the same contribution with each new sweep, while the noise will tend to cancel itself out. If many samples are taken and the entire set is averaged, the signal is enhanced and the noise is significantly reduced. The effects of the noise cannot be removed completely, but in some cases, a signal can be extracted from data where in any given sampling, the signal is completely obscured. This technique can improve enormously the signal-to-noise ratio, the ratio of the signal amplitude to a measure of the effective noise amplitude.

• •   Load ST7, signal averaging (see Fig. 19.7).

A data sequence of N points, consisting of signal plus noise, is sampled M times. The signal has amplitude B, which may be more or less (you adjust) than the noise amplitude, C. To improve the signal-to-noise ratio, we sum the different data sequences and take the average. The signal emerges gradually from the noise.

In the example, the noise is generated using the rnd function, and the data are generated using the sine function. (Note the subscript on t.) With each pass of N data points, the signal repeats. The summation is the means by which we perform the averaging. The data index b corresponds to the different data values in a particular sample; a is the sampling index which specifies which data set we are considering. For each given value of b in the data sequence, we sum each of the sampled values of a.

It is instructive to see the progression of the averaged signal as the number of samples increases. Start out by observing one sample; let $X = 0$. Then gradually increase the limit on the sum; let X take on successively larger values, from 0 to $M - 1$, and observe the signal as it emerges from the noise.

Increase M to 64, and see what effect this change has on the quality of the average. In actual experiments, signals may be determined after thousands or even millions of sequences.

With a modest M, how large can the ratio C/B be and still expect to extract some signal information?

Store the data and take the FFT of S_0 and S_{M-1}. Compare the frequency compositions for an impressive view of the noise reduction. Would digital filtering be as effective as the averaging process?

Signal averaging

Sixteen sweeps of a data set containing 64 samples.

M := 16   N := 64   a := 0 ..M − 1   b := 0 ..N − 1

noel := M·N   i := 0 ..noel − 1   ω := 6

B := 1 $t_b := 2 \cdot \pi \cdot \dfrac{b}{N}$ C := 1 $noise_i := rnd(2 \cdot C) - C$

$A_i := B \cdot \sin\left[\omega \cdot t_{mod(i,N)}\right] + noise_i$ X := M − 1

$s_b := \displaystyle\sum_a A_{b+a \cdot N} \cdot (a \le X)$ $s_b := \dfrac{s_b}{X + 1}$ $y_b := B \cdot \sin\left[\omega \cdot t_b\right]$

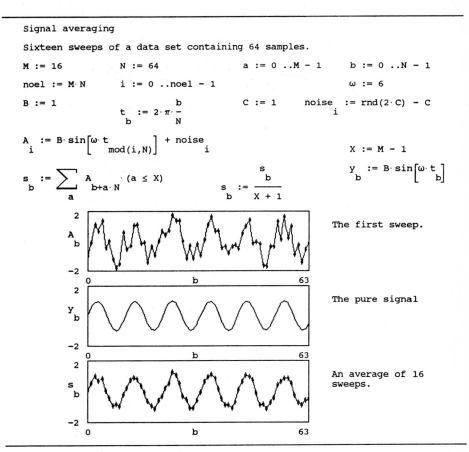

The first sweep.

The pure signal

An average of 16
sweeps.

Figure 19.7 ST7, signal averaging.

"...because you don't take care of me, or want me,
or want to make any kind of commitment to me.
I'm completely finished with you, Zack.
You just find some other girl to be your little pet
— that doesn't seem to be too difficult for you anyway
— because I've had it with you, and with your stupid music,
and this is just really boring... ."

"I guess it's over between us."

Down by Law

Index

Addison-Wesley Publishing Company

9 780201 547368

ISBN 0-201-54736-8

90000>